INSTRUMENTATION
Devices and Systems

London
Toronto

McGraw-Hill Offices

New Delhi
New York
St Louis
San Francisco
Auckland
Bogota
Guatemala
Hamburg
Lisbon
London
Madrid
Mexico
Montreal
Panama
Paris
San Juan
São Paulo
Singapore
Sydney
Tokyo
Toronto

Instrumentation
Devices and Systems

C S RANGAN
National Aeronautical Laboratory
Bangalore

G R SARMA
Kakatiya Institute of Technology and Science
Warangal

V S V Mani
Integrated Process Automation
Bangalore

Tata McGraw-Hill Publishing Company Limited
NEW DELHI

© 1983, TATA McGRAW-HILL PUBLISHING COMPANY LIMITED

Thirteenth Reprint 1994
RQRYYROJRXLRL

This edition can be exported from India only by the publishers,
Tata McGraw-Hill Publishing Company Limited

ISBN 0-07-451852-6

Published by Tata McGraw-Hill Publishing Company Limited,
4/12 Asaf Ali Road, New Delhi 110 002 and printed at
Taj Press, A-35/4, Mayapuri, Phase 1, New Delhi 110 064

FOREWORD

Measurement provides us with a means of describing various phenomena in quantitative terms. In fact any increase in our ability to make measurement increases the possibility of advancing our understanding of the laws of nature. Progress in science and technology is therefore closely linked to our capability to make accurate measurements. Electronics has now become an important part of measurement. Present-day electronic measurement techniques and instrumentation have influenced science and industry and many other fields of human activity. Therefore a course on electronic measurement and instrumentation should form an important part of the graduate student's curriculum in engineering education at most Indian universities. This calls for a good textbook or reference book covering the field in some detail.

I am happy that Mr C S Rangan, Dr G R Sarma and Dr V S V Mani have written the book *Instrumentation—Devices and Systems*, which fulfils this requirement. The extensive experience of the authors in instrumentation for science and industry is obvious in the wide coverage they have made of the subject. The treatment is simple and clear. I am certain that this book will be of use to students, scientists and engineers as a textbook and reference book.

I would like to congratulate and thank the authors for their effort in bringing out this book.

S RAMASESHAN
Director
Indian Institute of Science
Bangalore

PREFACE

The art of measurement plays an important role in all branches of engineering and science. With the advancement of technology, measurement techniques have also taken rapid strides during recent years with the introduction of many types of instrumentation devices, innovations, refinements and altogether new techniques. The object of this book is to bring these developments together within easy reach of students, practising engineers and technologists. The contents have been framed carefully, dealing specially with electrical transducers, signal conditioners and processors, with an exhaustive bibliography for professional engineers and a glossary for the novice. The book caters to the engineering and scientific community working in the broad disciplines of aeronautical, civil, electronic and mechanical engineering. There may be many books written on the subject; nevertheless it is the opinion of the authors that this is the first book of its kind with the unique feature of an exhaustive treatment of both electrical transducers and associated electronic instrumentation for signal conditioning and processing. The authors have endeavoured to present the discipline of instrumentation in a logical and conscise form—written strictly keeping the academic requirements in view and yet catering to practising engineers by treating the subject methodically. They strongly feel that the book can readily be utilized as a text for undergraduate and postgraduate students in Indian universities.

The primary emphasis of the book is on the measurement of physical and mechanical variables encountered in experimental investigations and industrial processes. Engineers in non-electrical engineering branches who have to get themselves involved with measurements of these physical and mechanical parameters by electrical transduction methods will find this book immensely useful in their work. In covering such a broad field of interest, it has been presumed that the reader will have some knowledge of one or two specialised subjects such as applied physics and electrical engineering. It is hoped that in this work, the authors have succeeded in maintaining a balance between theory and applications in the discipline of instrumentation science and engineering. It is presumed that the subject has been made sufficiently attractive through a treatise like this to tempt students to take up this discipline as a career, for research and development establishments as well as industrial organisations.

The book covers all aspects of major types of electrical transducers and associated instrumentation in 18 chapters. The first three chapters form an introduction to the concepts of measurement, essential to appreciate problems associated with instrumentation. The basic characteristics, sources of error and the behaviour of first -and second-order systems are covered in these chapters. Different electrical transduction principles employed in the measurement of the various physical and mechanical parameters, commonly encountered in almost every branch of engineering and science are exhaustively treated in Chapters 4 to 10. Some of the unique features in this presentation, not found elsewhere are the analysis of force-balance devices, analysis of elastic diaphragms for both small and large deflections, practical aspects on the performance characteristics of thermocouples, and digital transduction techniques.

It may be noted that in many of the other standard books on transducer technology, electronic-measurement aspects covering signal conditioners and modifiers, filters, analysers and output display and recording devices are rarely included in a single volume. However the authors have considered this as essential to appreciate modern instrumentation systems and have treated them thoroughly in later chapters. Chapters 11, 12 and 13 are completely devoted to various input signal-conditioning and analogue-processing systems and filters, which are highly essential to transform the signal to a form suitable for processing and storage. The subsequent two chapters cover the instrumentation aspects on data acquisition, conversion and processing. The modern trend instrumentation and control systems is to use microprocessors to advantage for a variety of functions, and in fitness to its importance, a separate chapter on microprocessors has been included. Further, for the sake of completeness from the measurement systems point of view, a description of peripheral equipment of digital systems, electronic power supplies and a few standard test equipment are also included. Wherever required, practical circuits are included to enable the reader to experiment upon and design his own instrumentation system. The emphasis given to general components and to a number of specialized circuits such as protection circuits for power supplies etc. are deliberate and reflects the authors' opinion that the importance given to them in other similar works appears to be less than what is due.

The authors have been engaged in the research and development of a variety of electrical transducers and associated measurement systems at the Systems Engineering Division of the National Aeronautical Laboratory, Bangalore, for more than a decade. They have, on many occasions, participated in workshops and lectures where they had disseminated the knowledge gained by their experience. Further, they were involved in drafting the syllabi and conducting special courses on Instrumentation and examiners for under-graduate and post-graduate courses for a number of universities. In this process, they found a lacuna in not being able to follow a single volume wherein all aspects of instrumentation devices as well as systems are treated exhaustively. This motivated the authors to undertake the preparation of this book. They are greatly indebted to the National Aeronautical Laboratory for giving permission to take up this endeavour in their spare time.

The authors wish to thank the University Grants Commission for granting the necessary funds for writing this book and the National Book Trust for subsidizing the publication. They wish to acknowledge the help received from their colleagues in the preparation of the manuscript by way of discussions and perusal of the manuscript. The authors are particularly indebted to Mrs Sarala Udayakanth for typing the manuscript patiently, Mr C Jayachandran and Mr H S Subramanya for drafting and Mr Shyam Chetty and Mr Nagaraj N Murthy for perusal of the manuscript.

Further they wish to thank the publishers for the sustained interest shown by them during the entire work. In this venture, a vast literature on the subject is required to be consulted and the authors acknowledge with due courtesy the source consulted to adapt some of the information. The authors look forward to any constructive criticism and suggestions to improve the quality of the book.

C S Rangan
G R Sarma
V S V Mani

CONTENTS

1
BASIC CONCEPTS OF MEASUREMENT

1.1 INTRODUCTION

The art of measurement is a wide discipline in both engineering and science, encompassing the areas of detection, acquisition, control and analysis of data. It involves the precise measurement and recording of a physical, chemical, mechanical, or an optical parameter and plays a vital role in every branch of scientific research and industrial processes interacting basically with control systems, process instrumentation, and data reduction. Recent advances in electronics, physics, material sciences, and other branches of science and technology have resulted in the development of many sophisticated and high precision measuring devices and systems, catering to varied measurement problems in such disciplines as aeronautics, science and technology, space, medicine, oceanography, and industry in general.

Measurement provides us with a means of describing a natural phenomena in quantitative terms. As a fundamental principle of science, Lord Kelvin stated: "When you can measure what you are speaking about and express them in numbers, you know something about it and when you cannot measure it or where you cannot express in numbers, your knowledge is of a meagre and unsatisfactory kind. It may be the beginning of knowledge, but you have scarcely in your thought advanced to the stage of science". In order to make constructive use of the quantitative information obtained from the experiment conducted, there must be a means of measuring and controlling the relevant properties precisely. The reliability of control is directly related to the reliability of measurement.

Widespread use of instrumentation in industry started in 1930 with the introduction of electronics, advancement of physics and allied disciplines, and with the availability of reliable electrical instruments for continuous measurement and recording of many of the physical parameters. The number of variables which require measurement has since then been continuously extended, as novel techniques and methods based on newly-found physical and chemical phenomena are developed. During the last four decades, the measuring techniques have improved considerably, meeting the exacting demands of scientists, engineers, and technologists.

1.2 SYSTEM CONFIGURATION

A generalized measurement system comprises the following elements, as shown in Fig. 1.1.

(a) The transducer which coverts the measurand (measured quantity, property or condition) into a usable electrical output.

(b) The signal conditioner which converts the transducer output into an electrical quantity suitable for control recording and/or display.

(c) The display or readout devices which display the required information about the measurand, generally in engineering units.

(d) The electrical power supply which provides the required excitation to the transducer and the necessary electrical power to the signal conditioners and display devices.

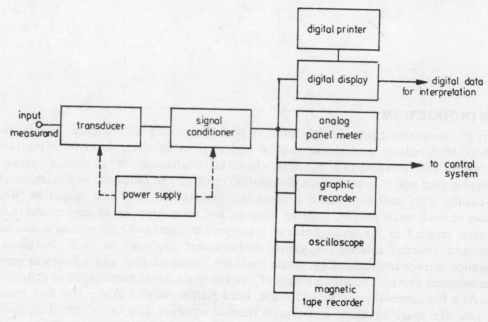

Fig. 1.1 A generalized measurement system

The transducer is defined as a device which, when actuated by one form of energy, is capable of converting it to another form of energy. The transduction may be from mechanical, electrical, or optical to any other related form.

The signal conditioner can vary in complexity from a simple resistance network or impedance matching network to complex multistage amplifiers with or without detectors, demodulators, and filters. Alternately, they are termed as signal modifiers or signal processors. The output signal may be an analog or digital quantity.

The readout or display devices may be in analog or digital format. The simplest form of a display device is the common panel meter with some kind of calibrated scale or pointer. With the advancement of computer technology, the analog signals are invariably converted to a digital format through an analog to digital converter and are displayed in derived units with a digital panel meter. Numerical print-outs are obtained whenever a permanent record is necessary. The analog signal itself can be recorded permanently on a self-balancing type potentiometric strip chart recorder, or an ultra-violet galvanometer-type oscillograph. Graphic pen type galvanometer recorders are also employed in cases where the signal frequency is low. If the signal is digital, the information can be printed out and stored on a paper with a teleprinter, line printer, or mosaic printer or recorded in a paper tape, punch card, magnetic tape (cassette), or floppy disc. The main advantages of these devices are high accuracy, high speed, and elimination of human operational errors.

1.3 PROBLEM ANALYSIS

In any measurement problem it is very essential to have a clear understanding of the choice of the electrical transducer, associated signal conditioner, and display or recording instruments before conducting the experiment. It is advantageous to draw-up the complete specifications of the devices as well as the total system configuration for the detailed design.

The following eight golden rules may be followed in every measurement problem:

(a) Establish the minimum performance required for the instrumentation. Ascertain the following details *a priori*:

Statement of the problem
Primary and secondary goal
Accuracy desired
Reliability demanded
Possible consequences of failures in individual components
Physical dimensions
Cost
Test procedure and schedule.

(b) Collect, systematize, and analyse the existing facts and information that will help to crystallize the problem and aid its solution. Investigate the problem with a questionnaire:

(i) Is conventional instrumentation adequate? If not, in what respects?
(ii) Can techniques of similar instrumentation already available be applied to solve the problem?
(iii) Can any of the recent developments in the field be applied?
(iv) Is any basic research needed from theoretical considerations?
(v) Is it essential to attempt the problem with a specialized instrumentation approach?

(c) Determine absent facts or missing information, and conduct component testing to supplement known design criteria. The technical data on all the components must be obtained. Essential tests on those parameters which will affect the overall performance of the system must be carried out.

(d) Choose the logical approach and establish design specifications. Engineering judgement must be exercised. Any approach that promises greatest chance of success shall be decided upon.

(e) Fabricate the instrumentation device and system, employing the minimum number of unfavourable compromises. Incorporate definite quality control measures and improve normal workmanship standards at reasonable cost.

(f) Perform all calibration and bench tests that are feasible to ensure the required accuracy under given operating environmental conditions. Provide graphs or data on errors expected. Emphasise on 'precision' (referring to reproducibility of data) and 'accuracy'.

(g) Provide professional coverage on technical details during the tests. Sometimes, good systems get scrapped, whereas marginal systems get accepted and later fail.

(h) Assist in evaluation of data. The data should be presented in a usable form to solve the original problem. Calibration data must be supplied with expected degrees of accuracy.

1.4 BASIC CHARACTERISTICS OF MEASURING DEVICES

The function of a measuring device is to sense or detect a parameter encountered in an industrial process or in scientific research, such as pressure, temperature, flow, motion, resistance, voltage, current, and power. The measuring device must be capable of faithfully and accurately detecting any changes that occur in the measured parameter. For control purposes, the measuring instrument either generates a warning signal to indicate the need for a manual change or activates a control device automatically. For obtaining optimum performance, a number of basic characteristics are to be considered. Each one of them, with its relevance to measurement, is discussed separately.

1.4.1 Accuracy

The accuracy of a measurement or reading is purely a relative term. In measurement, it is influenced by static error, dynamic error, drift, reproducibility, and non-linearity. It is defined as the 'closeness with which the reading approaches an accepted standard value or the true value'. Absolute accuracy as such has no significance in the measurement of a physical quantity. In any experiment, accuracy is influenced by the limits of intrinsic error, limits of variation in indication, instability of the electrical zero, and environment. It is numerically equal to the referred error value, i.e. degree of error in the final result.

The accuracy is determined by calibration under certain operating conditions and is expressed as within plus or minus a certain specified amount or a percentage at a certain point of scale or between specified points of scale. All devices and instruments are classified and designated into different "grades" or "classes", depending upon the accuracy of the product.

The accuracy of a complete system is dependent upon the individual accuracies of the primary sensing element, secondary element, and the manipulating devices. Each unit contributes to the accuracy with separate limits specified. If $\pm a_1$, $\pm a_2$ and $\pm a_3$ are the accuracy limits of a typical system, and A is the overall accuracy, the lowest limit of accuracy can be expressed as $A = \pm(a_1 + a_2 + a_3)$, and the root mean square accuracy can be expressed as $A = \sqrt{(a_1^2 + a_2^2 + a_3^2)}$. In practice, the root mean square accuracy is often specified, since it is not probable that all the units of the system will have the greatest static error at the same point and at the same time.

1.4.2 Precision

Another characteristic that is often referred to in measurement is the 'precision' of the device. Precision is the closeness with which individual measurements are distributed about their mean value. It refers to the degree of agreement of a set or group of measurements among themselves. It is equal to the mean value of the scatter of individual measurements. It combines the uncertainty due to both random differences in results in a number of measurements and the smallest readable increment in scale or chart (given as the deviation of mean values). It has no guarantee of accuracy.

1.4.3 Error

An ideal or theoretical output versus the measurand relationship exists for every transducer. It the transducer was ideally designed and made from appropriate materials with ideal workmanship, the output of this ideal transducer would continuously indicate the true value of the measurand. It would follow exactly the prescribed or known theoretical curve which specifies the relationship of the output to the applied measurand over the transducer's range. Such a relationship can be expressed in the form of a mathematical equation, graph, or table of values. The ideal output would be obtained regardless of the ambient environmental conditions and the operating conditions to which the device is subjected to.

In actual practice, however, the output of a transducer is affected by the non-ideal behaviour of the device which causes the indicated measurand value to deviate from the true value. The algebraic difference between the indicated value and the true value of the measurand is termed the error of the device. This error is usually expressed in per cent of the full scale output (%F.S.). The ratio of this error to the full scale output is a measure of the accuracy of the device.

The above mentioned error is contributed by the existence of a large number of individual errors. In actual measurement the effect of these errors on the transducer behaviour should be known clearly. The knowledge of these individual errors, which are described below, can be often used to correct the final data and thereby increase the overall accuracy of the measurement.

(a) Intrinsic, Absolute and Relative Errors

The error observed when the instrument is under the reference condition is termed as the intrinsic error. The absolute error is the difference obtained by substracting the true value of a quantity from the observed value. The relative error is the ratio of the absolute error to the true value. In certain cases, it may be necessary to express this as relative linearity error K which can be written as

$$K = \frac{K_a - K_b}{K_a}$$

where K_a = average slope measured over the central 80% of F.S., and K_b = average slope measured at the lower extreme 10% of F.S.

(b) Uncertainty and Random Error

Uncertainty and random errors are indicated when repeated measurements of the same quantity result in differing values. The magnitude and direction of these errors are not known and as such are considered indeterminate. They are caused by such effects as friction, spring hysteresis, noise, and other phenomena. The contributing factors are any random changes in input signal, combined with noise and drift in the signal conditioner. Such errors occur more in dynamic data analysis. The uncertainty is expressed as the average deviation, probable error, or statistical deviation. The error value is estimated as the amount by which the observed or calculated value departs from the true value.

(c) Systematic and Instrumental Error

Other errors resulting from the characteristics of materials used in fabricating the measuring device or system are systematic and instrumental errors.

Systematic errors are relatively constant errors occurring due to such effects as sensitivity drift, zero effect, known non-linearities, etc. The phenomenon is frequently hidden and not evident in direct observations. The value is obtained by a statistical procedure based on repetitive measurements, carried out under different conditions or with different equipment or by new methods. They are eliminated by suitable corrections.

The instrumental error is a measure of precision at which the readings are taken with the instrument. It is a part of the total measurement error, expressing the accuracy of measurement. The error is reduced by applying corrections to the readings taken by the observer. Another error, similar to this in characteristic, is the equipment error caused by calibration linearity, zero drift, and sensitivity changes during measurement.

The above mentioned errors are compensated by algebraic corrections.

(d) Interference Errors

The unwanted disturbances superimposed on low level input signals due to noise, hum, line pickup, ripple, switching transients and line transients are termed as interference errors. They are created by noise from electrical machines, magnetic fields, thermal sources, atmospheric interferences, arcing contacts in switches and relays, electrostatic noise, and cable noise. The error is reduced by isolation or frequency discrimination. The isolation (shielding) may be electrical, electromagnetic, or electrostatic.

(e) Installation Errors (Application Errors)

These errors are created due to incorrect or improper application and faulty installation. Such errors are predominant if the device is used beyond the range or at excess temperature and vibration, or if the impedance matching to the signal conditioner is poor. All the devices and instruments must be used in accordance with design specifications and manufacturers' recommendations.

(f) Operational Errors (Human Errors)

This type of error is introduced as part of the total error, if the operational techniques employed is poor, even though the system is accurate and carefully selected and applied. The error occurs due to improper adjustment, use of defective standards, incorrect scale marking or reading, parallax error, and poor instrument operator training. A typical case is the failure to adjust the set zero, and balance the position and full-scale gain before starting the experiments in a multichannel strain measuring bridge. Care should be taken to ensure that the standards employed to check the resistance, voltage, pressure, temperature, etc. are precisely calibrated beforehand. Repeated readings with trained observers and independent checks of the measured variables should be taken wherever possible. Another related error, known as personnel error, is caused due to carelessness, bias on the part of the observer, lack of experience, or individual limitations. This can be overcome by having the readings taken by more than one observer.

(g) Zero Drift

'Zero drift' is the deviation observed in the instrument output with time from the initial value, when all the other measurement conditions are constant. This can be caused by a change in component values due to variation in ambient conditions or due to ageing.

(h) Error due to Sensitivity Changes

Sometimes, the errors due to drift at zero or full-scale setting may be large and completely random in nature. Correction in such cases is difficult, even though test calibratior signals can be inserted to check the performance of the instrument during the measurement. The maximum difference occurs at the start of the operation and the error reduces after the warm-up period. These errors are due to changes in sensitivity, caused by changes in temperature or fluctuations in the applied voltage. They are reduced by incorporating temperature compensation and voltage regulation and by the use of a balanced differential amplifier or chopper stabilized amplifier. The error created by the uncertainty in readings is reduced to a minimum by taking a large number of static calibrations with repeated observations, keeping the input constant. A random error of this nature often follows a Gaussian distribution.

(i) Statistical Errors

The statistical errors in a measurement can be considered in terms of the statistical mean and the standard deviation. If $x_1, x_2 \cdots x_n$ represent a set of measured values of a quantity, the statistical mean $\bar{x}$ of these readings is given by

$$\bar{x} = \frac{1}{n} \sum_{i=1}^{n} x_i$$

The standard deviation, indicating the degree of dispersion of readings about a mean value, can be expressed as

$$\sigma = \sqrt{\frac{1}{n} \sum_{i=1}^{n} d_i^2}$$

where σ is the standard deviation, d_i is the deviation of the individual points from the mean, $| x_i - \bar{x} |$ and n is the number of observations.

(j) Weighting of Errors

In certain experiments the errors cannot be computed directly. As an example, the error observed in the measurement of the Mach number depends very much on the measurement errors of the two pressure values. The error depends upon those associated with each individual measurement as well as on those involved in the interaction of errors in the final computation. Also each error does not affect the final result in the same manner.

1.4.4 Linearity

Most of the transducers are designed to provide a linear "output versus measurand" relationship, primarily because this tends to facilitate a more accurate data reduction. Linearity is defined as the ability to reproduce the input characteristics symmetrically, and this can be expressed by the equation $y = mx + c$ where y is the output, x the input, m the slope, and c the intercept. The closeness of the calibration curve to a specified straight line is the linearity of the transducer. The non-linearity may be due to non-linear elements in the device, the electronic amplifier, mechanical hysteresis, viscous flow or creep, and elastic after-effects in the mechanical system.

The linearity is expressed as a percentage of the departure from the linear value, i.e. maximum deviation of the output curve from the best-fit straight line during any calibration cycle. Absolute linearity relates to the maximum error in calibration at any point on the scale to the absolute measurement or theoretical straight line. The value is given as $\pm x\%$ of F.S.

The term linearity by itself means very little, and any value given is sometimes misleading. As such, the linearity is further classified under the following categories.

"Theoretical slope linearity" is referred to a straight line between the theoretical end points. The line is drawn without referring to any measured values.

"Terminal linearity" is a special case of theoretical slope linearity for which the theoretical end points are exactly 0% and 100% of the full-scale output.

"End point linearity" is referred to a straight line between the experimental end points. Such end points can be specified as those obtained during any one calibration cycle or as an average of readings during two or more consecutive calibration cycles.

"Independent linearity" is referred to the best straight line, a line midway between the closest possible two parallel straight lines enclosing all the output values obtained during one calibration cycle. This can be drawn only when the curve is drawn with all the output readings including the end point readings.

"Least square linearity" is referred to the straight line for which the sum of the squares of the residuals are minimized. The residuals refer to the deviations of output readings from their corresponding points on the best-fit straight line. A relative term is the "scatter" which can be defined as the deviation of the mean value of repeated measurements from the best fit line. The graphs indicating different aspects of linearity are shown in Fig. 1.2 (a, b, c).

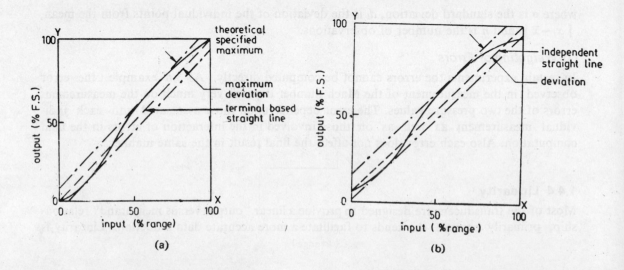

(a)   (b)

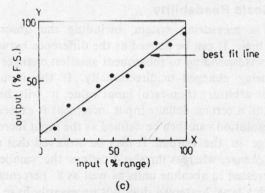

best fit line

(c)

Fig. 1.2 (a) Terminal linearity;
(b) Independent linearity;
(c) Least square fit linearity

1.4.5 Hysteresis

When a device is used to measure any parameter, first for increasing values of the measurand and then for decreasing values of the measurand, the two output readings obtained usually differ from each other, primarily because of a certain amount of internal or external friction in the response of the sensing element. The maximum difference in any part of output readings so obtained during any one calibration cycle is the hysteresis of the device and is shown in Fig. 1.3. Like magnetic hysteresis, this value, observed mostly in mechanical devices, depends on the past history of input reversals, time elapsed from previous cycle, backlash of gears, coulomb friction, lost motion, linkage pivots, and elasticity of materials. The error is encountered in primary detectors as well as in analog indicating and recording devices. The error is reduced by proper design and selection of the mechanical components, introducing greater flexibility, and providing suitable heat treatment to the materials. Hysteresis is usually expressed as a percentage of the full-scale output measured at 50% F.S. level. The hysteresis obtained when only a portion of the range is covered is less than the total hysteresis. Inherent hysteresis will be lower for smaller deflection of the transducer element.

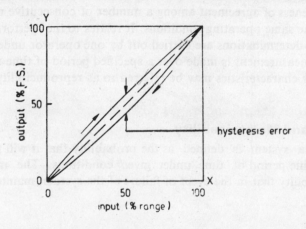

hysteresis error

1.4.6 Resolution and Scale Readability

Resolution is the ability of a measuring system, including the observer, to discriminate between nearly equal values. It can be defined as the difference between two input values of the measured quantity corresponding to subsequent smallest changes in the output information, input quantity being changed unidirectionally. If the input to an instrument is slowly increased from some arbitrary (non-zero) input value, it will be observed that the output does not change until a certain definite input increment is exceeded. This increment is termed as resolution. Resolution can then be defined as the input increment that produces a definite perceivable change in the output. It may be observed that resolution defines the smallest measurable *input change*, whereas threshold defines the smallest measurable *input*. Both the terms can be expressed in absolute units as well as a percentage of the full-scale output. An instrument with a large hysteresis does not necessarily have poor resolution.

Scale readability is a characteristic that depends on both the instrument and the observer. It indicates the number of significant figures that can be recorded in the data. In the case of analog meters, the factor depends upon the scale marking and the thickness of the deflection pointer. In digital meters, the least significant digit gives the measure of scale readability.

1.4.7 Threshold

If the instrument input is very gradually increased from zero, there will be some minimum value below which no output change can be observed or detected. This minimum value defines the threshold of the instrument. The phenomenon is specified by the first detectable output change which is noticeable or measurable. In many cases it is preferred to give a quantitative value when considering the reproducibility of the threshold data. The term can then be defined as the definite numerical value in the output for a corresponding change in the input.

"Dead space", "dead band", and "dead zone" are some of the other terms used to express threshold in many instruments. They form a part of the total range of input values possible for a given output and contribute to the total hysteresis.

1.4.8 Repeatability

Repeatability is defined as the measure of the deviation of test results from the mean value. It indicates the closeness of agreement among a number of consecutive measurements of the same input under the same operating conditions. It relates to the performance of the unit or systems when all determinations are carried out by one operator under the same conditions. When the measurement is made over a specified period of time and when hysteresis is also included, this characteristics may be referred to as reproducibility.

1.4.9 Reliability and Maintainability

The reliability of a system is defined as the probability that it will perform its assigned functions for a specific period of time under given conditions. The maintainability of a system is the probability that in the event of failure of the system, maintenance action under given conditions will restore the system within a specified time. Both the factors are extremely significant for complex systems. Estimates of reliability and maintainability must be included in the initial trade-off between performance, cost, and schedule.

The reliability of a device or system is affected not only by the choice of individual parts in system but also by manufacturing methods, quality of maintenance, and the type of user.

1.4.10 Span

The range of the measurand variable for which an instrument is designed to measure linearly is called the span. Sometimes, it specifies the linear operating range of the total scale. A related term which implies the dynamic fidelity of the equipment is termed as the "dynamic range". This is the ratio of the largest to the smallest dynamic input that the instrument will faithfully measure. The value is usually given in decibels.

1.4.11 Dynamic Accuracy

If a measurement system is subjected to rapidly-varying inputs, the relation between the input and output becomes different from that in the static or quasistatic case. The dynamic response of the system can be expressed by means of a differential equation. If this is a linear differential equation, the system is dynamically linear. The basic dynamic characteristics depend on the order of the differential equation of the system.

First-order instruments (e.g. temperature sensors) can be characterized by one parameter known as the time constant τ (in seconds) of the system. The differential equation representing the system is

$$\tau \dot{y} + y = x(t) \tag{1.1}$$

where $x(t)$ is the time function of the input and y is the output of the system.

The two parameters that characterize the second order type of transducers are the natural frequency ω_n and the damping ratio ζ of the system. With these parameters, the differential equation can be written as

$$\frac{1}{\omega_n{}^2}\ddot{y} + \frac{2\zeta}{\omega_n}\dot{y} + y = x(t) \tag{1.2}$$

where ω_n is expressed in rad/sec and ζ is a non-dimensional quantity. Higher-order systems also result when more than one lower order system is in series, e.g. if the output of a second-order transducer is fed to a second-order filter, the overall system becomes a fourth-order system.

The parameters mentioned above for first-order and second-order systems are very useful for analysing the output response to simple input-time functions and for evaluating the dynamic errors arising out of them. In the case of first-order systems, a lower time constant represents fast response and hence minimum dynamic errors. In the case of second-order systems, the natural frequency is an index of the speed of response. The damping ratio indicates the relative stability of a second-order system. A poorly-damped system exhibits oscillatory output in response to a transient input, whereas a highly-damped system exhibits sluggish response, thereby taking considerable time to reach the steady state value.

An extensive treatment of the dynamic behaviour of the measurement systems of different orders is presented in Chapter 3.

1.5 CALIBRATION

Calibration is an essential part of industrial measurement and control. It can be defined as the comparison of specific values of the input and output of an instrument with a corresponding reference standard. It offers a guarantee to the device or instrument that it operates with the required accuracy and the range specifications under the stipulated environmental conditions. Calibrated devices permit a manufacturer or processor to produce a quality product with desirable or required specifications. By this process, the errors and corrections are revealed.

Calibration must be performed periodically to test the validity of the performance of the device or the system and requires the use of a standard for comparison of values. These comparisons require operator skill, availability of good reference standards, and standard environments. Calibration does not guarantee the performance of an instrument but is usually a good indication whether or not its performance can meet the accuracy and range specifications for which the device is to be used. Recalibration is carried out if the device has been adjusted, aged, repaired, modified, or abused at any time. The records obtained act as manufacturer's verification and offer confidence to the user as evidence of compliance.

The accepted standards can be classified under three categories, "primary", "secondary", and "working standards".

A primary standard is an extremely accurate and absolute unit certified by the national standards institution to be within allowable tolerances. These standards are very expensive to own and maintain. 'Absolute' is used in the sense of being independent, invariant, and not relative but finite.

The reference calibrated standards, designed and constructed from absolute standards are termed as secondary standards. These can be established at a number of institutions with traceability to the primary standard. The calibration interval for secondary standards depends on the accuracy and the type of standard being maintained.

The normal standards needed by the industrial establishments and laboratories, having one order of accuracy lower than the secondary standards are termed as working standards.

A well-equipped industrial calibration facility should maintain primary/secondary standards and associated calibration equipment for displacement, velocity, acceleration, force, pressure, flow, temperature, voltage, current, time, and frequency, as required by the industry being served. Some of the standards normally maintained with the accuracies achievable are given in Table 1.1. The standard should be at least an order more accurate than the instrument being calibrated. The reference standard need only be as reliable and accurate as required for the application.

In all calibration procedures, it is advisable to take readings both in the ascending and descending order. In a mechanical or electro-mechanical transducer, this procedure normally reveals losses due to friction, hysteresis, and similar type of phenomena, and in a purely electrical device, the non-linearity and magnetic reluctance get exhibited.

TABLE 1.1 CALIBRATION STANDARDS FOR PHYSICAL PARAMETERS

Parameter	Primary Standard	Secondary and Working Standards
Displacement/ velocity/ acceleration	Length standard with Krypton 86 lamp (1×10^{-8}); motion measurement with standard gauges; vibrating and rotating table simulation; laser interferometer (1×10^{-6})	Precision micrometer and other gauges (1×10^{-5}); gyroscopes; standard accelerometers (2×10^{-4})
Pressure	Air dead weight testers; precision manometers $(3 \times 10^{-5}$ to $1 \times 10^{-6})$	Oil dead-weight testers, quartz bourdon tube; force balance transducers; mercury and water manometers $(1 \times 10^{-5}$ to $3 \times 10^{-4})$
Force/torque	Standard dead weights $(1 \times 10^{-7}$ to $1 \times 10^{-8})$	Standard load cells; universal testing machines; precision torque meters $(1 \times 10^{-4}$ to $1 \times 10^{-5})$
Flow	Volume, mass and time measurements (1×10^{-5})	Pitot tubes rotameters turbine flow meters $(1 \times 10^{-4}$ to $1 \times 10^{-3})$
Temperature	Precision potentiometers/bridges; boiling and melting points of metals $(2 \times 10^{-3}K)$	Standard thermocouples; platinum resistance thermometers; standard potentiometers; radiation pyrometers $(20 \times 10^{-3}K)$; rubidium beam standards
Time/frequency	Cesium beam standards (Time 0.2 μs/day, frequency 1×10^{-12}/day)	Quartz crystal oscillators (Time 20 μs/day, frequency 1×10^{-10}/day)
Voltage/current	Josephson effect-potential related to frequency (1×10^{-6})	Standard voltmeters; standard potentiometers (1×10^{-5})

Typical accuracies are given in parentheses.

EXERCISES

1.1 (a) Enumerate the various sources of error encountered in a measurement system.

(b) The output of a pressure transducer is recorded over its full-scale range of 50 bars, as shown below.

Calibration Pressure	Output Reading Bars
0	0
5.0	5.0
10.0	9.8
15.0	14.8
20.0	19.9
25.0	25.1
30.0	30.1
35.0	35.3
40.0	40.2
45.0	45.1
50.0	50.0

(i) Determine the static sensitivity of the device.

(ii) Calculate the maximum non-linearity of the device.

(iii) If the error due to hysteresis is observed to be ± 0.1 bar, calculate the overall accuracy of the device.

1.2 The calibrated Mach number M in a Mach metre is obtained from the measurements of pressures q_c and p_s, related by the equation

$$M = \sqrt{5\left[\left(\frac{q_c}{p_s}+1\right)^{2/7}-1\right]} \text{ for } M \leqslant 1$$

Obtain the error in Mach number if (a) error in q_c and p_s is $\pm 0.1\%$ F.S. individually, (b) error in q_c is $+0.1\%$ F.S. and p_s is -0.1% F.S., and (c) error in q_c is $\pm 0.1\%$ F.S. and p_s is -0.2% F.S.

BIBLIOGRAPHY

Adams, L.F., *Engineering Measurements and Instrumentation*, The English University Press Ltd., London, 1975.

Barry, B.A., *Errors in Practical Measurements in Science, Engineering and Technology*, Wiley Inter Science, New York, 1978.

Bass, H.G., *Introduction to Engineering Measurements*, McGraw Hill-New York, 1967.

Beckwith, T.G. and Buck, N.L., *Mechanical Measurements*, Addison Wesley, Reading, Massachusetts, 1969.

Bragg, G.M., *Principles of Experimentation and Measurement*-Prentice-Hall, New Jersey, 1974.

Born, G.J. and Durbin, E.J., "Theory of measurement", *Instrumentation and Control Systems*, Vol. 41, No. 11, pp. 63-67, 1968.

Burgeos, J.A., "Spotting trouble before it happens (Reliability), *Machine Design*, Vol. 42, No. 23, pp. 150-155, Sept. 17, 1970.

Cerni, R.H. and Foster, L.E., *Introduction for Engineering Measurement*, John Wiley and Sons Inc., New York, 1962.

Churchman, C.W. and Raboosh, P., *Measurements, Definition and Theories*, John Wiley and Sons Inc., New York, 1959.

Considine, D.M., *Process Instruments and Controls Handbook*, McGraw-Hill, New York, 1974.

Cook, N.M. and Rabinowicz, E., *Physical Measurements and Analysis*, Addison Wesley, New York, 1963.

Doebelin E.A., *Measurement Systems, Application and Design*, McGraw-Hill, New York, 1966.

Eckman, D.P., *Industrial Instrumentation*, John Wiley and Sons Inc., New York, 1972.

Hand, B.P., "A technique for system error analysis", *Advances in Instrumentation*, Vol. 25, Part 3, paper 713, 1970.

Holzbock, W.G., *Instruments for Measurement and Control*, Reinhold, New York, 1963.

I.S.A., *Standards and Practices for Instrumentation*, I.S.A. Publication, Pittsburg, 1977.

I.S.A., *Transducer Compendium*, Instrument Society of America, Plenum Press, Pittsburg, 1967.

Korn, J. and Simpson, K., "Theory and experiments for teaching measurement", *Instrument Practice*, Vol. 25, No. 4, pp. 205-209, April 1971.

Labunets, V.S., et. al., "Relationship of actual and the normalized reliability of the means of measurement technology", *Measurement Technology*, Vol. 16, No. 6, pp. 800-801, June 1973.

Liptak, *Instrument Engineers Handbook*, Chilton Book Co., New York, 1969.

Lunas, L.J., "What is an accuracy specification?", *Instrument and Control Systems*, Vol. 46, No. 11, pp. 69-71, Nov. 1973.

Neubert, H.K.P,, *Instrument Transducers*, Clarendon Press, Oxford, 1975.

Norton, H.N., "The error band concept and its use in specifications and evaluation of transducer", *Microtechnic*, Vol. 26, No. 6, pp. 381-383, Aug. 1972.

Norton, H.N., *Handbook of Transducers for Electrical Measuring Systems*, Prentice-Hall, New Jersey, 1968.

Oliver, F.J., *Practical Instrument Transducers*, Pitman and Sons, London, 1972.

Quittner, G.F., "Sensors in automation", *IEEE Trans. Ind. Elect. and Control Inst.*, Vol. IECI 21, No. 1, pp. 3-12, February, 1974.

Reddip, R.J., "Reliability criteria", *Measurement and Control*, Vol. 10, pp. 201-203, June 1977.

Rohrbach, C., "Operating principles of mechanical modules for transducers and the most important sources of error", *Proc. 1972, Joint Measurement Conference (ISA 1972)*, pp. 125-134, Boulder, Colo, USA, June 1972.

Scheuk, H., *Theories of Engineering Experimentation*, McGraw Hill-New York, 1968.

Soissen, H.E., *Instrumentation in Industry*, Wiley Inter Science, New York, 1975.

Stein, P.K., *Measurement Engineering*, *Vol. 1*, *Basic Principles*, Stein Engineering Services, Tempe Arizona, 1962.

Stein, P.K., "Sensors/detectors, transducers, the basic measuring components", *Proc. 1972*, *Joint Measurement Conference*, Boulder Colo, USA, pp. 63-91, June 1972 (ISA 1972).

Striker, G., *Transducers for Industrial Measurements*, Acta IMEKO, Budapest, 1967.

Sydenham, P.H., "Nature and scope of measurement science", *Proceedings of the IMEKO Colloquim*, Budapest, p. 271 (Conference held at New England University, Adelaide), 1976.

Thomas, H.E., *Handbook of Biomedical Instrumentation and Measurement*, Reston, VA, Reston, 1974.

Wildhack, W.A., et al., "Accuracy in measurements and calibration", *NBS Technote 262*, Washington D.C., 1965.

2

TRANSDUCER CLASSIFICATION

2.1 INTRODUCTION

A transducer is defined as a device capable of being actuated by an energizing input from one or more transmission media, and in turn, generating a related signal to one or more transmission systems or media. It provides a usable output in response to a specific input measurand which may be a physical or mechanical quantity, property or condition. Actually, the energy in one form of information, transmission system or physical state is transferred to that of another system or state. The responding device may be mechanical, electrical, magnetic, optical, chemical, acoustic, thermal, nuclear, or a combination of any two or more of these.

An example of the mechanical transducer is the dial gauge or aneroid barometer, which has been in existence over a long period. Mechanical transducers possess high accuracy, ruggedness, relatively low cost, and operate without any external power supplies. But such types are not advantageous for many of the modern scientific experiments and process control instrumentation because of their poor frequency response, requirement of large forces to overcome mechanical friction, incompatibility when remote control or indication is required, and a host of other limitations. All these drawbacks have been overcome with the introduction of electrical transducers.

2.2 ELECTRICAL TRANSDUCER

An electrical transducer is a sensing device by which a physical, mechanical or optical quantity to be measured is transformed directly, with a suitable mechanism, into an electrical voltage or current proportional to the input measurand. The input versus output energy relationship takes a definite reproducible function. The output to input and the output to time behaviour is predictable to a known degree of accuracy, sensitivity and response, within the specified environmental conditions. The significant parameters which dictate the transducer capability are linearity, repeatability, resolution, and reliability.

The main advantages of an electrical transducer may be summarized as follows:

(a) The electrical output can be amplified to any desired level.
(b) The output can be indicated and recorded remotely at a distance from the **sensing** medium. Further, more than one indicator can be actuated simultaneously.

(c) The output can be modified to meet the requirements of the indicating or controlling equipment. The signal magnitude can be related in terms of the voltage or current. The analog signal information can be converted into frequency or pulse informations. The same output can be converted into a digital format for display, print-out or on-line computation.

Since the output can be modified, modulated, or amplified at will, the output signal can be easily adapted for recording on any suitable multichannel recording oscillograph which can cater to a number of electrical transducers simultaneously.

(d) The signals can be conditioned or mixed to obtain any combination with outputs of similar transducers or control signals as in an air data computer or adaptive control systems. A typical example is the Mach number measurement with two measurands.

(e) The size and shape of the transducer can be suitably designed to achieve the optimum weight and volume.

(f) The contour design and dimensions can be so chosen as not to disturb the measurand phenomena, as in the case of turbulence measurements. In certain cases the size can be made extremely small, thereby increasing the natural frequency to a high value. An example is the miniature piezoelectric pick-up employed for vibration measurements.

In spite of the merits described above, some disadvantages do exist in electrical sensors, creating problems in certain precision measurements. The device is sometimes less reliable than mechanical types because of the ageing and drift of the active components. Further, the sensing elements and associated signal conditioners are comparatively expensive. In some cases the accuracy and resolution attainable are not as high as in mechanical devices. The best accuracy achievable is of the order of 0.01%. With the availability of better materials, improved technology and circuitry, the range of accuracy and stability have been very much increased during recent years.

Special techniques, such as feedback indicating systems where zero or null indication is the criterion, can be employed to improve the accuracy, but this is carried out at the expense of increased circuit complexity, more space, lower natural frequency, and higher cost.

2.3 CLASSIFICATION

All electrical transducers are broadly classified under two categories, viz., active and passive transducers. Active transducers are self-generating devices, operating under energy conversion principles. They generate an equivalent electrical output signal, e.g. from pressure to charge or from temperature to electrical potential, without any external energizing source. Passive transducers operate under energy controlling principles. They depend upon the change in the electrical parameter (resistance, inductance or capacitance) whose excitation or operation requires secondary electrical energy from an external source. A typical example is the case of the strain gauge excited by a dc voltage source or differential transformer energized by a carrier wave signal.

The various transduction principles under which the electrical transducers operate are given in Table 2.1. The basic input quantity involved in transduction and the measured parameter for which electrical transducers can be employed are given in Table

TABLE 2.1 CLASSIFICATION OF ELECTRICAL TRANSDUCERS

Active Transducers	Passive Transducers
Thermoelectric	Resistive
Piezoelectric	Inductive
Photovoltaic	Capacitive
	Photoconductive
	Piezoresistive
Magnetostrictive	Magnetoresistive
Electrokinetic	Thermoresistive
Electrodynamic	Elastoresistive
Electromagnetic	Hall effect
Pyroelectric	Synchro
Galvanic	Gyro
	Radio-active absorption
	Ionic conduction

TABLE 2.2 DIMENSIONAL RELATIONSHIP BETWEEN PARAMETERS

Basic Quantity	Measured Parameter (Derived Quantity)
Linear displacement	Length, width, thickness, position, level, wear, surface quality, strain, velocity, acceleration
Angular displacement	Altitude, angle of incidence, angle of flow, angular vibration
Linear velocity	Speed, rate of flow, momentum, vibration
Angular velocity	Angular speed, rate of turn (roll, pitch and yaw), angular momentum, vibration
Linear acceleration	Vibration, impact (jerk), motion
Angular acceleration	Torque, angular vibration, angular impact, moment of inertia
Force	Weight, density, thrust, stress, torque, vibration, acceleration, pressure (absolute, gauge and differential) flow, fluid velocity, sound intensity
Temperature	Gas and liquid expansion, heat flow, heat conductivity, fluid flow, surface temperature, radiation pressure, gas velocity, turbulence, velocity of sound
Light	Light flux and density, temperature, spectral distribution, strain, length, force, torque, frequency
Time	Frequency, number of events, statistical distribution
Electromagnetic radiation	Wavelength, power, field strength

Each one of these quantities in Table 2.2 can be measured using various transduction principles given in Table 2.1, the actual type depending on specific requirements, performance specifications, and environmental conditions.

2.4 BASIC REQUIREMENTS OF A TRANSDUCER

A transducer is normally designed to sense a specific measurand or to respond only to that particular measurand. A complete knowledge of the electrical and mechanical characteristics of the transducer is of great importance while choosing a transducer for a particular application. Often, it is deemed essential to get details of these characteristics during the selection of instrumentation for the experiment concerned. The basic requirements are:

(a) Ruggedness: Ability to withstand overloads, with safety stops for overload protection.

(b) Linearity: Ability to reproduce input-output characteristics symmetrically and linearly. Overall linearity is the main factor considered.

(c) Repeatability: Ability to reproduce the output signal exactly when the same measurand is applied repeatedly under same environmental conditions.

(d) Convenient instrumentation: Sufficiently high analog output signal with high signal to noise ratio; digital output preferred in many cases.

(e) High stability and reliability: Minimum error in measurement, unaffected by temperature, vibration, and other environmental variations.

(f) Good dynamic response: Output is faithful to input when taken as a function of time. The effect is analysed as the frequency response.

(g) Excellent mechanical characteristics that can affect the performance in static, quasi-static, and dynamic states. The major effects are:

(i) Mechanical hysteresis—manifestation of imperfect response of the sensing elements, integrated over dimensions of the strained transducer. Effect depends on the raw material used, ageing, etc.

(ii) Viscous flow or creep—effect due to viscous flow in the material of the sensing element. Magnitude increases with increasing load and temperature. Materials with low melting point show larger creep values.

(iii) Elastic after effect—a continued deformation when the load is applied and kept constant. This effect decreases with time. Like creep, there is a similar relaxation towards the original position when the load is removed. Virtually no residual deformation is observed.

(h) Built-in integrated device with noise, asymmetry, and other defects minimized.

The technical specifications required for a typical pressure transducer are given in Table 2.3, wherein all aspects of the user's requirements are covered.

TABLE 2.3 TYPICAL SPECIFICATIONS FOR A PRESSURE TRANSDUCER

Parameter	Characteristics
General	
Manufacturer	As specified
Model/series	As specified
Identification	As specified
Measurand	Static/dynamic/absolute/gauge/differential pressure
Measurand media	Liquid/gas
Measurand range	Full-scale range; kg/cm^2
Limitations	Case pressure, temperature, special radiation
Applications	Industrial, aerospace, biomedical, geophysics, laboratory

(Contd.)

TABLE 2.3 (Contd.)

Parameter	Characteristics
Electrical Characteristics	
Operating principle-transduction	Resistive, capacitive, inductive, piezoelectric, piezoresistive
Sensing element	Diaphragm, bellows, capsules, bourdon tube
Sensitivity	m V/V/F.S.
Transfer function	Linear, logarithmic, error function
Excitation	Working level voltage—ac/dc V
Resolution	Smallest change recognizable (% E.S.)
Output Characteristics	
ac or dc	Nature, range, output voltage, output impedance
Voltage range (V)	dc/ac
Power range (W)	W
Impedance (Ω)	ohms
Frequency range	Range of operating frequency (Hz)
Non-linearity	% F.S.
Hysteresis and creep	% F.S.
Static error band	Deviation from transfer function (includes all errors)
Zero shift and sensitivity variation with temperature	% F.S. per °C
Repeatability	% F.S.
Threshold	% F.S.
Over range/over load	% F.S.
Natural frequencies	Hz
Dynamic response	Response characteristics indicated through its bandwidth in Hz
Acceleration response	% F.S. per *g* (where *g* is the acceleration due to gravity)
Rise time	Seconds
Stability	% F.S. over a period of time
Temperature range	Range of operation within specification
Calibration and zero adjustment	Facility provided in instrumentation
Mechanical	
Dimensions (size)	$l \times b \times h$, in cm
Weight	W in g
Mounting	Drawing specifications
Material of construction	Materials used for fabrication
Life expectancy	Number of cycles/operations, within specifications
Connections	
Pressure inlet	Types and dimensions
Electrical output	Types and dimensions
Accessories	Ancillary parts needed for installation
Operational limitations	Environmental and range conditions
Others	To be specified
Others	
Environmental characteristics	Effects of temperature, humidity, acceleration, shock, vibration, and magnetic field
Operating life	Hours of operation, within specification
Storage life	Hours/days, without determination

3

PERFORMANCE CHARACTERISTICS OF AN INSTRUMENTATION SYSTEM

3.1 INTRODUCTION

All measuring devices in an instrumentation system should have characteristics that can be expressed in a quantitative manner. These are normally expressed in numerical values, indicating the ability of the system to perform as required and the extent to which the parameters can be measured accurately. The measurement accuracy is generally interpreted as the basic characteristic of the system. Results of this property is judged by the precision and basic dynamic characteristics achieved.

The term "instrumentation system" includes the sensing element, variable conversion and manipulation elements, data transmission, and data presentation. These are realized with suitable transducers, signal conditioners and recording equipment. The performance characteristic of an instrumentation system is judged by how faithfully the system measures the desired input and how thoroughly it rejects the undesirable inputs. Quantitatively, it relates to the degree of approach to perfection. The system operation is defined in terms of static and dynamic characteristics. The former represents the non-linear and statistical effects and the latter generally represents the dynamic behaviour of the system. The static characteristic is represented by precision and accuracy. The accuracy may be influenced by the sensitivity, working range, non-linearity, hysteresis and other properties of the sensor. The dynamics of a real system is reflected by the time constant, damping coefficient, and the natural frequency. The response of cascaded elements possessing individual dynamic responses can be ascertained from the characteristics of the dominant elements, or combinations thereof.

3.2 GENERALIZED MEASUREMENTS

The dynamic characteristics of a measurement system can be studied by postulating a generalized mathematical model embodying the features pertinent to the characteristics of the dynamic relation between any particular input and output. Any measurement system can be considered as a transform of a measured signal $x_i(t)$ to an output signal $x_0(t)$. The relationship between them is normally determined by a set of differential equations obtained from physical principles and the scheme of measurement.

The most widely used mathematical model for the dynamic response studies is the ordinary linear differential equation with constant coefficients. The relationship can be represented in general as

$$a_n \frac{dx_o^n}{dt^n} + a_{n-1} \frac{dx_o^{n-1}}{dt^{n-1}} + \cdots + a_1 \frac{dx_o}{dt} + a_0 x_o$$

$$= b_m \frac{dx_i^m}{dt^m} + b_{m-1} \frac{dx_i^{m-1}}{dt^{m-1}} + \cdots + b_1 \frac{dx_i}{dt} + b_0 x_i \tag{3.1}$$

where a's and b's are constants depending upon the physical parameters of the system. The solution of equations of this type can be obtained by either the method of D operators or the Laplace transform method. The latter method is followed in this chapter.

3.2.1 Transfer Function Representation

The transfer function is defined as the ratio of the Laplace transform of the output quantity to the Laplace transform of the input quantity, when all initial conditions are zero.

The operational transfer function of Eq. (3.1) can be written as

$$\frac{x_o(s)}{x_i(s)} = \frac{b_m s^m + b_{m-1} s^{m-1} + \cdots + b_1 s + b_0}{a_n s^n + a_{n-1} s^{n-1} + \cdots + a_1 s + a_0} \tag{3.2}$$

where $x_o(s)$ is the Laplace transform of the output, $x_i(s)$ is the Laplace transform of the input, and s is the Laplace operator.

The system configuration can be symbolically represented as shown in Fig. 3.1.

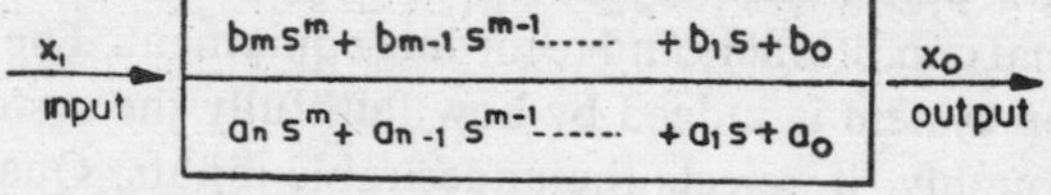

Fig. 3.1 Generalized operational transfer function

3.2.2 Sinusoidal Transfer Function

The quality of measurement under dynamic conditions can be assessed clearly by analysing the response of the system to certain standard inputs. The most important response is the steady state response to a sinusoidal input. The input quantity x_i takes the form of A_i sin (ωt). In all linear systems, under steady state, i.e. after the initial transients have died, the output quantity will be a sinewave of exactly the same angular frequency ω of the input. The amplitude may, however, differ from that of the input and a phase shift may also be present. The results are obtained as a particular solution by the method of undetermined coefficients.

The frequency response of the system will consist of curves sharing amplitude ratio and phase shift as a function of frequency. This is often represented as shown in Fig. 3.2.

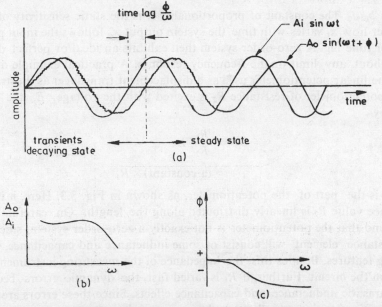

Fig. 3.2 Sinusoidal response characteristics: (a) input-output
waveforms; (b) amplitude ratio; (c) phase shift

The sinusoidal transfer function of a measurement system is obtained by substituting $j\omega$ for s wherever it appears in the operational transfer function (Eq. (3.2)) as shown below:

$$\frac{x_o}{x_i}(j\omega) = \frac{b_m(j\omega)^m + b_{m-1}(j\omega)^{m-1} + \cdots + b_1(j\omega) + b_0}{a_n(j\omega)^n + a_{n-1}(j\omega)^{n-1} + \cdots + a_1(j\omega) + a_0} \tag{3.3}$$

For any given frequency ω, the term $\frac{x_o}{x_i}(j\omega)$ is a complex number. This can also be represented in the polar form as

$$\frac{x_o}{x_i}(j\omega) = \frac{|x_o|}{|x_i|} \angle\phi = M\angle\phi \tag{3.4}$$

where M represents the amplitude ratio of the output to the input, and the angle ϕ represents the phase angle by which the output x_o leads the input x_i.

3.3 ZERO-ORDER SYSTEM

In a measurement system there are many special cases in practice where the performance characteristics are complex. The simplest possible form of Eq. (3.1) occurs when all the a's and b's other than a_0 and b_0 are assumed to be zero. The differential equation (3.1) then becomes a simple algebraic equation,

$$a_0 x_o = b_0 x_i \tag{3.5}$$

Any instrumentation system that closely obeys this equation over its range of operation is defined as a "zero-order system". The static sensitivity can be expressed as

$$x_o = \frac{b_0}{a_0} x_i = K x_i \tag{3.6}$$

where $K = b_0/a_0$. The constant of proportionality K is the static sensitivity of the system.

No matter how x_i varies with time, the system output x_o follows the input perfectly with no deviation or time lag. A zero-order system then exhibits an ideal or perfect dynamic performance without any limit on the frequency response. A practical example of the zero-order system is the linear potentiometer used as a displacement transducer as illustrated in Fig. 3.3. When the potentiometer of resistance R_2 is excited with the voltage, E, the output voltage e is given by

$$e = \frac{R_1}{R_2} E$$

$$= (\text{a constant}) \times R_1 \tag{3.7}$$

where R_1 is the part of the potentiometer, as shown in Fig. 3.3. Here, it is assumed that the resistance value R_2 is linearly distributed along the length. On careful examination, it may be found that the potentiometer is not exactly a zero-order system, since the potentiometer resistance element will consist of some inductance and capacitance, depending upon the winding features. Besides this, the impedance of the measuring instrument offers a loading effect on the circuit. Further, if R_1 is varied fast, the dynamic errors become dominant due to parasitic inductance and capacitance effects. Since these errors are small in magnitude, a potentiometer is normally termed as a zero-order system.

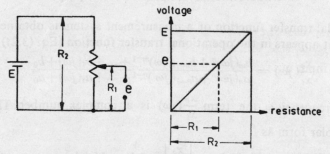

Fig. 3.3 Potentiometric device representing zero-order system

3.4 FIRST-ORDER SYSTEM

In Eq. (3.1), if all the terms other than a_1, a_0, and b_0 are assumed to be zero, we get

$$a_1 \frac{dx_o}{dt} + a_0 x_o = b_0 x_i \tag{3.8}$$

Any system following this equation is termed as a first-order system. Equation (3.8) may be rewritten as

$$\frac{a_1}{a_0} \frac{dx_o}{dt} + x_o = \frac{b_0}{a_0} x_i$$

By substituting $\frac{b_0}{a_0} = K$ (static sensitivity) and $\frac{a_1}{a_0} = \tau$ (time constant) and by taking the

Laplace transform with zero initial condition, the transfer function of the first-order system becomes

$$\frac{x_o}{x_i}(s) = \frac{K}{\tau s + 1} \tag{3.9}$$

Thermocouples and thermistors are examples of the first-order systems. As a specific case, consider a situation where a thermocouple is suddenly immersed in a gas medium and assume that the heat transfer is through convection only (no radiation and conduction). Then the rate at which heat is being stored in the thermocouple junction can be expressed mathematically as

$$h_c A (T_1 - T_2) = mc\frac{dT_2}{dt} \tag{3.10}$$

where h_c = coefficient of heat transfer by convection, A = heat transfer area of the junction, T_2 = junction temperature, T_1 = ambient gas temperature, m = mass of the junction, and c = specific heat of the junction.

The ratio of m/A for a thermocouple can be determined by measurement. Representing $(mc/h_c A)$ as τ (time constant) and rearranging, the above equation becomes

$$T_1 = T_2 + \tau\frac{dT_2}{dt} \tag{3.11}$$

thus representing a first-order response.

3.4.1 Step Response of First-Order System

Consider a first-order system which is initially in equilibrium. On the application of a step input, let the input quantity be increased instantaneously by an amount x_s. Then Eq. (3.9) becomes

$$(\tau s + 1) x_o = K x_s/s \tag{3.12}$$

A typical example of this case is a thermocouple in air suddenly immersed in boiling water, resulting in a step input change in the junction temperature. The step input can be represented mathematically by the relationship in time domain as:

$$x_i = 0, \text{ for } t = 0$$

and

$$x_i = x_s \text{ for } t \geqslant 0$$

In Laplace transform notation,

$$x_i(s) = \frac{x_s}{s} \tag{3.13}$$

Hence Eq. (3.12) becomes,

$$x_o(s) = \frac{K}{(\tau s + 1)}\frac{x_s}{s} \tag{3.14}$$

By partial fraction expansion,

$$x_o(s) = \left[\frac{1}{s} - \frac{1}{s + \dfrac{1}{\tau}} \right] K x_s \tag{3.15}$$

The inverse Laplace transform of Eq. (3.15) becomes

$$x_o(t) = (1 - e^{-t/\tau})\, Kx_s \tag{3.16}$$

Equation (3.16) shows that the speed of response depends only on the value of the time constant τ, and the response is faster if τ is smaller. Therefore, for a first-order system, minimizing the magnitude of τ helps to improve the dynamic response. Rewriting Eq. (3.16), we get

$$\frac{x_o}{Kx_s} = (1 - e^{-t/\tau}) \tag{3.17}$$

Plotting the normalized value of $\dfrac{x_o}{Kx_s}$ against t/τ, a response of the form shown in Fig. 3.4(a) is obtained. One of the important characteristics of such an exponential response curve is that, at $t = \tau$, $x_o = 0.632 Kx_s$. Expressing the same in a different way, in first-order systems when $t = \tau$, the response reaches 63.2% of its steady-state value x_s.

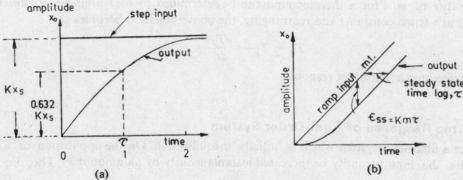

Fig. 3.4 (a) Response of a first-order system to a step input; (b) response of a first-order system to a ramp input

3.4.2 Ramp Response of First-Order System

Consider the case when a ramp input is applied to a first-order system which is initially in equilibrium. Let the input change with a slope m with respect to time t, then,

$$x_i(s) = \mathcal{L}(mt) = \frac{m}{s^2} \tag{3.18}$$

Substituting Eq. (3.18) in Eq. (3.9), we get

$$x_o(s) = \frac{K}{(\tau s + 1)} \frac{m}{s^2}$$

$$= Km\left(\frac{1}{s^2} + \frac{\tau}{s + \dfrac{1}{\tau}} - \frac{\tau}{s}\right) \tag{3.19}$$

The inverse Laplace transform of Eq. (3.19) gives

$$x_{ot} = Km(t - \tau + \tau e^{-t/\tau}), \quad \text{for } t \geqslant 0 \tag{3.20}$$

The dynamic error between the actual output and the input-ramp is given by

$$\epsilon(t) = Kmt - x_o(t)$$

$$= Km\tau(1 - e^{-t/\tau}) \tag{3.21}$$

As $t \to \infty$, $\epsilon_{ss} \to Km\tau$ thus indicating smaller values of steady-state error with smaller values of τ. The ramp input response curve of a first-order system is shown in Fig. 3.4(b).

3.4.3 Frequency Response of First-Order System

The transfer function for a sinusoidal input $x_i = A_i \sin(\omega t)$ is obtained by substituting $s = j\omega$ in Eq. (3.19) as

$$\frac{x_o}{x_i}(j\omega) = \frac{K}{j\omega\tau + 1} = \frac{K}{\sqrt{\omega^2\tau^2 + 1}} \angle \tan^{-1}(\omega\tau) \tag{3.22}$$

A first-order instrument approaches the ideal condition when τ tends to zero. For any other value of τ, the measurements will be accurate below a particular value of ω only.

For a pure sine-wave input, the amplitude and phase shift can be computed by simple calculations. If the input is complex, i.e. a combination of several sine waves of different frequencies, the transfer function at each frequency is to be computed and then interpreted.

3.4.4 Impulse Response of First-Order System

An impulse function is a rectangular pulse of infinitesimally short duration, infinitely high magnitude, and a finite area. If the area of the pulse is taken as unity, the value is termed as 'unit impulse function', $u(t)$. Such an input plays an important role in the dynamic analysis of a system.

The Laplace transform of an impulse function is the area under the impulse. Hence for a unit-impulse input, the Laplace transform of the input is unity, i.e.

$$u(s) = \mathcal{L}[u(t)] = 1 \tag{3.23}$$

It should be noted that an impulse that has infinite magnitude and zero duration is a mere mathematical hypothetical case that actually does not occur in any of the physical systems whatsoever. However, if the magnitude of a 'pulse' is very large and its duration is very short when compared to the system time constants, it may be approximated to an impulse. For example, if a temperature input $f_T(t)$ is applied to a thermocouple for a very short duration t_0 ($t_0 \ll \tau$), where the magnitude f_T is sufficiently large so that the integral $\int_0^{t_0} f_T(t)\, dt$ is very high, then such an input can be considered as an impulse input.

Usually, for inputs in the form of a pulse with duration t_d the response of the system can be obtained by considering the input as two step inputs, one occurring at $t = 0$ and the other at $t = t_d$ in the reverse direction and superimposing the results. However, for a unit-impulse input, the response can be calculated by the simple inverse Laplace transformation of the transfer function, as the Laplace transform of a unit impulse is unity.

3.5 SECOND-ORDER SYSTEM

A second-order system is defined as one that follows the equation

$$a_2 \frac{d^2 x_o}{dt^2} + a_1 \frac{dx_o}{dt} + a_0 x_o = b_0 x_i \tag{3.24}$$

Taking the Laplace transform of the above equation, it can be shown that

$$\frac{x_o}{x_i}(s) = \frac{K}{\dfrac{s^2}{\omega_n^2} + \dfrac{2\zeta}{\omega_n} s + 1} \tag{3.25}$$

where $\omega_n = \sqrt{\dfrac{a_0}{a_2}}$, undamped natural frequency (rad/s); $\zeta = \dfrac{a_1}{2\sqrt{a_0 a_2}}$, damping ratio; and $K = b_0/a_0$, static sensitivity.

Typical examples of second-order systems are single degree-of-freedom spring-mass systems employed for acceleration and force measurements.

3.5.1 Step Response of Second-Order System

For a step input of magnitude Eq. (3.25) can be rewritten as

$$\frac{x_o}{K x_s} = \frac{\omega_n^2}{s(s^2 + 2\zeta\omega_n s + \omega_n^2)} \tag{3.26}$$

since the Laplace transform of the step input is $1/s$.

To solve this equation, three practical situations must be identified, depending upon the magnitude of ζ. The roots of the second term in the denominator of the above equation become real and separate if the damping ratio is greater than unity (over-damped system); the critically-damped case ($\zeta = 1$) gives rise to real and repeated roots, and the under-damped case ($\zeta < 1$) gives a complex conjugate pair of roots. The three solutions for Eq. (3.26) will then be

(a) for $\zeta > 1$ (over damped),

$$\frac{x_o}{K x_s}(t) = -\frac{\zeta + \sqrt{\zeta^2 - 1}}{2\sqrt{\zeta^2 - 1}} \exp\left(-\zeta + \sqrt{\zeta^2 - 1}\right)\omega_n t$$

$$+ \frac{\zeta - \sqrt{\zeta^2 - 1}}{2\sqrt{\zeta^2 - 1}} \exp\left(-\zeta - \sqrt{\zeta^2 - 1}\right)\omega_n t + 1 \tag{3.27}$$

(b) for $\zeta = 1$ (critically damped),

$$\frac{x_o}{K x_s}(t) = 1 - (1 + \omega_n t) \exp(-\omega_n t) \tag{3.28}$$

and

(c) for $\zeta < 1$ (under damped),

$$\frac{x_o}{K x_s}(t) = 1 - \frac{\exp(-\zeta\omega_n t)}{\sqrt{1 - \zeta^2}} \sin\left(\sqrt{1 - \zeta^2}\,\omega_n t\right) + \phi \tag{3.29}$$

where $\phi = \sin^{-1}\sqrt{1 - \zeta^2}$.

The values of (x_o/Kx_s) for a step input, as a function of $\omega_n t$ are shown in Fig. 3.5(a). In a second-order system, ω_n is a direct indication of the speed of response. For a given ζ, the normalized amplitude will attain the same value if ω_n is doubled and t is halved. An increase in damping reduces oscillations but slows down the response, i.e. the final value is reached after a longer duration. The time required for the oscillations to decrease to a specified absolute percentage of the final value and thereafter remain less than this value is normally called the setting time t_s. The magnitude of oscillations at any instant of time is never greater than the envelope defined by the exponential term $\exp(-\zeta\omega_n t)$. Thus, an underdamped system will reach 95% of its final value for a step input when $\zeta\omega_n t = 3$, and 98% when $\zeta\omega_n t = 4$.

The corresponding settling time will be

$$t_s = \frac{3}{\zeta\omega_n} \quad \text{(for 95\% settling)} \tag{3.30}$$

$$t_s = \frac{4}{\zeta\omega_n} \quad \text{(for 98\% settling)} \tag{3.31}$$

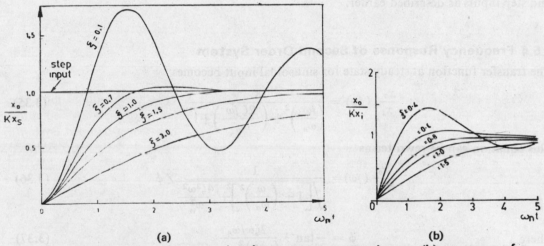

Fig. 3.5 (a) Response of a second-order system to a step input; (b) response of a second-order system to a ramp input (nondimensional)

3.5.2 Ramp Response of Second-Order System

Just as in the case of a first-order system, the response of a second-order system to a ramp input $x_i(t) = mt$ can also be obtained. The solutions in this case will be
(a) for over-damped case ($\zeta > 1$),

$$\frac{x_o}{Kx_i}(t) = \left[\left(Kmt - \frac{2\zeta}{\omega_n} \right) + \frac{2\zeta}{\omega_n} \exp(-\zeta\omega_n t) \left(\cosh \omega_n t \sqrt{\zeta^2-1} \right. \right.$$
$$\left. \left. + \frac{2\zeta^2-1}{2\zeta\sqrt{\zeta^2-1}} \sinh \omega_n t \sqrt{\zeta^2-1} \right) \right] \tag{3.32}$$

(ᵇ) for critically-damped case ($\zeta = 1$),

$$\frac{x_o}{Kx_i}(t) = \left[\left(Kmt - \frac{2\zeta}{\omega_n}\right) + \frac{2\zeta}{\omega_n}\left(\exp(-\omega_n t)\left(1 + \frac{\omega_n t}{2}\right)\right)\right]$$ (3.33)

(c) for under-damped case ($\zeta < 1$),

$$\frac{x_o}{Kx_i}(t) = \left[\left(Kmt - \frac{2\zeta}{\omega_n}\right) - \frac{\exp(-\zeta\omega_n t)}{\omega_n\sqrt{1-\zeta^2}}\sin(\omega_n t\sqrt{1-\zeta^2}+\phi)\right]$$

where $$\phi = \tan^{-1}\frac{2\zeta\sqrt{1-\zeta^2}}{2\zeta^2-1}$$ (3.34)

The normalized response of a second-order system to a ramp input is shown in Fig. 3.5(b).

3.5.3 Terminated Ramp Response of Second-Order System

The response of a second-order instrument to perfect the step input is sometimes misleading, since such a perfect step input does not occur in nature. A realistic approach to this is the terminated ramp input. The response for such an input can be obtained in terms of ramp and step inputs as described earlier.

3.5.4 Frequency Response of Second-Order System

The transfer function at steady state for sinusoidal input becomes

$$\frac{x_o}{x_i}(j\omega) = \frac{K}{\left(\frac{j\omega}{\omega_n}\right)^2 + \left(\frac{2\zeta j\omega}{\omega_n}\right) + 1}$$ (3.35)

This equation can be rewritten as

$$\frac{x_o}{Kx_i}(j\omega) = \frac{1}{\sqrt{\left[1 - \left(\frac{\omega}{\omega_n}\right)^2\right]^2 + \frac{4\zeta^2\omega^2}{\omega_n^2}}}\angle\phi$$ (3.36)

where $$\phi = -\tan^{-1}\frac{2\zeta\omega/\omega_n}{\left(\frac{\omega}{\omega_n}\right)^2 - 1}$$ (3.37)

The frequency and phase responses are shown in Fig. 3.6.

3.6 DEAD-TIME ELEMENT

A dead-time element or transport lag is defined as a system in which the output is exactly of the same form as that of the input, but the event occurs after a time delay τ_d. Mathematically,

$$x_o(t) = Kx_i(t-\tau_d), \quad \text{for } t \geqslant \tau_d$$ (3.38)

Such cases can be observed in pneumatic signal transmission systems. A pressure input at one end of a length of pneumatic tubing will be observed at the other end after the time

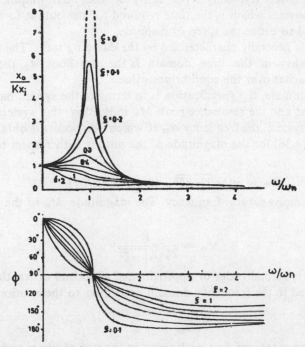

Fig. 3.6 Frequency response of a second-order system

required for propagation through the distance between the two ends. Taking the speed as equal to the speed of sound, the dead time for a 300 m length of tubing is of the order of one second.

The consideration of this phenomenon is important in hydraulic and pneumatic instrumentation systems.

3.7 SPECIFICATIONS AND TESTING OF DYNAMIC RESPONSE

The specifications for the dynamic response of a total measurement system comprising a transducer, signal conditioner, filter, and output display/recorder or the basic transducer alone are the same as that of a typical linear control system. There are basically two factors in specifying the dynamic performance, viz., the speed of response and relative stability or damping. If the system considered is higher than a second-order system, usually the dominant modes are specified in terms of a basic first order or second order system. The dynamic performance of the system can be defined in either the time domain or frequency domain. Most dynamic performance terms are usually interpreted in terms of the definitions of a linear second order system. These include the damped natural frequency and damping ratio.

The transient response to a step input is a common means of specifying the dynamic performance in the time domain. The terms that are used in specifying the speed of response are the rise time t_r, which is the time for the output to rise from 10 to 90 per cent of the final value and the settling time t_s which is the time required for the output to remain within a certain percentage (typically 5 per cent) of the final output. For a first order system, the time constant which is the time required for the output to reach 63 per cent of its final value is used to define the speed of response.

Relative stability is generally characterized by the damping ratio. The term usually used to define relative stability in the time domain is the overshoot M_p, the maximum value to which the output reaches over the equilibrium value.

In the frequency domain, the specification is in terms of the system bandwidth indicating the speed of response and the resonance peak M_m indicating the system relative stability. For a second order system, the frequency ω_m at which M_m occurs is obtained by differentiating the term in Eq. (3.36) for the magnitude of the output with respect to ω and equating it to zero,

$$\omega_m = \omega_n \sqrt{1-2\zeta^2}, \quad \text{(for } \zeta \leqslant 0.707) \tag{3.39}$$

where ω_n is the undamped natural frequency. The magnitude M_m of the peak value is given by

$$M_m = \frac{1}{2\zeta\sqrt{1-\zeta^2}} \tag{3.40}$$

For a system that is second order or approximated as second order, the response in the time domain is related to the frequency domain according to the relationship

$$t_p = \frac{\pi}{\omega_m} \tag{3.41}$$

where t_p is the time to reach the first peak value in the step response and ω_m is the frequency at which M_m occurs.

As can be observed from the earlier discussion, the specifications are in terms of the response to a step input in the case of time domain or a sine-wave input in the case of frequency domain. In order to actually perform the dynamic test on a measurement system to obtain its performance specifications, the choice of whether to use a step-type input or sine-wave input function is a matter of convenience, depending upon the actual physical parameter involved. Either type of input when properly used will yield the same information about the system. The step input does offer a distinct advantage in cases where the generation of sinusoidal input signal is difficult, such as is the case of calibrating temperature or pressure transducers. However, transient response data require fairly extensive data reduction to provide all the required information.

EXERCISES

3.1 A linear second-order, single-degree-of-freedom system has a mass of 8×10^{-3} kg and a stiffness of 1000 N/m. Calculate the natural frequency of the system. Determine the damping constant necessary to just prevent overshoot in response to a step input of force.

3.2 A temperature probe having a first-order response with a time constant of 1 sec is given a step input of 50°C from 0°C. Calculate the temperature indicated 0.6 s after the application of the input. Plot the temperature response characteristics at every 0.2 s interval up to 2 s.

3.3 The damping ratio of under-damped, second-order system is experimentally determined by subjecting the system to an impulse input and recording the decay curve. Determine the damping ratio as a function of the amplitude reduction per cycle. Discuss the sources of error and limitations of the method.

3.4 For a second-order, single-degree-of-freedom accelerometer, plot the maximum ratio of the input frequency to the natural frequency as a function of its damping ratio.

3.5 A second-order instrument is required to measure the input signals up to 100 Hz with an amplitude inaccuracy of less than 1%. Calculate the natural frequency requirements, if the damping ratios are 0.3 and 0.6 respectively. Determine the phase shift in each case at 50 and 75 Hz.

3.6 The thrust experienced by a solid-propellent rocket motor, test fixed in a test facility, is measured by a deflection of a spring element attached to the front end of the motor. If the thrust developed after ignition can be idealized by a step input, estimate the time required for the measuring system to read full thrust steadily, with the following parameters:

Mass of the motor: 30 kg

Spring constant: 70 kg f/cm

Damping ratio: 0.70

BIBLIOGRAPHY

Baird, D.C., *Experimentation-Introduction to Measurement Theory*, Prentice Hall-New Jersey, 1975.

Boiten, S.G., "Mechanics of instrumentation", *Proc. of I. Mech. Engrs.*, (U.K.), pp. 177-269, 1963.

Bragg, G.M., *Principles of Experimentation and Measurement*, Prentice-Hall, New York, 1974.

Bushell, K.W., "The rapid estimation of transient response of a cascade instrument elements", *Proc. Inst. Mech. Engrs.*, Vol. 180, Pt 3G, paper 10, 1965-66.

Dack, D., "System identification by online correlation", *Control Engineering*, Vol. 17, No. 3, pp. 64-70, March 1970.

Davies, J., *Introduction to Dynamic Analysis and Automatic Control (Response of overall systems)*, John Wiley, New York, 1965.

Doebelin, E.O., *Measurement Systems, Application and Design*, McGraw-Hill Book Co., New York, 1975.

Doebelin, E.O., *System Dynamics—Modelling and Response*, Columbus O.H., Merril, 1972.

Draper, C.S. and McKay, W. and Lees, S., *Instrument Engineering*, 3 Vols., McGraw-Hill, New York, 1952.

Elias, N.R. and Lambert, T.H., "Relationship between transient and steady state performance criteria for control systems", *Measurement and Control—Transactions*, Vol. 10, pp. 223-228, June 1977.

Gnoevoi, A.V. and Isaev, L.K., "Simplified method for computing the damping of instruments", *Meas. Tech.*, Vol. 16, No. 7, pp. 980-982, July 1973.

Johnson, W.C., *Mathematical and Physical Principles of Engineering Analysis*, McGraw-Hill, New York, 1944.

Klein, V., "Evaluation of basic performance characteristics of an instrumentation system", *Report Aero-22*, Cranfield Institute of Technology Cranfield, England, 1973.

Luppold, D.S., *Precision DC Measurements and Standards*, Chapter I, Addison Wesley, Reading, Massachusetts, 1968.

Neubert, H.K.P., *Instrument Transducers*, Clarendon Press, Oxford, 1975.

O' Higgins P.J., *Basic Instrumentation—Industrial Measurement*, McGraw-Hill Co., New York, 1966.

Richard Graham A., *An Introduction to Engineering Measurements*, Prentice-Hall Inc., New Jersey, 1975.

Stein, P.K., *Measurement Engineering, Vol. I,* Stein Engineering Services, Tempe Arizona, 1962.

Tse, F.S., Moise, I.E. and Hinkle, R.T., *Mechanical Vibrations—Theory and Applications*, Second Edition, Allyn and Bacon, Boston, 1978.

4

DISPLACEMENT

4.1 INTRODUCTION

Displacement is the vector representing a change in position of a body or a point with respect to a reference It may be linear or rotational motion, expressed in absolute or relative terms. Many of the modern scientific and industrial observations need a very accurate measurement of this parameter. Being a fundamental quantity, the basic sensing device is widely adapted with suitable linkages for the measurement of many derived quantities, such as force, stress, pressure, velocity, and acceleration. The magnitude of measurement ranges from a few microns to a few centimetres in the case of linear displacement and a few seconds to 360° in the case of angular displacement.

A majority of displacement transducers sense the static or dynamic displacement by means of a sensing shaft or similar links mechanically coupled to the point or body whose motion is measured. Such attachments of both linear and angular transducers are usually of simple mechanical configurations, but the coupling must be primarily designed to avoid any slippage after it is fastened and thereby keep the back-lash minimum. For linear-displacement measurements, the common types employed are the threaded end, lug, clevis, and bearing couplings. Spring-loaded shafts may also be used for certain applications. A number of specialized types of displacement transducers operate without use of a mechanical linkage between the transducer and the object whose displacement is to be measured, as in the case of some of the electromagnetic, capacitive, and optical transducers.

4.2 PRINCIPLES OF TRANSDUCTION

Displacement transducers can be classified primarily on the basis of the transduction principle employed for the measurement. In this chapter only the electromechanical transducers which convert displacement quantities into electrical voltages/currents are dealt with.

The major electrical transduction principles used are:

(i) Variable resistance—potentiometric/strain gauge
(ii) Variable inductance linear variable differential transformer/variable reluctance
(iii) Variable capacitance
(iv) Synchros and resolvers.

A number of additional types are also designed, depending upon the convenience and measurement accuracy required, such as digital output transducers, electro-optical devices, and the radio-active devices. In practice, potentiometric- and inductive-type devices are most widely used in scientific and engineering applications. The performance characteristics of a few selected variety displacement transducers are shown in Table 4.1.

4.2.1 Variable Resistance Device

Displacement transducers using potentiometric variable resistance transduction elements are invariably shaft-coupled devices. The sensing element is basically a resistance-potentiometer with a movable wiper contact attached to an insulated plunger type shaft, mechanically linking the point under measurement. The contact motion can be translation, rotation, or a combination of the two, thus allowing measurements of rotary or translatory displacements. They are relatively simple in construction, in the sense that a sliding contact (wiper) is made to move linearly over a resistance element which may be in the form of a wire or a conductive plastic film. The resistivity and temperature coefficient of the resistance element should be of such a value that the device operates with appreciable constant sensitivity over a wide temperature range. The constructional features of linear and rotary potentiometers are shown in Fig. 4.1. The three major elements critical in a potentiometric device are the winding wire, winding former, and wiper as shown in Fig. 4.1(a) and (b).

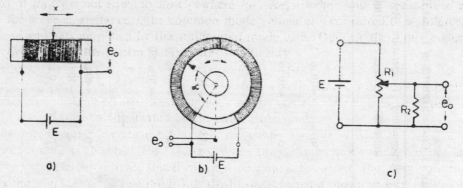

Fig. 4.1 Potentiometric displacement transducer. (a) linear motion;
(b) angular motion; (c) circuit arrangement

The winding wire is a precision drawn resistance wire with a diameter of about 25 to 50 microns and is wound over a cylindrical or a flat mandrel of ceramic, glass, or anodized aluminium. The wire is annealed in a reducing atmosphere to avoid any surface oxidation. Resistivity may vary normally from 0.4 $\mu\Omega$-m to 1.3 $\mu\Omega$-m, and temperature coefficient may vary from 0.002%/°C to 0.01%/°C. The wire should be strong, ductile, and protected from surface corrosion by enamelling or oxidation. The dimensional tolerance should be less than 1%, and the resistance stability with time should be of a very high order. The materials commonly employed are the alloys of copper-nickel, nickel-chromium, and silver-palladium. The winding can be linear, toroidal, or helical, and should possess uniform spacing and constant tension. The outer surface, except for the linear track of the wiper, is covered with a suitable insulating material to protect against dust and abrasion.

A number of additional types are included for ready reference. Both the environment and measurement accuracy requirements must be considered before making a choice of device and the respective characteristics. The last three types are most widely used and the rest, included only for the sake of completeness, are very rarely used in industry. The relative merits are given in brief.

4.2.1 Variable Resistance Transducers

Displacement measurement using a variable resistance transducer element is invariably made by a device commonly known as a resistance potentiometer with a suitable mechanism for converting the mechanical movement into electric signal. The measurement depends on a linear relationship between the resistance and the length of a conductor of uniform cross-section. Potentiometers are relatively simple to construct. In this scale that couples a signal (wiper) is made to move linearly over a resistance element which may be in the form of a conductive coating or the resistive wire. Any reference conditions exist the sensory element should be of such size that the device operates with appreciable sensitivity over a wide temperature range. The constructional features of linear and rotary potentiometers are shown in Fig. 4.1. The three major elements of a potentiometer are the winding, the former and the wiper along with its holder and bearings.

TABLE 4.1 CHARACTERISTICS OF LINEAR DISPLACEMENT TRANSDUCERS

Transduction Principle	Range mm	Linearity % F.S.	Repeatability (microns)	Temperature Range (°C)	Resolution (microns)	Frequency Response (Hz)	Remarks
1. Resistive wire-wound potentiometer	100	0.25	50	−10 to 75	50	5	Long ranges, economical, high output, and minimum electronics
Conductive strip potentiometer	100	0.5	5	−10 to 75	10	10	Poor resolution and high noise
Cantilever with strain gauges	10	0.5	50	−10 to 70	10	100	Versatile, small size, low range, and large reaction forces
2. Inductive/variable reluctance	5	0.5	0.5	−20 to 75	2	100	Small size, high resolution, non-contact type, and low range
Linear variable differential transformer	50	0.1	0.5	−10 to 75	1	1000	Good linearity, high resolution, but interference due to magnetic field
Eddy current (proximity)	10	0.75	5	−20 to 80	2	5000	Non-contact type, and high output
3. Capacitive							Easy mechanical design, high temperature operation, error due to stray capacitance
(a) Variable area	50	0.1	0.5	−40 to 200	50	50	
(b) Variable gap	5	0.5	2	−10 to 500	0.1	2000	
4. Digital transducer	10 to 500	0.1	0.5	− 0 to 55	0.5	100	Long range, digital output, high accuracy and resolution, expensive and bulky

FIG. 4.1 Potentiometer displacement transducer (a) linear movement, (b) angular movement, (c) circuit arrangement.

The winding of a practical wire-wound element, which varies from about 25 to 50 micron dia is wound over a circular or flat strip of ceramic, glass, or anodized aluminium. The wire is annealed and reducing atmospheres to avoid any surface oxidation. Resistivity may vary appreciably from a few to about 1 or 2 ohm per cm. The resistance coefficient may vary from 0.001 to 0.01 per °C to which the resistance wire is subjected. From surface corrosion the element material should be as inert as possible. The deterioration should be less than 1%, and this is achieved by suitable selection of the material. In highly corrosive environments noble metals are used. Gold-platinum and silver-palladium are typical materials. The winding is made as uniform as possible to obtain a smooth, stepless, and continuous resistance variation as the contact moves over it. The former is always coated with a suitable insulating material to protect against dust and abrasion.

The wipers are spring elements made from tempered phosphor-bronze, beryllium-copper, or other precious metal alloys and are suitably shaped to move over the resistance element with minimum friction. The wiper contact force and contact resistance are important factors in the overall accuracy of the device. In some cases conductive lubricants are also used to reduce the friction. Leaf spring and dual wipers are designed for better contact and ability to withstand high shocks and vibration.

The main requirements for winding formers are good dimensional stability and surface insulation. Some of the recommended materials are ceramic, steatite, anodized aluminium, and moulded epoxies.

The whole transduction element described above can be employed for linear as well as angular displacement. The linear range depends very much on the mechanical design. The resistance value and the current-carrying capacity are chosen to suit the desired application; normal values are range 2 to 10 cm F.S., resistance 100 to 50,000 ohms, and current capacity 0.5 to 5 mA. The resolution of the device depends upon the wiper width, diameter of the resistance wire, and spacing between the windings. An optimum choice is sought for the highest precision and resolution. In the case of the wire wound element, the wiper wire diameter to spacing ratio is normally 10, and the resolution achievable is 0.05% to 0.1%. A linearity of the order of 0.1% can be achieved easily, as wires of uniform diameter and specific resistance are available. The plastic-film type is ideal for infinite resolution purposes, even though it is difficult to get a resolution better than 5 microns in practice.

Electrical noise is another factor normally exhibited by these devices and they are random in nature. Further, they depend on the current and speed of motion of the wiper. Wire-wound devices are relatively free from Johnson noise. But the contact noise caused by variation in contact resistance when the wiper moves along the potentiometer track is not negligible in many cases. The noise level increases with wear and tear and also with the contamination or oxidation of the track and the wiper surfaces. Sometimes, thermoelectric effects due to dissimilar materials used for the wiper and wire can also generate a voltage acting as a noise source. This is particularly true when the device is operating at higher temperatures. Yet another type of noise exhibited is the vibrational noise or high-velocity noise caused by jumping or bouncing movements of the wiper. This is reduced by adjusting the contact pressure and oscillatory characteristics of the wiper structure.

The sensitivity of the device is normally given as volts per full-scale mechanical travel of the wiper. The input excitation voltage is limited by the dissipating wattage which causes the temperature of the winding wire to rise to a specified level. This voltage level depends upon the cooling conditions, the thermal characteristics of the potentiometer wire, and the transducer housing design.

Inherent linearity depends on the minimum resolution achievable in the device. If the apparent resolution is $n\%$ of F.S., the linearity error cannot be smaller than $\pm 1/2\, n\%$ of F.S. Further, the linearity is a function of the winding pitch, variations in wire diameter, and any irregularity in former dimensions and wiper movements. The normal value achievable for a standard unit is 0.1%.

The resistance measurement can be carried out with a simple circuit, as shown in Fig. 4.1(c). The circuit linearity is determined by the ratio of the total potentiometer resistance R_1 to the load resistance R_2 as indicated in the figure. A better scheme for measurement is the Wheatstone's bridge network with a suitable detector system (the bridge is analysed in detail in Chapter 5).

The major disadvantages of the potentiometer-type displacement transducer are poor dynamic response, susceptibility to vibration and shock, poor resolution, and presence of noise in signal.

Displacement transducers for very short stroke lengths can be designed with high precision using a bonded/unbonded strain-gauge type sensor. The motion to be measured is transferred to an elastic element, such as a cantilever beam, and the stresses developed on application of displacement is related to the motion. This principle is extended very much in the design of force, pressure, and acceleration transducers.

4.2.2 Variable Inductance Transducer

A simple and more popular type of displacement sensor is the variable-inductance type wherein the variation of inductance as a function of displacement is achieved either by variation in mutual inductances or self inductances. Devices operating on these principles are more widely known as linear variable differential transformers and variable reluctance sensors respectively.

(a) Linear Variable Differential Transformer (LVDT)

Linear variable differential transformer type of transducers find a number of applications in both measurement and control systems. The extremely fine resolution, high accuracy, and good stability make the device particularly suitable as a short-stroke, position-measuring device. Since a number of physical quantities, such as pressure, load, and acceleration can be measured in terms of mechanical deflection. LVDT forms the basic sensing element in all such measurements. The LVDT device is widely used as the basic element in extensometers, electronic comparators, thickness-measuring units, and level indicators. Some of the other important applications are in numerically-controlled machines and creep-testing machines.

The basic construction of the differential transformer is shown in Fig. 4.2(a) at three different core positions.

The linear variable differential transformer consists of a primary coil and two identical secondary coils, axially-spaced and wound on a cylindrical-coil former, with a rod-shaped magnetic core positioned centrally inside the coil assembly providing a preferred path for the magnetic flux linking the coils. The displacement to be measured is transferred to the magnetic core through suitable linkages.

When the primary coil is energized with an ac carrier wave signal, voltages are induced in each secondary section, the exact value depending upon the position of the magnetic core with respect to the centre of the coil assembly. If the core is symmetrically placed (electrically) with respect to the two secondary coils, equal voltages are induced in the two coils. When these two outputs are connected in phase opposition as shown in Fig. 4.2(b), the magnitude of the resultant voltage tends to a zero value. Such a balance point is termed 'the null position'. In practice, a small residual voltage is always present at a null position due to the presence of harmonics in the excitation signal and stray capacitance coupling between the primary and secondary windings. When the core is now displaced from the null position

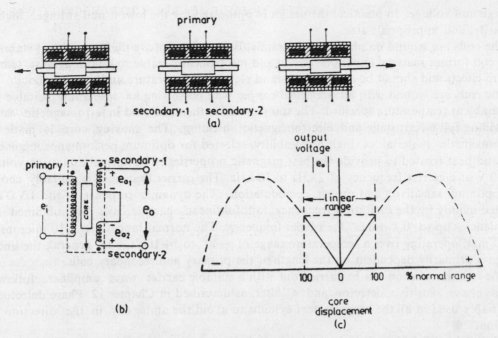

Fig. 4.2 Linear variable differential transformer: (a) basic construction; (b) connection of secondary windings; (c) transfer characteristic

the induced voltage in the secondary towards which the core has moved increases while that in the other secondary decreases. This results in a differential voltage output from the transformer.

The signal output e_o in relation to the other characteristics of the coil is given by[2]

$$e_o = \frac{16\pi^3 f I_p n_p n_s}{10^9 \ln\left(\frac{r_o}{r_i}\right)} \frac{2bx}{3w}\left(1 - \frac{x^2}{2b^2}\right) \qquad (4.1)$$

where f = excitation signal frequency, I_p = primary current, n_p = number of turns in primary, n_s = number of turns in secondary, b = width of the primary coil, w = width of the secondary coil, x = core displacement, r_o = outer radius of the coil, and r_i = inner radius of the coil.

With proper design of coils, the magnitude of the output signal is made to vary linearly with the mechanical displacement of the core on both sides with respect to the null position, as shown in Fig. 4.2(c). While the magnitude of the output voltages are ideally the same for equal core displacements on either side of the null, the phase difference between the output and input voltages changes by 180° when the core moves through the null position. In actual measurement, this phase change-over is measured with a phase-sensitive detector.

The sensitivity is proportional to the frequency f and the primary current I_p, and for best linearity $x \ll b$. However, larger I_p produces core saturation and an increase in the temperature of the coil, and hence results in larger harmonics at null position, making adjustment difficult. An increase in frequency produces a greater effect of stray capacitance, and in turn a large null voltage. In practice, the design is optimized for the lowest null voltage, highest linearity, and appropriate size.

The coils are wound on phenolic or ceramic formers to improve the dimensional stability. The coil former material should be strong and mechanically stable to guard against temperature effects and should be able to withstand elevated temperature and thermal shock.

The coils are wound with an enamelled copper wire possessing an insulation suitable for the ambient temperature specified. The transformer is then enclosed in ferromagnetic cases, providing full electrostatic and electromagnetic shielding. The moving core is made of ferromagnetic material of high permeability, selected for optimum performance in general use and heat treated to provide the best magnetic properties. The normal excitation voltage is 1.0 V at a carrier frequency of 2 kHz to 10 kHz. The carrier frequency is suitably chosen for optimum sensitivity and proper demodulation. The dynamic response of the LVDT is limited mainly by the excitation frequency; faithful linear characteristics are obtained for frequencies up to 0.1 times the carrier frequency. The normal ranges are ± 10 microns to ± 10 mm, operating over a temperature range of $-40°$ to $+100°C$. In general, the linear range is primarily dependent on the length of the primary and secondary coils.

The instrumentation can be carried out with a suitable carrier wave amplifier, followed by a phase sensitive detector and a filter, as described in Chapter 12. Phase detector is invariably used in all the measurement systems to avoid the ambiguity in the direction of motion.

With the availability of miniature integrated circuits, it is feasible to incorporate the oscillator and demodulator within the transducer housing itself, thereby enabling the device to operate as a dc-dc system. An output voltage of 0 to 5 V can be obtained with an input supply of ± 15 V dc.

The main advantages of the LVDT type of displacement sensors are:

(i) *Mechanical*: Simplicity of design and ease of fabrication and installation, wide range of displacement; frictionless movement of core and hence infinite resolution; rugged construction; negligible operating force (core weight being low), and ability to operate even at higher temperatures.

(ii) *Electrical*: Output voltage is a linear and continuous function of mechanical displacement (linearity better than 0.25%), high sensitivity (2 mV/volt/10 microns at 4 kHz excitation); low output impedance (100 ohms); ability to operate over a wide range of carrier frequencies (50 Hz to 20 kHz); infinite resolution in output (theoretically limiting factors being signal to noise ratio and input stability conditions); and very low cross sensitivity.

(b) Angular Displacement Measurement

A rotary variable differential transformer is a very convenient device for the measurement of angular displacement. The device operates on the same principle as LVDT explained earlier, where the output voltage varies linearly with the angular position of the shaft. A typical unit is illustrated in Fig. 4.3.

A cardioid-shaped cam (rotor) of a magnetic material is used as the core. The input shaft fastened to the core is mounted at the centre of the coil former on which the primary and secondary are wound symmetrically. The cardioid shape of the rotor is so chosen as to produce a highly linear output over a specified angle of rotation. The shaft is mounted with miniature precision ball bearings to minimize friction and mechanical hysteresis. The main advantages of the unit are infinite resolution and linear operation (better than $\pm 0.5\%$ of the full range). The signal conditioner employed here is the same as that for LVDT type transducers.

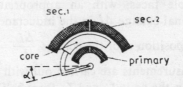

Fig. 4.3 Rotary variable differential transformer

(c) *Variable Reluctance Transducer*

The variable reluctance type displacement sensor is very useful for certain laboratory measurements of stress, thickness, vibration, and shock. In one of the configurations, two coils L_1 and L_2 are wound continuously over a cylindrical bobbin with a ferromagnetic core moving within it. Any variation in the position of the core will change the self-inductances of the coils L_1 and L_2, as illustrated in Fig. 4.4. In another type, an E-shaped magnetic core having two windings at the end limbs is used with an armature mounted suitably covering

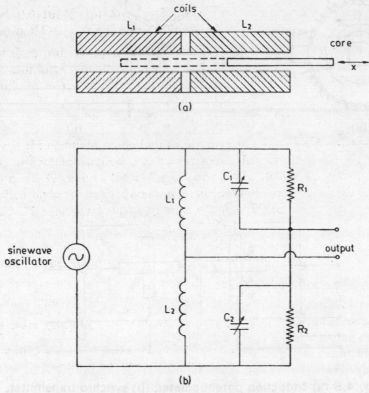

Fig. 4.4 Variable reluctance displacement transducer:
(a) coil assembly; (b) detector circuit

the pole faces, with an appropriate air gap. In either case, it can be shown that the fractional change ΔL in the inductance L is approximately related to the fractional change Δx in position x of the core as $\dfrac{\Delta L}{L} = -\dfrac{\Delta x}{x}$ for small displacements.

Measurements are carried out with a Wheatstone's bridge network as shown in Fig. 4.4(b) wherein the coils L_1 and L_2 form half of the bridge and the other two arms are completed with two fixed resistors R_1 and R_2 with capacitors C_1 and C_2 in parallel to achieve both amplitude and phase balance. The main advantages of the device are its high sensitivity and good linearity of 0.5 to 1% even for long stroke lengths of 50 cm (overall length should be double that of a stroke length). The device can be operated under severe environmental conditions, with encapsulation of the coils in an epoxy resin and hermetically-sealed bobbin. With appropriate modification, it can be employed for velocity and acceleration measurements also.

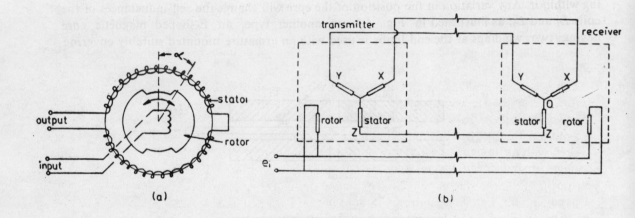

(a)   (b)

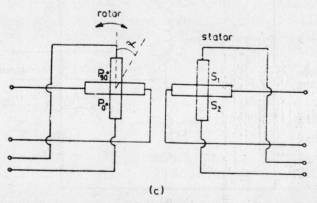

(c)

Fig. 4.5 (a) Induction potentiometer; (b) synchro transmitter; (c) resolver

4.2.3 Induction Potentiometers

Induction potentiometers are linear synchro devices which provide an accurate, linear indication of the shaft rotation about a reference position in the form of a polarized voltage whose magnitude is proportional to the angular displacement and whose phase relationship indicates the direction of the shaft rotation. The device comprises a rotor attached to the transmitting shaft on which the primary is wound and its stator is wound with the secondary winding as shown in Fig. 4.5(a). The windings are so designed that the output voltage is directly proportional to the angular position of the rotor. Good linearity is feasible for angular displacements in the range of $\pm 45°$ only, even though the shaft rotation is continuous. Some of the errors that can arise are due to the variable output impedance, mechanical asymmetry, and thermal effects. These devices are analogous to resistance potentiometers but since they are induction-type components, they have less restraining forces acting upon the rotors and hence are capable of providing higher resolution.

4.2.4 Synchros and Resolvers

Synchros and resolvers are basically a class of ac electromechanical, variable-coupling transformer devices primarily employed for angular data transmission and computing systems. The angular shaft position data is transmitted from one location to another through converted electrical signals.

The basic electromagnetic structure of a synchro consists of a wound rotor and a wound stator, concentrically arranged to give adjustable mutual coupling between the windings of the two members. The rotor is wound with a single-phase concentrated winding and the stator is wound with three-phase distributed windings connected in a Y-configuration. The rotor is excited with an ac signal, and by the transformer action between the rotor and stator windings, voltages are induced in the stator coils. The magnitudes of these voltages depend upon the angular position of the rotor with respect to the stator. The output voltage varies sinusoidally, depending upon the position of the rotor with respect to the stator. In a typical practical set-up, a pair of synchros are used: one acts as a transmitter and the other as a receiver, as shown in Fig. 4.5(b).

An inductive resolver is essentially a variable transformer with a rotary electromagnetic coupling between the primary and secondary windings. In a typical angle-positioning resolver, two windings are provided at right angles to one another for both the stator and rotor. The windings are located in such a manner that the output voltage has an amplitude proportional to the sine or cosine of the input shaft position of the rotor with respect to the stator. Depending upon the designer's particular application, either the rotor or stator may be used as the primary. The electrical connections of a resolver are shown in Fig. 4.5(c).

The main advantages of synchros and resolvers are:

(i) Infinite resolution
(ii) No wear of rotation, except at slip rings
(iii) System operating at much higher speeds
(iv) Relatively insensitive characteristics to stray cable capacitances
(v) High reliability and accuracy (0.01% feasible)
(vi) Useful operating angle of 360° and capable of continuous rotations.

4.2.5 Variable Capacitance Transducer

The variable capacitance type transducer finds considerable usage in specific and limited areas in the field of displacement measurement. They are ideally suited as non-contact type dynamic sensors, especially, in the studies of vibration in very light structures such as thin walls and diaphragms. The non-contact type sensor is desirable when a transducer is needed to measure the mechanical displacement without causing any additional mechanical loading on the vibrating object. Some of the advantages of this device are that it has high stability, good linearity, compactness, and good temperature range. Further, its performance in the contact-type version is superior to other comparable transducers in large displacement ranges of 0 to 25 cm.

The most common form of the variable capacitor used for displacement measurement is a parallel-plate capacitor with a variable gap. The capacitance variation in a parallel-plate capacitor can be achieved by changing the gap width between the plates d, the common area of the plates A, or the dielectric constant k, as shown in Fig. 4.6.

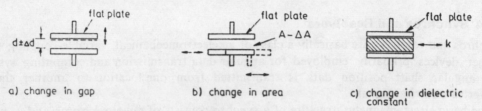

Fig. 4.6 Variable capacitance devices

The capacitance C of such a parallel-plate capacitor is given by

$$C = \frac{kA}{d} \tag{4.2}$$

In a typical device one plate of the transducer is kept fixed and the other plate is moved or deflected depending upon the displacement measurement. The variable dielectric system is employed in the case of level measurements in liquid columns, as in the fuel gauge system of an aircraft or level indicator in a chemical plant. The resultant change in capacitance in all the above cases can be converted to an useful electrical signal by means of a variety of circuitry.

For small changes Δd in position with respect to an initial value, the capacitance variation ΔC can be written as

$$\frac{\Delta C}{C} = \frac{-\Delta d}{d} \tag{4.3}$$

where higher-order terms are neglected.

Similarly, if ΔA is the change in area and Δk is the change in the dielectric constant, then

$$\frac{\Delta C}{C} = \frac{\Delta A}{A} \tag{4.4}$$

and

$$\frac{\Delta C}{C} = \frac{\Delta k}{k} \tag{4.5}$$

Equations (4.4) and (4.5) represent exact relationship, indicating that the variable area and variable dielectric constant configurations produce a linear relationship without restrictions on the range.

A linear variable capacitance device in a practical application comprises a cylinder moving concentrically inside two other identical cylinders with a constant air gap. With the movement of the central cylinder, the capacitance area of one section increases while the other correspondingly decreases. The resultant change in capacitance is directly proportional to the displacement of the inner cylinder. The main advantages of the device are good stability, and a linearity better than $\pm$ 0.2% over a 25-cm range.

A simple instrumentation system for single-ended measurements using an operational amplifier is shown in Fig. 4.7. This circuit arrangement gives a linear output in cases where (a) C_2 is a fixed capacitance and C_1 is the transducer capacitance operating on the principle of capacitance variations due to area change or dielectric constant change, as can be seen from the relationship,

$$e_o = - \frac{C_1}{C_2} \cdot e_i \qquad (4.6)$$

$$= - \frac{1}{C_2} \frac{kA}{d} \cdot e_i \qquad (4.7)$$

$$e_o \propto k \text{ or } A \qquad (4.8)$$

(b) C_1 is a fixed capacitor and C_2 is the transducer capacitance, operating on the principle of variation in gap, giving rise to

$$e_o = - \frac{C_1}{C_2} \cdot e_i$$

$$= - \frac{C_1 d}{kA} \cdot e_i \qquad (4.9)$$

$$e_o \propto d \qquad (4.10)$$

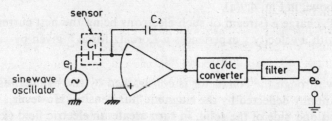

Fig. 4.7 Operational amplifier circuit configuration for capacitance type displacement transducers

For higher accuracy a closed loop ac servo bridge system is normally used as illustrated in Fig. 4.8. Any out-of-balance of the bridge due to the change in transducer capacitance is amplified to actuate a servomotor. The motor in turn positions a reference capacitance, till the bridge output becomes zero. The output is then read in terms of the position of the motor shaft with a high accuracy. Capacitance-type sensors find wide use in gauging and inspection systems in metrology and in checking dimensions of gauges in grinding operations and roll spacing in strip-rolling mills. Very low drift and high accuracy over long ranges allow very precise control over the final product. The device can be used as an extensometer in the measurement of creep and tensile properties of materials over long pe riods. Capacitance strain gauges, fabricated with ceramic and nimonic materials, can be profitably employed for displacement measurements up to 600°C. With suitable design features, the device can be adopted for the measurement of pressure and force in the instrumentation of aircraft, other vehicles, and process control.

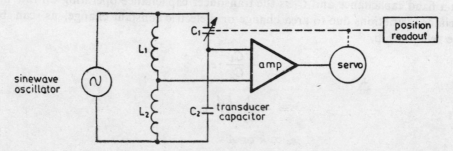

Fig. 4.8 AC servo bridge arrangement for variable capacitance devices

4.2.6 Hall Effect Devices

One of the numerous applications of the Hall effect is in position measurements, particularly for measuring angular displacements of shafts.

The Hall effect occurs when a transverse magnetic field is applied to a current-carrying conductor.[3] It results in an electric field perpendicular to the directions of both the magnetic field and current with a magnitude proportional to the product of the magnetic field strength and current. The schematic arrangement of the conductor, the magnetic field, and current flow are shown in Fig. 4.9(a).

An electron of charge e (stream of such electrons being the nett current) travelling in a magnetic field $\mathbf{B}$ with a velocity $\mathbf{v}$ experiences a Lorentz force $\mathbf{F}$ given by

$$\mathbf{F} = e(\mathbf{v} \times \mathbf{B}) \tag{4.11}$$

The current flow through the conductor is constrained by the boundaries of the solid, and the electrons are initially deflected by the magnetic flux density. However, the build up of the charges toward one side of the solid, in turn create an electric field (known as the Hall field) that counterbalances the Lorentz force acting on the bulk of the current carriers. The current continues to flow in the original direction as if unaffected by the magnetic field. The time required to reach this equilibrium is of the order of 10^{-14} s.

The electric field is given by

$$\mathbf{E}_H = \mathbf{v} \times \mathbf{B} \tag{4.12}$$

If ρ and e represent the density and charge of the carriers, then the current density $\mathbf{i}$ is given by

$$\mathbf{i} = \rho\mathbf{v} \tag{4.13}$$

The Hall field represented by single electron velocity is therefore

$$\mathbf{E}_H = \frac{1}{\rho}\mathbf{i}\times\mathbf{B} \tag{4.14}$$

The factor $\frac{1}{\rho}$ is termed as the 'Hall coefficient', R_H, which is inversely proportional to the carrier density in the solid. Thus, the Hall effect is much more pronounced in semiconductors than in metals. For practical applications, it is advantageous, if the effect is expressed in terms of the electric potential rather than the electric field.

From Fig. 4.9(a), it can be seen that $V_H = wE_H$, and $I = iwd$; therefore, the Hall potential is given by

$$V_H = \frac{R_H}{d}IB \tag{4.15}$$

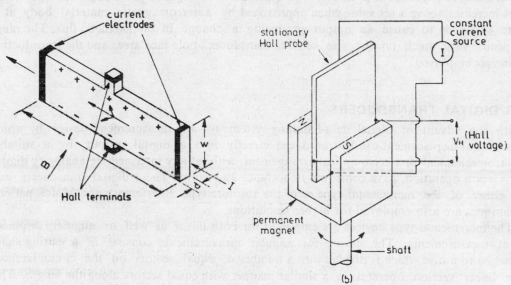

(a)

Fig. 4.9 (a) Hall effect principle; (b) Hall effect angular displacement transducer

The equilibrium between the Lorentz force and Hall field can only be attained by current carriers with a single velocity. Since the current in the Hall element is limited by the heat dissipation and permissible temperature rise for maximum power output, the Hall element should be made of materials with highest mobility. Such materials are compounds of groups III-V. like Indium Antimonide and Indium Arsenide. Some problems associated with the Hall-effect phenomena are current noise generated in the device, residual voltages due to misalignment of the terminals, and magnetoresistance due to non-uniform velocities of the carriers.

A typical transducer arrangement applying the Hall-effect phenomena for producing an output which is directly proportional to small rotary shaft displacements is shown in

Fig. 4.9(b). The Hall probe is rigidly suspended between the poles of a permanent magnet fixed to the shaft as shown in the figure; the probe remains stationary as the shaft (with the magnet mounted) rotates. With a constant control current supplied to the electrical contacts at the end of the probe, the voltage generated (Hall voltage) across the probe is directly proportional to the sine of the angular displacement of the shaft. Hence, the linear scale between the rotation and output voltage can be obtained up to $\pm 6°$ of the rotation.

The main advantage of such transducers is that they are non-contact devices with high resolution and small size. Some of the other applications are in measurements of velocity, rpm, sorting, limit sensing, and non-contact current and magnetic field measurements.[4]

4.2.7 Proximity Devices

Although not normally considered as transducers, proximity devices are in fact non-contact displacement transducers having a discrete increment in the output at one point within the travel range. Such devices are developed employing electromagnetic, inductive, reluctance, or capacitance principles. In a typical electromagnetic proximity device, the output increases above a set value when approached by a ferromagnetic material body at a rate sufficient to cause an output producing a change in the magnetic flux. The range depends very much on the size of the transducer, pole-face area, and the transduction principle employed.

4.3 DIGITAL TRANSDUCERS

With the advent of digital data-handling systems for any measurement, devices by which mechanical displacement can be transduced directly into a digital output, by a suitable electromechanical or electro-optical arrangement, without any intermediate analog to digital conversion operation, have come into importance and utility. These digital transducers can be either of the incremental type or of the absolute type. Interference and Moire pattern techniques are also employed for higher resolutions.

The incremental-type devices are employed for both linear as well as angular displacement measurements. The device for angular measurements consists of a sensing shaft attached to a disc which is divided into a number of equal sectors on the circumference. The linear version operates in a similar manner with equal sectors along the length. The sensing mechanism can be a direct electrical contact with a wiper or brush or a photo-electric device with slots acting as optical windows. Each time an incremental motion of the sensor occurs, pulses are generated which are measured in a counter.

A gear with a large number of shaped teeth with a direct electrical contact or electromagnetic induction pick-up can also be used for angular measurements. The counting of the pulse train is again carried out with a counter. A direction sensing feature is incorporated to sense the direction of motion, positive/negative or clockwise/anti-clockwise. In the case of angular transducers, the performance of the electromagnetic transduction gets affected, if the angular speed is either too low or too high. Similar devices can be developed with the pick-up operating on the variable reluctance or capacitance principle.

The absolute digital displacement transducer is similar in construction to the incremental type described above, except that a unique coded information is obtained identifying a given position. This is achieved with a linear encoder or a shaft position encoder as shown in Fig. 4.10.

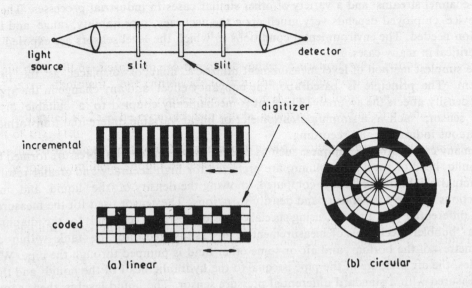

Fig. 4.10 Details of a digital encoder for linear and angular displacement measurement

The principle of encoder is based on the on-off switching of a multiple track (each track representing a bit), each track divided into conducting or insulating sections with the smallest increment suitably chosen for the highest possible resolution. As the device moves under the brushes or optical windows, the respective circuits are switched 'on' and 'off' and the code is either displayed in decimal format with a suitable translator or fed directly to a processor.

A variety of codes are used in encoders for proper identification. The choice depends on such factors as the available computing circuitry, nature of the display required, total number of counts and degree of reliability. The most compact code is the natural binary code with the bits in terms of 2^0, 2^1, 2^2 and 2^3. A binary decimal code is a combination of the binary system and the Arabic decimal system used as 8421 BCD system. Each digit in Arabic is repeated by a binary code

$$8473 = 1000 \quad 0100 \quad 0111 \quad 0011$$

The main disadvantage of the binary and 8421 coding systems is that two or more bits have to change simultaneously during a single position change. This is overcome by a binary coded decimal (BCD) system, such as the "gray code", wherein only one-bit change takes place in the transition between any two consecutive numbers. Another modification based on the cyclic decimal system is the Datex Code, patented by Giannini Corporation, USA. By this there is only one decimal digit shift for each number sequence from 0 to any other number in the Arabic structure.

4.4 LEVEL MEASUREMENTS

Liquid-level measurements are widely employed to monitor as well as measure quantitatively the liquid content in vessels, reservoirs, and tanks, or the liquid column height in open-channel streams and a variety of other similar cases in industrial processes. The type of device employed depends very much upon the accuracy, repeatability, range and instrumention needed. The environmental conditions to which the level sensors are exposed to are also critical in many cases.

The simplest method of level measurement utilizes a float or displacer as the primary element. The principle is based upon the buoyancy effect and any change in the apparent mass density affects the accuracy. The float is mechanically coupled to a suitable displacement sensor, such as a simple potentiometer or linear variable differential transformer for continuous indication and recording.

In many cases, other techniques, such as measuring the differential pressure formed by the hydraulic head of the liquid column, are preferred for high accuracy and greater resolution. The actual height of the fluid is computed, knowing the density of the liquid and making corrections for the temperature and density variations. The sensor used for the measurement is the differential pressure cell, using special corrosion-resistant materials for the diaphragms. In the "bubbler" technique of measurement, a pipe is inserted into the tank within a few centimetres of the bottom and air or some other fluid is pumped through the pipe. When it bubbles, the air pressure in the pipe is equal to the hydraulic head of the liquid and this can be measured with a standard differential pressure sensor. The liquid level is then computed knowing the specific gravity of the liquid.

Two of the most common type of level sensors having wide application are the capacitance sensor and ultrasonic transducer. The capacitance device essentially consists of a concentric-type electrical probe inserted into the tank, and the liquid acts as the dielectric of the capacitance formed. The probe capacitance C varies as the level varies and this change in C can be measured precisely with an ac bridge system or as a change in the frequency when coupled with a tank circuit of a high-frequency oscillator. As any change in temperature can affect the dielectric constant, suitable corrections are made to minimize the error in measurement. The main disadvantage is that the system is not applicable for conducting liquids. Such sensors are widely used to measure the level in fuel tanks of aircrafts and industrial plants. Ultrasonic devices can be readily used for gas-liquid, liquid-liquid or gas-solid interfaces. The principle of measurement is the same as that of the ultrasonic flow meters described in Chapter 8. A variety of configurations are employed in actual practice either as an on-off damped sensor or on-off transmitter, or as a continuous monitoring device. In the continuous type, the propagation time of an ultrasonic beam from a transmitting device to a receiver through the fluid is measured accurately and the level is interpolated. The accuracy is adversely affected by any change in the density of the liquid.

The liquid level in a container can be inferred by weighing the vessel with its contents and computing the level, knowing the density of the liquid. Using suitable electronic circuits, the base weight of the container can be tared off to give the exact quantity of the liquid. Using high precision electrical load cells, the system accuracy can be very much enhanced. Though it is an expensive system, the main advantages are that continuous measurement can be done with processing compatability and that sensing devices are not in contact with the liquid.

Nuclear level-measuring instruments using gamma radiations, though unsafe in certain cases, are ideal for many applications considering their accuracy and reliability, with almost all types of liquids and solids. A source of nuclear gamma radiation is beamed through the contents of the vessel to a receiving detector, and the amount of radiation absorbed by the mass of the liquid or solid in its path is taken as a measure. The measuring instrument is calibrated in terms of the level, knowing the amount of radiation. The leakage rate in the system has to be maintained to a bare minimum, to protect the operating personnel. The system is not affected by corrosive materials and is ideal for continuous level measurement. The interface position of liquids and slurries in process vessels, tanks, pumps, or solids in silos can be easily measured. A unique advantage is that the gauge does not come in physical contact with the material.

EXERCISES

4.1 A LVDT type displacement transducer with a primary of 300 turns and a secondary of 500 turns in each section is excited with a carrier wave signal of 1 kHz, 5 mA current. The width of the primary coil and each secondary coil is 10 mm, the thickness of the windings is 4 mm and the radius of the outer coil is 8 mm. Calculate the sensitivity of the device and the percentage of output linearity, at 10% and 20% of the primary coil width.

4.2 Obtain the percentage non-linearity in terms of the percentage change in separation between the two electrodes in a variable air-gap type capacitance displacement transducer.

REFERENCES

1. "Electromechanical design", *PPMA Conference Report*, April 1964, p. 8.
2. Neubert, H.K.P., *Instrument Transducers*, Clarendon Press, Oxford, 1975, Ch. 4, p. 206.
3. Epstein, M. "Hall effect devices", *IEEE Trans. on Magnetics*, Vol. Mag. 3, No. 3, September 1967, pp. 352-359.
4. *Siemens Data Book: Galvanomagnetic Devices*, Siemens Co., Munich, West Germany, 1977, pp. 23-45.

BIBLIOGRAPHY

Ahrendt, W.R. and Savant, C.J., *Servomechanism Practice*, McGraw-Hill, New York, 1960.

Anon, "Continuous measurement of liquid levels", *Design and Component Engineering*, Vol. 17, No. 16, pp. 6-13, Sept. 15, 1971.

Anon, "Capacitance transducer challenges potentiometer as position sensor", *Product Engineering*, Vol. 42, No. 7, March 29, 1971.

Atkinson, P.D. and Hynes, R.W., "Analysis of a linear differential transformer", *Elliot Journal*, U.K., Vol. 2, pp. 144-151, 1954.

Beckwith, T.G. and Buck, N.L., *Mechanical Measurements*, Addision Wesley, Reading, Massachusetts, 1961.

Bews, J., "Potentiometer performance is vital to servo system accuracy", *Electronic Engineering*, Vol. 44 No. 531, pp. 27-29, May 1972.

Canfield, E.B., *Electromechanical Control System and Devices*, John Wiley and Sons, New York, 1965.

Chass, J., "The differential transformer", *I.S.A.*, Vol. 9, pp. 5 and 6, 1962.

Cummings, T.C.L., "Advantages of capacitor sensing", *Electronic Equipment News*, Vol. 13, No. 4, pp. 32-37 July/Aug. 1971.

Davis, S.A. and Ledgerwood, B.K., *Electromechanical Components for Servomechanisms*, McGraw-Hill, New York, 1961.

Doebelin, E.O., *Measurement Systems*, McGraw-Hill, New York, 1968.

Dummer, G.W.A., *Variable Resistors and Potentiometers*, Isaac Pitmans and Sons, London, 1956.

Ferris, S.A. et al. "The magnetoresistor as a displacement transducer element", *J. Phy. E. Scientific Instr.*, Vol. 3, No. 8, pp. 639-642, Aug. 1970.

Garratt, J.D., "Survey of displacement transducers below 50 mm", *J. Phy. E. Scientific Insrt.*, Vol. 12, No. 6, pp. 563-573, July 1979.

Hardway, E.V., "Position sensor combines low cost with high accuracy and reliability", *Electronics*, Vol. 44, No. 17, pp. 86-88, Aug. 16, 1971.

Herceg, E.E., *Handbook for Measurement and Control*, Schaevitz Engineering Co., Pennsauken, New Jersey, 1972.

Jones, R.V. and Richards, J.C.S., "The design and some applications of sensitive capacitance micrometers", *J. Phy. E. Scientific Instr.*, Vol. 6, No. 7, pp. 589-600, July 1973.

Keast, D.N., *Measurements in Mechanical Dyamics*, McGraw-Hill, New York, 1967.

Lewis, M.G., "A miniature mutual inductive proximity transducer", *J. Phy. E.*, Vol. 7, No. 4, p. 269, April 1974.

Lion, K.S., *Instrumentation for Scientific Research*, McGraw-Hill, New York, 1959.

London, F.H., "Laser Interferometer", *Instruments and Control Systems*, Vol. 37, No. 11, pp. 87-89, Nov. 1964.

Marmorstone, R.J., "Digital techniques in precision dimensional measurement", *Automatic Control*, Vol. 17 No. 7, pp. 32-34, July 1962.

Mason, P.J. "Product survey: Liquid level indicators and controllers", *Engineering Materials and Design*, ol. 13, No. 11, pp. 1393-1411, Nov. 1970.

Norton, H., *Handbook of Transducers for Electrical Measuring Systems*, Prentice-Hall, Princeton, 1969.

Oliver, F.J., *Practical Instrument Transducers*, Pitman & Sons, London, 1972.

Roberts, H.C., *Mechanical Measurements by Electrical Methods*, Instruments Publishing Co., Pittsburg, Pa, 1951.

Rohrbach, C., *Handbuch für Elektrisches Messen Mechanischer Grössen*, V.D.I. Verlag, Düsseldorf, 1967.

Ross, E.A., "Nema standard digital position rotary incremental transducers", *Control Engg.* Vol. 14, No. 16, p. 85, October 1967.

Sarma, G.R. and Bapat, Y.N., "Extending the range of seismic transducers", *Instruments and Control Systems*, Vol. 45, No. 2, pp. 111-112, February 1972.

Starer, R.L., "Electro-optical tracking techniques", *Instruments and Control Systems*, Vol. 40, No. 2, pp. 103-105, Feb. 1967.

Stevens, R. et. al. "A digital angle display unit", *Scientific Inst.* Vol. 4, No. 2, pp. 139-142, February 1971.

Wiles, A.P., "Digital position measurement", *Instruments and Control Systems*, Vol. 43, No. 9, pp. 129-131, Sept. 1970.

Wong, G S.K., "A sensitive null setting angle detector", *Scientific Instruments*, Vol. 4, No. 3, pp. 195-197, March 1971.

5

STRAIN

5.1 INTRODUCTION

In the design and construction of machines and structures, the strength of the material plays a very important role. A theoretical knowledge of this property is essential to estimate whether the mechanical components can carry the loads demanded of them, without excessive deformation or failure. These load-carrying abilities are normally characterized in terms of stress, which is defined as the force experienced per unit area, and is expressed in pressure units. Stress itself cannot be measured directly and is normally deduced from the changes in mechanical dimensions and the applied load. The mechanical deformation formed due to stress is measured with strain-gauge elements. The relationship between load and elongation is characterized in terms of strain which is defined as the change Δl in length l per unit length and is expressed as $\Delta l/l$ in microstrains.

The precise measurement of the parameter 'strain' is an important aspect in measurement engineering, as it is very often encountered in many fields of engineering and technology, especially in experimental stress analysis. Further, a large number of mechanical and physical parameters can be related with devices operating on the principle of strain measurement.

The stress to strain relationship in a simple tension or compression test is expressed as

$$E = \frac{\sigma_a}{\epsilon_a} \text{ kg/cm}^2 \tag{5.1}$$

where E is the Young's Modulus of the material in kg/cm², σ_a is the axial stress in kg/cm², and ϵ_a is the axial strain m/m.

The relation is linear so long as the stress is kept below the elastic limit. The stress-strain curve for a typical metal specimen is given in Fig. 5.1.

The deformation of a strut under simple tension loading is given in Fig. 5.2. The length is increased by Δx and the cross-section is decreased by $\Delta y \times \Delta z$. If the strain is measured in either of the planes perpendicular to the applied load, a strain with a lesser magnitude and with opposite sign is developed in this plane and this effect is known as Poisson's effect. The magnitude is expressed as the Poisson's ratio ν which is a function of the material. ν is approximately 0.3 for most of the materials. The relationship between stress and strain is valid only in the direction of the applied load.

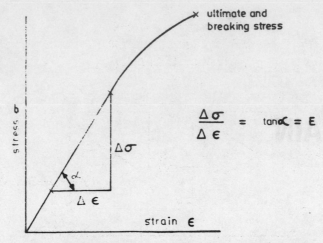

Fig. 5.1 Stress-strain curve for a typical metal

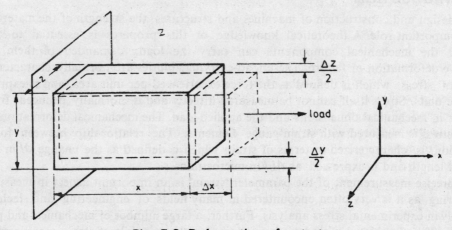

Fig. 5.2 Deformation of a strut

In the example shown in Fig. 5.2 the stress components ϵ_x, ϵ_y and ϵ_z can be written in terms of the stress in the x direction σ_x as

$$\frac{\Delta x}{x} = \epsilon_x = \frac{\sigma_x}{E} \tag{5.2}$$

$$-\frac{\Delta y}{y} = \epsilon_y = -\frac{\nu\sigma_x}{E} \tag{5.3}$$

$$-\frac{\Delta z}{z} = \epsilon_z = -\frac{\nu\sigma_x}{E} \tag{5.4}$$

Similarly, if loads are applied simultaneously in the other two axes and the strain computed, it may be shown that

$$\epsilon_x = \frac{\sigma_x}{E} - \frac{\nu\sigma_y}{E} - \frac{\nu\sigma_z}{E} \tag{5.5}$$

$$\epsilon_y = \frac{\sigma_y}{E} - \frac{\nu\sigma_x}{E} - \frac{\nu\sigma_z}{E} \tag{5.6}$$

$$\epsilon_z = \frac{\sigma_z}{E} - \frac{\nu\sigma_x}{E} - \frac{\nu\sigma_y}{E} \tag{5.7}$$

Rewriting Eqs. (5.5)—(5.7) in terms of stresses,

$$\sigma_x = E\epsilon_x + \nu\sigma_y + \nu\sigma_z \tag{5.8}$$
$$\sigma_y = E\epsilon_y + \nu\sigma_x + \nu\sigma_z \tag{5.9}$$
$$\sigma_z = E\epsilon_z + \nu\sigma_x + \nu\sigma_y \tag{5.10}$$

In a two-dimensional strain system, where $\sigma_z = 0$, the above equations become

$$\sigma_x = \frac{E}{(1-\nu^2)} (\epsilon_x + \nu\epsilon_y) \tag{5.11}$$

$$\sigma_y = \frac{E}{(1-\nu^2)} (\epsilon_y + \nu\epsilon_x) \tag{5.12}$$

By measuring the strains in X and Y directions, the relative stresses can be computed.

5.2 FACTORS AFFECTING STRAIN MEASUREMENTS

Strain measurements are normally carried out on the free surface of a body. The three strains ϵ_x, ϵ_y, and ϵ_z defined in Sec. 5.1 adequately express the two-dimensional state of stresses existing on the surface. By measuring displacements corresponding to Δx in each direction and dividing it by the original length x, the strain can be determined. The strain magnitude is of the order of a few micrometers per metre expressed as microstrains. But it is difficult to measure such displacements directly, except in certain isolated cases, since the magnitude involved is very small. Therefore, a device or gauge which can yield surface strains directly is preferred. Such a device is popularly known as the "strain gauge". An accurate definition of strain on the surface requires the determination of the slopes of the displacement of the surfaces. The strains as such are likely to vary from point to point. Direct measurements of such small displacements over the entire surface of the body is also difficult. This is overcome by measuring one displacement component over a small portion of the body, along a short line segment. The strain measured in this manner may not be the true value, since the measurement is made over a finite length and not at a point. The error produced by this approach depends upon the strain gradient and the length of the line segment.

It is imperative to reduce the size of a strain gauge to improve the accuracy of measurements, but as the size is very much reduced, dimensional tolerances become very critical. If a strain value of the order of 1000 microstrains is to be measured to an accuracy of 5 microstrains over a gauge length of 5 mm, a displacement of 25×10^{-5} mm has to be accurately determined.

The basic characteristics of a strain gauge that one looks for are the gauge length, gauge width, gauge sensitivity, range of measurement, accuracy, frequency response and the ambient environmental conditions it can withstand. Since strain cannot be measured at a point, non-linear stress fields can give rise to errors, depending upon the gauge dimensions. Sensitivity, which is defined as the smallest value of strain that can be read, is of the order of ± 1 microstrain and can be attained with the aid of modern instrumentation techniques. The maximum strain measurable and the accuracy achievable depends very much upon the type of gauges used and the method of gauging employed.

5.3 TYPES OF STRAIN GAUGES

Strain gauges can be classified as mechanical, optical, or electrical depending upon the principle of operation and their constructional features. Of these, the electrical strain gauges and that too the electrical resistance type gauges, are the most popular because of the many advantages they offer in the process of measurement.

5.3.1 Mechanical Gauges

In mechanical gauges, the change in length Δl is magnified mechanically using levers or gears. Among them the Huggenburger type of extensometer is the most popular, wherein a lever system is employed to obtain the magnification of the movable knife-edge of the extensometer with respect to a fixed knife-edge. In a demountable type of strain gauge, the actual movement of the pivot is transferred to the spindle of a dial gauge, where the movement is magnified by a rack-and-pinion arrangement. Mechanical strain gauges are comparatively larger in size, and as such are suitable only in cases where sufficient area is available on the test specimen for mounting the gauge. Further, they are useful in cases where the strain gradient is negligible and the additional mass of the mechanical gauge does not contribute to any error. These gauges are employed for static strain measurements only and also in cases where the point of measurement is accessible for visual observation.

5.3.2 Optical Gauges

Optical strain gauges are very similar to mechanical strain gauges except that the magnification is achieved with multiple reflectors using mirrors or prisms. As such the inertia of the system is very much reduced. In Martin's mirror-type extensometer, a plain mirror is rigidly attached to a movable knife-edge. When subjected to stress the mirror rotates through an angle, and the reflected light beam from the mirror subtends an angle twice that of the incident light. The measurement accuracy is high and independent of temperature variations.

5.3.3 Electrical Strain Gauges

The principle of an electrical strain gauge is based upon the measurement of the changes in resistance, capacitance, or inductance that are proportional to the strain transferred from the specimen to the basic gauge element. The most versatile device for experimental determination of strain for the purpose of stress analysis is the bonded resistance type of strain gauge. Capacitance and inductance type are only employed for special applications. Therefore, the rest of the treatment in this book is mainly concerned with resistance gauges only.

The basic concept of an electrical resistance strain gauge is attributed to Lord Kelvin who in 1856 expounded the theory that the resistance of a copper or iron wire changes when subjected to tension. The resistance of the wire changes as a function of strain, increasing with tension and reducing with compression. Sensitivity differs from material to material. Such a change in resistance can be measured accurately using a Wheatstone bridge. Developed on this principle, the electrical resistance strain gauge is basically a metal wire or foil subjected to the same strain as that of the specimen under test, achieved through suitable bonding of the gauge to the specimen.

Another class of strain gauge which is of a recent origin is the semiconductor type, piezoresistive strain gauge. This gauge has the advantages of high sensitivity, small size, and adaptability for both static and dynamic measurements.

5.4 THEORY OF OPERATION OF RESISTANCE STRAIN GAUGES

Assume a conductor of length L and cross-sectional area A. If this conductor is strained axially in tension, causing an increase in length, the lateral dimensions will reduce as a function of the Poisson's ratio of the wire material. Since the resistance of the wire is dependent on its length, area of cross-section, and also its specific resistivity, the resultant change in resistance due to strain can be interpreted as due to a dimensional change of the wire or due to a change in the specific resistivity.

The resistance R (in ohms) of a uniform conductor (single, long wire) as shown in Fig. 5.3 is given by

$$R = \frac{\rho l}{A} \tag{5.13}$$

where ρ = specific resistance of the wire material in ohm-m, l = length of the wire in m, A = cross-sectional area of the wire in m^2.

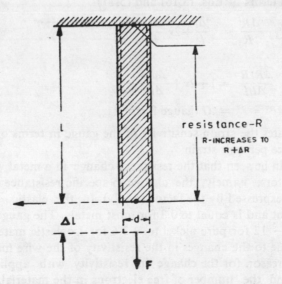

resistance—R

R–INCREASES TO
R+ΔR

**Fig. 5.3 Deformation of a resistance wire
under strain**

If a uniform stress σ is applied to this wire along its length, the resistance R will change because of dimensional changes (length and cross-sectional area) and because of the fundamental property of the material. Differentiating Eq. (5.13),

$$\frac{dR}{d\sigma} = \frac{d\left(\frac{\rho l}{A}\right)}{d\sigma} = \frac{\rho}{A}\frac{\partial l}{\partial \sigma} - \frac{\rho l}{A^2}\frac{\partial A}{\partial \sigma} + \frac{l}{A}\frac{\partial \rho}{\partial \sigma} \tag{5.14}$$

Multiplying Eq. (5.14) by $\left(\dfrac{1}{R}\right)$,

$$\frac{1}{R}\frac{dR}{d\sigma} = \frac{1}{l}\frac{\partial l}{\partial \sigma} - \frac{1}{A}\frac{\partial A}{\partial \sigma} + \frac{1}{\rho}\frac{\partial \rho}{\partial \sigma}$$

or

$$\frac{\Delta R}{R} = \frac{\Delta l}{l} - \frac{\Delta A}{A} + \frac{\Delta \rho}{\rho} \tag{5.15}$$

Thus, for a finite stress variation, the total change in resistance is due to the fractional change in length $\Delta l/l$, the fractional change in cross-sectional area $\Delta A/A$, and the fractional change in resistivity $\Delta \rho/\rho$. For a wire of circular cross-section, expressing the change in area in terms of its diameter (for small changes),

$$\frac{\Delta A}{A} \simeq 2\frac{\Delta d}{d} \tag{5.16}$$

where d is the diameter of the wire in metres. The lateral concentration $\Delta d/d$ is related to the change in length $\Delta l/l$ by the Poisson's ratio ν of the wire material as given below.

$$\frac{\Delta d}{d} = -\nu\frac{\Delta l}{l} \tag{5.17}$$

Rewriting Eq. (5.15) in terms of Eqs. (5.16) and (5.17)

$$\frac{\Delta R}{R} = \frac{\Delta l}{l} + 2\nu\frac{\Delta l}{l} + \frac{\Delta \rho}{\rho} \tag{5.18}$$

or

$$\frac{\Delta R/R}{\Delta l/l} = 1 + 2\nu + \frac{\Delta \rho/\rho}{\Delta l/l}$$

$$= G \text{ (gauge factor)} \tag{5.19}$$

The gauge factor indicates the strain sensitivity of the gauge in terms of the change in resistance per unit resistance per unit strain.

From Eq. (5.19) it can be seen that the resistance change in a metal wire due to strain is produced by two factors, namely, the change in specific resistance $\Delta \rho$ and the change in dimensions of the wire expressed by the factor $(1+2\nu)$. In the elastic range, the Poisson's ratio ν is nearly constant and is equal to 0.3 for most metals. The gauge factor G for various materials ranges from -12 for pure nickel to $+3.6$ for isoelastic material, which indicates that the contribution due to the changes in the resistivity of the wire material can be considerable. The apparent reason for the change in resistivity with applied strain is due to changes in mobility and the number of free electrons in the material. However, the gauge factor determined experimentally is reasonably constant for a given material. In the purely elastic region of deformation of any material, a change in volume is not possible as the wire cannot store energy in these conditions, which means that there cannot be any change in resistivity. Therefore, under constant volume conditions, the gauge factor takes a different value, which is nearly 2.0. The factor is constant over its elastic region, thus providing a wide linear stress-strain relationship.

The expression for gauge factor given by Eq. (5.19) is for a single uniform length of a conductor. Usually the strain gauge used for actual measurement is in the form of a grid. This causes certain sections of the strain gauge to be located in a direction transverse to the direction of the actual strain. The transverse strain also produces a change in resistance of the wire in addition to the axial strain. The calibrated gauge factor given by the manufacturer is normally valid only when the transverse strain is related to the axial strain as given by the equation

$$\epsilon_{trans} = -0.285 \; \epsilon_{axial}$$

Such inaccuracies may be insignificant in many cases, since the Poisson's ratio is nearly the same for most metals.

5.5 TYPES OF ELECTRICAL STRAIN GAUGES

It is apparent from the analysis presented in the previous section that a single length of wire can as well be used as the sensing element in a strain gauge. However, the circuits which are used for measuring the resistance changes impose certain restrictions on the minimum resistance that a strain gauge should possess. This value depends upon the gauge current and gauge length. Higher resistance gauges offer higher changes in the resistance for a given gauge factor, and at the same time draw lower current and have less heat dissipation problems. A resistance of the order of 60 to 1000 ohms is normally chosen for optimum performance. To achieve this value, a grid pattern is formed, thereby increasing the length of the wire and at the same time keeping the gauge length and width minimum.

The sensing wires used in these electrical strain gauges are drawn out of special metal alloys which are discussed in Sec. 5.6. The gauges are classified into a number of categories depending upon the method of fabrication, but the two major types are the wire and the foil gauges. Two other types which are of very recent origin are the semiconductor and thin film gauges.

5.5.1 Wire Gauges

Wire strain gauges are normally of two types, namely, bonded and unbonded gauges depending on the method of fabrication. In the first type, the strain gauge is bonded directly to the surface of the specimen being tested with a thin layer of adhesive cement which serves to transmit the strain from the specimen to the gauge wires and at the same time serves as an electrical insulator. Keeping the surface area of the wire section larger than its cross-sectional area, stress relaxation and slippage are avoided. Wire gauges are fabricated in four basic varieties, viz. flat grid, wrap around, single wire, and woven.

Flat Grid Type

In this type the wire is wound back and forth as a grid, as illustrated in Fig. 5.4(a). This grid structure is bonded to a backing material, such as paper or epoxy, with an adhesive that can hold the wire element to the base firmly, permitting a good transference of strain from the base to the wires. Since the ends of each section of the wire are looped around, transverse strains also cause changes in resistance in such sections of the wire. In order to reduce the cross sensitivity, such loop lengths should be minimized or joined through a different material having a lower sensitivity to strain than that of the actual material used for the strain gauge. In a standard gauge the cross sensitivity should not be greater than 2% of the sensitivity of the major axis. The wire grid plane should be as close to the specimen surface as possible to achieve maximum transfer of strain from the specimen and to keep the creep and hysteresis minimum.

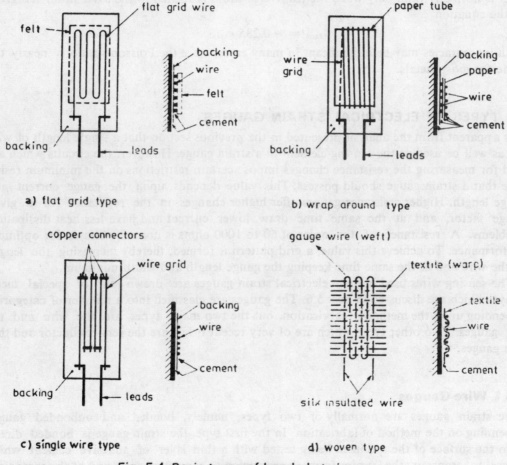

Fig. 5.4 Basic types of bonded strain gauges

Wrap-Around Type

This type of gauge is wound on a flattened tube of paper, or alternately, on a thin strip or card as shown in Fig. 5.4(b). Gauge lengths smaller than that of the flat-grid type can be achieved for the same resistance value, but the gauge exhibits greater surface thickness since the grid wire is in two planes, introducing different transfer characteristics from that of the flat type and resulting in larger hysteresis and creep.

Single-Wire Gauges

Single-wire types were developed to eliminate the cross-sensitivity factor. In this device single wires are stretched across and laid as shown in Fig. 5.4(c). Instead of loops formed by the same wires, thick copper wires are welded at the ends, reducing the cross sensitivity considerably. These gauges are not very popular and are intended for large gauge lengths only.

Woven Type

This method of fabrication, as shown in Fig. 5.4(d), is employed in gauges intended for the measurement of large strains. A silk-insulated Eureka wire is wound as the weft on a rayon wrap to form a woven-type gauge, which is useful for tests on fabrics and leather. High-temperature gauges of this type are developed with a glass fibre weave but they are not popular for common engineering applications.

For good sensitivity and faithful transmission of strain to the gauge, it is essential that the gauge wire should have high resistivity and large surface area. Such a high resistance can be achieved only with a thin wire of long length. The gauge is usually fabricated with a constantan wire of 20 microns diameter, wound in a grid format with as many loops as possible, laid side by side. In spite of its small diameter, the wire can withstand tension and compression easily, mainly because of the fact that the surface area is very large compared to its cross-section. This large bonded area controls the movements of the wire almost perfectly with no buckling. The sensitivity of the bonded wire gauge under compression is lower than that at tension by 1 to 2% only. A large length to width ratio in the grid structure is also desirable, to keep the transverse sensitivity minimum.

Wire strain gauges of the bonded type are easy to manufacture in large numbers at relatively low cost. The normal gauge factor value is between 2.0 and 2.2, and materials having a higher gauge factor are not normally recommended because of their poor temperature characteristics. For materials having higher gauge factors, the transverse sensitivity is also considerable, unless they are specially reduced during manufacture. The current-carrying capability is usually limited because of the low area of cross-section of the wire, the normal value being 10 to 20 mA. It may be noted that stress concentrations can occur at the terminal and wire joints, causing fatigue failures.

5.5.2 Unbonded Strain Gauges

An unbonded strain gauge device is basically a free filament-sensing element where strain is transferred to the resistance wire directly without any backing. In a typical device, a few number of loops of high tensile strength resistance wire of 25 micron diameter is wound between insulated pins, one of them attached to a stationary frame and the other to a movable frame, so that the winding experiences an increase or decrease of stress for a given force input. The schematic diagram of a typical displacement transducer wherein the measuring forces are transmitted to the platform containing the unbonded wire structure by means of a force rod is shown in Fig. 5.5. The main advantage of this device lies in its radial symmetry which assists in the cancellation of spurious signals from transverse forces. The other advantages are very low hysteresis and creep (since the wire backing and bonding are avoided, unlike in the case of bonded gauges), miniaturization of the transducing element by integration of the force-summing unit and the force-sensing components, and adaptability

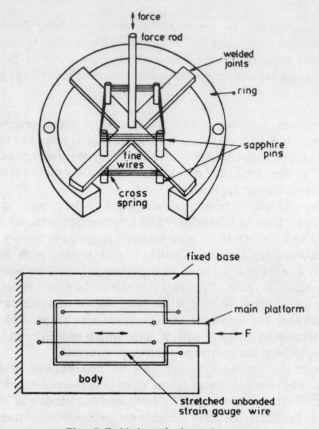

Fig. 5.5 Unbonded strain gauge

for high-temperature environments due to the welded construction. The main applications are in displacement transducers, pressure transducers, and accelerometers.

5.5.3 Foil Gauges

The foil strain gauge is basically an extension of the wire gauge, differing in its constructional features and having certain advantages in actual measurement. In foil gauges, the required grid pattern is formed with a very thin foil of the same material as that used for wire gauges, as shown in Fig. 5.6. On account of the larger surface area to area of cross-section ratio, it has a higher heat dissipation capability and hence better thermal stability. Since the grid element in the foil gauge is many times wider than its cross-section, a larger ratio of the bonding area to the cross-sectional area is achieved compared to the wire gauges. This in turn enables a higher heat dissipation and better bonding properties. The strain reproducibility is also excellent. By making the perpendicular sections of the foil wide, the response of the gauge to the traverse strain can be considerably reduced.

In the foil type of gauges, there is no stress concentration at the terminals due to the absence of joints, thereby extending the life of the gauge. By virtue of the versatile photo-

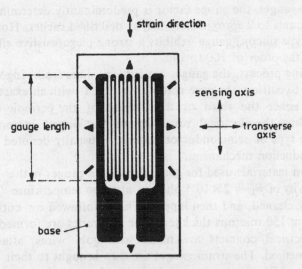

Fig. 5.6 Foil strain gauge

chemical etching process, any type of complex pattern of any small size can be fabricated easily, such as circular gauges, diaphragm gauges, orthogonal arrays for shear measurement and transducer applications as well as many types of Rosettes for two-dimensional stress analysis.

5.5.4 Semiconductor Strain Gauges

Semiconductor strain gauges employ the piezoresistive property of doped silicon and germanium. In the metal alloy strain gauges described earlier, the strain sensitivity is mainly due to the dimensional change with a lesser contribution due to the resistivity changes. Semiconductor strain gauges, developed as an offshoot of the integrated circuit technology, are fabricated from single crystals of silicon and germanium, where the strain sensitivity is mainly due to resistivity changes in the semiconductor material itself. A unique feature of the device is that the change in resistance due to strain is 40 to 100 times more than that of the conventional metal alloy types. In addition to the high gauge factor, other advantages are chemical inertness, freedom from hysteresis and creep effects, good fatigue life, and low cross sensitivity.

The gauge factor for the semiconductor type strain gauge is given by the expression

$$G = \frac{\Delta R/R}{\epsilon} = 1 + 2v + m \tag{5.20}$$

where G = Gauge factor,
ϵ = Strain in the semiconductor,
v = Poisson's ratio at uniaxial stress (0.3 for metals), and $m = \pi E$, in which
π = Coefficient of piezoresistance, along the axis of the gauge, and
E = Young's modulus of the gauge along its length.

In Eq. (5.20), the first term relates to elongation, second to lateral contraction due to the longitudinal stress, and the last term to the predominant piezoresistive effect.

In the case of wire gauges, the gauge factor is predominantly determined by the geometrical change and amounts to approximately 2.0, as described earlier. However, the semiconductor (p-type or n-type silicon) gauge exhibits a strong piezoresistive effect, resulting in a high gauge factor of the order of 100 to 140.

In the manufacturing process, the gauges are cut in slices from ingots of cylindrically-shaped silicon. Prior to cutting, the pure material is doped with an exact amount of foreign impurity atoms of either the third or fifth group of the periodic table, to achieve the required resistivity. Since the electrical resistivity of the doped material varies with the degree of doping, the type of semiconductor material is usually denoted by its characteristic conductivity and conduction mechanism.

One of the common materials used for general purpose gauges is the p (iii)-type silicon doped with a resistivity of $\rho_0 = 2 \times 10^{-4}$ ohm-m, at room temperature. The material is first groove-cut into slices, cleaned, and then lapped. This is followed by cutting the pieces to thin filaments of about 150 microns thickness. The electrodes are formed by vapour deposition and ohmic electrical contacts are made with gold wires, attached by means of a thermocompression method. The strain gauges are then brought to their nominal resistance by electrolytic etching. For use as a strain gauge element, they are embedded on a film backing of phenolic, bakelite or epoxy. Some of the common arrangements of types manufactured are shown in Fig. 5.7.

The main characteristics specified for a semiconductor gauge are:

(a) Filament material—p- or n-type silicon
(b) Gauge factor—positive or negative
(c) Gauge length
(d) Gauge resistance
(ε) Temperature coefficient
(f) Backing or encapsulation
(g) Bonding (cementing or welding)
(h) Lead geometry.

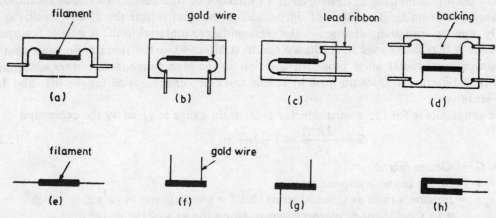

Fig. 5.7 Semiconductor strain gauges

The bonding techniques employed are similar to that for wire or foil gauges, except that greater care must be taken in handling, because of their brittleness. Special solder material (cadmium-tin) is used for soldering the leads to the circuit. The semiconductor strain gauges are available with both positive and negative gauge factors, for p- and n-type silicon respectively. This enables to form bridge circuits with two active arms at one location itself, even when both the gauges are subjected to the same strain value. In the application of these gauges in transducers, the strain-sensitive diaphragm and other elements are fabricated as bonded gauges, or by diffusion technique, as p-n junctions on silicon substrates. Some of the properties of these gauges are discussed below.

(a) Gauge Sensitivity

The variation of gauge factors of p- and n-type silicon as a function of resistivity and crystal orientation, is illustrated in Fig. 5.8. The sensitivity of semiconductor gauges at low strain limits at room temperature is computed from the equation,

$$G = \frac{\Delta R/R}{\Delta l/l} = 1+2\nu+\pi E \tag{5.21}$$

Since the product πE is well in excess of 100, the contribution towards the sensitivity from the gauge geometry is insignificant when compared with the piezoresistive effect. Unlike wire gauges, a small apparent strain is observed due to the gauge current, depending upon the magnitude and direction of current flow, even at very low rates of self heating.

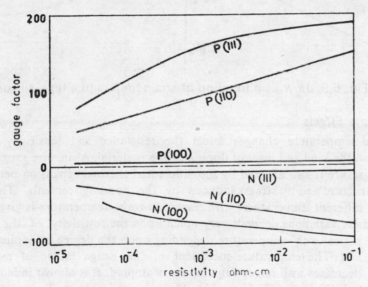

Fig. 5.8 Variation of gauge factor as a function of resistivity and crystal orientation

(b) Linearity

In contrast to wire and foil gauges, the sensitivity of the gauge depends strongly on strain level, thereby exhibiting non-linearity in resistance variation with strain as shown in Fig. 5.9.

The relative resistance change at constant temperature is given by the equation

$$\frac{\Delta R}{R} = c_1\epsilon+c_2\epsilon^2+c_3\epsilon^3+\cdots \tag{5.22}$$

where c_1, c_2, c_3, ... are constants, R is the unstrained gauge resistance and $\epsilon = \Delta l/l$ is the strain.

For a heavily-doped p-type silicon with resistivity $\rho_0 = 2 \times 10^{-4}$ ohm-m, the expression becomes $\Delta R/R = 119.5\epsilon + 4000\epsilon^2$, and for an n-type silicon gauge with resistivity $\rho_G = 3.1 \times 10^{-4}$ ohm-m, $\Delta R/R = -110\epsilon + 10{,}000\epsilon^2$.

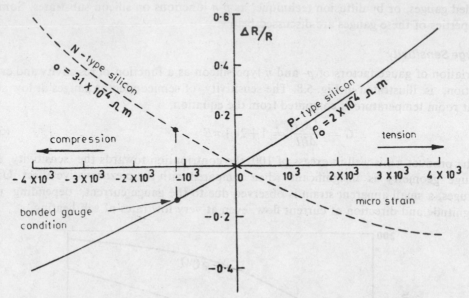

Fig. 5.9 $\Delta R/R$ as a function of strain for p- and n-type silicon

(c) Temperature Effects

Environmental temperature changes affect the resistance and sensitivity of the gauge, depending upon the kind and level of doping of the material. As in wire gauges, the unstrained gauge resistance is also affected by the differential thermal expansion between the gauge and the test structure and by strains induced by the bonding cements. The variation in resistance at different temperatures with respect to room temperature is given in Fig. 5.10. The slope of these variations depends very much upon the resistivity of the material. The gauge factor varies with temperature depending upon the degree of doping (resistivity) as shown in Fig. 5.11. The temperature coefficient of the gauge factor of p-type silicon is negative and decreases with increasing amount of doping. It is almost independent of temperature, at very high degrees of doping, i.e. for $\rho_0 < 10^{-5}$ ohm-m. Temperature compensation for the gauge factor is more complex than in wire gauges, because of high gauge factors. This is achieved to some extent by suitable circuit design techniques in the signal conditioner.

(d) Temperature Compensation

Temperature compensation for resistance variations is carried out either by self-compensation or circuit-compensation. Self-compensation is obtained by using n-type gauges which have positive temperature coefficient of resistivity, balanced to some extent by its negative temperature coefficient of gauge factor. Employing selected materials for the gauges, good

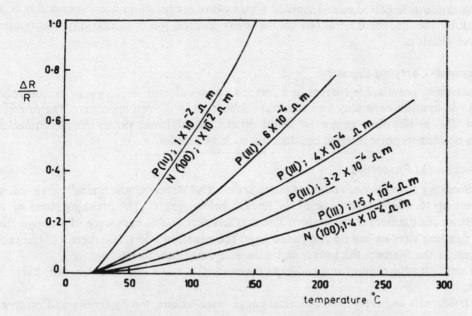

Fig. 5.10 $\Delta R/R$ as a function of room temperature variations

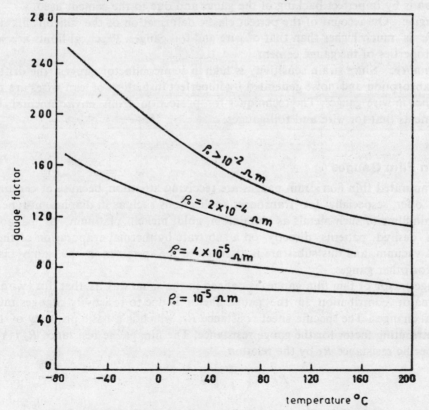

Fig. 5.11 Variation of gauge factor with temperature

compensation is achieved over a limited temperature range. Circuit compensation is accomplished by the use of differential and dummy gauges, p-n combinations, and temperature sensitive resistors.

(e) Current-Carrying Capacity

The maximum permissible current in a bonded semiconductor strain gauge is controlled by its heat-dissipation capability and thermal conduction to the test specimen. The normal safe current for a 120 ohm gauge is about 30 mA. Much lower values are recommended for gauges bonded to poor thermal conductors, such as plastics.

(f) Mechanical Properties

(i) *Breaking strength and radius of curvatures*: The stress versus strain curve of silicon filaments up to the fracture point is linear, below 450°C. The breaking stress of silicon depends on the filament cross-section. The smallest permissible curvature of a gauge filament under bending stresses can be computed from the equation $r = t/2\epsilon$, where r is the radius of curvature, t the filament thickness, and ϵ the safe maximum strain.

The smallest safe radius for a rod-type filament is 7 to 8 cm and for whiskers 0.3 to 0.5 cm.

(ii) *Hysteresis and creep*: In practical gauge installations, the hysteresis and creep experienced are very small due to the integrated format of the actual gauge itself. The major contribution is by imperfect backing of the gauge and due to the cement used.

(iii) *Fatigue*: On account of the perfect elastic deformation of the silicon filament, the fatigue life is much higher than that of wire and foil gauges. Practical limits are set by the bonding properties of the gauge cement.

(iv) *Humidity*: Since strain sensitivity is high in semiconductor gauges, the drift due to moisture absorption and noise generated by imperfect insulation of lead wires are relatively less than that in wire gauges. The techniques for protection from environmental humidity are the same as that for wire and foil gauges.

5.5.5 Thin Film Gauges

Of late, evaporated thin film strain gauges are receiving attention, because of certain advantages they offer, especially for transducer applications such as in diaphragm-type pressure gauges. Thin films of such metals as aluminium, gold, nickel, platinum, or palladium are formed in desired patterns directly on a substrate by thermal evaporation of the desired material in vacuum, and this substrate is attached to the specimen in the same manner as that used for other gauges.

The gauge factor of thin film gauges is defined in the same way as that for wire gauges, but the major contribution in the gauge factor is due to resistivity changes rather than geometrical changes. The specific sheet resistance R_f, which is a basic property of the film, is the contributing factor for the gauge resistance. The film gauge resistance R_g is related to the film specific resistance R_f by the relation

$$R_f = \left(\frac{W}{l} \right) R_g \tag{5.23}$$

where W is the width of the film and l is the length of the film. Since $R_g = \dfrac{\rho_f l}{A}$, where ρ_f

is the film resistivity in ohm-m and A is the film cross-sectional area, R_f can be written as ρ_f/t, where t is the thickness of the film. The specific resistance R_f is a measure of the film thickness. However, it may be noted that ρ_f changes as a function of the film thickness, increasing with decreasing film thickness. As such, the sheet resistance is a non-linear function of the film thickness. For very thin films having a thickness of the order of 50 Å, R_f may be as large as 10^6 ohm-cm. Therefore, it is possible to obtain thin film gauges of high resistance values with smaller dimensions, which give rise to higher sensitivity and low power consumption.

The gauge factor of thin films of cobalt and platinum varies with the resistivity as shown in Fig. 5.12. Except for some special metals, such as tellurium, the gauge factor is low and approaches the value obtained for bulk materials. The gauges can operate over a wide temperature range from $-200°C$ to $+400°C$ with good stability. The sensitivity is also high because of a high gauge factor and high gauge resistance. These gauges are rugged and have very low hysteresis and creep.

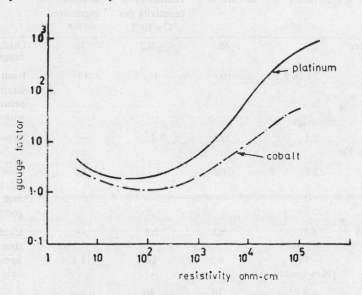

Fig. 5.12 Variation of gauge factor with resistivity in thin
film gauges

5.6 MATERIALS FOR STRAIN GAUGES

The materials employed for the fabrication of electrical strain gauges and their installation for stress measurements should possess a few basic qualities and minimum standards in order to achieve high accuracy, excellent reproducibility, good sensitivity, long life, and ability to operate under the required environmental conditions. Some of these qualities are attained by choosing materials having high specific resistance, low temperature coefficient of resistance, constant gauge factor, and constant strain sensitivity over a wide range of strain values. The material used for the backing and the bonding cement should offer high insulation resistance and excellent transmissibility, and must be immune to moisture effects.

5.6.1 Wire Resistance Material

Not all the materials used for strain gauge fabrication will have all these ideal characteristics. Table 5.1 shows the various types of materials used for strain gauges, their composition, and other characteristics. The most common materials used for wire strain gauges are advance or constantan alloys, as they exhibit high specific resistance, constant gauge factor over a wide strain range, and good stability over a reasonably large temperature range. The isoelastic alloys are also employed in commercial gauges because of their high gauge factor of 3.6 compared to 2.1 for Advance. This alloy is extremely sensitive to temperature variations, and the gauge factor changes at high strain values (above 1000 microstrain); as such it is employed for low strain measurements only and is ideally suited for dynamic strain measurements.

TABLE 5.1 PROPERTIES OF MATERIALS FOR WIRE AND FOIL GAUGES

Material	Gauge factor	Resistivity Ω cm $\times 10^{-8}$	Temperature coefficient of resistivity per °C $\times 10^{-6}$	Coefficient of linear expansion $\times 10^{-6}$	Remarks
Constantan Advance 45% Ni/55% Cu	2.1	48	± 0.2	16	Useful temperature range 0°-300°C
Nichrome 80% Ni/20% Cr	2.1 to 2.5	100	1	13	Used for dynamic strains. Can be temperature compensated with platinum
Karma 74% Ni/ 20% Cr/3% Al/3% Fe	2.1	125	0.2	—	Same as nichrome
Isoelastic 36% Ni/ 8% Cr/0.5% Mo/ 55.5% Fe	3.5	80	1.75	7.2	Poor temperature stability; ideal for dynamic measurements; good sensitivity
Alloy 479-92 Pt/8W	4.7	62	2.4	—	Used for unbonded strain gauges
Nickel—pure	−12 (Non-linear)	6.5	68	12.8	Special applications only
Platinum—pure	4.8	10	40	—	—

5.6.2 Backing Material

The backing material is that portion of the strain gauge to which the strain sensitive grid structure is attached. In addition to the primary electrical insulation backing, it also helps retain the geometric shape of the grid pattern and provide protection to the gauge. The choice of the backing material is dictated by the ambient conditions. The type of backing materials used, their temperature ranges, and other characteristics are given in Table 5.2.

5.6.3 Gauge Bonding Cement

Bonding cements are adhesives used to fix the strain gauge onto the test specimen. Since this cement serves the vital function of transmitting the strain from the specimen to the

TABLE 5.2 STANDARD BONDING TECHNIQUES FOR WIRE RESISTANCE STRAIN GAUGES

Gauge backing material	Adhesive	Curing time and pressure	Type	Temperature range/ remarks
Paper	Nitro cellulose/ acetone duco (Durofix)	12 to 40 h at 80°C; 7-35 kPa	Solvent setting	0°-60°C (up to 100°C with slight drift); useful for curved surfaces
Epoxy paper/ phenolic (bakelite)	Cyano acrylate acrylic cement (Eastman 910)	1 to 5 min. at room temp. 10-17 h at room temp. or 2-10 h. at 150°C 35-100 kPa	Pressure setting or chemical action setting	0-150°C. Ideal for electrical transducers
Phenolic (bakelite) Fibre glass	Phenolic (bake-lite) cement or epoxy type (Araldite)	5 to 8 h at 180°C; 350-700 kPa	Chemical action setting	0-200°C (up to 300°C for short periods) good for electrical transducers — requires high bonding pressure
Transfer gauge (glass weave or none)	Silicone varnish	1 to 2 h	—	Up to 400°C; Dynamic strain mainly
Transfer gauge (glass weave or none)	Ceramic cement (Rockhide process)	—	—	Above 400°C dynamic strain only

gauge-sensing element, the choice of the suitable cement and its correct application are of utmost importance. Improper bonding of the gauge to the specimen can cause many errors, such as hysteresis, creep, temperature induced zero drift, and low insulation resistance. In long-term strain measurements, an improperly-cured cement gives rise to stability problems. In many cases, guidelines are supplied by the manufacturers themselves on the choice of cement to be used, cement proportions, surface conditions and curing for obtaining the best performance.

Basically, the cement can be classified under two categories, viz. solvent-setting cement and chemically-reacting cement. Duco cement is an example of solvent-setting cement which is cured by solvent evaporation. Epoxies and phenolic bakelite cements are chemically-reacting cements which are cured by polymerization. Acrylic cements are contact cements that get cured almost instantaneously.

Table 5.2 also gives the various types of cements used for bonding strain gauges, their curing times, and temperature ranges.

5.7 GAUGING TECHNIQUES AND OTHER FACTORS

The proper functioning of a strain gauge is wholly dependent on the quality of bonding which holds the gauge to the surface of the structure undergoing the test. If the bond does not faithfully transmit the strain from the test piece to the wire or foil of the gauge, the results obtained on measurement can never be accurate. The greatest weakness in the entire technique of strain measurement by means of wire or foil gauges is because of imperfections in the bonding of strain gauges to the test piece.

5.7.1 Installation

The selection of the size of the strain gauge for any particular application is an important consideration for obtaining the overall faithfulness needed in the measurement. The first limitation of gauge size is purely physical, namely, whether the given gauge will fit into the available surface of the specimen. A second limitation is the strain gradient at the location where the strain gauge is to be mounted. The gauge will essentially average out the strain beneath its strain-sensitive grid. Thirdly, the wave lengths of the vibratory strains to be measured must be large as compared to the length of the gauges, to reduce the errors in the dynamic response. For good fidelity in strain magnitude reproduction, the gauge length should be less than 1/20th of the wavelength of the vibration. In general, the largest possible size of gauge should be used, since such gauges will have lower hysteresis, creep, and zero shift, and larger current-carrying capability. As far as the gauge resistance is concerned, the highest resistance commensurate with a gauge grid geometry chosen is preferred, especially when the instrumentation following the strain gauge circuit has a high input impedance.

The performance of the gauge is very much influenced by the cement chosen for bonding and the procedure followed in fixing the gauge at the location, and as such great care must be taken in mounting and subsequent bonding. The surface should be smooth enough, but not too highly polished, since polishing does not promote good adhesion. All scales, rust, paint, and other surface contaminations must be removed from the metal surfaces. In surface preparation as well as in installation, fine grid abrasive paper or emery cloth is ideal for cleaning. The surface is further cleaned to remove any traces of grease or dirt using such solvents as acetone, trichloroethylene, or toluene with surgical cotton. Light rubbing with a dilute acid can also be helpful. The strain gauge backing should be cleaned with a solvent such as acetone to remove oil and grease contamination and dried under a 60 W lamp, to be completely free from any moisture. A fairly generous layer of the recommended cement is spread on the prepared clean surface of the specimen as well as on the gauge backing. The gauge is then laid at the location very carefully, pressed with a thumb or pressure pad to the exact pressure recommended by the manufacturer, and then cured as specified. The pressure level applied is normally 35 to 180 kPa and the temperature for curing varies from 60° to 200°C, maintained for a period of 6 to 12 hours. Particular care should be taken to avoid any air gap between the gauge and the specimen surface. The insulation resistance between the gauge and the surface of the specimen should be checked after curing. This must be very high, of the order of 1000 MΩ for a test voltage of 30 V dc. Further curing is recommended if higher insulation resistance is required.

5.7.2 Hysteresis

The bonded strain gauge should sense exactly the same amount of strain as experienced by the surface to which it is bonded. If the relative resistance variation in the gauge is plotted in terms of strain, the resultant hysteresis loop with cycle loading will be as shown in Fig. 5.13. Normally, repeated cycling to a strain level higher than that actually required will reduce this hysteresis effect. Sometimes, a large hysteresis arises from faulty bonding techniques, and such defects may not get eliminated by cycling.

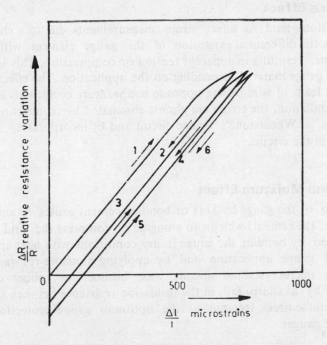

Fig. 5.13 Hysteresis in strain gauge installation

5.7.3 Creep

For good bonding with faithful transmission of the strain to the gauge, it is essential that both the backing material in which the gauge filament is embedded, and the bonding cement holding the gauge in position is much stronger than the filament itself. If this is not the case, the gauge filament relaxes under strain, and strain indication is less than the true strain value, becoming increasingly non-linear as strain increases. Creep arises from a number of sources, but mainly due to a faulty structure in the gauge itself, faulty bonding of the gauge to the specimen, or an increase in the operating temperature. Unlike hysteresis, creep is time dependent and is more when the gauges are initially installed. Static strain tests are more affected than dynamic tests. The effect is more significant in smaller gauges because of their small bonding area.

5.7.4 Fatigue

In dynamic strain tests, fatigue failure arises due to stress reversals occurring at the point where the connecting leads are attached to the gauge. Fatigue can also cause decay in the gauge base or fixing cement, leading to filament relaxation. Etched foil gauges are preferred to wire gauges in many cases for dynamic tests. Isoelastic gauges are the most suitable. In all cases, the gauge leads should be well secured to prevent relative motion between the gauges and the leads, and they should have no abrupt change in area at the joints.

5.7.5 Temperature Effect

Temperature variations tend to affect strain measurements due to a change in the gauge resistance as well as the differential expansion of the gauge element with respect to the structural membrane, resulting in apparent tension or compression. This is avoided by proper selection of the gauge material, depending on the application. The effect can be reduced by connecting short leads of wire having opposite temperature coefficients in series with the gauge. In actual installation, the errors are almost eliminated by connecting the gauges in differential pairs in a Wheatstone's bridge circuit and by incorporating temperature-compensation elements in the circuit.

5.7.6 Humidity and Moisture Effect

Moisture absorption by the gauge backing or bonding cement causes volume changes (swelling or contraction of the cement) which can elongate or compress the grid. Such humidity effects are eliminated by bonding the gauge in dry conditions with heat applied during the whole operation of gauge application and by applying moisture-resistant water-proofing compounds, such as microcrystalline silicone wax, bitumen, or rubber compounds. The defect is observed by a sharp fall in the insulation resistance between the gauge and the specimen. Most manufacturers recommend the optimum gauge protection techniques to be adopted for their gauges.

5.8 STRAIN GAUGE CIRCUITS

The measurement of the changes in resistance in the gauges is accomplished by electrical circuits using potentiometer or Wheatstone bridge networks, as shown in Figs. 5.14 and 5.15. The potentiometer circuit, also known as the Ballast circuit, consists of a dc voltage E (or at times ac voltage, depending upon the application) applied across the resistance network R_1 and R_2, in which one or both can be the strain gauges. The voltage e that appears across R_2 (assuming that a high input impedance device is used to measure the voltages) is given as

$$e = E \frac{R_2}{R_1 + R_2} \tag{5.24}$$

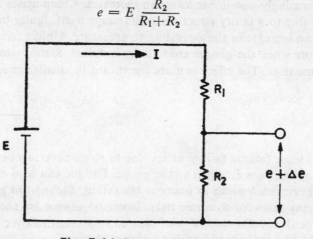

Fig. 5.14 Potentiometer circuit

The change in output voltage Δe due to changes ΔR_1 and ΔR_2 in the resistances R_1 and R_2 can be written as (assuming zero source resistance and infinite load resistance)

$$e + \Delta e = E \left[\frac{R_2 + \Delta R_2}{R_1 + \Delta R_1 + R_2 + \Delta R_2} \right] \tag{5.25}$$

or

$$\Delta e = \left[\frac{R_2 + \Delta R_2}{R_1 + \Delta R_1 + R_2 + \Delta R_2} - \frac{R_2}{R_1 + R_2} \right] E \tag{5.26}$$

On simplification, it can be shown that

$$\Delta e = E \frac{R_1}{R_2} \frac{\left[\dfrac{\Delta R_2}{R_2} - \dfrac{\Delta R_1}{R_1} \right]}{\left[1 + \dfrac{R_1}{R_2} \right]^2 \left[1 + \dfrac{\dfrac{\Delta R_1}{R_2} - \dfrac{\Delta R_2}{R_2}}{1 + \dfrac{R_1}{R_2}} \right]} \tag{5.27}$$

Rewriting the denominator term in Eq. (5.27) as

$$1 + \frac{\dfrac{\Delta R_1}{R_2} + \dfrac{\Delta R_2}{R_2}}{\left(1 + \dfrac{R_1}{R_2} \right)} = 1 + \frac{\left(\dfrac{R_1}{R_2} \dfrac{\Delta R_1}{R_1} \right) + \dfrac{\Delta R_2}{R_2}}{\left(1 + \dfrac{R_1}{R_2} \right)}$$

and substituting $R_1/R_2 = a$, Eq. (5.27) can be rewritten as

$$\Delta e = E \left[\frac{a}{(1+a)^2} \left(\frac{\Delta R_2}{R_2} - \frac{\Delta R_1}{R_1} \right) (1 - N) \right] \tag{5.28}$$

where N is a non-linear term given as

$$N = \left[1 - \frac{1}{1 + \dfrac{1}{(1+a)} \left(a \dfrac{\Delta R_1}{R_1} + \dfrac{\Delta R_2}{R_2} \right)} \right]$$

If R_2 is a strain gauge and R_1 is a fixed resistor, i.e. $\Delta R_1 = 0$ (with one active gauge only), by neglecting the non-linearity term N, Eq. (5.28) becomes

$$\Delta e = \frac{a}{(1+a)^2} \frac{\Delta R_2}{R_2} E \tag{5.29}$$

Substituting for the gauge factor G (i.e. the change in resistance per unit resistance per unit strain),

$$\Delta e = \frac{a}{(1+a)^2} G \epsilon E \tag{5.30}$$

The circuit voltage sensitivity S_e is determined as

$$S_e = \frac{\Delta e}{\epsilon} = \frac{a}{(1+a)^2} GE \tag{5.31}$$

When $\qquad R_1 = R_2,$

$$S_e = \frac{1}{4} GE \tag{5.32}$$

It can be seen from Eq. (5.28) that the useful range of the potentiometer circuit is limited by the admissible values of non-linearity determined by term N which depends upon the strain level and resistance ratio a. Another important factor is the voltage sensitivity S_e of the circuit, defined as the ratio of the change in the output voltage Δe to the strain ϵ, as given in Eq. (5.31). From Eqs. (5.28), (5.31), and (5.32), it may be shown that the error introduced by the circuit non-linearity is relatively small for normal strain measurements of the order of 1000 microstrains. If a strain gauge with a gauge factor of 2 is used in place of R_2, the error approaches about 2% for the ranges up to 10% strain, depending upon the value of a of the circuit. As the ratio a is decreased from 9 to 2, the useful measurement range reduces from 10% to 2% strain. Thus the range of the potentiometer circuit is sufficient enough for normal strain measurements, in the elastic region of materials. In a practical design the supply voltage E is dictated by the maximum allowable current permissible for the gauge. To understand the influence of these parameters on the sensitivity more explicitly, Eq. (5.31) can be rewritten as

$$S_e = \frac{E}{(1+a)} \frac{a}{(1+a)} G \qquad (5.33)$$

$$= IR_2 \frac{a}{(1+a)} G \qquad (5.34)$$

where I is the current through R_1 and R_2.

It may be seen that for a given value of gauge current and gauge resistance, sensitivity increases with a, at the cost of a higher excitation voltage. This condition also reduces non-linearity.

The disadvantage of a potentiometer circuit is that it exhibits some initial voltage under zero strain condition. This has to be balanced to a zero value to monitor the small variations of voltage appearing due to strain. This drawback can be circumvented in a Wheatstone bridge circuit analysed below.

5.8.1 Wheatstone Bridge Circuit

A typical four-arm active Wheatstone's bridge normally employed for strain measurements is shown in Fig. 5.15. It may be seen that the potential difference between the points B and D is given by

$$e = E_{BA} - E_{DA}$$

$$= E\left[\frac{R_1}{R_1+R_2} - \frac{R_4}{R_3+R_4}\right]$$

$$= E\left[\frac{R_1 R_3 - R_2 R_4}{(R_1+R_2)(R_3+R_4)}\right] \qquad (5.35)$$

This output voltage e is zero when $R_1 R_3 = R_2 R_4$. Under this condition the bridge is said to be balanced. Thus, the bridge arms can always be adjusted to satisfy the equality to obtain zero voltage under zero strain condition.

Consider a bridge where all the four resistors are active strain gauges whose resistance values change by ΔR_1, ΔR_2, ΔR_3, and ΔR_4 respectively on application of strain. Then,

$$e = E\left[\frac{(R_1+\Delta R_1)(R_3+\Delta R_3) - (R_2+\Delta R_2)(R_4+\Delta R_4)}{(R_1+\Delta R_1+R_2+\Delta R_2)(R_3+\Delta R_3+R_4+\Delta R_4)}\right] \qquad (5.36)$$

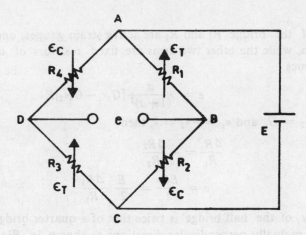

Fig. 5.15 Four-arm active Wheatstone bridge

Neglecting the second-order non-linearity terms and imposing the initial condition for balance, it can be shown that

$$e = E \left[\frac{\Delta R_1}{R_1} - \frac{\Delta R_2}{R_2} + \frac{\Delta R_3}{R_3} - \frac{\Delta R_4}{R_4} \right] \frac{R_1 R_2}{(R_1 + R_2)^2} \tag{5.37}$$

or

$$e = \frac{a}{(1+a)^2} \left[\frac{\Delta R_1}{R_1} - \frac{\Delta R_2}{R_2} + \frac{\Delta R_3}{R_3} - \frac{\Delta R_4}{R_4} \right] E \tag{5.38}$$

where

$$a = \frac{R_1}{R_2} = \frac{R_4}{R_3}.$$

If the gauge factors of the gauges are G_1, G_2, G_3, and G_4 and the strains developed are ϵ_1, ϵ_2, ϵ_3, and ϵ_4 respectively, then Eq. (5.38) becomes

$$e = \frac{a}{(1+a)^2} \left[G_1 \epsilon_1 - G_2 \epsilon_2 + G_3 \epsilon_3 - G_4 \epsilon_4 \right] E \tag{5.39}$$

The inherent property of algebraic addition of four strain values in the bridge gives rise to a number of applications of the bridge in strain measurements and, in particular, for transducer applications of strain gauges.

Various practical configurations of the bridge are considered below.

(a) Quarter Bridge

In this configuration, one arm of the bridge R_1 is active, and the other three arms contain fixed resistors having a value equal to that of the initial value of R_1, i.e. $R_1 = R_2 = R_3 = R_4$ and $\Delta R_2 = \Delta R_3 = \Delta R_4 = 0$. From Eq. (5.39)

$$e = \frac{EG\epsilon_1}{4} = \frac{E}{4} \frac{\Delta R_1}{R_1} \tag{5.40}$$

(b) Half Bridge

When two arms of the bridge R_1 and R_2 are active strain gauges, one in tension and the other in compression, while the other two arms are fixed resistors of identical value, the output voltage becomes

$$e = \frac{a}{(1+a)^2}[G_1\epsilon_1 - G_2\epsilon_2]E \tag{5.41}$$

If $R_1 = R_2$, $G_1 = G_2 = G$, and $\epsilon_1 = -\epsilon_2 = \epsilon$, then

$$\frac{\Delta R_1}{R_1} = -\frac{\Delta R_2}{R_2}$$

and

$$e = \frac{EG\epsilon}{2} = \frac{E}{2}\frac{\Delta R_1}{R_1} \tag{5.42}$$

Thus, the sensitivity of the 'half bridge' is twice that of a quarter bridge. If the gauges R_1 and R_2 are placed at mutually perpendicular directions as shown in Fig. 5.16(a) (Poisson's configuration), then

$$e = \frac{a}{(1+a)^2}[G_1\epsilon_1 - G_2(-0.3\epsilon_1)]E \tag{5.43}$$

$$= 0.325EG\epsilon \tag{5.44}$$

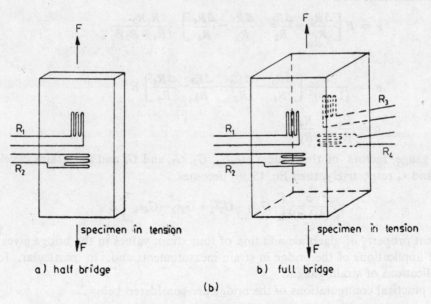

(b)

Fig. 5.16 Strain gauges connected in Poisson configurations:
(a) Half bridge; (b) full bridge

(c) Full Bridge

Consider a case of full-bridge configuration when all the four arms of the bridge are active gauges, two in tension (R_1 and R_3) and the other two in compression (R_2 and R_4). If $R_1 = R_2 = R_3 = R_4$, $G_1 = G_2 = G_3 = G_4 = G$ and $\epsilon_1 = -\epsilon_2 = \epsilon_3 = -\epsilon_4 = \epsilon$, then the output voltage will be

$$e = EG\epsilon = E\frac{\Delta R_1}{R_1} \tag{5.45}$$

If the full bridge is in the Poisson's arrangement as shown in Fig. 5.16(b), the output voltage is given by

$$E = \frac{E}{4}[G_1\epsilon_1 - G_2(-0.3\epsilon_1) + G_3\epsilon_1 - G_4(-0.3\epsilon_1)] \tag{5.46}$$

If the gauges are assumed to be identical ($G_1 = G_2 = G_3 = G_4 = G$),

$$e = 0.65EG\epsilon = 0.65E\frac{\Delta R_1}{R_1} \tag{5.47}$$

It may be noted that in all the cases, the circuit voltage sensitivity S_e under constant voltage excitation condition is related to the gauge factor by the relation

$$S_e = \frac{e}{\epsilon} = \frac{a}{(1+a)^2}EG \tag{5.48}$$

and the sensitivity is maximum when $a = 1$, i.e. in an equal-arm bridge configuration.

5.8.2 Strain Gauge Balancing Circuits

Strain gauge measurements can be carried out in two different ways, depending upon the balancing technique employed for the bridge. The first type is known as "out-of-balance" or "direct reading" type, in which the output voltage variations as a result of the strain, for an initially-balanced bridge condition, are calibrated directly in terms of microstrains. Such a measurement is ideally suited for dynamic strain measurements, in addition to the normal static strain measurements. The only source of error in this arrangement is the effect of possible variations in the excitation voltage and gain instability of the signal amplifier.

An alternate method of measurement employed is the null balance technique, wherein the resistance of one or more arms of the bridge is varied to match the effective change in resistance of the strain gauge. This method is ideally suited for static strain measurements. Since the reading is independent of the excitation voltage and gain of the amplifier used, the accuracy achievable is very high. A typical null-balance arrangement is illustrated in Fig. 5.17(a).

The resistors R_5 and R_6 are part of a calibrated potentiometer R_p which is usually a ten-turn helical potentiometer. The condition for balance is $R_{AB}R_{CD} = R_{AD}R_{BC}$, suffixes indicating the respective arms of the bridge as shown in the figure. If R_2 is the strain gauge, then the resultant unbalance due to strain can be nullified and the bridge brought back to balance, by the adjustment of the potentiometer R_p. The extent to which the potentiometer position is changed is calibrated in terms of the strain values directly. The effective values of the resistances in each arm can be written by referring to Fig. 5.17(a) as

$$R_{AB} = \frac{R_1 R_6}{R_1 + R_6}$$

and

$$R_{AD} = \frac{R_4 R_5}{R_4 + R_5} \tag{5.49}$$

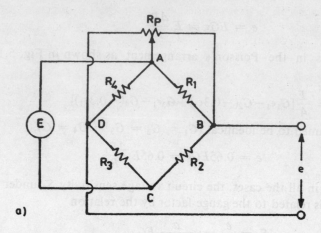

a)

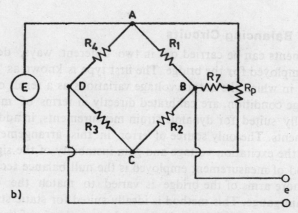

b)

Fig. 5.17 Methods of balancing Wheatstone bridge

To bring the bridge to the balance condition, R_5 and R_6 are changed by ΔR_5 and ΔR_6. For an equal arm bridge network $\Delta R_5 = -\Delta R_6$, for balance. The fractional changes in R_{AB} and R_{AD} can be computed by giving corresponding increments, and it may be shown that

$$\epsilon = \frac{2}{G} \frac{\Delta R_5}{R_P} \frac{1}{\left(1 + \dfrac{\Delta R_5}{R_4}\right)} \qquad (5.50)$$

Equation (5.50) shows that the strain can be read directly in terms of changes in the potentiometer position as indicated by ΔR_5; the non-linearity will be insignificant if $\Delta R_5 \ll R_4$, indicating a certain maximum allowable strain for a particular design. Equation (5.50) also shows that the indication is independent of the excitation voltage but depends only on the gauge factor. Null balance can also be obtained by putting R_P across the excitation leads as shown in Fig. 5.17(b). In this case, the arrangement can be considered as an addition of the extra potential at point B through a series resistor R_7, exactly equal in magnitude and opposite in polarity to the unbalanced voltage across *BD*. Resistance R_7 determines the span of measurement.

In certain other cases, it may be more convenient to measure the bridge unbalance voltage itself, very precisely, by employing a nulling technique as shown in Fig. 5.18; the nulling voltage is derived from the same source that excites the bridge, thus cancelling the variations in excitation. When the active arms are subjected to strain, the unbalance voltage of the bridge I is balanced with an equivalent but opposite in phase voltage from a dummy bridge II, by a suitable adjustment of the resistor R_5. This change in the second bridge is taken as a measure of the strain being measured. The main advantage is that both initial and null balances are performed by the reference bridge II in the instrument This technique is widely employed in precision strain measuring bridges.

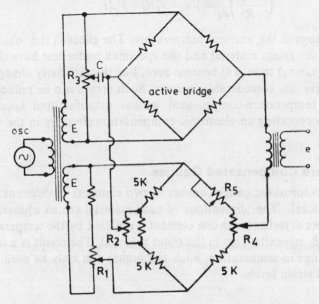

Fig. 5.18 Null balance with additional bridge

5.8.3 Circuits for Semiconductor Strain Gauges

The semiconductor type of strain gauges exhibit large non-linearity in the gauge factor and large variation of resistance with strain as well as variation of gauge factor with temperature. The normal method of excitation with a constant voltage supply, as is done for wire- and foil-type gauges, is no longer applicable. For good linearity in the output voltage with respect to strain, the desirable condition is to keep the gauge current constant. The constant-current operation by using a constant-current bridge excitation or by suitable modification to produce constant current in the bridge arm in addition to constant voltage, is ideal. Normal methods of achieving this are either to introduce a high resistance in series with the bridge excitation or to use an operational amplifier circuit in constant current mode. Alternatively, a sensing device such as a thermistor can be utilized to control the excitation voltage automatically in such a manner as to maintain the bridge arm current constant.

5.9 TEMPERATURE COMPENSATION

In practical applications, strain measurements are carried out over long periods of time. Consequently, in a particular gauge installation, the gauges are subjected to change in the ambient temperature. This will result in two effects, namely, a change in resistivity in the material of the gauge and an apparent strain due to the differential expansion of the gauge and the specimen to which the gauge is bonded.

If α_g is the coefficient of linear expansion of the gauge material, α_s is the coefficient of linear expansion of the specimen, and β is the coefficient of resistivity of the gauge material with respect to temperature, then the combined effect due to the ambient temperature variation can be written as

$$\left(\frac{\Delta R}{R} \right)_{\Delta_t} = [(\alpha_s - \alpha_g)G + \beta]\Delta t \tag{5.51}$$

where Δt is the change in the ambient temperature. The effect is the observation of a net apparent strain. If the gauge material and the specimen under test have the same coefficient of expansion, the $(\alpha_s - \alpha_g)$ term will become zero, but the resistivity change will still persist which can give rise to considerable errors. Such errors can be reduced substantially by employing either temperature-compensated gauges manufactured specifically for such purposes or by incorporating an electronic-compensation circuitry in the system.

5.9.1 Temperature Compensated Gauges

The temperature-compensated gauge consists of two elements of different materials, such as constantan and nickel. The dimensions of each material are so chosen that the temperature-induced changes of resistance in one element is nullified by the temperature-induced resistance changes with opposite sign in the other material. The result is a minimum apparent strain due to a change in temperature. Such techniques can only be used for limited ranges of temperature and strain levels.

5.9.2 Compensation through Bridge Arrangement

Temperature compensation in a strain-measuring system is also achieved by proper placement of the strain gauges in the bridge circuits. The change in resistance in a gauge can be attributed to two causes, one being due to the actual strain experienced by the gauge and the other due to temperature variations. Thus for any gauge

$$\frac{\Delta R}{R} = \left(\frac{\Delta R}{R} \right)_\epsilon + \left(\frac{\Delta R}{R} \right)_t \tag{5.52}$$

where the subscripts ϵ and t indicate the changes due to strain and temperature respectively.

To obtain temperature compensation, the term $\left(\dfrac{\Delta R}{R} \right)_t$ should be minimized.

In a bridge with a single arm, a second strain gauge of the same specification is placed in the adjacent arm and exposed to the same temperature variations. This gauge may or may not be subjected to any strain but must be subjected to the same environmental conditions as that of the active gauge fixed on the specimen. Referring to Fig. 5.15, the following cases may be obtained.

Case 1: R_1 is the active gauge subjected to the strain being measured and R_2 is a compensating gauge subjected to the same ambient temperature as that of R_1 but not subjected to any strain. R_3 and R_4 are assumed to be fixed resistors.

Then, Eq. (5.38) for output voltage e may be written as

$$e = \frac{a}{(1+a)^2}\left[\left(\frac{\Delta R_1}{R_1}\right)_e + \left(\frac{\Delta R_1}{R_1}\right)_t - \left(\frac{\Delta R_2}{R_2}\right)_t\right]E \qquad (5.53)$$

If $R_1 = R_2$, then $\left(\frac{\Delta R_1}{R_1}\right)_t = \left(\frac{\Delta R_2}{R_2}\right)_t$ and $a = 1$. Hence Eq. (5.53) becomes

$$e = \frac{1}{4}\left(\frac{\Delta R_1}{R_1}\right)_e E = \frac{EG\epsilon}{4}$$

and the bridge sensitivity S_e is obtained as

$$S_e = \frac{e}{\epsilon} = \frac{EG}{4} \qquad (5.54)$$

If I is the current passing through the gauge, $E = 2IR_1$. The sensitivity S_I in terms of gauge current is expressed as

$$S_I = \frac{IR_1G}{2}$$

or

$$\frac{S_I}{I} = \frac{R_1G}{2} \qquad (5.55)$$

Case 2: Consider that R_4 is the compensating gauge instead of R_2, R_1 being the active gauge. The current sensitivity can then be shown to be

$$\frac{S_I}{I} = \frac{e}{\epsilon I} = \frac{a}{(1+a)}R_1G \qquad (5.56)$$

The current sensitivity can thus be higher than that obtained in the earlier case for $a > 1$. However, this implies that a larger excitation voltage is required to maintain the same gauge current.

It may be concluded that temperature compensation can be achieved by employing an identical strain gauge exposed to the same environment in either of the adjacent arms of the active gauge in the bridge circuit. This procedure is widely employed in strain gauge instrumentation.

5.10 APPLICATIONS

Electrical strain gauges are employed for a variety of electrical transducer devices, mainly because of the ease in instrumentation, high accuracy, and excellent reliability. One of the most common configurations used in pressure, force, displacement, and acceleration transducers is the cantilever beam in which four strain gauges are employed, as shown in Fig. 5.19. Gauges R_1 and R_3 are subjected to tension while R_2 and R_4 are subjected to compression for the load F. These gauges constitute the four active arms of a measuring bridge. Since these are located at the same section of the beam, they are exposed to the same temperature environment, thereby achieving temperature compensation automatically. This configuration is invariably used in almost all transducer applications.

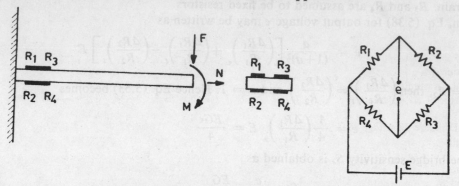

Fig. 5.19 Full bridge for force measurement

A measuring system with four active arms, as shown in Fig. 5.19, can be advantageously employed to resolve the components of forces acting on a specimen. If the specimen is subjected to usual loading as indicated by F, as well as a load in the perpendicular direction as indicated by N, the output voltage of the bridge is proportional to the bending only, since the load N causes all the four gauges to have identical strain change in resistance with the same sign. Expressing them in the form of an equation,

$$\frac{\Delta R_1}{R_1} = \frac{\Delta R_3}{R_3} = \frac{\Delta R_{1N}}{R_1} + \frac{\Delta R_{1F}}{R_1} = \frac{\Delta R_{3N}}{R_3} + \frac{\Delta R_{3F}}{R_3} \qquad (5.57)$$

and

$$\frac{\Delta R_2}{R_2} = \frac{\Delta R_4}{R_4} = \frac{\Delta R_{2N}}{R_2} - \frac{\Delta R_{2F}}{R_2} = \frac{\Delta R_{4N}}{R_4} - \frac{\Delta R_{4F}}{R_4} \qquad (5.58)$$

where N and F subscripts denote the perpendicular and bending forces. Since the gauges are symmetrically placed, it follows that

$$e = \frac{1}{4} \left[\sum \frac{\Delta R_{1F}}{R_1} \right] E \qquad (5.59)$$

Thus, the output voltage is proportional to change in resistance due to bending force only.

EXERCISES

5.1 The static calibration of strain gauge bridges are carried out by connecting a standard resistor shunted across one of the arms. If the strain gauge used has a resistance of 120 ohms and a gauge factor of 2.0, calculate the shunt resistance needed to obtain equivalent microstrain levels of (a) 300, (b) 2000, and (c) 5000.

5.2 Two active strain gauges are connected in series in one of the arms of a Wheatstone bridge network, and the bridge is adjusted initially for balance. Assuming both the strain gauges to be identical, derive the sensitivity of the bridge. Discuss the salient features of the arrangement.

5.3 Design a null balance Wheatstone bridge arrangement capable of measuring incremental strains of 1 microstrain, for a standard 120 ohms, four-arm active bridge. Determine the range attainable with this set up.

5.4 A single arm active strain gauge with 120 ohms resistance and a gauge factor of 2.0 is placed in an equal-arm Wheatstone bridge. With a bridge supply current of 20 mA, the output of the bridge corresponds to 30 units for 1000 microstrains. What would be the output if the current was increased to 30 mA, under identical conditions?

With the bridge current at 20 mA, what will be the output if the gauge factor of the strain gauge was 3.5 under the same strain?

5.5 Four strain gauges are placed symmetrically in Poisson's configuration centrally on a steel bar of 5 cm dia. Assuming that all the gauges are identical having a resistance value of 120 ohms and a gauge factor of 2.1, calculate the bridge sensitivity in terms of μV/kg axial load, if the bridge is excited with 6 V dc.

Estimate the bridge output, if one of the gauges is shunted with a 500 kohms resistor. Interpret the unbalance created in terms of equivalent strain.

5.6 R_1, R_2, R_3, and R_4 are the four arms of a Wheatstone bridge connected sequentially in a clockwise direction. Of these, R_1 and R_2 are active strain gauges of resistance 120 ohms and gauge factor 2.1, and R_3 and R_4 and fixed resistors of 500 ohms each. Calculate the bridge sensitivity if the bridge is excited with 6 V dc. Compare the result with the case where R_1 and R_4 are the strain gauges, and R_2 and R_3 are the fixed resistors with the same values as in the earlier case.

5.7 In an equal-arm Wheatstone bridge, the single active gauge has a nominal resistance 120 ohms, and is made of 'advance' having a thermal expansion coefficient of 30×10^{-6} m/m-°C and temperature coefficient of resistance of 12×10^{-6} ohm/ohm-°C. The other three arms are fixed resistors having negligible temperature coefficients. If the gauge is bonded to steel having a thermal coefficient of expansion of 13×10^{-6} m/m-°C, calculate the bridge output for a 60°C rise in specimen temperature, if the gauge current is 25 mA.

BIBLIOGRAPHY

B.L.H., *Stain Gauge Handbook*, Bulletin 4311A, Baldwin Lima Hamilton, Massachusetts, 1962.

B.L.H., *Semiconductor Strain Gauge Handbook*, Baldwin Lima Hamilton, Massachusetts, 1967.

Dally, J.W., and Riley, W.F., *Experimental Stress Analysis*, McGraw-Hill, New York, 1965.

Dean, M., *Aerodynamic Measurements*, Technology Press, Cambridge, 1956.

Dean, M. and Douglas, R.D. (Ed.), *Semiconductor and Conventional Strain Gauges*, Academic Press, New York, 1962.

Dobie, W.B. and Isaac, P.C.G., *Electrical Resistance Strain Gauges*, English University Press, London, 1948.

Dorsey, J., *Semiconductor Strain Gauge Handbook, Parts I-VI*, Baldwin Lima Hamilton, Massachusetts, 1968.

Hetenyi, M. (Ed.), *Handbook of Experimental Stress Analysis*, Chapman and Hall, London, 1950.

Higson, G.R., "Recent advances in strain gauges", *J. Sc. Inst.*, Vol. 41, pp. 405-414, 1964.

Jackson, P., "The foil strain gauge", *Instrument Practice*, Vol. 7, pp. 775-787, 1953.

Jones, E. and Malson, K.R., "The physical characteristics of wire resistance strain gauges", Aeronautical Research Council Research Memorandum 2661, Her Majesty's Stationery Office, London, 1952.

Lee, G.H., *Introduction to Experimental Stress Analysis*, Wiley & Sons, New York, 1950.

Lion, K.S., *Instrumentation in Scientific Research*, McGraw-Hill, New York, 1959.

Mathewson, C.E., "Dimensionless strain gauge", *Instruments and Control Systems*, Vol. 34, No. 10, pp. 1870-1871, October 1961.

Murray, W.M. and Stein, P.K., *Strain Gauge Techniques*, M.I.T. Press, Cambridge, Massachusetts, 1956.

N.B.S., *Characteristics and Applications of Resistance Strain Gauges*, N.B.S., Washington, D.C., 1954.

N.B.S., "Development of high temperature strain gauges", *N.B.S. Monograph*, 26, Washington, D.C., 1961.

Neubert, H.K.P., "Elasto resistive effects in metal wires and films", *Technical Report No. 69277, Royal Aircraft Establishment*, Faranborough, 1969.

Neubert, H.K.P., *Instrument Transducers*, Clarendon Press, Oxford, 1963.

Neubert, H.K.P., *Strain Gauges, Kinds and Uses*, Macmillan, London, 1967.

Norton, K., *Handbook of Transducers*, Prentice Hall, Princeton, 1969.

Parker, R.L. and Krinsky, A., "Electrical resistance strain gauges, characteristics of thin evaporated metal films", *J. of Applied Physics*, Vol. 34, pp. 2700-2708, 1963.

Perino, P.R., "Thin film strain gauge transducers", *Instrumentation and Control Systems*, Vol. 38, No. 12, pp. 119-121, Dec. 1965.

Perry, C.C. and Lisner, H.R., *The Strain Gauge Primer*, McGraw-Hill, New York, 1962.

Philips, L.G., *Self Adhesive Strain Gauges*, Royal Aircraft Establishment, Technical Report No. 67025, Faranborough, 1967.

Potma, T., *Strain Gauges—Theory and Applications*, Iliffe, London, 1967.

Roark, R.J. and Young W.C., *Formulas for Stress and Strain*, McGraw-Hill, New York, 1976.

Rohrbach, C., *Handbuch for Elektriches Messen Mechanischer Grössen*, V.D.I. Verlag, Düsseldorf, 1967.

Sanchez, J.C. and Wright, W.V., "Recent advances in flexible semiconductor strain gauges", *Journal of Instrument Society of America*, Pitisburg, Vol. 8, 1967.

Seredenin, V.I., "Thermocompensated differential transformer displacement transducer", *Measurement Technology*, Vol. 16, No. 4, pp. 509-511, April 1973.

Shields, J., "Strain gauge adhesives", *Metron*, Vol. 2, pp. 163-71, February 1970.

Smith, C.S., "Piezoresistive effect in germanium and silicon", *Physical Review*, Vol. 94, p. 42, 1954.

Stein, P.K., *Strain Gauges—Measurement Engineering*, Stein Engineering Services, Phoenix, 1972.

Timoshenko, S.P. and Goodier, J.N., *Theory of Elasticity*, McGraw-Hill, New York, 1951.

Whitehead, R.J., "Protective coating for strain gauges", *ISA Journal*, Vol. 11, pp. 71-73, March 1964.

6

VIBRATION

6.1 INTRODUCTION

Vibration and shock are the two main physical characteristics that define the motion in structures and machine components. Acceleration, velocity, and displacement as well as forces and stresses in vibrating bodies comprise the bulk of vibration and shock parameters. Vibration can be due to unbalance of rotating parts, misalignments, or external forces. For each of these measurements various types of transducers have been designed, although in some specific applications it may be possible to derive one quantity from the other, based upon their inter-relationship; e.g., velocity can be obtained from acceleration measurements by integration. The choice of the transducer for a particular measurement depends upon the application as well as the cost of instrumentation.

Vibration measurements are made, in general, for three major reasons, viz.

(a) Obtaining the response of a body or structure, such as the response of an aircraft wing to various load conditions.

(b) Defining the vibratory environment surrounding a vibratory source, viz. floor vibrations surrounding a high-speed compressor or generator.

(c) Monitoring and/or control of a system, such as in maintaining acceleration at a desired level in electromagnetic exciters or in an inertial navigational system.

The first application of determining the response of a structure requires the analysis of signals in addition to actual measurements. For the second application, a judicious selection of the number of measurement stations and their location at which vibration is measured is important. The investigation includes a number of field tests carried out under varying environmental conditions. For the third application, measurements made are mainly on the acceleration levels, acceleration-time waveforms, and spectral density distribution. All experiments are carried out with suitable velocity or acceleration transducers. In planning a vibration test, it is often mandatory to specify the types of measurements that should be made along with details of the frequency response, signal conditioning, and method of analysis and data presentation.

6.2 CHARACTERISTICS OF VIBRATION

Most of the vibrations encountered in practice are not pure simple harmonic motions that can be described by a simple mathematical function. For pure harmonic motion, the magnitude expressed in terms of the peak value is quite useful. If the frequency is known, the peak value describes the instantaneous values of the vibration magnitude as well with respect to time. For complex motions, other descriptive quantities such as the average values and root mean square values are needed to obtain information regarding the time history.

6.2.1 Periodic Motion

For the analysis of complex vibrations, a complete knowledge of the effect of vibrations on other associated elements is also required in addition to the basic quantities. One of the most powerful tools for this purpose is the Fourier frequency analysis. In this method, any steady-state complex periodic motion, however complex it may be, can be represented as a combination of a number of pure sinusoidal motions with harmonically related frequencies, as expressed by the equation

$$F(t) = X_0 + X_1 \sin(\omega t + \phi_1) + X_2 \sin(2\omega t + \phi_2) + X_3 \sin(3\omega t + \phi_3)$$
$$+ \cdots + X_n \sin(n\omega t + \phi_n) \tag{6.1}$$

As more and more terms are added to the above series, the description of the non-harmonic periodic motion becomes more precise. Signals of various frequencies constitute a frequency spectrum. Examples of periodic time functions and their frequency spectra are shown in Fig. 6.1.

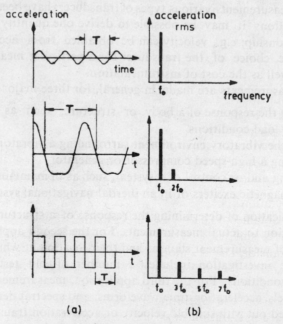

Fig. 6.1 Some periodic time functions and their
frequency spectra

6.2.2 Random Vibrations

In random vibrations, the vibration amplitudes are irregular with respect to time and never exactly repeat in time. To obtain a complete description of this vibratory process, an infinitely long record is required. Instead, statistical methods can be used to describe the random process. In the study of continuous processes, such as stationary random vibration, the probability density function is more appropriate, rather than the probability itself. This density gives the probability of finding instantaneous amplitude levels within a certain amplitude interval, divided by the magnitude of the interval. Further, it indicates in an average, how the instantaneous amplitudes are distributed without any consideration of the time history or frequency content. In the case of the auto-correlation function, the manner in which a particular instantaneous amplitude of the signal is dependent upon the previous instantaneous values is described. It is possible to obtain the mean square spectral density and frequency information using frequency analysers. The details of frequency analysers are presented in Chapter 13.

6.2.3 Shock

In certain cases, the effect of a shock or transient vibration on a particular mechanical system is important. Shock can be defined as the transmission of (kinetic) energy to a system which takes place in a relatively short time compared to the natural period of the system and which is followed by a decay of the natural oscillatory motion developed in the system. Shock phenomena originate from explosions, impacts, and other spasmodic releases of energy. It may be measured in terms of acceleration, velocity, or displacement; for a complete description, it is necessary to give the value of the exact amplitude in relation to the time history of the quantity in question. The shock pulse contains energy, spread over all frequencies from zero to infinity, spectra being continuous without any discrete frequency component. On the other hand, in the transient phenomena, such as in the case of the periodic wave, the magnitude of the spectral components tend towards zero at zero frequency as well as when the frequency approaches infinity. To describe the non-stationary random process, the variations in the statistical properties described earlier need to be taken into account. This can be described by the 'ensemble average' which is an average taken over a large number of repeated experiments.

6.3 ANALYSIS OF VIBRATION-SENSING DEVICES

The principle of operation of electrical transducers employed for vibration and shock measurements can be obtained by analysing linear mathematical models. The device may be basically considered as a single degree-of-freedom spring-mass system along with a suitable electrical sensor for transforming the motion to an equivalent electrical signal. Understanding the behaviour of such a system is essential for estimating the response of more complicated structures.

A generalized theory on the operating principle of similar measuring devices has been given in Chapter 3; but for vibration measurements, the treatment of the most popular device, namely, the seismic accelerometer can be very useful since it is inertially referenced and gives absolute values. The other types of transducers need a stationary reference, although velocity and displacement can be measured with a seismic configuration under limited conditions in certain applications.

6.3.1 Generalized Second-Order System

A typical device with a single degree-of-freedom arrangement is shown in Fig. 6.2. The system comprises a mass 'm', a linear spring of stiffness 'K' and a viscous damper 'c' all mounted on a foundation support. The mass is constrained to move only in an axis perpendicular to the foundation.

The equation of motion can be represented as

$$\ddot{x}(t) + 2\zeta\omega_n\dot{x}(t) + \omega_n^2 x(t) = \ddot{y}(t) = a(t) \tag{6.2}$$

where $a(t)$ is the acceleration of the foundation support equal to $\ddot{y}(t)$, and x and y are the displacements of the mass and foundation respectively, as indicated in Fig. 6.2.

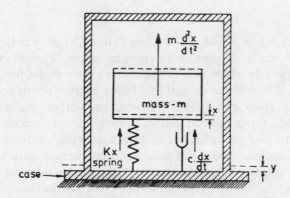

Fig. 6.2 Single degree-of-freedom seismic spring mass system

The absolute motion y of the foundation is transformed into a relative motion x through this arrangement. The coefficient of the terms x and $\dot{x}$ in the above equation have physical significance in the sense that the term $\omega_n = \sqrt{k/m}$ represents the undamped natural frequency of the system and the term $\zeta = \dfrac{c}{2\sqrt{km}}$ is the damping ratio (ratio of the actual damping to the critical damping).

The response of such a system to various types of inputs has been exhaustively dealt with in Chapter 3, as a generalized second-order system. The same study is valid for seismic-type vibration transducers also. However, vibration transducers require a single degree-of-freedom of system that senses the relative displacement x between the mass and platform. It gives an electrical output proportional to x. Since x is being taken as a measure of input vibrations, from Eq. (6.2) the transfer function can be written as a function of the Laplace variable s as

$$\frac{x}{s^2 y} = \frac{1}{s^2 + 2\zeta\omega_n s + \omega_n^2} \tag{6.3}$$

6.3.2 Absolute Displacement

A critical examination of Eq. (6.3) shows that a simple second-order spring-mass system of the type described can be used to measure absolute displacement, velocity, and acceleration.

Equation (6.3) may be written as

$$\frac{x}{y} = \frac{s^2/\omega_n^2}{\frac{s^2}{\omega_n^2} + 2\zeta\frac{s}{\omega_n} + 1}$$ (6.4)

For sinusoidal excitation at a frequency ω, by substituting $s = j\omega$, Eq. (6.4) becomes

$$\frac{x}{y} = \frac{-(\omega/\omega_n)^2}{1 - \left(\frac{\omega}{\omega_n}\right)^2 + 2j\zeta\left(\frac{\omega}{\omega_n}\right)}$$ (6.5)

If

$$\frac{\omega}{\omega_n} = \beta$$ (6.6)

then

$$\frac{x}{y} = \frac{-\beta^2 e^{j\phi}}{\sqrt{(1-\beta^2)^2 + (2\zeta\beta)^2}}$$ (6.7)

where $\phi = -\tan^{-1}\left[\frac{2\zeta\beta}{(1-\beta^2)}\right]$ Equation (6.7) shows how the displacement x of the seismic mass is related to the input displacement y in terms of the ratio of the excitation frequency ω to the system natural frequency ω_n. A plot of Eq. (6.7) is shown in Fig. 6.3.

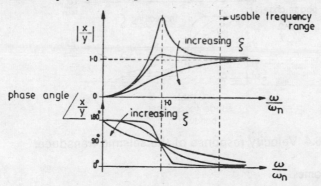

Fig. 6.3 Displacement response of seismic transducer

From Fig. 6.3, it may be observed that for large values of β (i.e. when the input frequencies are much larger than the system natural frequencies), all the curves converge at $x/y = 1$, thus making the displacement of the mass relative to the case identical to that of the input displacement. Typically, for $\beta > 5$, the amplitude ratio will be within 1% of unity, even if damping is very small ($\zeta < 0.1$). However, measurements at lower frequencies (i.e. $\beta < 5$) can be carried out to some extent if the damping ratio is higher; unfortunately, a noticeable phase shift is present at lower frequencies. With $\zeta = 0.7$ and $\beta \geqslant 1.2$, the absolute displacement measurement can be made with an accuracy of 5%. As can be seen, there is no high frequency limit for measurements. To cater to measurements down to very low frequencies, the natural frequency of the system should be as low as possible; for this, the mass of the seismic element should be large. Thus, a direct measurement of the seismic displacement is rarely attempted at very low frequencies because of the large sizes involved. In such cases, displacements are obtained after integration using either velocity or acceleration measurements, as discussed later in this chapter. The displacement of the mass with respect to the case can be measured with any of the conventional displacement devices operating on variable resistance, capacitance, or inductance principles.

6.3.3 Absolute Velocity

The relative displacement x of the mass with respect to the case can be made proportional to the input velocity $\dot{y}$, rather than input displacement, under certain conditions. These conditions can be obtained by rewriting Eq. (6.7) as

$$\frac{x}{\dot{y}} = \frac{1}{\omega_n} \cdot \frac{-\beta\, e^{j(\phi+\pi/2)}}{\sqrt{(1-\beta^2)^2+(2\zeta\beta)^2}} \tag{6.8}$$

A plot of the above equation is illustrated in Fig. 6.4.

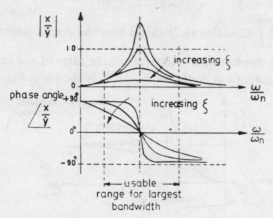

Fig. 6.4 Velocity response of the seismic transducer

At $\beta = 1$, Eq. (6.8) becomes

$$\frac{x}{\dot{y}} = \frac{1}{2\zeta\omega_n} \tag{6.9}$$

Thus, around $\beta = 1$, in the above system, the relative displacement x of the seismic mass with respect to the case is proportional to the input velocity $\dot{y}$. As can be seen from Fig. 6.4, with large values of ζ, the system can be used to measure input velocities over a fairly wide range of frequencies. However, the sensitivity of the transducer is compromised by increasing the damping, since the relative displacement x reduces with increased damping.

An alternative way of measuring the seismic velocity is to use the basic seismic displacement configuration as discussed in the earlier section and incorporate a relative velocity transducer of the electromagnetic type to obtain velocity outputs.

6.3.4 Absolute Acceleration

A large number of practical accelerometers have the same second-order type of single-degree-of-freedom configuration described earlier. They differ only in details, such as the spring element, type of sensor employed to measure the relative motion, and the damping system provided.

In the second-order system shown in Fig. 6.2, the relative motion x must be proportional to the input acceleration for an accelerometer. It may be shown from Eqs. (6.2), (6.6) and (6.7) that

$$\frac{x}{\ddot{y}} = \frac{1}{\omega_n^2} \frac{e^{j\phi}}{\sqrt{(1-\beta^2)^2 + (2\zeta\beta)^2}} \tag{6.10}$$

A plot of the response obtained from the above equation is shown in Figs. 6.5(a) and (b). It can be seen that for $\beta \ll 1$, the relative displacement x is proportional to the input acceleration. For a damping ratio of 0.6, the response is flat up to about $\beta = 0.7$.

An examination of Eq. (6.10) reveals that the sensitivity is inversely proportional to the square of the natural frequency. However, to obtain good bandwidths it is necessary to have higher natural frequencies. In practice, the appropriate choice is a compromise between the two factors.

For most vibration measurements, the choice of an accelerometer is invariably favoured when compared to the velocity and displacement transducers. This is so because the accelerometer is usually small in weight and size, and has large bandwidth and good sensitivity.

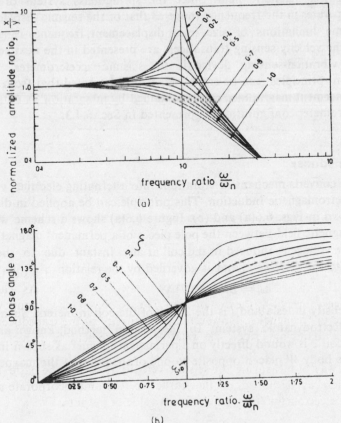

(a)

(b)

Fig. 6.5 Acceleration response of the seismic transducer

6.4 VIBRATION-SENSING DEVICES

Various transduction methods based on the resistance, capacitance or inductance, change or any other principle can be employed to measure the seismic mass motion with respect to the case and the absolute displacement, velocity, or acceleration of the vibration can be determined.

In the second-order spring-mass system described earlier, when $\beta (=\omega/\omega_n)$ is substantially greater than 1.0 (see Eq. (6.7)), the displacement of the mass with respect to the case is directly proportional to the input absolute displacement. Under this condition, the transducer becomes a seismic displacement-measuring device. The addition of substantial damping makes the transducer useful for indicating displacements over a wide range of frequencies, limited by the distortions introduced due to the phase shift. Variable resistance (potentiometers, strain gauges), variable capacitance, variable reluctance, or LVDT devices have been successfully employed to sense the true motion of the mass with respect to the case. To obtain low natural frequencies the mass has to be kept relatively large, thereby increasing the size of the transducer. Due to these limitations, such types of transducers are seldom used for vibration displacement measurements.

The vibration velocity can be measured directly either in terms of absolute or relative values. Usually, a spring-mass transducer for measuring velocity is a device with a low natural frequency, utilizing the frequency range above its natural frequency. The relative velocity dx/dt between the mass and the case is measured with a velocity-sensing transducer element, such as a coil moving in a magnetic field. Since the spring-mass system of an absolute velocity transducer operates in the frequency range as that of the seismic displacement transducer, it has the same limitations of size, input displacement, frequency range, and phase shift. The details of the velocity sensing transducers are presented in the next section.

The most popular vibration-sensing device is the seismic accelerometer, where again different transduction principles can be employed. It may be noted that from acceleration, the velocity and displacement magnitudes can be obtained by integration. A detailed analysis of the various accelerometer configurations is presented in Sec. 6.4.3.

6.4.1 Velocity Transducer

A velocity transducer converts mechanical vibrations into alternating electrical voltages using the principle of electromagnetic induction. This principle can be applied in different ways, two of which are shown in Figs. 6.6(a) and (b). Figure 6.6(a) shows a scheme wherein a coil is suspended in a magnetic field between the pole pieces of a permanent magnet with springs from the housing. The voltage e_o induced in the coil at any instant due to the motion is directly proportional to the velocity $\dot{x}$, and is governed by the relation

$$e_o = Bl\dot{x} \times 10^{-12} \text{ V} \tag{6.11}$$

where B is the flux density in tesla and l is the length of the coil in meters. Such a system is usually called the electrodynamic system. In the second method, known as the electromagnetic system, the coil c is wound directly on a permanent magnet as shown in Fig. 6.6(b). When a ferromagnetic body W placed opposite to one of the poles of the magnet is moved with respect to the magnet, a change in the flux ϕ linking the coil c obtained. This causes a voltage proportional to $d\phi/dt$ generated in the coil. The voltage in this case, may be expressed as

$$e_o = k \frac{d\phi}{dt} = k \frac{d\phi}{dy} \frac{dy}{dt} = k \frac{d\phi}{dy} \frac{d(y_0+x)}{dt}$$

$$= k \frac{d\phi}{dy} \frac{dx}{dt} \qquad (6.12)$$

where y is the instantaneous gap, y_0 is the average gap between the magnet face and the ferromagnetic body, and k is a proportionality constant.

As can be seen from Eq. (6.12), the induced voltage is directly proportional to the velocity of movement, but is also dependent on the gap y. Thus, $d\phi/dy$ forms the sensitivity factor indicating that as the average distance increases, sensitivity reduces.

In principle, both methods can be employed to measure absolute or relative velocities. In the case of absolute velocity measurement, the coil and the magnet form the single-degree-of-freedom, second-order, spring-mass system arrangement. It has been shown in Sec. 6.3.1 that at frequencies sufficiently above the natural frequency of the system, the displacement of the seismic mass is equal to the input displacement. In this frequency range, instead of sensing the seismic displacement, the velocity of the seismic mass can be sensed using the above principle, thereby obtaining seismic velocity values. It may be noted that the coil can be stationary and the magnet movable or vice versa. Natural frequencies of the order of 10, to 12 Hz with damping ratios of about 0.5 make the transducer useful above about 20 Hz. Usually, in these types of transducers eddy-current damping is provided making the damping invariant with temperature. The electromagnetic principle is widely used for proximity switches or in the measurement of speed of rotating bodies.

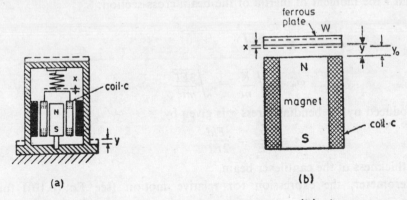

Fig. 6.6 Configurations of: (a) electrodynamic; (b) electromagnetic transducers

The advantages of these devices are: (a) self-generating principle, requiring no external supplies and (b) high sensitivities of the order of 200 mV/cm/s is obtainable, without amplification. However, unless special precautions are taken in the construction, strong external magnetic fields can adversely affect the performance of the devices.

6.4.2 Bonded Strain Gauge Accelerometer

One of the simplest devices to measure vibration characteristics is the bonded strain gauge sensor. Strains developed due to bending in a cantilever beam subjected to vibrations can be made to be proportional to the unknown acceleration, by using a simple accelerometer configuration as shown in Fig. 6.7. A seismic mass m is attached to the end of a cantilever beam of length l. When this is subjected to an acceleration, a relative displacement x of the mass with respect to the case is developed.

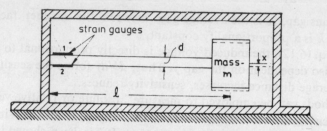

Fig. 6.7 Bonded strain gauge accelerometer

The spring constant K of the system is

$$K = \frac{\text{Force } F}{\text{Deflection } x}$$

The deflection x of the mass is given by

$$x = \frac{Fl^3}{3EI} \tag{6.13}$$

where F is the force acting on the mass, l is the length of the cantilever beam, E the modulus of elasticity, and I the moment of inertia of the beam cross-section.
Since,

$$K = \frac{3EI}{l^3} \tag{6.14}$$

$$\omega_n = \sqrt{\frac{K}{m}} = \sqrt{\frac{3EI}{ml^3}} \tag{6.15}$$

The strain ϵ produced by the bending stress σ is given by

$$\epsilon = \frac{\sigma}{E} = \frac{Fld}{2EI} \tag{6.16}$$

where d is the thickness of the cantilever beam.

In an accelerometer, the expression for relative motion (see Eq. (6.10)) for $\beta \ll 1$ becomes

$$x = -\frac{\ddot{y}}{\omega_n^2} \tag{6.17}$$

From Eqs. (6.13), (6.16), and (6.17), it can be shown that

$$-\frac{\ddot{y}}{\omega_n^2} = \frac{1}{3} \frac{Fl^3}{EI}$$

$$= \frac{2}{3} \cdot \frac{\epsilon l^2}{d} \tag{6.18}$$

Therefore,

$$\frac{\epsilon}{\ddot{y}} = \frac{-3d}{2\omega_n^2 l^2} \tag{6.19}$$

Substituting for ω_n^2 from Eq. (6.15),

$$\frac{\epsilon}{\ddot{y}} = -\frac{mdl}{2EI} \tag{6.20}$$

Equations (6.20) and (6.15) indicate the static sensitivity and frequency response relationships for this type of accelerometer. In order to have higher sensitivities, m and l should be made larger, but this reduces the natural frequency as indicated in Eq. (6.15). The ultimate choice is a compromise between the two.

In this particular configuration, it is rather difficult to obtain high natural frequencies beyond a few tens of hertz because of the lower limitations of the size of the beam on which the gauges are mounted. To improve the bandwidth, fluid-filled damping is provided. The strain gauges employed are standard wire, foil, or semiconductor gauges, two in compression and two in tension, completing a Wheatstone bridge network. The instrumentation requirements for strain gauges have been discussed in Chapter 5.

An alternative to the cantilever beam-type accelerometer described so far, which gives a higher frequency response, is a configuration where the seismic mass m is supported by a solid structure, mostly cylindrical in form, as shown in Fig. 6.8. The supporting structure acts as the spring. Strain gauges bonded on the surface of the support measure the strain due to accelerations. The deflection is relatively small, and the natural frequency is much higher than that of the cantilever type. The internal damping provided by the solid cylinder itself is adequate for proper functioning.

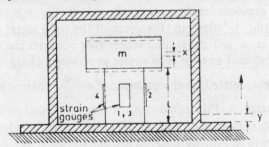

Fig. 6.8 Solid cylinder accelerometer

The spring constant K of the system shown in Fig. 6.8 is given as

$$K = \frac{F}{x} \tag{6.21}$$

where F is the force acting on the cylinder due to mass m.

Substituting $x = \epsilon l$,

$$x = \frac{\sigma}{E} l \tag{6.22}$$

$$= \frac{F}{A \cdot E} \cdot l \tag{6.23}$$

where l is the length of the cylinder, A is the area of cross-section, and σ is the stress developed, all in appropriate units.

Therefore,

$$K = \frac{AE}{l} \qquad (6.24)$$

and

$$\omega_n = \sqrt{\frac{AE}{ml}} \qquad (6.25)$$

The strain produced due to acceleration $\ddot{y}$ is given by

$$\frac{\epsilon}{\ddot{y}} = \frac{m}{AE} \qquad (6.26)$$

Natural frequencies of the order of a few thousands of hertz with the response right from static values can be obtained depending upon the particular design. To obtain higher sensitivities, semiconductor strain gauges can be employed. It may be noted that although bonded strain gauges have been illustrated in the above configurations, it is equally possible to employ other devices, such as variable inductance or variable capacitance to measure displacement, rather than strain.

6.4.3 Piezoelectric Accelerometer

The development of a piezoelectric accelerometer is based on the same principle as that described for the previous configuration, shown in Fig. 6.8, except that a force-sensitive piezoelectric crystal is used in the place of the solid metal cylinder. The main advantage here is that it is a self-generating sensor that converts the dynamic force or acceleration into equivalent electrical energy. The device generates a charge q when a force F is applied across the element, related by the equation $F = \frac{q}{d}$ where d is the piezoelectric constant.

The accelerometer is fabricated with a mass mounted in direct contact with the crystal element. The mass is preloaded with a stiff spring, and the whole assembly is mounted in a metal housing with a sturdy base. When the device is subjected to acceleration, the mass exerts a variable force on the piezoelectric disc, which is linearly proportional to the acceleration. The charge developed across the disc is in turn proportional to the acceleration of the mass.

The sensitivity of the piezoelectric crystal is a complex value and is defined as the ratio of the electrical output to the mechanical input, and is expressed as volts or charge per unit acceleration. The voltage sensitivity $S_e(f)$ and the charge sensitivity $S_q(f)$ may be written as

$$S_e(f) = \frac{v(f)}{a} \qquad (6.27)$$

and

$$S_q(f) = \frac{q_0(f)}{a} \qquad (6.28)$$

where $v(f)$ and $q_o(f)$ are the voltage and change generated respectively. Both $S_e(f)$ and $S_q(f)$ are frequency dependent and are characterized by their inherent capacitance and resistance as well as the loading conditions.

In the frequency range where the sensitivity of the accelerometer is constant, the piezoelectric equation in terms of the output voltage is

$$E = -g_{33}T + \frac{D}{\epsilon^T} \tag{6.29}$$

where E is the output voltage, D is the dielectric displacement, g_{33} is the piezoelectric voltage constant (stress constant), T is the mechanical stress and ϵ^T is the premittivity of the crystal material at constant stress. The suffixes of the voltage constant g_{33} refer to the direction of the electric field (first suffix) and the direction of the mechanical stress (second suffix).

In the approximation of an open-circuit condition, the dielectric displacement D will be zero and Eq. (6.29) becomes

$$[E]_{D=0} = -g_{33}T \tag{6.30}$$

For an accelerometer, in which the seismic mass m is many times greater than the mass of the piezoelectric transducer, the mechanical stress T in the transducer is

$$T(t) = a(t) \cdot \frac{m}{A}, \text{(compression)} \tag{6.31}$$

where A is the cross-sectional area of the piezoelectric crystal and a is the acceleration. The open-circuit voltage sensitivity S_{e_0} of the accelerometer can be derived from Eqs. (6.30) and (6.31). Taking $e = E \cdot h$ where h is the thickness of the crystal, and assuming $m \gg$ crystal mass, the load resistance is infinity and the load capacitance is zero, the voltage sensitivity becomes

$$S_{e_0} = \frac{e}{a} = g_{33} \frac{h}{A} m \tag{6.32}$$

If the seismic mass m is not many times greater than the mass m' of the transducer disc, then m may be replaced by $m + (\frac{1}{2})m'$ in Eq. (6.32). In the limiting case, $m = 0$ and only $(1/2)m'$ acts as the seismic mass; then the voltage sensitivity relationship is modified as

$$S_{e_0} = g_{33} \frac{h}{A} \cdot \frac{m'}{2} = \frac{1}{2} \rho g_{33} h^2 \tag{6.33}$$

where ρ is the density of the crystal material. Thus, the voltage sensitivity of the piezoelectric crystal sensor, without seismic mass, increases as the square of the disc thickness h and is independent of the surface area A.

A short circuit condition arises, when the current following through the load capacitor C_c (offered by the cable) is the same as that when the crystal terminals were shorted. Expressing the dielectric displacement in terms of the piezoelectric charge constant d_{33},

$$D = d_{33}T + \epsilon^T E \tag{6.34}$$

In the above short-circuit condition, the voltage across the device $E = 0$, and hence

$$[D]_{E=0} = d_{33}T \tag{6.35}$$

Consequently, the charge sensitivity S_q of the sensor is given by

$$S_q = \frac{q}{a} = d_{33}\left(m + \frac{1}{2}m'\right) \tag{6.36}$$

showing that S_q is independent of the disc dimensions.

The material constants which determine the voltage and charge sensitivities are the voltage constant g_{ij} and charge constant d_{ij} where i and j are the crystal axes. Both these are dependent on temperature and have opposite signs. By selecting a mode of operation between open and short circuit, it is possible in principle to compensate the temperature characteristics of the material constants. In practice, the piezoelectric charge sensitivity can be reduced considerably by having a large thermal time constant and large seismic mass (high sensitivity). The other aspects of piezoelectric transducers are given in Chapter 7.

Fabrication and Mounting

The accelerometer is fabricated in various modes with the seismic mass mounted in direct contact with the crystal element as shown in Fig. 6.9. The crystal itself acts as a spring supporting the mass, thus the spring constant of the system is mainly decided by the stiffness of the piezoelectric crystal element in that particular mode. The devices should be so designed that they can be excited by only one component of vibration. The appearance of shear or flexural vibrations causes a directional sensitivity. Shear forces readily appear in a sensor intended for axial excitation, if the crystal disc and seismic mass are not exactly aligned with respect to their centres of gravity. Flexural stresses occur mostly with thin piezoelectric discs when the faces of the discs as well as the surfaces with which the disc is in mechanical contact are not perfectly flat. Lateral forces appear because the adhesive bond hinders the lateral expansion and contraction of the disc. These forces are caused by the different coefficients of thermal expansion and compliances of the piezoelectric material, sensor base and seismic mass. Basically, all lateral forces reduce the sensitivity of the sensor.

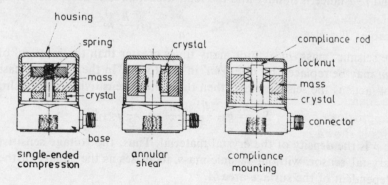

Fig. 6.9 Different configurations of piezoelectric accelerometers

Shear and compliance types are the best for overall performance. In the case of shear mounting, it permits excellent isolation of the sensing elements from the case, and provides minimum problems of cable whip, acoustics, and thermal transients; but the overall sensitivity is limited and the cross sensitivity is not negligible. In the case of compliance rod mounting, the sensor exhibits high sensitivity, complete isolation from stress membrane, and very low cross sensitivity. The performance parameters for various modes of operation of piezoelectric crystals employed for accelerometers and pressure transducers, where the basic sensor is in the form of a disc, plate, or cantilever, are given in Chapter 7 (Fig. 7.16 and Table 7.2).

For an accelerometer to generate accurate and useful data, the device must be properly coupled to the vibrating system under test. The mounting must be rigid over the frequency range of interest. The main advantages of the sensor are:

(a) Self generating
(b) Wide frequency response
(c) Small size and weight
(d) Electrical output directly proportional to the acceleration.

Environmental Effects

In actual usage, the performance of a piezoelectric accelerometer is normally affected by various environmental conditions. A major factor is the temperature which causes variation in some of the basic parameters, such as charge sensitivity, permittivity, dissipation factor, and leakage resistance. The insulation resistance is also affected due to any increase in humidity. Another factor is the error introduced by the transverse sensitivity factor, when a linear accelerometer is subjected to any acceleration in the radial direction perpendicular to the direction of the main axis of polarisation. This effect is minimum in quartz-type accelerometers.

Piezoelectric accelerometers are also sensitive to air-borne high intensity sound or random acoustical noise. The error is as high as $\pm 0.1g$ where g is the acceleration due to gravity for a noise level of 160 dB. The vibration of a structure on which the transducer is mounted can also create similar problems. Such interference errors are reduced by incorporating suitable filters in signal conditioners. In many of the installations, tribo-electric signals are caused during the flexing and squeezing of the lead cables of the device. The effect is mainly due to frictional separation as a result of improper mating in the two leads of the concentric coaxial cable. The electrostatic induction at the point of separation generates appreciable voltages across the load. Low loss cables with special conductive coatings on the inner and outer conductors, to lead away the charges, are recommended.

Charge Generator Model of the Accelerometer with Cable

A good approximation of the charge generator model for frequencies well below the natural frequencies is shown in Fig. 6.10.

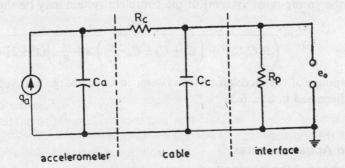

Fig. 6.10 Charge generator model of the piezoelectric accelerometer

The electrical characteristics of the connecting coaxial cable between the piezoelectric accelerometer and the signal conditioner is included in the mathematical representation of the complete accelerometer model, since these parameters directly affect the overall transfer function. Referring to Fig. (6.10) the output voltage e_o can then be expressed as

$$e_o = \frac{Ksx}{R_c C_a C_c s^2 + \left(C_c + C_a + C_a \dfrac{R_c}{R_p} \right) s + \dfrac{1}{R_p}} \qquad (6.37)$$

where C_a = internal capacitance of the accelerometer, R_c = cable resistance, C_c = cable capacitance, R_p = interface input resistance, K = proportionality constant, and x = deflection in the crystal.

The deflection x is related to the equivalent charge q_a as $q_a = D_q x$ where D_q is th characteristic constant of the piezoelectric material.

The basic limitation of this type of accelerometer can be inferred from Eqn. (6.37) wherein

$$e_o(j\omega)\Big|_{\omega=0} = 0 \qquad (6.38)$$

To compensate for this lack of dc response, several schemes of circuitry are possible in the signal conditioner that interfaces with the accelerometer. One technique is to integrate the signal so that the integrated output

$$e_c(s) = \frac{e_o(s)}{s} \qquad (6.39)$$

A second method (voltage amplifier) uses an amplifier with an extremely high input impedance to minimize the loading. Assuming that $R_c = 0$, Eq. (6.37) becomes

$$e_o(s) = \frac{Ksx}{(C_a + C_c)s + \dfrac{1}{R_p}} \qquad (6.40)$$

If the input impedance of the signal conditioning stage R_p is very large, the circuit provides a very low cut-off frequency.

In terms of the input acceleration $\ddot{y}$, the overall transfer function (including the dynamic response of the spring-mass system) of the complete system may be shown to be

$$\frac{e_o}{y} = \frac{Ks}{\left(R_c C_a C_c s^2 + \left(C_c + C_a + C_a \dfrac{R_c}{R_p} \right) s + \dfrac{1}{R_p} \right)(s^2 + 2\zeta \omega_n s + \omega_n^2)} \qquad (6.41)$$

The total response of the accelerometer system, in both charge and voltage amplifier modes are further discussed in Sec. 6.5.

6.4.4 Servo Accelerometer

The measurement of the vibration of large structures involves special problems. The natural modes of large massive structures tend to occur at low frequencies, and associated accelerations expected under many conditions of measurement are small. Under these conditions, the accelerometer should be very sensitive and suitable for use right from static conditions. Unlike many other applications, the motion of large structures is relatively unaffected by the loading of the accelerometer mass during measurement. This allows the use of accelerometers which are relatively heavy when compared to piezoelectric devices. For such applications, a servo accelerometer (also known as force-balance accelerometer) which operates on measuring forces required to keep the seismic mass at rest with respect to the instrument frame under acceleration, is ideally suited. The device was originally developed mainly for inertial guidance systems in aircraft and missiles. Its high accuracy and reasonable frequency response make it suitable even as a secondary standard.

Basically, servo accelerometers measure the acceleration of a structure or vehicle on which it is mounted by measuring the force required to constrain the proof mass to move with the vehicle, or in other words, the force needed to prevent the mass moving relative to the instrument frame. A displacement transducer produces a signal proportional to the relative movement of the mass with respect to the instrument frame, and this signal is amplified and fed back as direct current to the force coil suspended in a magnetic field. The effect of this current is to generate the required restoring force for equilibrium. Ideally, therefore, the current required to constrain the mass is a measure of the input acceleration (on the frame) along the direction in which the mass is free to move.

A schematic arrangement of the servo accelerometer is shown in Fig. 6.11.

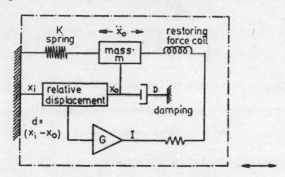

Fig. 6.11 Schematic arrangement of the servo accelerometer

Referring to the diagram, we have

$$m\ddot{x}_0 = Kd + FI + Dd \tag{6.42}$$

where K is the linear spring rate, F is the force produced on the mass per unit current, D is the viscous-damping coefficient, and I is the current.

Further, $\qquad d = x_i - x_o \qquad$ and $\qquad \ddot{x}_o = \ddot{x}_i - \ddot{d}$

Therefore,

$$m\ddot{x}_i = Kd + FI + D\dot{d} + m\ddot{d} \tag{6.43}$$

Then, under the condition that $I = Gd$, where G is the gain of the amplifier,

$$m\ddot{x}_i = \frac{m}{G}\ddot{I} + \frac{D}{G}\dot{I} + \left(\frac{K}{G} + F\right)I \tag{6.44}$$

Hence,

$$\ddot{x}_i = \left[\frac{m}{FG} s^2 + \frac{D}{FG} s + \frac{K}{FG} + 1 \right] \frac{FI(s)}{m} \tag{6.45}$$

where s is the Laplace operator.

The static sensitivity is then expressed as

$$\frac{I}{\ddot{x}_i} = \frac{G}{s^2 + \frac{D}{m} s + \frac{K+FG}{m}} \tag{6.46}$$

This is the closed loop dynamic response equation giving a value for the current I required to make the seismic mass stationary for an input acceleration $\ddot{x}_i$. The undamped natural frequency of the system is given by

$$\omega_c = \sqrt{\frac{K+FG}{m}} \simeq \sqrt{\frac{FG}{m}} \tag{6.47}$$

for $K \ll FG$, i.e. for large values of G.

In steady state

$$\frac{I}{\ddot{x}_i} = \frac{Gm}{K+FG} \tag{6.48}$$

If G is very large,

$$\frac{I}{\ddot{x}_i} = \frac{m}{F} \tag{6.49}$$

The open loop characteristic is given by (assuming $F = 0$),

$$\frac{I}{\ddot{x}_i} = \frac{G}{s^2 + \frac{D}{m} s + \frac{K}{m}} \tag{6.50}$$

and the undamped natural frequency in this case is

$$\omega_o = \sqrt{\frac{K}{m}} \tag{6.51}$$

A flat frequency response from 2 to about 500 Hz can be obtained in these devices with high sensitivities.

In another design, the torque arising from linear acceleration on a suspended pendulum-type seismic element is precisely opposed by an equal capturing torque. This torque is exactly proportional to the level of the dc current generated by the servo in an electromagnetic force generator. By automatically maintaining the pendulum in this condition of force balance, the device provides a high-level voltage or current output signal, as a measure of the acceleration to which it is subjected to.

6.4.5 Digital Accelerometer

The principle of variation of the natural resonant frequency of a structural membrane, with an applied force, can be employed to measure acceleration in a digital format. One such type is the linear digital accelerometer which has the unique advantage of high reliability and accuracy in addition to small size and output frequency directly proportional to the acceleration. The disadvantage of the normal analog to digital conversion is also eliminated.

The accelerometer device is basically a double-ended closed quartz tuning fork. The sensing element is cut from crystalline quartz and excited at its mechanical resonant frequency. The precise configuration and dimensions are determined by the acceleration range and other environmental considerations.

Two quartz resonators are used in each instrument.[1] Each resonator is fastened to the instrument case and to an individually-suspended proof mass in a manner such that acceleration components, along their axis of sensitivity, place one resonator in tension and the other in compression as shown in Fig. 6.12. The resultant stresses cause precisely defined changes in the resonant frequency. Such a device finds unique application in inertial guidance systems for aircraft, and in guidance and telemetry systems for missiles.

The change in frequency as a result of applied acceleration is measured directly as a digital output. The symmetrical construction allows the parallel beams to vibrate in symmetry so that the moments due to bending, at the dual beam junctions, are cancelled out. The equation for a fixed-end beam of constant cross-section in transverse vibration is given by

$$EI \frac{d^4y}{dx^4} + T \frac{d^2y}{dx^2} + m \frac{d^2y}{dt^2} = 0 \qquad (6.52)$$

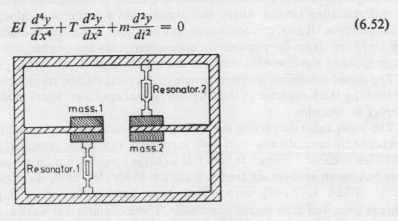

Fig. 6.12 Resonator type digital accelerometer

where E is modulus of elasticity in the axial direction, I is the moment of inertia of a plane section through the beam, y is the beam deflection at any point x, x is the position along the longitudinal axis of the beam, T is the axial load in tension, m is the mass per unit length, and t is time.

The solution of this differential equation for fixed end boundary conditions results in a transcendental equation. from which ω can be computed.

$$\omega = 5.59332 \left(\frac{2}{l}\right)^2 \sqrt{\frac{EI}{m}} \left[1 + 0.09831 \left(\frac{l^2T}{8EI}\right) - 0.00531 \left(\frac{l^2T}{8EI}\right)^2 \right.$$

$$\left. + 0.00055 \left(\frac{l^2T}{8EI}\right)^3 - \cdots \right] \qquad (6.53)$$

The result shows that the natural frequency of the resonator is a function of the tension T. Expressing in terms of acceleration, the frequency may be expressed as

$$f_T = f_o + K_1 a - K_2 a^2 + K_3 a^3 \tag{6.54}$$

$$f_c = f_o - K_1 a - K_2 a^2 - K_3 a^3 \tag{6.55}$$

where f_T is the frequency in tension, f_c is the frequency in compression, f_o is the frequency in no-load condition and K_1, K_2, K_3 are the coefficients.
Therefore,

$$f = f_T - f_c = 2K_1 a + 2K_3 a^3 \tag{6.56}$$

Usually, the third order term is small (less than 0.03% at 20g), and the difference frequency, as read with a counter, is directly proportional to the applied acceleration.

6.5 SIGNAL CONDITIONERS

The signal conditioning stage of vibration transducers depends upon the type of transduction employed. Starting with the connecting cable, the associated signal amplifier, integrating or differentiating circuits, filters, modulators, and demodulators, along with the balancing arrangements, if any, perform important functions in signal conditioning. Signal conditioning amplifier stages for piezoelectric transducers only are emphasized in this section, and the other types of signal conditioners are dealt with exhaustively in Chapters 11 and 12.

The signal-conditioning system employing a piezoelectric transducer comprises the cable connecting the transducer to the amplifier, signal amplifier, signal modifier, if any, and output display or recorder.

The input cable connecting the transducer is usually a low capacitance, low noise, low microphonic coaxial cable with high insulation resistance between the leads. The signal amplifier is either a voltage follower or a charge amplifier built with special operational amplifiers having an appropriate feedback circuit. In an ideal case, the operational amplifier can be visualized as having zero offset, large bandwidth, infinite input impedance, infinite voltage gain, and zero output impedance. These characteristics are closely met by some of the recent commercially available operational amplifiers in the frequency ranges of interest.

Voltage Amplifiers

The voltage follower amplifier suitable for piezoelectric devices is shown in Fig. 6.13(a), which is designed for non-inverting operation with unity gain. Figure 6.13(b) shows the equivalent circuit of the accelerometer along with the connecting table and voltage follower. This configuration takes advantage of the high input impedance of the amplifier, which results in very low leakage path across the transducer and cable capacitance. The low frequency response of the transducer, cable, and amplifier combination is thus improved. With operational amplifiers having FET input stages, an input impedance of the order of 10^{11} ohms can be obtained.

If the other characteristics of the amplifier are assumed to be ideal, then from Fig. 6.13(a), the input current of the amplifier i_{in} may be written as

$$\frac{e_i - e_o}{R_i} + \frac{e_i}{R_p} = i_{in} \tag{6.57}$$

where R_i is the internal input resistance of the amplifier and R_p is the resistance to ground. Since the open loop dc gain of the amplifier is very large (over 10^6), it can be shown that $e_o \cong e_i$. Then

$$\frac{e_i}{R_p} = i_{\text{in}} \tag{6.58}$$

Hence, voltage follower can be approximated by the equivalent circuit shown in Fig. 6.13(b).

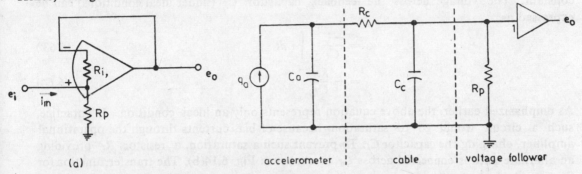

(a)   accelerometer   cable   voltage follower

Fig. 6.13 Equivalent representation of: (a) voltage follower; (b) accelerometer and voltage follower combination

The complete transfer function as given by Eq. (6.41) can be rewritten (neglecting cable resistance) as

$$e_o(s) = \frac{Ks}{(C_c + C_a)s + \dfrac{1}{R_p}} \frac{1}{s^2 + 2\zeta\omega_n s + \omega_n^2} \ddot{y} \tag{6.59}$$

Equation (6.59) can be written as

$$e_o(s) = \frac{K}{(C_c + C_a)} \frac{(C_c + C_a)R_p s}{R_p(C_c + C_a)s + 1} \frac{1}{s^2 + 2\zeta\omega_n s + \omega_n^2} \ddot{y} \tag{6.60}$$

$$= \frac{K}{C} \frac{\tau_1 s}{\tau_1 s + 1} \frac{1}{s^2 + 2\zeta\omega_n s + \omega_n^2} \ddot{y} \tag{6.61}$$

where $\qquad C = C_o + C_a$, and, $\tau_1 = R_p(C_o + C_a)$.

It can be seen from Eq. (6.61) that the static sensitivity is lower for higher values of cable and piezoelectric crystal capacitances. Apart from this, the steady-state response is zero. Thus, static response cannot be obtained in this mode of operation. In practice, the value of R_p and C are suitably chosen to obtain reasonably good sensitivity as well as required low frequency response. The high frequency limitation in this configuration is imposed by the response of the spring-mass system.

Charge Amplifier
In the voltage amplifier configuration, it is seen that the frequency response depends on the cable capacitance, and for each cable length only a particular calibration is valid. To obviate this difficulty, a charge amplifier configuration, where the charge generated by the device is converted to a proportional output voltage, is preferred.

The circuit arrangement of a basic charge amplifier configuration is as shown in Fig. 614(a). Assuming ideal conditions under which there would be no current flow into the input terminals of the operational amplifier,

$$\frac{dq}{dt} = i = K\dot{x} \tag{6.62}$$

where x is the deflection of the crystal due to input acceleration and K is a proportionality constant. The voltage across the feedback capacitor C_f (under ideal conditions) can be expressed as

$$e_o = \frac{-1}{C_f} \cdot \int i \, dt \tag{6.63}$$

$$= -\frac{Kx}{C_f} \tag{6.64}$$

As emphasized earlier, the above equation represents only an ideal condition. In practice, such a circuit would go to saturation because of bias currents through the operational amplifier, charging the capacitor C_f. To prevent such a saturation, a resistor R_f providing an alternate path is connected across C_f, as shown in Fig. 6.14(b). The transfer function for the circuit can be written as

$$\frac{e_o}{x}(s) = \frac{Ks\tau_2}{s\tau_2 + 1} \tag{6.65}$$

where,

$$\tau_2 = R_f C_f$$

The overall transfer function in this case is,

$$\frac{e_o}{\ddot{y}} = K \frac{s\tau_2}{s\tau_2 + 1} \quad \frac{1}{s^2 + 2\zeta\omega_n s + \omega_n^2} \tag{6.66}$$

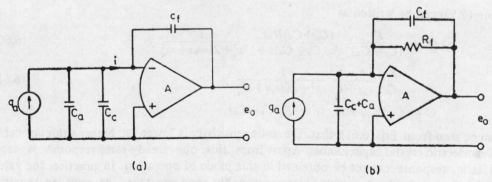

Fig. 6.14 Charge amplifier: (a) basic configuration; (b) modified configuration

Equation (6.66) is identical in form with that obtained for a voltage amplifier and piezoelectric accelerometer combination given by Eq. (6.61). This also exhibits similar low-frequency response limitations. However, the distinct advantage here is that both static sensitivity and low-frequency response are independent of the cable capacitance and crystal capacitance. Low-frequency response depends only on the circuit components C_f and R_f. Static sensitivity is not lost even with longer cables.

In general, it is a good practice to include signal filtering after the signal amplifier stage (either voltage follower or charge amplifier) in the instrumentation system. It is usually a low-pass filter adjusted to the cut-off frequency of the most frequency-restrictive component in the system, which is usually the accelerometer. The signal conditioner is suitably designed with a low-pass filter network to eliminate the accelerometer resonance errors and extraneous noise signals.

Signal transmission from the filter output to the recorder or other display is usually through a cable whose effect can be ignored, since the signals are of high amplitudes fed from low impedance sources. At times, telemetry is also used for long-distance transmission.

Practical Boot-strapped Circuit

Conventional designs are sometimes not used because of prohibitively large input resistors that are required for very good response. In a practical circuit, input resistances which are several orders of magnitude larger than the values of the dc return resistors can be obtained by boot-strapping, as shown in Fig. 6.15. In this, the lower cut-off frequency of the transducer is determined more by the $R_1 C_1$ product rather than the equivalent resistance and capacitance of the transducer and cable. $R_1 = 11$ MΩ and $C_1 = 10\ \mu$F, in the typical circuit shown in Fig. 6.15.

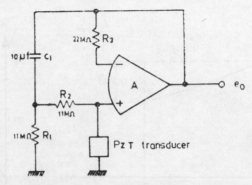

Fig. 6.15 A practical boot-strapped circuit for piezoelectric transducers

6.6 SHOCK MEASUREMENTS

The measurement of mechanical shocks requires special consideration. Often, the peak acceleration levels occurring during the shock are of vital importance, while in certain cases, quantities, such as the acceleration-time integral (total velocity change) and the spectral content of the shock pulse are required. For shock measurements, the frequency response of the measuring equipment should be linear over the frequency range determined by the spectral content of the shock pulse, and the phase response should also be good enough to produce minimum distortion. For ideal measurements, the bandwidth of the measuring system should be infinite. To study the effects of low-frequency and high-frequency response limitations, it is convenient to separate the effects for the purpose of study.

Limitation of the low-frequency response essentially means that there is no static response through the measurement system. In such cases, the peak value of the pulse cannot be retained, and the output amplitude E falls off gradually by an amount $e^{-T/RC}$ from its original value, where T is the pulse duration and RC the low frequency-time constant of the measuring system, as shown in Fig. 6.16(a), which shows normalized values. This response can be easily obtained mathematically by solving Eq. (6.61) or (6.66) for pulse inputs. Similarly, for sawtooth and half-sinewave inputs, the response is as shown in Figs. 6.16(b) and (c). In order to reduce this type of error to 5%, the factor $e^{-T/RC}$ should be 0.95 or higher for the rectangular pulse. This gives the value of T/RC of about 0.05, i.e. the time constant *RC* should be twenty times the duration of the pulse. For half sine and sawtooth pulses, the *RC* time constant should be about 12 and 9 times the duration of the pulses respectively for the same error. If initially the shock pulse does not have its maximum value at the beginning (half sine or sawtooth) there will be a reduction of peak value in the output and the magnitude of this will be equal to the undershoot.

Insofar as the effects caused by limitations in the high-frequency response, it is evident that dc transmission is present, but sudden changes (leading and trailing edges) are not reproduced accurately, as shown in Fig. 6.16(d). On the basis of considerations discussed above, it is possible to establish certain rules for guidance in determining the frequency range required for faithful reproduction of a shock pulse of a given duration. These are

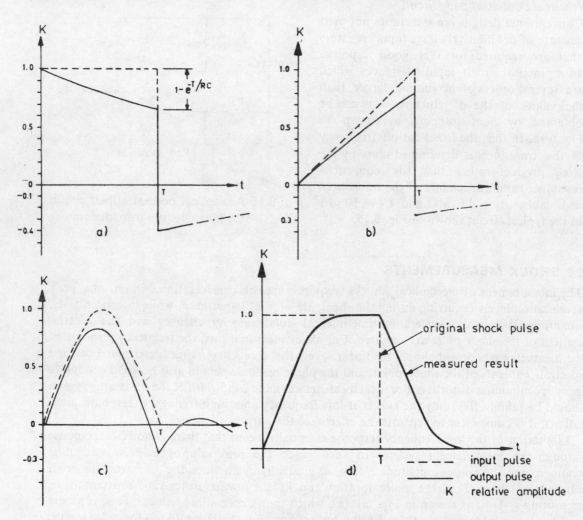

Fig. 6.16 Effect of low-frequency response limit on: (a) rectangular,
(b) sawtooth, (c) half-sinewave pulses; (d) effect of high
frequency response limit on rectangular shock pulse

graphically shown in Fig. 6.17. Thus for shock measurement, it is essential that the overall frequency response of the complete measuring system be adequate within allowed limits of error.

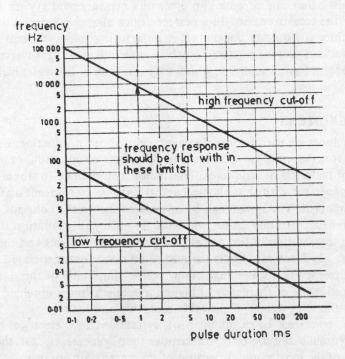

Fig. 6.17 Frequency range requirements for shock measurement
for given pulse durations

6.7 SYSTEM CHARACTERISTICS

So far the discussion had been limited to individual components of vibration and shock-measuring systems. But in a complete measurement system, the overall system characteristics comprising of accelerometer, cable, amplifier, and recorder or other display devices should be considered.

The first important characteristic of the complete measurement system is its frequency response. In this, the limiting factor is usually the response of the accelerometer. Since many of the accelerometers are lightly damped, one has to choose a device having the highest natural frequency, though this can lead to lower sensitivity. The other components of the chain usually do not introduce any frequency-response limitations.

Instrumentation elements exhibit linearity problems when they are used in an amplitude region above or far below their rated range. The linearity specifications are usually extremely good for piezoelectric accelerometers, amplifiers, and filters. However, some non-linearity can arise if the F.M. tape recorder is inadvertently operating outside the 40% deviation of its carrier frequency.

The sensitivity exhibited by a typical accelerometer depends upon the piezoelectric crystal material used and the total capacitance of the crystal and the cable. Typically with a 500 pf cable, sensitivity of the order of 5-10 mV/g can be obtained.

Another characteristic that can introduce an error in a measurement system is the transverse sensitivity of the accelerometers. In a perfect device all inputs normal to the sensitive axis should not produce any output, but due to manufacturing tolerances and internal element variations, practical accelerometers do exhibit a sensitivity to transverse inputs. This is usually less than 5% of basic sensitivity, which may not always be negligible.

6.8 VIBRATION EXCITERS

Vibration-testing machines are used for development, simulation, production, or exploration of vibration tests, for the purpose of studying the effects of vibration, or for evaluating physical properties of materials or structures. The major component in these tests is the vibration exciter or generator with suitable mechanical linkages to transmit a vibrating force to a structure or component. The system can be operated either in the constant displacement mode or in the constant acceleration mode, while the frequency of excitation is varied. The load consists of the total weight of test pieces (components under test) and the supporting platform or structure. The force capacity is the maximum rated force generated by the generator. The force corresponds to the maximum vector amplitude of the sinusoidal wave generated in the desired range of frequency. Maximum acceleration is obtained by dividing the force capacity by the total weight of the table assembly and load.

Vibration can be generated by a number of systems, viz. (a) electrical motor-driven systems, (b) electrohydraulic devices, or (c) electrodynamic generators. Of these, electrodynamic generators are the most popular because of their many advantages.

The direct-drive vibration machine consists of a rotating eccentric disc or cam driving a positive linkage mechanism, which creates a displacement between the base and table of the machine as illustrated in Fig. 6.18. With the base held in a fixed position, the table generates a time-varying displacement of constant amplitude, independent of the rpm. The drive is achieved with a variable speed dc or ac motor. The displacements and mechanical power can be large, but the frequency is limited to about 100 Hz; the displacement is not perfectly constant or sinusoidal as the frequency is increased. A modified version of the shaker table is the reaction-type generator, wherein the oscillating force is created with an unbalanced rotating mass attached to the main shaft. The most common rectilinear reaction-type vibration machine consists of two rotating unbalance masses, rotating in opposite directions and

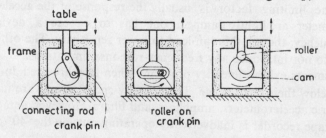

Fig. 6.18 Direct-drive vibration exciter

so phased that the unbalance forces add in the desired direction and cancel in the other directions. The effective force generated is midway between the two axes of rotation and is normal to a line connecting the two.

The electrohydraulic vibration generator is a device which transforms power in the form of a high-pressure flow of fluid from a pump to vibrations of the table in the machine. The reciprocatory motion is achieved with a two-stage electrohydraulic valve, used to deliver high-pressure fluid, first to one side of the piston in the actuator and then to the other side, thereby forcing the actuator to the required extent of motion (displacement). The valve may be solenoid operated or driven by a small electrohydraulic valve, with the operating pump pressure of the order 2×10^7 Pa. The main advantages of this type are large stroke lengths (as much as 20 cm) and high power capability, catering for heavy loads. However, the frequency is limited to about 25 Hz, although large forces and large velocities of motion are possible. Other advantages are: the size of the machine is small relative to the forces attainable, the electrical driving power for controlling the valve is low, the magnetic leakage flux is insignificant compared to electrodynamic shakers, and the operating frequency can be extended down to zero. But the machine is inherently non-linear with amplitude in terms of the electrical input or output velocity.

Electrodynamic Vibration Exciter

The most common type of exciter used for calibration and test purposes is the versatile electrodynamic vibration system, comprising an electrodynamic exciter, an associated amplifier and controllers, and vibration monitoring equipment.

In this device, the force causing the motion of the table is produced electrodynamically by the interaction between a current flow in an armature coil and an intense dc magnetic field in which the armature coil is suspended, as shown in Fig. 6.19. The table is structurally attached to the force-generating oil, and is concentrically located in the annular air gap of the dc magnetic circuit. The body can be energized either by an electromagnet or a

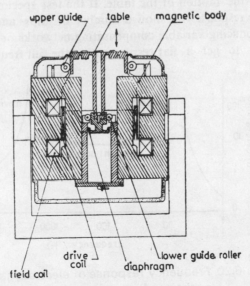

Fig. 6.19 Electrodynamic vibration exciter

permanent magnet (for smaller forces) generating a radially-directed field in the airgap which is perpendicular to the direction of current flow in the armature coil. In Fig. 6.19, field coils are provided to generate the dc magnetic field. The generated force in the armature coil is in the direction of the axis of the coil, perpendicular to the table surface, and is also perpendicular to the armature current direction and to the airgap field direction. The table to which the coil is attached rigidly is supported by elastic members from the machine body, permitting linear motion perpendicular to the surface. The table and coil should form one rigid unit so that all the points move in phase. The motion in the other direction is restricted by guided rollers; in an ideal case, the movement is perfectly one-dimensional. The whole assembly is mounted on a base with the trunnion shaft centerline passing horizontally through the centre of gravity of the body assembly, permitting the body to be rotated about its centre, thereby enabling tests to be carried out either in the vertical or horizontal direction or at any desired angle in between. For higher power exciters, cooling is carried out by convecting air currents from a blower or by recirculating fluid in conjunction with a heat exchanger.

The force F produced by the exciter can be expressed by Faraday's law as

$$F = BIl \times 10^{-5} \text{ N} \tag{6.67}$$

where B is the magnetic field in tesla, l is the total length of the armature coil in metres, and I is the armature current in amperes.

The response of the electrodynamic shaker under constant-current drive is shown in Fig. 6.20. The table movement is stiffness-controlled at low frequencies, i.e. the displacement amplitude is independent of frequency. As the frequency is increased, a resonance of the overall mass of the moving element and suspension occurs and the amplitude increases to a large value. Above this frequency, the movement is mass-controlled and the table moves with constant acceleration. At a very high frequency, the different parts of the moving table resonate once again and cause irregularities in the motion. Sometimes, the test specimen itself will influence the motion of the table. If the test specimen resonates at one or more frequencies, the table response will show a number of dips and peaks at these resonant frequencies. By introducing variable compensating networks or servo control of the moving table, it is possible to get a flat response over the full frequency range of interest. The

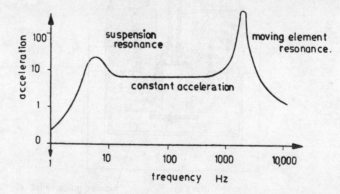

Fig. 6.20 Frequency response of electrodynamic vibration exciter under constant drive coil current

power amplifier employed for driving the shakers are specifically designed to match the coil impedance, required frequency response, and constant power level.

The main advantages of the electrodynamic shakers are: wide range of forces and operating frequencies (flat up to about 5000 Hz), simple control of the frequency and amplitude of excitation, pure sinusoidal motion at all frequencies and amplitudes, and adaptability to generate random vibrations. The system is also very versatile for many vibration tests. The leakage magnetic flux present in the main magnetic circuit can create problems in cases of low-level signal measurements. The device is best suited for an automatically-programmed calibration of vibration transducers.

6.9 CALIBRATION

The calibration of a vibration transducer is mainly carried out to assess the frequency response and sensitivity characteristics. Different methods can be adopted depending upon the magnitude of the above two parameters, and they can be broadly classified as low-frequency and low-acceleration methods, calibration by direct measurement, high-acceleration tests, and calibration by comparison methods.

The sensitivity factor of a linear vibration pickup is defined as the ratio of the electrical output to the mechanical input applied in a specified direction, and this is determined at a specific frequency. This factor is often a complex quantity as it includes the amplitude and phase information. In practice, the sensitivity for all transducers varies with frequency but with suitable designs it can be kept substantially constant over a specified range of frequencies. The change in sensitivity is mainly due to the resonances occurring in seismic elements and other mountings, variation in ambient temperature, or variation in the damping. The vibration pickup exhibits good linearity over a range of amplitudes. Beyond a maximum, the linearity factor changes due to nonlinear performance of the mechanical elements of the sensing device, and below a minimum, the variation in linearity occurs due to friction, resolving power of the sensing element, and electrical noise. The mechanical input given is displacement, velocity, or acceleration. Displacement is always expressed in terms of peak-to-peak, whereas velocity and acceleration are expressed either in peak or rms values. The phase lag in a vibration transducer is a measure of the time lag between the mechanical input and the electrical output, and is often proportional to the frequency.

Static Calibration System

The earth's gravitational field provides a convenient means of applying small constant acceleration levels to a sensor and is ideally suited for static, low-acceleration calibration. The change in acceleration in a sensor when moved from a positive direction along its sensing axis to a negative direction (0 to 180°) is 2g, where g is the acceleration due to gravity. Using this principle, certain sensors having an inherent dc response can be calibrated with a tilting support calibration table as shown in the Fig. 6.21. With a high resolu-

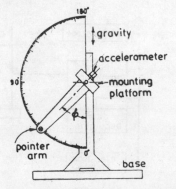

Fig. 6.21 Static calibration set up for $\pm 1g$

tion graduated scale, the arm can be set at any angle ϕ, and the acceleration a experienced by the transducer can be measured to a high order of accuracy by using the following equation

$$a = g \cos \phi \tag{6.68}$$

Centrifuge System

A direct method of calibration uses centrifuge systems wherein constant acceleration can be exerted on accelerometers. In this, the sensor is mounted on a centrifuge table with its axis of sensitivity carefully aligned along the radius of the circle of rotation. If the angular velocity is ω radians per second, the acceleration a acting on the sensor is given as $a = \omega^2 r$ where r is the distance from the centre of gravity of the mass element of the pickup to the axis of rotation. The deflection of the mass element should be negligible while computing the value of r. The output of the device is then plotted as a function of acceleration for successive values of ω, and from the slope of the curve obtained, the calibration factor can be computed. Care should be taken to keep the angular velocity constant during each experiment and to read ω and r very accurately.

Electrodynamic Calibration

The most versatile method usually adopted for calibration is the rectilinear electrodynamic exciter which provides a means of applying undistorted sinusoidal motion over a range of displacement amplitudes, starting from a displacement value of 2 cm at the lowest frequency of 5 Hz to a few microns at 10,000 Hz. The equivalent acceleration generated can be as much as 100g.

The sensor to be calibrated is mounted on the platform table (with its centre of gravity centred on the table) of a standard electrodynamic shaker. The armature and table should be fixed as rigid as practicable, to minimize table bending and to increase the first axial resonance to as high a frequency as possible. The motion obtained will be sinusoidal when the armature is excited with a sine-wave signal. The magnitude of displacement is proportional to the power input fed to the armature coil. Peak-to-peak displacement is measured accurately with the help of a synchronized stroboscope and a graticule scale of a telescope, as shown in Fig. 6.22. The dynamic velocity and acceleration levels are then calculated. The

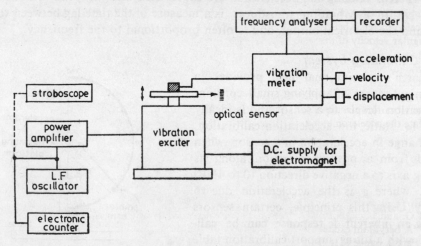

Fig. 6.22 Vibration exciter set up for calibration of accelerometers

sensor sensitivity, which is the ratio of the sensor output and input motion is then computed at various frequencies and displacement levels. For high precision and resolution for displacement measurement, Ronchi rulings, gratings, or the laser interferometer can be employed with advantage.

Another precise method of calibrating an accelerometer is to compare the readings of the test specimen with that of a reference standard accelerometer. In this set-up, both the devices are mounted symmetrically back to back on the vibrating table of the exciter, and the readings from both the units in terms of the ratios of their voltages are taken and interpreted in terms of the sensitivity and frequency response. The standard accelerometer has to be calibrated periodically against a primary standard which should be at least one order better in accuracy than that of the test piece.

EXERCISES

6.1 A seismic vibration pickup having a damping ratio of 0.70 and a natural resonant frequency of 8 Hz is mounted on a vibration shaker table. If the relative amplitude of the seismic mass recorded is 1.2 mm, when the table is vibrated at 20 Hz, determine the amplitude of vibration of the shaker table.

6.2. Design a cantilever-type accelerometer which produces 50 microstrains/g and has a natural frequency of 100 Hz. Specify the damping ratio required to obtain a settling time of about 0.01 s.

6.3 A piezoelectric accelerometer, represented by a single-degree-of-freedom spring-mass system has a natural frequency of 20 kHz and a damping ratio of 0.01. The acceleration a (in g's) given to the accelerometer is described by the equation,

$$a = 100t, \text{ for } 0 \leqslant t \leqslant 0.05 \text{ s}$$
$$= 5 \text{ for } t > 0.05 \text{ s}$$

Plot the output versus the input acceleration.

6.4 A piezoelectric accelerometer system has the following features: natural frequency = 30 kHz, damping ratio = 0.01, crystal capacitance = 50 pf, cable capacitance = 1000 pf, input impedance of the voltage amplifier = 10 MΩ, and cable resistance = 1.0 Ω. Plot the frequency response of the total system.

6.5 It is proposed to improve the bandwidth of a piezoelectric accelerometer by increasing the damping by means of a circuit arrangement. Develop a circuit configuration (passive or active device) that will perform the required function, and deduce the side effects of introducing such a system.

6.6 Design a servo accelerometer of the type discussed in Sec. 6.4.4 which gives an output of 10 mA/g with a natural frequency of 100 Hz.

6.7 An accelerometer is being calibrated in a centrifuge system. The expected error in the measurement of the angular velocity of the centrifuge is ±0.05%, and the error in the measurement of distance of the transducer centre of gravity from the centre of rotation is ±0.01%. Calculate the calibration error that would arise in the worst case?

6.8 An accelerometer of natural frequency 25 kHz and a vibration pickup of natural frequency 8 Hz and a damping ratio of 0.7 are both mounted on a vibration shaker table. When the table is vibrated at 12 Hz, the vibration pickup showed a relative amplitude of 3 mm and the accelerometer output was 9 mV. Calculate the accelerometer sensitivity in mV/g.

BIBLIOGRAPHY

Anderson, R.A., *Fundamental of Vibration*, Macmillan, New York, 1967.

Beckwith, T.G. and Buck, N.L., *Mechanical Measurements*, Addison Wesley, New York, 1969.

Bell, C.W., "A beryllium exciter for the calibration of vibration transducers", *Advances in Instrumentation*, Vol. 25, Part 2, paper 611, 1970.

Butler, R.I. and McWhirter, M., "Current practices in shock and vibration sensors", *Instrumentation Technology*, Vol. 14, No. 3, pp. 41-45, March 1967.

Cameron, L.B., "Vibration analysis—its growth as a routine servicing tool", *Br. J. Non-Destr. Testing*, Vol. 15, No. 3, pp. 90-93, May 1973.

Coon, G.W. and Harrison, D.R., "Miniature capacitor accelerometer", *Instrumentation Technology*, Vol. 14, No. 3, pp. 51-53, March 1967.

Corey, V.B., "Measuring angular acceleration with linear accelerometers", *Control Engineering*, Vol. 9, No. 3, pp. 79-81, March 1962.

Day, P.E. and Marples, V., "Phase calibration of displacement sensitive vibration transducer systems", *Scientific Instruments*, Vol. 4, No. 2, pp. 137-138. February 1971.

di Cenzo, C.D., "Digital techniques simplify angular velocity measurements", *Electronic Engineering*, Vol. 44, No. 531, pp. 30-32, May 1972.

Doebelin, E.O., *Measurement Systems—Application and Design*, McGraw-Hill, New York, 1966.

Endevco, *Piezoelectric Accelerometer Manual*, Endevco, California, 1975.

Evans, R.H. and Haigh, G.G., "Accelerometers with integration in the feedback loop to give velocity output", *Royal Aircraft Establishment Tech. Report 64005*, Faranborough, 1964.

Harris, C.M. and Crede, C.E. (Ed), *Shock and Vibration Control Handbook*, McGraw-Hill, New York, 1976.

I.S.A., "A specification and tests for piezoelectric acceleration transducers", RP-37.2, ISA Pittsburg, 1964.

Jako, C., "An angular accelerometer", *Advances in Instrumentation*, Vol. 25, Part 2, Paper 605, 1970.

Kulizyk, W.K. and Davis, Q.V., "Laser Doppler instrument for measurement of moving turbine blades", *Proc. IEE*, Vol. 120, No. 9, pp. 1017-23, Sept. 1973.

McLaren, I., "Open and closed loop accelerometers", *Agardograph*, No. 160, Vol. 6, July 1974.

Ioskowitz L., "Accelerometer calibration Parts 1 and 2", *Instrumentation and Control Systems*, Vol. 34, Nos. 2 and 3, pp. 257-260, 467-470, Feb/March 1961.

Neubert, H.K.P., *Instrument Transducers*, Clarendon Press, Oxford, 1975.

Norton, H.N., *Handbook of Transducers for Electrical Measuring Systems*, Prentice-Hall, New Jersey, 1968.

Rasanan, G.K. and Wigel, B.M., "Accelerometer mounting and data integrating", *Sound and Vibration*, Vol. 1, November 1967.

Ruzicka, J.E., "Mechanical vibration and shock terminology", *Sound and Vibration*, Vol. 1, May 1967.

Sabin, H.B., "17 ways to measure acceleration", *Control Engineering*, March 1965.

Szabados, B. et al., "A new digital instrument for measuring angular velocity and acceleration", *Proc., IEEE*, Vol. 60, No. 4, pp. 455-456, April 1972.

Thomas, I.L. and Evans, R.H., "Performance characteristics and methods of testing of force feedback accelerometers", *Aeronautical Research Council, Research Memorandum* 3601, 1967.

Thomas, P.P., "Sources of error in precision force feedback accelerometer and methods of testing", *RAE Tech. Note*, IAP 1076, Jan. 1960.

Timoshenko, S., Young, D.H. and Weaver, Jr. W., *Vibration Problems in Engineering*, 4th Edn., John Wiley and Sons, New York, 1967.

Tse, F.S., Morse, I.E. and Hinkle, R.T., *Mechanical Vibrations, Theory and Applications*, II Edition, Allyn and Bacon Inc., Boston, 1978.

Vick, G.L., "A feasibility study of solid state acceleration sensing technique", *Report No. FDL-TDR-64-55*, Wright Patterson Airforce Base, USA, 1964.

Woodward, M.H., "Automated vibration calibration data acquisition system", *Advances in Instrumentation*, Vol. 27, 1972, Part 2, paper 620, 1972.

7
PRESSURE

7.1 INTRODUCTION

Pressure is basically a mechanical concept that can be expressed in terms of the primary dimensions of mass and length, and is a physical parameter encountered in many fields. It is defined as the force acting per unit area, measured at a given point or over a surface. This can be in absolute, gauge, or differential units, depending upon the reference taken. The measurement involved can be of a static or dynamic nature. The unit for pressure is expressed as gravitational units of force per unit area, and the magnitude range from a few microns of mercury to hundreds of kilograms per cm². At very low magnitudes, the parameter is expressed in terms of cm of water column or mm of mercury column at 0°C. In SI units, the magnitude is expressed in pascals (N/m²).

Pressure is one of the significant properties of a fluid and is characterized by a compressive stress exerted uniformly in all directions. When the fluid is in equilibrium, the pressure exerted at a point is identical in all directions and is independent of the orientation. This condition is referred to as the static pressure. In the case of a moving fluid, various pressure components may exist in the medium.

Pressure transducers can be classified into gravitational and elastic types. In the gravitational type, the familiar manometer is the simplest device. In elastic transducers the pressure exerts a force over the area of an elastic device. The force responsive elastic member is in the form of a diaphragm, capsule, bellows, or bourdon tube as shown in Fig. 7.1. The resultant displacement or strain developed is measured with an appropriate electrical sensor. The conversion of this mechanical phenomenon to an equivalent electrical signal is achieved by a variety of linkage mechanisms. The transduction principles used are deflection measurements with resistive, inductive, and capacitive principles or measurement of change in natural resonance frequency of a stretched member. In transducer terminology they are classified as: potentiometric, bonded and unbonded strain gauge, piezoresistive, inductive, linear variable differential transformer, capacitive, piezoelectric, or vibrating-element types The characteristics of these transducers are given in Table 7.1.

7.2 DIAPHRAGMS

The most common type of pressure-sensing elastic element used in a transducer is the

TABLE 7.1 CLASSIFICATION OF PRESSURE TRANSDUCERS

Characteristics	Strain gauge Bonded	Strain gauge Unbonded	Diffused semiconductor	Reluctance	Capacitance	Potentiometer	LVDT	Force balance	Piezoelectric	Vibrating diaphragm
Pressure range in kPa	10 to 2×10^5	3 to 7×10^4	0.1 to 7×10^4	0.1 to 7×10^4	0.1 to 10×10^3	30 to 7×10^4	100 to 7×10^4	0.1 to 3×10^4	10^2 to 7×10^4	10 to 300
Sensitivity (nominal) per 10 kPa	3 mV/V	4 mV/V	20 mV/V	40 mV/V	5 V (F.S.)	5 V (F.S.)	2 mV/V	5 V (F.S.) (Servo)	3 p.c.	100 Hz
Accuracy in % FS	0.15	0.25	0.25	0.5	0.1	0.5	0.5	0.1	1	0.2
Frequency response in Hz	2000	5000	10^5	1	3000	50	400	10	10^5	1
Temperature range in °C	−40 to 100	−40 to 125	−40 to 100	−40 to 300	−10 to 300	−20 to 120	−20 to 100	10 to 150	−40 to 200	−20 to 100
Immunity to acceleration sensitivity	Very good	Good	Excellent	Very good	Fair	Poor	Poor	Fair	Excellent	Fair
Remarks	Good linearity and repeatability; high ruggedness; temp. effect small; can be adapted for high temp. experiments	High stability; small size	High sensitivity, high dynamic response; small size good repeatability	High sensitivity; good for differential pressure measurements; rugged; susceptible to stray magnetic field	Good dynamic response; ideal for low and differential pressure measurements; small size	Low cost; high output; poor resolution; short life	Good linearity; susceptible to stray magnetic field	High accuracy; high output; large size; low dynamic response	Excellent high frequency response; high ruggedness; low dynamic output; sensitive to temp; useful for dynamic pressure only	Good accuracy and repeatability; digital output; feasible; useful for remote operations

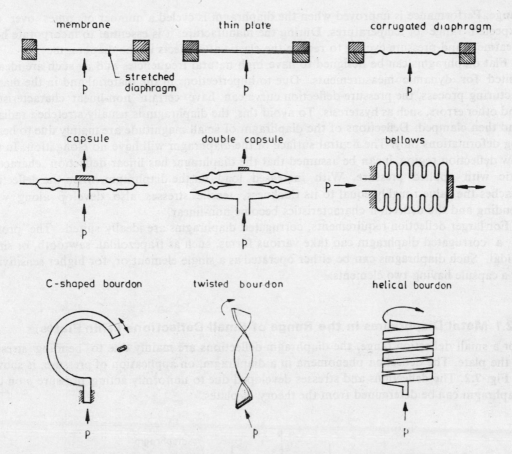

Fig. 7.1 Various elastic elements for pressure measurements

diaphragm. The diaphragm is essentially a thin circular plate stretched and fastened at its periphery. The structure of the diaphragm may be flat or corrugated, as shown in Fig. 7.1. Diaphragms are widely used as a sensing element for high accuracy and good dynamic response. They can respond to pressure values ranging from a few millimeters of water column to several atmospheres. The main characteristics of the diaphragm are ruggedness, excellent stability and reliability, low hysteresis and creep, and good dynamic response. The other characteristics such as the effect of environmental conditions, material of the diaphragm, size, weight, and fabrication technology vary enormously, depending upon the transduction principle used, range, and actual application.

Sensing diaphragms are made from elastic metal alloys, such as bronze, phosphor bronze, beryllium copper, and stainless steel or from proprietory alloys, such as Monel, Inconel-X and Nickel-Span-C (a ferrous-nickel alloy). The diaphragms are fabricated by pressing, stamping, or spinning from sheet stock or they are integrally machined with their supporting wall from a bar. The main considerations while selecting a suitable diaphragm material are the chemical nature of the fluid which is expected to come in contact with the diaphragm, temperature range, effects of shock and vibration, and frequency response requirements. Ni-Span-C is unique in that it has constant elastic properties over a wide temperature range. Performance is improved when the diaphragm is cycled a number of times over the expected range of temperatures. During the manufacture, it is essential to incorporate heat treatment and pressure cycling to reduce the elastic aftereffects in the diaphragm.

Flat diaphragms can be designed to have high natural frequencies and as such are ideally suited for dynamic measurements. Due to imperfections in the material and in the manufacturing process, the pressure-deflection curve can have certain non-linear characteristics and other errors, such as hysteresis. To avoid this, the diaphragm is usually stretched radially and then clamped. Deflections of the diaphragm of small magnitude are mainly due to bending deformations only. The neutral surface of the diaphragm will have no elongation. In the low deflection region, it can be assumed that the diaphragm has linear deflection characteristic with applied pressure. With increased load on the diaphragm, when the deflection reaches the value roughly equal to its thickness, tensile stresses also develop along with bending and the deflection characteristics become non-linear.

For larger deflection requirements, corrugated diaphragms are ideally suited. The profile of a corrugated diaphragm can take various forms, such as trapezoidal, sawtooth, or sinusoidal. Such diaphragms can be either operated as a single element or, for higher sensitivity, as a capsule having two elements.

7.2.1 Metal Diaphragms in the Range of Small Deflections (Thin Plates)

For a small deflection range, the diaphragm deflections are mainly due to bending stresses in the plate. The deflection phenomena in a diaphragm, on application of pressure, is shown in Fig. 7.2. The deflections and stresses developed due to uniformly acting pressure p on the diaphragm can be determined from the theory of plates.

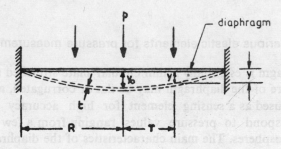

Fig. 7.2 Deflection in a diaphragm due to pressure

The deflection y at any point on the diaphragm is given by[1]

$$y = \frac{3}{4} \cdot \frac{(1-\nu^2)}{Et^3} \, p \left(\frac{r^4}{4} - R^2 \, \frac{r^2}{2} \right) + c \tag{7.1}$$

where, expressed in appropriate units, p = pressure difference across the diaphragm, t = thickness of the diaphragm, E = modulus of the elasticity of the material of the diaphragm, ν = Poisson's ratio of the material of the diaphragm, r = radius at any point, R = Radius of the diaphragm, and c = a constant, depending upon the boundary conditions.

With the diaphragm clamped on the periphery, y will be zero at the periphery at $r = R$. The value of c can then be computed as

$$c = \frac{3pR^4(1-\nu^2)}{16Et^3} \tag{7.2}$$

Hence, the equation for small deflections of the elastic surface of a flat diaphragm takes the form

$$y = \frac{3}{16} p \frac{(1-\nu^2)}{Et^3} \cdot (R^2 - r^2)^2 \tag{7.3}$$

The deflection at the centre of the diaphragm y_0 (where $r = 0$) valid for $y \ll t$ is given by

$$y_0 = \frac{3}{16} p \frac{(1-\nu^2)}{Et^3} R^4 \tag{7.4}$$

Equation (7.4) shows the relation between applied pressure and deflection at the centre of the diaphragm. It has been found that this relation is valid without appreciable non-linearity (less than 2%) for deflections up to 30% of the thickness of the diaphragm.

The radial and tangential stresses σ_r and σ_t respectively, at any radial distance r from the centre are given by

$$\sigma_r = \frac{3}{8} p \frac{R^2}{t^2} \left[(3+\nu) \frac{r^2}{R^2} - (1+\nu) \right] \tag{7.5}$$

$$\sigma_t = \frac{3}{8} p \frac{R^2}{t^2} \left[(3\nu+1) \frac{r^2}{R^2} - (1+\nu) \right] \tag{7.6}$$

The principal stresses σ_1 and σ_2 at the centre of the diaphragm are due to tangential stress alone and are obtained from Eqs. (7.5) and (7.6) as

$$\sigma_1 = \sigma_2 = -\frac{3}{8} (1+\nu)p \frac{R^2}{t^2} \tag{7.7}$$

The equivalent stress σ_{eq} at the centre is given by

$$\sigma_{eq} = \sqrt{\sigma_1^2 + \sigma_2^2 - \sigma_1 \sigma_2} \tag{7.8}$$

From Eq. (7.7),

$$\sigma_{eq} = \frac{3(1+\nu)}{8} p \frac{R^2}{t^2} \tag{7.9}$$

For $\nu = 0.3$,

$$\sigma_{eq} = 0.488p \frac{R^2}{t^2} \tag{7.10}$$

At the edge of the diaphragm,

$$\sigma_1 = \sigma_r = \frac{3}{4} p \frac{R^2}{t^2} \quad \text{and} \quad \sigma_2 = \sigma_t = \frac{3}{4} p \frac{\nu R^2}{t^2}$$

Substituting these values in Eq. (7.8),

$$\sigma_{eq} = \frac{3}{4} p \frac{R^2}{t^2} \sqrt{1-\nu+\nu^2} \tag{7.11}$$

For $\nu = 0.3$, at the edges,

$$\sigma_{eq} = 0.666 \, p \, \frac{R^2}{t^2} \tag{7.12}$$

Thus, the equivalent stresses at the edge of the diaphragm will be more than those at the centre. The maximum pressure allowable can be determined from the condition,

$$\sigma_{eq} = 0.666p \, \frac{R^2}{t^2} < \sigma_{max} \tag{7.13}$$

where σ_{max} is the safe allowable stress for the material, determined from the yield strength and safety factor.

The maximum allowable pressure, p_{max} is thus given as

$$p_{max} = 1.5 \left(\frac{t}{R}\right)^2 \sigma_{max} \tag{7.14}$$

It can be seen from Eq. (7.14) that the maximum allowable pressure increases with the ratio of thickness to the radius of the diaphragm.

The relation between the magnitude of the stresses in the diaphragm and its deflection can also be determined as given below.

The radial and tangential stresses on the surface at the edges $(r = R)$, referring to Eqs. (7.4), (7.5) and (7.6) can be shown to be

$$\sigma_r = \frac{4y_0Et}{(1-\nu^2)R^2}; \quad \sigma_t = \nu\sigma_r \tag{7.15}$$

At the centre of the diaphragm $(r = 0)$, the surface stress magnitude will be

$$\sigma_r = \sigma_t = \frac{2y_0Et}{(1-\nu)R^2} \tag{7.16}$$

Thus, for small deflections, the stresses in the diaphragm are linearly proportional to the deflection.

The value of the maximum allowable deflection can be found from Eqs. (7.4) and (7.14) as

$$y_{0max} = 0.256 \, \frac{R^2}{Et} \, \sigma_{max} \tag{7.17}$$

It follows, therefore, that the allowable maximum deflection increases with reduced thickness and increased radius of the diaphragm.

7.2.2 Metal Diaphragms in the Range of Large Deflections (Membranes)

A thin diaphragm operating with very large deflections greater than the thickness of the diaphragm itself can be considered as being absolutely flexible. The tensile stresses in such a diaphragm will be much larger than the bending stresses, and hence the flexural rigidity can be neglected. Under the action of pressure, the membrane assumes a nearly spherical shape.

The relation between the pressure and deflection of a membrane can be written for $\nu = 0.3$ as

$$p = 3.58 \, \frac{Et}{R^4} \, y_0^3 \tag{7.18}$$

The above formula shows that in the range of very large deflections, when the diaphragm operates mainly in tension, the relationship between pressure and deflection is non-linear (cubic). Maximum stresses in such a case occur at the centre of the membrane and is given by[1]

$$\sigma_r = \sigma_t = \frac{3-\nu}{1-\nu} \frac{E_0 y_0^2}{4R_0^2} \tag{7.19}$$

From Eq. (7.19) it is seen that the stresses increase with the square of the deflection.

7.2.3 Flat Diaphragms

In the earlier sections, two limiting cases of diaphragms have been considered, where (a) diaphragm deflections are much smaller than the thickness of the diaphragm and (b) diaphragm deflections are very large when compared to the diaphragm thickness. A complete solution of the problem of flat diaphragms for any value of deflection is often required to design diaphragms to obtain a desired non-linear relation between pressure and deflection in many applications.

Deflection Eqs. (7.4) and (7.18) can be rewritten in a dimensionless form as

$$\frac{pR^4}{Et^4} = 5.86 \frac{y_0}{t} \text{ (for small deflections due to bending only)} \tag{7.20}$$

and

$$\frac{pR^4}{Et^4} = 3.58 \left(\frac{y_0}{t}\right)^3 \text{ (for large deflections due to tension only)} \tag{7.21}$$

For the small deflection region, as already noted, the deflections are mainly due to bending, while in the large deflection region, they are due to tension only. The solution for any value of deflection is obtained by superposing these two results.[2]

In practice, the deflection is a combination of both bending and tension, and the characteristic of a flat diaphragm at any deflection can be written by combining Eqs. (7.20) and (7.21) as

$$\frac{pR^4}{Et^4} = 5.86 \frac{y_0}{t} + 3.58 \left(\frac{y_0}{t}\right)^3 \tag{7.22}$$

Equation (7.22) can be helpful in designing diaphragms for any desired characteristic.

7.2.4 Dynamic Considerations of Diaphragm Elements

In many instances, the pressure to be measured is highly oscillatory in nature, such as the pressures encountered in the operation of turbines or compressors, in the flutter of aerofoils, and in many other fields. A suitable diaphragm is used to convert this dynamic pressure variation into an equivalent electrical signal. Such a pressure receiver containing the diaphragm element is always characterized by its sensitivity and natural frequency. The lowest natural frequency is of utmost importance as this is the frequency that determines the limit within which pressure measurements can be made without introducing objectionable dynamic errors. Further, if the pressure transducer is simultaneously subjected to mechanical vibration, undesirable signals are introduced by this interfering input. Because of these effects, the natural frequency of the transducer diaphragm element must be considerably high.

For practical purposes, the pressure transducer can be represented by a mechanical system having a certain elastic constant k and equivalent mass m_{eq}, the ratio of which determines the undamped natural frequency f_n.

$$f_n = \frac{1}{2\pi} \sqrt{\frac{k}{m_{eq}}} \qquad (7.23)$$

The elastic constant k and the effective area A of the pressure sensitive element determine the sensitivity S, which is given by

$$S = \frac{A}{k} \qquad (7.24)$$

Thus, the natural frequency can be written as

$$f_n = \frac{1}{2\pi} \sqrt{\frac{A}{S m_{eq}}} \qquad (7.25)$$

Equation (7.25) shows that the natural frequency is increased for decreasing values of the sensitivity or the effective mass per unit area of the pressure transducer element. Thus, for a given area, the mass per unit area of the elastic element becomes the basic criterion for design purposes. This design parameter becomes a controlling factor at high frequencies. Therefore, efforts towards improving high frequency performance must include minimization of the mass per unit area, consistent with manufacturing limitations.

7.2.5 Corrugated Diaphragms

Frequently, corrugated diaphragms are also encountered in pressure measurements, especially where larger deflections are required than those normally obtained with flat diaphragms. Diaphragm profiles take different forms, such as sawtooth, trapezoidal, and sinusoidal shapes, as shown in Fig. 7.3. The design and accuracy of manufacture of the clamping rings, base, and the correct shape for the flange are important in single diaphragm sensors. The design of the diaphragm assembly is considerably simplified if two identical diaphragms are connected along their flanges to form a diaphragm capsule. The main advantage in this is that the deflection characteristics under a given pressure is twice as large as that of a single diaphragm. A typical deflection range of a corrugated diaphragm is 2% of its diameter. Diaphragms with a fine sawtooth profile are simple to manufacture and are stable at small overloads. The manufacture of diaphragms with a deep sawtooth profile is somewhat more difficult due to the possibility

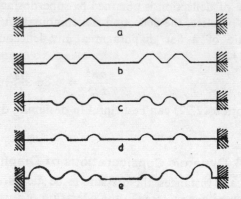

Fig. 7.3 Various profiles of corrugated diaphragms: (a) fine sawtooth; (b) trapezoidal; (c) sinusoidal; (d) toroidal bead; (e) sinusoidal-variable depth

of cracks developing at crests due to stress concentration. The fabrication of diaphragms having a sinusoidal or other continuous profiles requires more complex tools; such profiles are adopted for diaphragms of larger thickness and in cases where the stress concentration should be minimum. Corrugated diaphragms are susceptible to vibrations due to their large resilience and as such are used only for static measurements.

The characteristic of a corrugated diaphragm is described by a cubic equation, just as in the case of a flat diaphragm (Eq. (7.22)), and is of the form

$$p = Ay_0 + By_0^3 \qquad (7.26)$$

where A and B are constants.

Here again, the linear term corresponds to the diaphragm's resistance to bending and can be solved by considering the equation for small deflections only. The cubic term characterizes the diaphragm's resistance to tension. In Eq. (7.26) A and B are constants depending upon the shape of diaphragm profile, and are related to the profile geometry as

$$A = \frac{Et^3}{R^4} a \qquad (7.27)$$

$$B = \frac{Et}{R^4} b \qquad (7.28)$$

where E = modulus of elasticity of the material, t = thickness of the diaphragm, and R = radius of the diaphragm.

In Eqs. (7.27) and (7.28), the parameters a and b are given by

$$a = \frac{2(3+\alpha)(1+\alpha)}{3K_1\left(1-\dfrac{v^2}{\alpha^2}\right)} \qquad (7.29)$$

$$b = \frac{32K_1}{(\alpha^2-9)}\left[\frac{1}{6} - \frac{(3-v)}{(\alpha-v)(\alpha+3)}\right] \qquad (7.30)$$

where v = Poisson's ratio, $\alpha = \sqrt{K_1K_2}$, $K_1 = \dfrac{A}{y}$, $K_2 = \dfrac{12}{t^2l}\displaystyle\int_0^A y^2\,dA + \dfrac{1}{l}\displaystyle\int_0^A \cos^2\theta\,dA$,

A = arc length of one full wave of the corrugation profile, l = wavelength of the profile, y = profile height, and θ = slope angle of the tangent at any point.

7.3 OTHER ELASTIC ELEMENTS

The other basic types of elastic pressure-sensing elements used in electrical transducers are capsules, bourdon tubes, and bellows.

7.3.1 Capsule

A capsule, otherwise referred to as an aneroid, consists of two identical annular corrugated metal diaphragms sealed together at the periphery to obtain a shell-like enclosure. One of the diaphragms is provided with a central reinforced port to admit the pressure to be measured, and the other is linked to a mechanical member. The displacement of this member is proportional to the difference of the inner and outer pressures. The seal is made by brazing, soldering, or electron-beam welding, and the whole capsule is heat treated to relieve the stresses built up during welding and subsequent cooling. The factors influencing the deflections of the capsule are the same as those for the diaphragms, and larger displacements are achieved by stacking multiple capsule elements coupled in tandem as shown in Fig. 7.1.

7.3.2 Bourdon Tube

The bourdon tube is a curved or twisted metallic tube having an elliptical cross-section, and sealed at one end. The tube tends to straighten out on the application of pressure, and the angular deflection of the free end is taken as a measure of the pressure. The deflection sensitivity is a function of the aspect ratio of the tube cross-section. The main advantages are high sensitivity and good repeatability.

The different configurations mainly employed for this device are 'C', helical, spiral, and twisted tubes as shown in Fig. 7.1. The C-shaped tube has a total angle of curvature of 180 to 270°, and the angular deflection is normally measured with a mechanical pointer moving over a calibrated scale or with a potentiometric or LVDT transducer. The helical bourdon tube is similar in its deflection behaviour to a C tube, except that the tube is coiled into a multiturn helix with 5 to 10 turns. In the case of the spiral tube model where the radius of curvature increases with each turn, the tip travel due to its multiturn configuration increases depending upon the number of coils. The twisted bourdon tube is basically a flattened tube twisted along its central axis throughout its length. In some versions the twist rate is also made variable.

The deflection of a bourdon tube varies with the ratio of its major to minor cross-sectional axis, tube length, difference between the internal and external pressures, radius of curvature, and angle of twist. It also varies inversely with the tube-wall thickness and the modulus of elasticity of the material used.

The angular deflection of the helical-type and C-type bourdon tubes can be expressed by the equation

$$\frac{\phi}{\phi_0} = \frac{1.16pr^2}{tEb} \tag{7.31}$$

where ϕ = angle of rotation of the tip of the tube, ϕ_0 = angle of tube/total angle of helix, p = pressure in pascals, r = radius of the tube/helix in metres, t = wall thickness in metres, E = Young's modulus of material in pascals, and b = minor axis of the tube, measured from the middle of one wall to the middle of the other wall, in metres.

Bourdon tubes are almost invariably fabricated with metal alloys, such as cold-worked brass, phosphor bronze, beryllium copper, stainless steel, and nickel alloys. Nickel-span-C is a popular material owing to its negligible variation in modulus of elasticity with temperature. Helical bourdon tubes made of fused quartz having very low hysteresis, creep, and fatigue are widely used as secondary standards. Bourdon tubes are more sensitive to shock and vibrations than diaphragms, and are therefore used mostly for static measurements. The range covered varies from 10^6 to 10^8 pascals.

7.3.3 Bellows

Bellows are thin-walled cylindrical shells with deep convolutions, and are sealed at one end. The sealed end moves axially when pressure is applied to the other end, as shown in Fig. 7.1. The number of convolutions varies from 5 to 20 depending upon the pressure range, displacement required, and operating temperature. The stiffness is proportional to Young's modulus of the material, and is inversely proportional to the outside diameter and to the number of convolutions of the bellow. The deflection y of the bellows can be expressed by the equation,

$$y = 2nA_Q \frac{pR_x^2}{Et^3} \qquad (7.32)$$

where t = wall thickness, n = number of convolutions, E = modulus of elasticity, R_x = average radius of the bellows, and A_Q = effective area of the bellows.

Bellows are normally used for low-pressure measurements requiring large stroke lengths. They are sensitive to vibrations. In certain applications, the bellows can be furnished with a restraining spring which opposes their axial deflection. This allows their usage for extended pressure ranges with increased life. The materials used for the fabrication are phosphor bronze, beryllium copper, stainless steel, or nickel alloys.

7.4 TRANSDUCTION METHODS

Electrical pressure transducers based on the principle of variable capacitance, resistance, and inductance have been developed for a variety of pressure measurements, for converting the deflections or stresses developed in elastic elements into corresponding electrical signals.

7.4.1 Potentiometric Device

The potentiometric-type pressure transducer is one of the earliest type of electrical pressure sensors. In this, a diaphragm, capsule, bellows, or bourdon tube is linked to a free-sliding wiper contact moving on a resistive element, as shown in Fig. 7.4. The wiper is driven by the elastic element in response to the applied pressure, and the changes in the voltage at the wiper point is related to the pressure. Depending upon the design of the resistance element, the output voltage can be made linear, square root, or any other function of the applied pressure. The main advantages of this type are high range, ruggedness, and simple instrumentation. Finite resolution, limited life, large size, poor frequency response, tendency to develop noise as slider wears off, and susceptibility to vibration are some of the disadvantages.

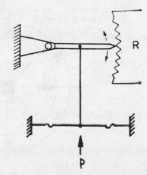

Fig. 7.4 Potentiometric pressure transducer

Typical characteristics are resolution of 0.2%, linearity of $\pm 1.0\%$, repeatability of $\pm 0.25\%$, and hysteresis of $\pm 0.5\%$, all with respect to F.S.R.

7.4.2 Strain Gauge Transducer

An elegant arrangement of a bonded strain gauge device is to fix the strain gauges directly onto the diaphragm. The strain gauges may be bonded or unbonded types. The range of application of this method is limited by the non-linearity of the strain-pressure relationship above a certain strain value.

For a clamped circular diaphragm of radius R, thickness t, and pressure difference p, as shown in Fig. 7.2, the maximum radial stress at the edges can be obtained from Eq. (7.5); by substituting $r = R$, Eq. (7.5) becomes

$$\sigma_r = \frac{3}{4} \, p \, \frac{R^2}{t^2} \tag{7.33}$$

within the linear range, the strain is obtained from the relation

$$\epsilon = \frac{3}{4} \, p \, \frac{R^2}{Et^2} \tag{7.34}$$

where E is the Young's modulus of the material. It has been found that for very thick diaphragms $(R/t \simeq 10)$, the calibration would be linear for a pressure of up to 70×10^6 pascals. However, the corresponding stress level at that pressure is quite high imposing a restriction on the usual higher limit. For a thin diaphragm $(R/t \simeq 100)$, the maximum pressure for linear operation is limited, resulting in low strain values. The advantages of this type of transducer, besides its simplicity, are its high natural frequency (and hence low sensitivity to acceleration) and good dynamic response. Since both tensile and compressive stresses exist on the surface of the diaphragm, the strain gauges can be located as shown in Fig. 7.5(a). Gauges 1 and 3 bonded near the periphery respond to radial strain, while 2 and 4 near the centre respond to tensile strain. This arrangement yields high sensitivity and fairly good temperature stability. The bridge circuit for this application is shown in Fig. 7.5(b).

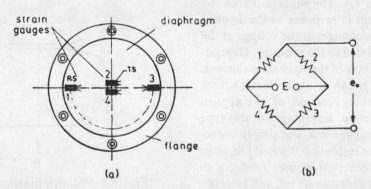

Fig. 7.5 Diaphragm type strain gauge pressure transducer: (a) physical location of strain gauges; (b) bridge circuit for measurement

Another configuration, in which excellent linearity can be achieved for a wide range of pressure magnitudes, incorporates a double cantilever beam mechanically coupled to the diaphragm as shown in Fig. 7.6(a). In this design, the pressure-sensing diaphragm is coupled symmetrically to the cantilever with a rigid pin. Four thermally matched strain gauges are bonded near the roots of the cantilever beam to measure the compressive and tensile strain. The main advantages of this design are its ruggedness, good linearity, and wide range. The diaphragm is mechanically aged for minimum long-term drift. Excellent temperature compensation over a range of −10° to 80 °C can be easily achieved. The transducer resolution is limited by the instrumentation only. In both the devices described above, sensitivity can be very much enhanced by the use of semiconductor gauges instead of wire or foil gauges.

Instead of a cantilever deflection system, the pressure measurement can be achieved by a strain tube where the stresses developed are measured with gauges bonded on the surface of the cylinder, as shown in Fig. 7.6(b).

In the case of unbonded gauge type pressure transducers, in one of the configurations, four bare strain gauge wires are stretched to a known initial tension and are mounted by linking the pressure sensing diaphragm and the case, as shown in Fig. 7.7. The four wire sections form the active arms of a Wheatstone bridge circuit. On application of pressure, the elastic element (diaphragm) displaces the armature through a mechanical linkage, causing two of the gauges to elongate while reducing the tension in the remaining two gauges. By a suitable design, the electrical output of the bridge can be made proportional to the applied pressure. The main advantages of this type of device are high sensitivity, good frequency response, and excellent stability, but they are sensitive to vibrations.

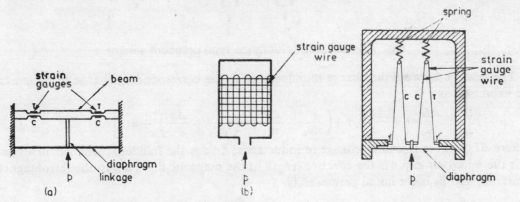

Fig. 7.6 Strain gauge pressure transducers: (a) double cantilever; (b) strain tube

Fig. 7.7 Unbonded strain gauge pressure sensor

7.4.3 Variable Reluctance Sensor

Pressure measurements can also be carried out using variable inductance principle, wherein the reluctance of a magnetic path is changed in proportion to the pressure. An extremely compact pressure transducer with a flat stretched metal diaphragm is shown in Fig. 7.8. An elastic ferromagnetic diaphragm D is mounted symmetrically between the faces of two circular ferromagnetic cores with a pressure port in each section. Two inductance coils are wound on the central section of each core. The difference in pressure between the two sections causes the diaphragm to deflect, resulting in a change in the air gaps between the core faces and the diaphragm. This leads to a change in the inductance of each coil. The coils are connected in the adjacent arms of an ac bridge circuit, and the bridge output is proportional to the magnitude of the differential pressure. A unique feature is that the dynamic response is improved by the absence of any mechanical linkage or any other form of loading on the diaphragm. The sensitivity being high, the device is ideally suited for very low pressure measurements. It is rugged and insensitive to vibrations. In another configuration, the elastic member can be a flat rectangular strip coupled to a twisted bourdon tube, and the inductance coils are wound on stacked E-core laminations.

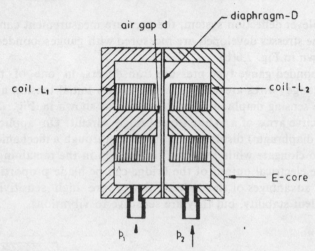

Fig. 7.8 Variable reluctance type pressure sensor

The relation between the change in inductance to the corresponding change in air gap can be expressed as

$$\pm \frac{\Delta L}{L} = \mp \frac{\Delta d}{d} \left[1 + \left(\frac{l}{d\mu_0} + \frac{\Delta d}{d} \right) + \left(\frac{l}{d\mu_0} + \frac{\Delta d}{d} \right)^2 + \cdots \right] \qquad (7.35)$$

where $\Delta L/L$ is the fractional change in inductance, $\Delta d/d$ is the fractional change in air gap, d is the initial air gap, l is the effective length of the magnetic flux path in the ferromagnetic material, and μ_0 is the initial permeability.

7.4.4 LVDT Type Transducer

One of the most popular types of pressure transducers is the Linear Variable Differential Transformer type device in which the LVDT is used as the sensing element. The elastic element, normally a diaphragm or bourdon tube is coupled to the core of the LVDT through a suitable mechanical linkage, as illustrated in Fig. 7.9. On application of pressure, the movement of the core as a result of the diaphragm deflection is sensed precisely, and the appropriate electrical output is interpreted in terms of pressure values. However, the deflections have to be kept small for obtaining reasonable linearity in a limited size. The dynamic response of this device is normally limited because of the core mass.

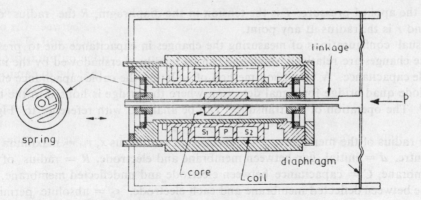

Fig. 7.9 LVDT type pressure sensor

7.4.5 Variable Capacitance Device

For the measurement of very low pressures, an equally suitable device is the variable capacitance transducer. In this configuration a stretched metal diaphragm is positioned symmetrically between the two stationary plates separating two volumes, as shown in Fig. 7.10. The capacitance between these plates and the electrically-grounded diaphragm varies as a function of the deflection of the diaphragm, which is proportional to the differential pressure applied. The changes in the two capacitances can be measured by an ac bridge, a tuned circuit, or by many other techniques. For small deflections, the relation between the deflection y at any point and the pressure is given by[1]

$$y = \frac{p}{4} \cdot \frac{(R^2 - r^2)}{T} \qquad (7.36)$$

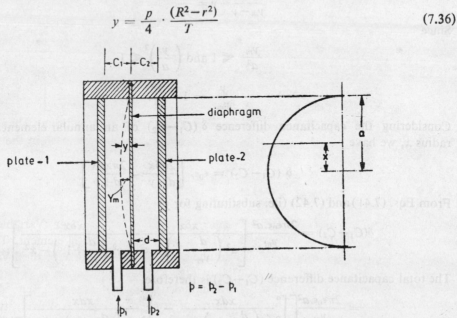

Fig. 7.10 Principle of variable capacitance type pressure sensor

where p is the applied pressure, T is the tension in the diaphragm, R the radius of the diaphragm, and r is the radius at any point.

In the usual configurations of measuring the changes in capacitance due to pressure, the capacitance changes are relatively small and can be readily overshadowed by the instabilities in the cable capacitance. A very good method of isolating the cable capacitance effects is by using a diode quad bridge for signal detection where the bridge is housed in the transducer case itself[3]. The operation of the transducer can be analysed with reference to Fig. 7.10 as follows:

Let a = radius of the membrane, y = deflection at any radius x, y_m = maximum deflection at the centre, d = initial gap between membrane and electrode, R = radius of curvature of the membrane, C = capacitance between electrode and undeflected membrane, C_1, C_2 = capacitance between deflected membrane and each electrode, ϵ_0 = absolute permittivity of free space, and ϵ_r = relative permittivity of pressure medium.
Then,

$$(y_m - y)[2R - (y_m - y)] = x^2 \tag{7.37}$$

Therefore,

$$2R = (y_m - y) + \frac{x^2}{(y_m - y)} \tag{7.38}$$

Also,

$$2R = y_m + \frac{a^2}{y_m} \tag{7.39}$$

Equating Eqs. (7.38) and (7.39),

$$\frac{x^2}{y_m - y} - y = \frac{a^2}{y_m} \tag{7.40}$$

Since

$$\frac{y_m}{a^2} \ll 1 \text{ and } \left(\frac{y}{a}\right)^2 \ll 1$$

$$\frac{y}{y_m} = 1 - \frac{x^2}{a^2} \tag{7.41}$$

Considering the capacitance difference $\delta(C_1 - C_2)$ of an annular element of width δx at radius x, we have

$$\delta(C_1 - C_2) = \epsilon_0 \epsilon_r \left[\frac{2\pi \delta x}{d - y} - \frac{2\pi x dx}{d + y}\right] \tag{7.42}$$

From Eqs. (7.41) and (7.42) (i.e. substituting for y)

$$\delta(C_1 - C_2) = \frac{2\pi \epsilon_0 \epsilon_r a^2}{y_m} \left[\frac{x \delta x}{a^2 \left(\dfrac{d}{y_m} - 1\right) + x^2} - \frac{x \delta x}{a^2 \left(\dfrac{d}{y_m} + 1\right) - x^2}\right] \tag{7.43}$$

The total capacitance difference $(C_1 - C_2)$ is therefore

$$= \frac{2\pi \epsilon_0 \epsilon_r a^2}{y_m} \left[\int_0^a \frac{x dx}{a^2 \left(\dfrac{d}{y_m} - 1\right) + x^2} - \int_0^a \frac{x dx}{a^2 \left(\dfrac{d}{y_m} + 1\right) - x^2}\right]$$

$$= \frac{\pi \epsilon_0 \epsilon_r a^2}{y_m} \cdot \log_e \cdot \frac{\left(\dfrac{d}{y_m}\right)^2}{\left[\left(\dfrac{d}{y_m}\right)^2 - 1\right]} \tag{7.44}$$

Under equal pressure conditions

$$C = \frac{\pi \epsilon_0 \epsilon_r a^2}{d^2} \tag{7.45}$$

and the fractional capacitance change is given by

$$\frac{\Delta C}{C} = \frac{d}{2y_m} \cdot \left[1 + \frac{y_m^2}{2d^2} + \frac{y_m^4}{3d^4} + \cdots \right] \tag{7.46}$$

From Eq. (7.46), it can be seen that high linearity can be obtained if $\frac{y_m}{d} \ll 1$. Thus, the linearity is improved at the cost of sensitivity.

The main advantages of the capacitance transducers are small size, good high frequency response, adaptability for high-temperature operation, good linearity, and resolution. However, it needs complex electronic circuitry; also, the cable capacitance effects should be taken care of. It may often be required to locate the preamplifier nearer the transducer.

7.4.6 Thin Film Pressure Transducer

Thin film pressure transducers are widely employed for the measurement of surface pressures on structures such as aerofoils, without any modification of the surface. Typical thickness of these transducers is in the range of 10 to 50 microns. The main advantages of this device are:

(a) The transducer can be attached to the surface with a simple bonding technique.
(b) The structure on which this transducer is mounted may be very thin so that the use of the other types of transducers is not feasible for direct measurement.
(c) Loading effects due to the transducer are insignificant.

The first two advantages are particularly applicable in the case of measurements of pressure on aerofoils, such as that of a fan or compressor blade, because the mounting of the transducer does not necessitate any machining of the structure. The third advantage is applicable in the case of supersonic flow studies, as long as the boundary layer thickness is much larger than the geometrical discontinuity that is created by the pressure of the pressure sensitive element. Also, the geometrical shape and dimensions of the sensitive area can be arbitrary so that any specific requirement can be easily fulfilled.

The transducer consists of a thin film of a dielectric, having constant modulus of elasticity over a wide temperature range (e.g. polyamides), with metal-film coatings on both faces which serve as electrodes. One of the two electrodes is bonded to the profile base and the other one, which is free to move, is subjected to the pressure as shown in Fig. 7.11. The variation in capacitance ΔC as a result of the variation of applied pressure ΔP can be related by the equation,

$$\frac{\Delta C}{C_0} = \frac{\Delta P}{E} \tag{7.47}$$

where C_0 is the initial value of the capacitance and E is the Young's modulus of the dielectric material. Metal coating or etching can also be adopted to provide a guard ring and output lead connections. The sensitivities of the order of 50 mV/bar can be obtained, depending upon other considerations. The high-frequency response limitation of the transducer is dependent on the dielectric material, and is typically 100 kHz, while the low-frequency response limitation depends on the electronic circuit used. It is apparent that the final calibration of the device should always be done on line, after the installation.

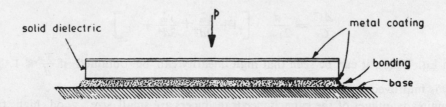

Fig. 7.11 Thin film pressure sensor

7.5 FORCE-BALANCE TRANSDUCER

The performance of the transducers based on the measurement of deflection of elastic elements, such as diaphragms, membranes, capsules or bellows is essentially dependent on the long-term stability characteristics of elastic elements. Properties such as material hysteresis and creep can degrade the accuracy. For higer sensitivity, these elements must have low stiffness and/or large area. Consequently, the transducer may be bulky and will be affected by vibration.

To overcome some of the above problems, feedback principles employing balance of forces have been applied with considerable success. In principle, force balance transducers employ electrodynamic devices or electrostatic force generators to balance the forces produced by the elastic element which is subjected to the pressure. In order to understand the performance of such a transducer system, an analysis of the closed loop feedback system in terms of the transfer function can be very helpful.

A typical force-balance system using electrodynamic force balancing principle is shown in Fig. 7.12. Any pressure difference between inside and outside of the bellows gives rise to a force F at the point A. The resultant displacement of the balancing beam is detected by an appropriate displacement transducer, such as a LVDT located at point B. The electrical output from the transducer is amplified causing a current I to flow through the balancing coil attached to the beam. At the balance position, the electrodynamic force exerted by the coil opposes the force exerted by the bellows, and the current I required to get such a balance is taken as a measure of the unknown pressure p acting on the bellows. If the loop gain is large, an extremely small deflection of the bellows is sufficient to activate the loop, and achieve the balance condition. The variations in spring constant of the bellows, zero setting of the spring and fulcrum, and gain and stability of the displacement detector and amplifier will be almost insignificant, as can be seen from the following analysis.

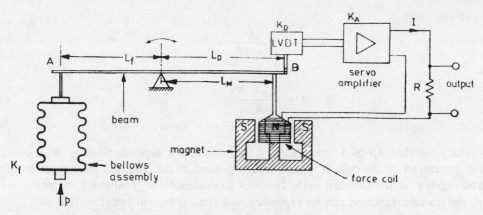

Fig. 7.12 Schematic of force-balance pressure transducer

7.5.1 Analysis

For determining the equation of motion, the sum of the forces due to the inertia of the movable part, the damping, and stiffness is equated to the net force produced by the bellows and electrodynamic system. Referring to Fig. 7.12,

$$m\ddot{x} + D\dot{x} + Kx = FL_f - K_m L_M I \tag{7.48}$$

where, x = displacement of the beam with respect to a reference point, K_m = force coil constant, F = force exerted by the bellows due to the applied pressure, m = mass of the movable part of the transducer, D = damping coefficient of the movable part, I = output current, K = spring constant of the bellows, L_f = fulcrum to bellows-centre distance, and L_M = fulcrum to force-coil distance.

Taking Laplace transform, the displacement may be written as

$$x(s) = \frac{FL_F - K_m L_M I}{ms^2 + Ds + K} \tag{7.49}$$

The displacement x is sensed by a suitable transducer, and an output current which is proportional to the input voltage is obtained from the amplifier as shown in Fig. 7.13. If FL_f is taken as the input to the system, the transfer function of the system is given by

$$\frac{I}{FL_f} = G(s) = \frac{\dfrac{L_D K_D K_A}{ms^2 + Ds + K}}{1 + \left(\dfrac{L_D K_D K_A}{ms^2 + Ds + K}\right)(K_m L_M)} \tag{7.50}$$

where L_D is the distance of the displacement-transducer from the fulcrum, K_D is the gain of the displacement-transducer, and K_A is the servo amplifier gain as shown in Fig. 7.12.

Under static conditions, i.e. when $s = 0$,

$$G(o) = \frac{L_D K_D K_A / K}{1 + \dfrac{L_D K_D K_A L_M K_M}{K}} \tag{7.51}$$

This is of the form

$$G(o) = \frac{A}{1+AB} \qquad (7.52)$$

where,

$$A = \frac{L_D K_D K_A}{K} \qquad (7.53)$$

$$B = K_m L_M \qquad (7.54)$$

If A is large so that $AB \gg 1$, then $G(o) = 1/B$; this factor depends only on $K_m L_M$ and in no other parameter of the system, hence reducing most of the common transducer errors like drift and ageing in the forward path. In order to evaluate the frequency response of the system, the transfer function can be expressed as a typical second-order system as

$$G(s) = \frac{G(o)}{\dfrac{s^2}{\omega_n^2} + \dfrac{2\zeta}{\omega_n}s + 1} \qquad (7.55)$$

where

$$\omega_n = \sqrt{\frac{K + L_D K_D K_A L_M K_m}{m}} = \sqrt{\frac{K}{m}(1+AB)} \qquad (7.56)$$

$$\zeta = \frac{D}{2\sqrt{m(K + L_D K_D K_A L_M K_m)}} = \frac{D}{2\sqrt{mK(1+AB)}} \qquad (7.57)$$

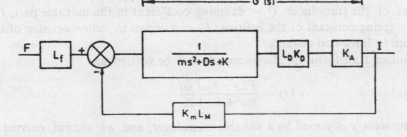

Fig. 7.13 Block diagram representation of force balance pressure
transducer

In order to decrease the hysteresis and static errors of the system, it is desirable that the loop gain AB be made as large as possible. Reduction of the spring constant of the bellows element in the system, therefore, produces a more favourable condition. The transient response characteristic as well as the stability of the system are influenced by the values of natural frequency ω_n and damping ratio ζ. A large loop gain which is favourable for low hysteresis error, will also reduce the ζ value, thereby causing instability. Obviously, a smaller mass of the moving system improves the dynamic response. The overall system performance depends upon the judicious choice of the electrical parameters K_A, K_D and K_m.

The above analysis presented is only for a typical case; there can be many variations in the actual design depending upon the requirements, such as introducing a centring spring to get initial balance at any desired point, using two bellows of which one is evacuated for absolute pressure measurements, introducing a bucking coil for linearity correction of flux density with current, and good centring by means of additional weights to reduce acceleration effects.

One disadvantage of the force-balance system based on the electrodynamic principle discussed above is that it tends to be heavy because of the magnet-and-coil assembly and hence limits the frequency response to about 100 Hz. In principle, the system can be designed to measure low pressures depending upon the spring rates (deflection per unit pressure) of the bellows available. Because of the closed loop null seeking action, the device exhibits high accuracy and good sensitivity. As such, it is often used as a secondary standard.

7.5.2 Electrostatic Feedback Device

Another type of force-balance system specially suited for low pressure measurements uses the force balance principle with electrostatic force generation[4]. The transducer consists of two pressure chambers separated by a thin conductive circular membrane which is lightly stretched such that it performs the role of a movable electrode. On either side of the membrane, metal electrodes covering the entire diameter of the membrane are present along with guard rings, across which a potential is applied to establish the required field.

If the flat membrane is situated midway between two electrodes which are maintained at potentials V^+, and V^- then the transfer function of the electrostatic generator is given by

$$K_f = \frac{F_e}{V_0} = \frac{2\epsilon_0\epsilon_r V}{d^2} \qquad (7.58)$$

where K_f = transfer function of the electrostatic generator (N m^{-2}, V^{-1}), F_e = generated electrostatic pressure (N/m^2), V_0 = membrane potential (V), $2V$ = potential across the electrodes (V), d = gap between membrane and each electrode (m), ϵ_0 = absolute permittivity of free space, and ϵ_r = relative permittivity of the pressure medium.

When the electrode potential V, the gap width d and the relative permittivity ϵ_r remain constant and the membrane remains flat, and when the system is in pressure balance, the membrane potential V_0 is a precise measure of the electrostatic pressure, and hence of the applied pressure. Sensitivity of the order of 30 V/(N/m^2) and frequency response of the order of 30 Hz have been reported with this device.

7.6 SOLID-STATE DEVICES

Recent advances in microelectronic circuit technology have been successfully applied for the development of solid-state transducers, especially for pressure measurements. There are two varieties in this category. The first is based on the piezoresistance effect, and the second utilizes the piezojunction effect.

The piezoresistive-type transducer consists of a monocrystalline silicon diaphragm with four piezoresistive strain gauges formed integrally in a Wheatstone bridge configuration diffused on it to measure the stresses developed due to the applied pressure. The salient features of this device are: (a) the mechanical properties of the monocrystalline silicon show low hysteresis and high repeatability, (b) piezoresistive semiconductor gauges formed on the silicon diaphragm exhibit much higher sensitivity compared with conventional bonded or unbonded wire gauges mounted on metal diaphragms, (c) piezoresistive gauges diffused directly onto the diaphragm surface are not likely to suffer from the creep and hysteresis effects inherent in bonded strain gauges, (d) miniaturization of the transducer is easy without any sacrifice in performance and, (e) they exhibit excellent thermal characteristics.

Being integral in nature, the lead fatigue and undesirable secondary resonances caused by internal vibrations are eliminated, thereby withstanding extremely high shock and vibrations without deterioration. With the miniaturization feature, the natural frequency is very high. The devices are ideally suited for high sensitivity, static, and dynamic pressure measurements in aerospace, oceanography, and medical sciences. The theory of piezoresistive strain gauges has been presented in Chapter 5.

The other type of solid-state pressure transducer employs the piezojunction effect, i.e. the variation in the sensitivity of the V-I (volt-ampere) characteristics of a p-n junction to stress. This piezojunction effect occurs at high stress levels ($\sigma > 10^8$ N/m^2 in silicon), and is characterized by an exponential increase in the minority carrier density as the stress is increased above the threshold level, and hence is found to be a highly sensitive mechanism. The minority carrier density is approximately linearly related to the current in a forward-biased p-n junction. An increase in the minority carrier density can be readily detected in the V-I characteristics of the junction. The exponential relationship between the stress and the minority carrier density, and consequently, the forward current in a p-n junction makes the piezojunction effect particularly attractive as a stress-transducing mechanism. Therefore, configurations, which permit measurement of physical parameters such as pressure and acceleration by variation of the stress applied to a p-n junction, provide a powerful family of sensitive piezojunction solid-state transducers.

The electrical characteristics of semiconductors and piezojunction phenomenon are conveniently described in terms of the energy-band structure. However, for transducer applications, the main consideration is the effect of the applied stress σ on p-n junction characteristics. This effect can be described in terms of the ratio ν of the stressed and unstressed minority carrier density. The variations of ν as a function of compressional and tensional stresses respectively for different values of D_u' (where D_u' is the deformation potential coefficient) are shown in Fig. 7.14. For a hydrostatic and uniaxial stress [100]. ν is independent of D_u'. The exponential increase in ν with stress is the basic characteristic of the piezojunction phenomenon. It is evident from Fig. 7.14 that ν is most sensitive to a [100] compressional stress and least sensitive to a [III] stress. It should also be noted that piezojunction effect is significant at stress levels greater than 10^8 N/m^2. The mechanical strength of silicon limits the maximum stress that can be applied to the p-n junction in silicon and is the basic limitation that restricts the change in ν from being very large. The fracture strength of silicon varies from sample to sample and depends to a large extent on the surface conditions. However, several order of magnitude changes in ν have been observed.

In calculating the current changes in the forward-biased p-n junction due to stress, it is assumed that the changes in the other parameters are assumed to be negligible when compared with the exponential change of ν, when the stress is above 10^8 N/m^2. The contribution of surface generation-recombination currents are also neglected in these calculations.

The total current I_T in a p-n junction is the sum of the ideal current I_I and the generation-recombination current I_R.

$$I_T = I_I + I_R \tag{7.59}$$

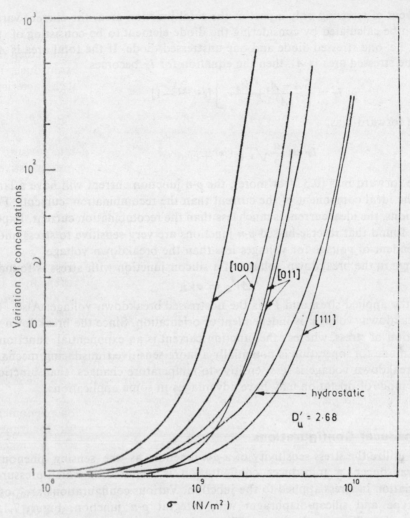

Fig. 7.14 Variation of ratio of stresses (ν) as a function of stress (σ) in piezoresistance devices

For forward-biased conditions, the bulk generation-recombination current is given by

$$I_R = \frac{av[e^{(qV/kT)} - 1]}{1 + b\sqrt{v}\ e^{qV/kT}} \tag{7.60}$$

and the ideal current is given by

$$I_I = cv[e^{qV/kT} - 1] \tag{7.61}$$

Thus,

$$I_T = \frac{av[e^{qV/kT} - 1]}{1 + b\sqrt{v}\ e^{qV/kT}} + cv[e^{qV/kT} - 1] \tag{7.62}$$

where a, b, and c are constants, k = Boltzmann's constant, V = junction voltage, v = carrier density ratio, T = absolute temperature, and q = charge of an electron.

In the event of stressing only a part of the total-junction area, the current variations due to stress can be calculated by considering the diode element to be consisting of two diodes in parallel, i.e. one stressed diode and one unstressed diode. If the total area is A, and if for example, the stressed area is A_s, then the equation for I_T becomes

$$I_T = \left[\frac{A - A_s}{A} + \frac{A_s}{A} v \right] [e^{qV/kT} - 1] \tag{7.63}$$

For a large forward-bias,

$$I_T \simeq \frac{a}{b} \sqrt{v} \, e^{qV/kT} + cve^{qV/kT} \tag{7.64}$$

For a large forward bias (0.3 V or more), the p-n junction current will have a larger dependence on the ideal component of the current than the recombination current. For reverse-bias conditions, the ideal current is much less than the recombination current. Experimentally, it has been found that reverse-biased p-n junctions are very sensitive to stress and are relatively independent of voltage for voltages less than the breakdown voltage.

The change in the breakdown voltage of a silicon junction with stress is found to be[5]

$$\Delta V_B = \sigma V_B \tag{7.65}$$

where σ is the applied stress and V_B is the unstressed breakdown voltage. Also, the change in the breakdown voltage is independent of orientation. Since the breakdown voltage is a linear function of stress, whereas the junction current is an exponential function of stress, the latter mode of operation is potentially a more sensitive transducing mechanism. However, the breakdown voltage is less sensitive to temperature changes than junction currents and such a mode of operation may have advantages in some applications.

7.6.1 Transducer Configurations

In order to utilize the stress sensitivity of a p-n junction as the sensing phenomenon in a pressure transducer, a transducer configuration is required in which pressure variations cause a variation in stress applied to the junction. Various configurations are possible, such as needle-type and silicon-diaphragm with integral p-n junction. Figure 7.15 shows the construction of a silicon-needle sensor. The p-n junction can be fabricated in the needle tip by adapting planar-processing techniques. A rigid housing positions the needle sensor firmly against the diaphragm. The differential pressure variations across the diaphragm vary the stress applied to the needle sensor and cause changes in the V-I characteristics of the sensor. The diaphragms are typically made with silicon or quartz. A basic limitation of these transducers is the dynamic range. Transducers for low differential pressure have to be mechanically biased into the stress-sensitive region.

In another configuration, the pressure differential is applied across a silicon diaphragm with the p-n junction located at the centre. This design has the advantages of mechanical simplicity, large area stresses, and ease of fabrication with silicon planar technology. Problems, such as creep, alignment, and hysteresis, which are associated with the mechanical housing are reduced in this configuration. It is advantageous to stress the entire area to obtain higher sensitivity, but extremely large biasing stresses are required. Also, in this diaphragm type, stresses are tensional, whereas compressional stresses are more desirable, as

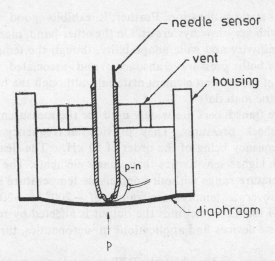

Fig. 7.15 Solid-state needle pressure sensor

the variation in ν is significantly greater in the latter case. In a typical transducer, the radius and thickness of the silicon diaphragm are of the order of 8 mm and 50 microns respectively.

Suitable measuring circuits for these types of transducers are the standard bridge configurations. In addition, temperature compensation is essential as the stress sensitive elements are sensitive to temperature also.

7.7 PIEZOELECTRIC PRESSURE TRANSDUCER

Certain types of materials generate an electrostatic charge or voltage when mechanical stresses are applied across them. An opposite effect is also observed when an electrostatic charge or voltage is applied to the crystal, resulting in the mechanical deformation of the device. This property of piezoelectricity has been utilised in the design of pressure transducers, wherein the mechanical stress is generated by the diaphragm subjected to pressure. The stress distribution in the crystal will depend not only on the load applied but also the manner in which this is applied, and upon the size and shape of the sensing element. Such devices find wide application in the measurement of acceleration and force (see Chapters 6 and 10).

The important parameters considered are sensitivity, natural frequency, non-linearity, hysteresis, temperature effects, acceleration response, and cross sensitivity. The performance of a crystal element depends upon the magnitude of the crystal's piezoelectric constants. In addition, other related properties are relative permittivity, the natural time constant of the material, the elastic constants, density, and the change of piezoelectric constants with temperature.[1]

Although a very large number of materials are piezoelectric, the most popular ones having significant values of piezoelectric constants and sensitivity are natural quartz, Rochelle salt, ADP, and a variety of synthetic ceramic materials like barium-titanate and lead-zirconate-titanate. Of these, natural quartz is the most stable device for many applications. It has a lower temperature sensitivity and a higher resistivity, thus giving an inherently long time constant which permits static calibration. Further, it exhibits good linearity over a wide range of stress levels with very low hysteresis. On the other hand, piezoelectric ceramics have considerably higher sensitivity and wide adaptability, though the temperature characteristics are poor. The design of both pressure transducers and associated electronic circuitry is affected by the choice of the sensing element materials, although the basic design approach is similar in all piezoelectric materials.

Piezoelectric pressure transducers are widely used for the measurement of rapidly-varying pressure as well as shock pressures. They provide flat frequency response from 1 Hz to 20 kHz, the natural frequency being of the order of 50 kHz. The lead-zirconate-type ceramic crystals have much higher sensitivities than quartz elements. The transducers can operate over a wide temperature range without appreciable temperature induced errors. Quartz devices can be used over a temperature range of $-200°$ to $+300°C$; whereas ceramic devices are limited to $+100°C$. Sometimes the output is affected by relatively little known pyroelectric effects. These devices find applications in aeronautics, turbines, pumps, hydraulics, and acoustics.

The various configurations under which the PZT (piezoelectric transducer) material can be employed for pressure (force) measurements are given in Fig. 7.16. The shape of the element may be a disc, plate, or tube, which may be operated under normal, transverse, or shear modes. Beam and disc-shaped bimorph types are also quite popular in certain applications.

In practical transducers, it is possible to stack a number of identical plates one above the other, electrically connected in series or in parallel. In this case, the charge sensitivity q_P increases by a factor equal to the number of plates, and the natural frequency f_0 decreases. The product $q_P f_0$ is a useful figure of merit and remains constant indicating the mode effectiveness. The sensitivities, static capacitance, and natural frequencies for a number of configurations of the PZT$-$5A lead zirconate elements shown in Fig. 7.16 are given in Table 7.2. It may be noted that the plate undergoing transverse compression is similar to that in direct compression, but the d_{31} constant replaces d_{33}, thereby reducing the sensitivity by a factor of two or three. The bending modes invariably use elements of bimorph construction. These consist of two similar plates with conducting plating on the upper and lower faces, which are connected mechanically and electrically along their common surface. They are polarized along its thickness. By appropriate electrical connection, the potential differences may be added. Alternatively, by using plates polarized in opposite directions, an added output can be obtained across the outer surfaces.

It would appear that the mode with the highest charge sensitivity-natural frequency product is the only one that need be considered, but with the limitations imposed by transducer size, it is often not possible to obtain sufficiently high sensitivity using this mode. In such circumstances, a mode with lower value of $q_P f_0$ may be chosen sacrificing the natural frequency.

Table 7.2 shows that a disc or plate under bimorph configuration in normal compression gives the largest value of $q_P f_0$. For direct-pressure measurement, the normal compressive mode and the bimorph disc in the bending mode are the best. A typical complete assembly of a normal compressive mode transducer is as shown in Fig. 7.17.

7.8 VIBRATING ELEMENT PRESSURE SENSORS

The vibrating element pressure sensor is one of the new generation devices wherein the

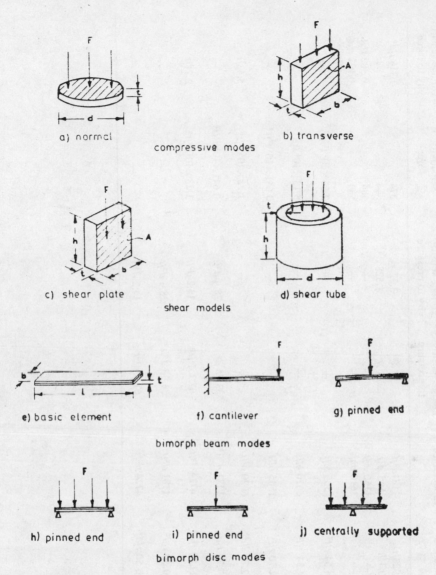

Fig. 7.16 Various loading configurations of piezoelectric elements in pressure transducers

applied pressure is directly converted to a proportional frequency. The principle is based upon the change in the natural resonant frequency of an elastic element such as a diaphragm as a function of the applied pressure[6]. A typical configuration of such a device is illustrated in Fig. 7.18. The diaphragm assembly is attached to a sturdy frame, forming a perfect pressure seal for the pressure chamber. A small magnet attached to the centre of the diaphragm and coupled to a coil suspended from the frame forms the driving element of the transducer. In practice the chamber volume between the outer cover and the diaphragm is evacuated for the absolute pressure measurement. A dummy coil having identical characteristics as that

TABLE 7.2 FIGURE OF MERIT, CAPACITANCE AND SENSITIVITIES OF DIFFERENT CONFIGURATIONS OF PZT MATERIALS

PZT elements	f_0—kHz natural resonance frequency	C_0—pF inherent capacitance	Q_p—pC/torr charge sensitivity to pressure	V_p—mV/torr voltage sensitivity to pressure	Q_F—pC/N charge sensitivity to force	V_F—V/N voltage sensitivity to force
Normal compression disc	$923/t$	$1181\,d^2/t$	$3.92\,d^2$	$3.32\,t$	374	$0.316\,t/d^2$
Plane transverse	$70.1/h$	$1505\,A/t$	$2.28\,A$	$1.528\,t$	—	—
Shear plate	—	$1150\,A/t$	—	—	584	$0.382\,t/A$
Shear tube	—	$3610\,dh/t$	—	—	584	$0.122\,t/dh$
Cantilever beam—series connected	$4.54\,t/l^2$	$1505\,bl/t$	—	—	$2.56\times10^4\,l^2/d^2$	—
Cantilever beam—parallel connected	$4.54\,t/l^2$	$6020\,bl/t$	—	—	$5.13\times10^4\,l^2/t^2$	—
Pinned end beam—parallel connected	$12.70\,t/l^2$	$1505\,bl/t$	—	—	$0.641\times10^4\,l^2/t^2$	—
Pinned end beam—series connected	$12.70\,t/d^2$	$6020\,bl/t$	—	—	$1.28\times10^4\,l^2/t^2$	$5.43/t$
Pinned edge disc—series connected	$27.70\,t/d^2$	$1181\,d^2/t^2$	$33.55\,d^4/l^2$	$28.4\,d^2/t$	$0.641\times10^4\,l^2/t^2$	—
Pinned edge disc—parallel connected	$27.70\,t/d^2$	$4724\,d^2/t$	$67.1\,d^4/l^2$	$14.2\,d^2/t$	$1.28\times10^4\,l^2/t^2$	$2.71/t$
Centrally supported disc—series connected	$20.50\,t/d^2$	$1181\,d^2/t$	$33.35\,d^4/l^2$	$28.4\,d^2/t$	—	—
Centrally supported disc—parallel connected	$20.50\,t/d^2$	$4724\,d^2/t$	$67.1\,d^4/l$	$14.2\,d^2/t$	—	—

t—mm
d, l, b, h—cm
A—cm^2

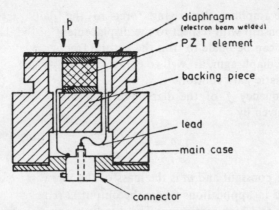

Fig. 7.17 Assembly of a piezoelectric pressure transducer

of the driver coil is also enclosed within the transducer housing and is connected to form a bridge along with the drive coil as shown in Fig. 7.18. The bridge output is amplified and fed back for excitation; any small disturbance in the bridge output will excite the diaphragm at its natural resonant frequency. The value of the natural resonant frequency depends upon the pressure difference existing across the diaphragm. The driver coil generates an induced voltage proportional to the velocity of the diaphragm; i.e., the driver coil voltage will be leading the displacement of the diaphragm by 90°. In practice the dummy coil separates the induced voltage in the driver coil from the excitation voltage and feeds it to the amplifier, because of the bridge configuration. The amplifier output provides necessary current to generate a driving force to sustain the oscillations at the natural resonance frequency. With

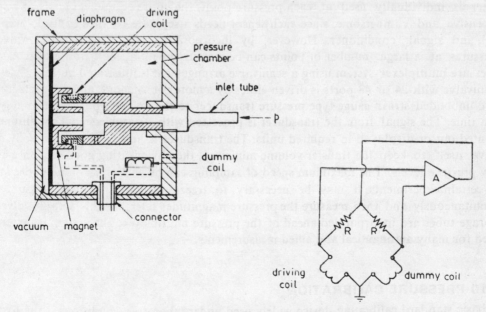

Fig. 7.18 Vibrating diaphragm pressure transducer

180° phase shift in the amplifier, the driving force to the diaphragm will be having the required phase relationship with respect to the displacement of the diaphragm at its natural frequency. Provisions can be made to trim the natural frequency of the diaphragm by adjusting the tension in the diaphragm, as well to control the amplitude of the oscillations by incorporating an automatic gain control.

The resonance frequency f of the diaphragm in terms of standard equation for simple harmonic motion is given by

$$f = \frac{1}{2\pi}\sqrt{\frac{K}{m}} \tag{7.65}$$

where K is the spring constant and m is the mass of the vibrating system respectively. The device is ideally suited in applications where the output is required in a direct digital format with high sensitivity and high resolution. The disadvantages are the variation of its sensitivity with temperature and difficulty in determining the modal points for mounting. Mounting at a point other than the modal point will introduce stresses in the diaphragm. This in turn will produce changes in stiffness which itself may vary as a function of temperature. This difficulty can be circumvented by using a thin-walled cylinder, with modal ends formed by a cap at the top and a mounting flange at the bottom. By mounting at only one point at the bottom (the bottom flange), an unrestrained resonance can be induced using the magnetic drive and pick-up coil.

7.9 PRESSURE MULTIPLEXER

In certain experiments, such as wind-tunnel testing of models, a simultaneous measurement of pressures at various locations is required for detailed investigations. If a pressure transducer is individually used at each pressure point, the entire equipment tends to be large, expensive, and cumbersome, since each sensor needs a separate balance control, zero control, and signal conditioner. However, by incorporating a pressure-transfer valve, the pressures at a large number of points can be measured with a single transducer. A typical pressure multiplexer system using a scanivalve arrangement is illustrated in Fig. 7.19. The scanivalve with 24 or 48 ports is driven either by a motor or solenoid, and connects a miniature unbonded strain gauge-type pressure transducer to the pressure ports sequentially, one at a time. The signal from the transducer is processed with a suitable signal conditioner and printed out or displayed in required units. The transducer is housed within the body of the valve itself to keep the transfer volume minimum, thereby ensuring good response even at low pressure levels. The maximum speed of sampling can be as high as 48 ports per minute. In certain experiments, it may be necessary to freeze several unknown pressure values simultaneously and then measure the pressure magnitudes later; for this, cut-off valves with storage tubes are incorporated ahead of the pressure multiplexer. The system is extensively used for many aeronautical and allied measurements.

7.10 PRESSURE CALIBRATION

A basic standard calibrating device widely used under laboratory conditions is the hydraulic or pneumatically-operated dead weight tester, using piston gauges. A free piston gauge for

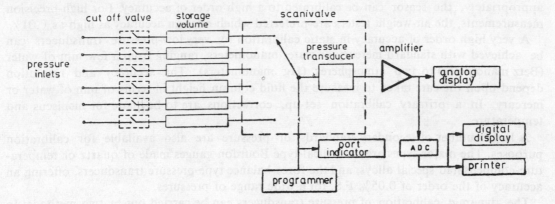

cut off valve   storage
volume

scanivalve

pressure
inlets

pressure
transducer

amplifier

analog
display

port
indicator

ADC

digital
display

printer

programmer

Fig. 7.19 Pressure multiplexer

the precise determination of steady pressures can be utilized to calibrate pressure transducers over a wide range, from about 50 to 50×10^6 Pa, in steps as small as 0.1% of the range, with a calibration uncertainty in the range of 0.01 to 0.5% of the reading.

The dead-weight tester consists of two accurately machined cylinders, honed to micron tolerances, inserted into two closed and known cross-sectional areas coupled together to a reservoir, as shown in Fig. 7.20. One of the cylinders is fitted with a close-fitting precision piston with a top platform where accurately known weights in the form of discs can be loaded. The transducer under test is connected to the other cylinder. The fluid pressure is then gradually applied until the force is large enough to just lift the precision piston-weight

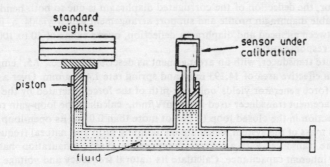

standard
weights

sensor under
calibration

piston

fluid

Fig. 7.20 Standard deadweight tester for pressure calibration

combination. When the piston is floating freely, the piston gauge with arranged weights is in equilibrium with the pressure developed in the cylinder. The relationship can be expressed as $F = pA$, where F is the equivalent force of the piston weight combination (total mass × acceleration due to gravity) corrected for local gravity and air buoyancy, p is the pressure, and A is the equivalent area of the piston cylinder combination corrected for piston cylinder friction, pressure level, and temperature. It is necessary that the cylinder and piston head are perfectly vertical for the above equation to hold good. In order to reduce the friction created by the fluid film, the piston is rotated or vibrated. By changing the weights appropriately, the sensor can be calibrated to a high order of accuracy. For high-precision measurements, the air-weight testers are preferred which offer an accuracy as high as 0.01%.

A very high order of accuracy in static calibration for very low-pressure transducers can be achieved with standard mercury or water manometers, ranging from a few mm of water (Betz manometer) to two atmospheres (Hg manometers). The accuracy and resolution depend upon the care taken to measure the fluid column height in terms of mm of water or mercury. In a primary calibration set-up, corrections are to be made for meniscus and temperature.

A large number of secondary standards of pressure are also available for calibration purposes. The major types are the helical-type Bourdon gauges made of quartz or temperature-compensated special alloys, and the force-balance type pressure transducers, offering an accuracy of the order of 0.05% F.S. for a wide range of pressures.

The dynamic calibration of pressure transducers can be carried out by two methods. In the first method the transducer is subjected to a fluctuating pressure created by an electrically-driven vibrating piston or diaphragm in a closed chamber. But in this method the frequency range is limited to about 100 Hz. Alternatively, the response characteristic can be precisely determined by subjecting the transducer to a step-pressure input, generated with a shock tube, wherein rise times as low as 1 ms can be achieved.

EXERCISES

7.1 In a variable capacitance pressure transducer, the diaphragm and housing are made out of a single piece of steel, where the diaphragm thickness and diameter are 0.5 and 12.5 mm respectively. The stationary electrode of 10 mm dia is separated by a gap of 0.25 mm from the diaphragm. Calculate: (a) the natural frequency of the diaphragm, (b) pressure sensitivity, and (c) maximum proof pressure.

7.2 In an airspeed indicator, the deflection of the corrugated diaphragm is due to both bending and tensile stresses. Design a suitable diaphragm profile and support arrangement which yields a linear relationship (within $\pm 5\%$) between airspeed and diaphragm deflection, over a range of 10 to 100 m/s
    Plot the expected response curve.

7.3 A force-balance pressure transducer, with an arrangement as described in Sec. 7.5, employs stainless steel bellows having an effective area of 14.193 mm² and spring rate 1.43 kg/mm. Over a pressure range of 0 to 70 kPa, the force generator yields only one-fifth of the force generated by the bellows. If the sensitivity of the displacement transducer used is 100 mV/mm, calculate the loop-gain requirements to make the bellows deflection in the closed loop to be not more than 0.01 of its open-loop values.
    Estimating the total mass of the system, calculate its damping ratio and natural frequency.

7.4 A piezoelectric pressure transducer with a normal compression disc configuration has 7.84 pC/torr sensitivity and 200 pF inherent capacitance. Calculate its natural frequency and voltage sensitivity.

7.5 A diaphragm-type pressure transducer is mounted on a vehicle, and the acceleration level in the direction normal to the diaphragm due to vibrations of the vehicle is estimated to be 2 m/s². If the mass per unit area of the diaphragm is 7 kg/m², calculate the error in the pressure reading due to vibrations.

7.6 The deflection of a pressure-sensing diaphragm under large deflection conditions is non-linear with respect to the pressure difference across the diaphragm. Using this feature to advantage, discuss how a linear relationship between air speed and deflection can be obtained from a pitot-static tube.

REFERENCES

1. Neubert, H.K.P., *Instrument Transducers*, Clarendon Press, Oxford, 1975, p. 58.

2. Andreeva, L.E., *Elastic Elements of Instruments*, Israel Programme of Scientific Publications, Jerusalem, 1966.

3. Harrison, D.R. and Dioneff, J., "A diode-quad bridge circuit for use with capacitance transducers", *Review of Scientific Instruments*, Vol. 44, No. 10, pp. 1468-1471, Oct. 1973.

4. McDonald, W.R. and King, C., "An electrostatic feedback transducer for measuring very low pressures", *Royal Aircraft Establishment, Technical Report* 71022, Faranborough, 1971.

5. Hauser, J.R. and Wortman, J.J., "Some effects of mechanical stress on the breakdown voltage of *p-n* junctions", *Journal of Applied Physics*, Vol. 37, No. 10, pp. 3884-3892, Sept. 1966.

6. Frishe, R.H., "Pressure sensors", *Sperry Rand Engineering Review*, Vol. 22, No. 4, Dec. 1969, pp. 45-48.

BIBLIOGRAPHY

Arrendale, H., "Precision pressure measurements", *Instruments and Control Systems*, Vol. 43, No. 10, pp. 73-75. October 1973.

Beckwith, T.G. and Buck, N.L., *Mechanical Measurements*, Addison Wesley, New York, 1969.

Bruce, C.F., "Fused Quartz diaphragm-type pressure transducer", *Scientific Instruments*, Vol. 4, No. 10, pp. 790-792, October 1971.

Cook, N.H. and Rabinowicz, *Physical Measurement and Analysis*, Addison Wesley Publishing Co. Inc., Reading, Mass., 1963.

Damrel, J.B., "Quartz bourdon gauge", *Instrument and Control Systems*, Vol. 36, No. 2, pp. 87-89, Feb. 1963.

Doebelin, E.O., *Measurement Systems—Applications and Design*, McGraw-Hill, New York, 1968.

ISA Transducer Compendium, Instrument Society of America, Pittsburg, 1973.

Johnson, D.P. and Newhall, D.H., "The piston gage as a precision pressure measuring instrument", *Instruments and Control Systems*, Vol. 35, No. 4, pp. 42-46, April 1962.

Lederer P.S. and Smith R.O., "An experimental technique for the determination of fidelity of the dynamic response of pressure transducers", *NBS Rept.* 7862, 1963.

Lion, K.S., *Instrumentation in Scientific Research*, McGraw-Hill, N.Y., 1959.

Liptak, *Instrument Engineers Handbook*, Chilton Book Co., N.Y., 1970.

Maddox, G.A., "Precision pressure measurements", *Instruments and Control Systems*, Vol. 39, No. 9, pp. 91-95, Sept. 1966.

Mallon, J.R., "The solid state approach to pressure measurement", *Microtecnic*, Vol. 25, No. 5, pp. 325-328, June 1971.

Mayer, R.C., "A new digital pressure sensor", *Advances in Instrumentation*, Vol. 27, Part 2, paper 601, 1972.

Minaev, I.G., Trofimov, A.I., "Calibration characteristics of static pressures (efforts) piezoelectric transducers", *Measurement Tech.*, Vol. 16, No. 4, pp. 619-620, April 1973.

Nemergut, P.J., "Determination of piezoelectric parameters by mechanical drive techniques", *Exp. Mech.*, Vol. 13, No. 10, pp. 33 N, October 1973.

Norton, H.N., *Handbook of Transducers for Electronic Measuring Systems*, Prentice-Hall, New Jersey, 1969.

Paros, J.M., "Precision digital pressure transducer", *Advances in Instrumentation*, Vol. 27, Part 2, paper 602, 1972.

Rohrbach, C., *Handuch für Elektriches Messen Mechanischev Grossen*, V.D.I, Verlag, Dusseldorf, 1967.

Schweppe, J.L. et al., "Methods for the dynamic calibration of pressure transducers", *NBS Monograph*, 67, 1963.

Taroni, A, et al., "Semiconductor sensors, Part 2, Piezoresistive devices", *IEEE Trans. Ind. Elec. Control Instr.*, Vol. IECI-17, No. 6, pp. 415-421, Nov. 1970.

Werner, F.D., "The design of diaphragms for pressure gauges which use wire resistance strain gauges", *Society of Experimental Stress Analysis Proc.*, Vol. 11, No. 1, 1953.

8
FLOW

8.1 INTRODUCTION

Quantitative determination of flow rates and mass flow of gases and liquids is important in many fields of engineering, especially process control. The type of fluid and its properties are the major factors which dictate the method of measurement most suitable for the purpose.

In general, flow meters can be divided into mechanical and electrical types. In mechanical devices, the most common method followed for flow measurement is to place an obstruction in the flow pipe so as to produce a secondary effect such as the torque developed on vanes or the pressure difference across an orifice plate. The electrical potential developed in a coil by a liquid moving in a magnetic field, frequency of rotation of a turbine, change in velocity of sound in a moving fluid, and change in resistance of an element placed in the fluid path are some of the basic principles used in an electrical type of flow meter. It is possible to obtain an electrical output from the basic mechanical types also by employing electrical-transducing techniques to convert the secondary effect into a proportional electrical signal. Since the choice of measurement technique is dictated by the properties of the fluid in question, the details given in Table 8.1 can be followed as guidelines for proper selection.

8.2 CLASSIFICATION OF FLOW METERS

Flow measurements are classified under two headings: (i) quantity, and (ii) rate of flow. A quantity meter is defined as one in which the fluid passing through a primary element is accurately quantified in terms of the weight or volume of the fluid. Examples are the positive-displacement meters, reciprocating piston, nutating discs, etc. For gases, the conventional wet-gas meter is perhaps the best-known example.

By contrast, the rate-of-flow meter can be defined as one in which the fluid passes through the primary element in a continuous stream. The movement of the fluid has an effect on the primary element according to some physical load, known or unknown, and as a result, the quantity of flow per unit time is defined. In practice, the relationship between the flow rate and signal obtained is always an empirical one established for the type of device from experience and calibration. Examples include the orifice plate, turbine, and electromagnetic flow meters.

The three most important factors which form the basis for the type of device applicable, either for flow measurement or flow metering, are repeatability, reliability, and accuracy, in that order of priority. The term accuracy comprises of linearity, response, and calibration factors. Other important constraints are operational convenience, maintenance, and cost.

All flow-rate meters can be classified under the following types, depending upon the physical principles of operation as well as other characteristics:

1. Head-type flow meters based on differential pressure measurements: (a) orifice plate, (b) venturi tube, (c) flow nozzle, and (d) pitot tube.
2. Electromagnetic-flow meters
3. Rotameters (variable-area meters)
4. Mechanical-flow meters: (a) positive displacement, and (b) turbine
5. Anemometer
6. Ultrasonic-flow meter
7. Vortex-flow meters
8. Others.

Relative characteristics of the various types of flow meters are given in Table 8.1.

8.3 HEAD-TYPE FLOW METERS

The primary head-type of flow-metering devices have a common feature in that they produce a pressure difference (head difference) when a fluid flow is maintained through them. The differential pressure so obtained has an accurate relationship to the mean dynamic pressure within the conduit and hence to the square of the flow rate.

The head type of flow measurement follows from Bernoulli's theorem which states that in a fluid stream, the sum of the pressure head, velocity head, and elevation head at a point is equal to their sum at any other point removed in the direction of flow from the first point, plus the loss due to the friction between the two points.

Consider a flow tube of varying cross-sectional area and having a difference in level as shown in Fig. 8.1. An incompressible fluid of density ρ is assumed to be steadily flowing through the pipe, with its axis inclined above the datum line XY. Making use of the principle of conversion of energy, the work done on a mass of fluid, minus the work done by it is equal to its change in potential and kinetic energy. Applying this principle, the relationship for the fluid flow under equilibrium conditions can be expressed as

$$\frac{p_1}{\rho} + \frac{v_1^2}{2g} + h_1 = \frac{p_2}{\rho} + \frac{v_2^2}{2g} + h_2 = k \tag{8.1}$$

where p_1 = pressure per unit area at BD, p_2 = pressure per unit area at FH, v_1 = the fluid velocity (mean value) at BD, v_2 = the fluid velocity (mean value) at FH, ρ = fluid density, g = acceleration due to gravity, h_1 = height of centre of gravity of volume $BCED$ above datum line, h_2 = height of centre of gravity of volume $FGIH$, above datum line, and k = a

TABLE 8.1 COMPARISON OF FLOW METERS

Type of flowmeter	Fluid Application						Performance							Remarks
	Liquid non-corrosive	Liquid corrosive	Cryogenic	Slurry	Liquid viscous	Gas non-corrosive/corrosive	Range m^3/s	Rangeability	Linearity	Repeatability % F.S.	Accuracy % F.S.	Pressure loss	Immunity to viscosity effects	
Orifice	A	A	NA	L	L	A	1×10^{-7} to 5	4	S	0.1	2	High	Good	Low cost; not recommended for slurries.
Venturi	A	A	NA	L	L	A	-do-	5	S	0.1	2	Medium	-do-	High cost; handles suspended solids; good for large flows.
Flow nozzle	A	A	NA	L	L	A	-do-	4	S	0.1	2	-do-	-do-	Recommended for high pressure/temperature steam flow; limited to moderate pipe sizes.
Pitot tube	NA	NA	NA	NA	NA	A	—	5	S	0.05	1	Nil	Poor	Mostly for aerodynamic measurements.
Rotameters	A	A	A	L	A	A	1×10^{-7} to 0.1	5	0.1% F.S.	0.5	2	Low	-do-	Low cost; handles wide variety of corrosives; limited to small pipe sizes and capacities.
Electromagnetic	A	A	A	L	L	NA	5×10^{-2} to 5	10	0.2% F.S.	0.1	0.5	Nil	Good	Only for conductive fluids; high cost; large pipe sizes and capacities; available in several materials of construction.
Positive displacement	A	A	NA	NA	L	L	5×10^{-3} to 1	10	0.2% F.S.	0.1	0.5	Low	-do-	Good accuracy, especially for low flow rates; easy to install and maintain; moderate cost; limited pipe size.

Device													Remarks
Turbine meter	A	L	A	L	NA	5×10⁻³ to 1	15	0.2% F.S.	0.2	0.5	-do-	-do-	Excellent repeatability; limited range for viscous materials; easy to install and maintain.
Hot wire/Film Anemometer	NA	NA	NA	NA	L	—	4	S	0.02	0.2	Nil	Poor	Applicable for aerodynamic measurements and flow in water channels.
Ultrasonic	A	NA	A	NA	NA	5×10⁻³ to 1	25	0.5% F.S.	0.1	1	-do-	Good	Applicable to sonically conductive liquids
Vortex	A	A	NA	A	L	5×10⁻³ to 0.1	25	0.5% F.S.	0.1	0.5	Low	-do-	High cost; handles variety of chemicals, including slurries; good response speed; applicable for gas mass flow measurements

A—applicable NA—not applicable L—limited application S—square-root relationship

constant, all in appropriate units. If the level of the pipe line is the same at both ends, then Eq. (8.1) becomes

$$\frac{p_1}{\rho} + \frac{v_1^2}{2g} = \frac{p_2}{\rho} + \frac{v_2^2}{2g} \tag{8.2}$$

If the flow is continuous, then the quantity of fluid Q_v passing per second at BD must be equal to that at FH, or

$$Q_v = A_1 v_1 = A_2 v_2 \tag{8.3}$$

where A_1 and A_2 are areas of cross-section at the points BD and FH. Thus, if $A_1 \neq A_2$, there exists pressure differential. Equation (8.2) can be rewritten as

$$v_2^2 - v_1^2 = \frac{2g(p_1 - p_2)}{\rho} \tag{8.4}$$

From Eq. (8.3),

$$v_1 = \frac{A_2}{A_1} v_2 = m v_2 \tag{8.5}$$

where $m = A_2/A_1$. Substituting Eq. (8.5) in Eq. (8.4),

$$v_2^2(1 - m^2) = \frac{2g(p_1 - p_2)}{\rho} \tag{8.6}$$

or

$$v_2 = \frac{1}{\sqrt{(1 - m^2)}} \sqrt{\frac{2g(p_1 - p_2)}{\rho}} \tag{8.7}$$

Multiplying both sides by A_2,

$$A_2 v_2 = \frac{A_2}{\sqrt{1 - m^2}} \sqrt{\frac{2g(p_1 - p_2)}{\rho}} \tag{8.8}$$

From Eq. (8.3), $Q_v = A_2 v_2$. Hence,

$$Q_v = E A_2 \sqrt{\frac{2g(p_1 - p_2)}{\rho}} \tag{8.9}$$

where the velocity approach factor,

$$E = \frac{1}{\sqrt{1 - m^2}} \tag{8.10}$$

Equation (8.9) shows that the flow rate can be computed conveniently, by an accurate measurement of the differential pressure developed and knowing the other constants.

In case the flow tube is not parallel to the reference XY, as shown in Fig. 8.1, Eq. (8.9) would take the form

$$Q_v = E A_2 \sqrt{\frac{2g[(p_1 - p_2) + (h_1 - h_2)\rho]}{\rho}} \tag{8.11}$$

In Eq. (8.11) the term $(h_1 - h_2)$ represents the head. Representing the term $[(p_1 - p_2) + (h_1 - h_2)\rho]$ as p_d; Eq. (8.11) can be rewritten as

$$Q_v = E A_2 \sqrt{\frac{2g p_d}{\rho}} \tag{8.12}$$

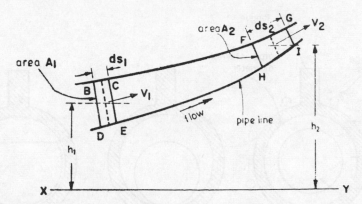

Fig. 8.1 Fluid flow through a varying cross-sectional area

With compressible fluids, such as gases and vapours, the density does not remain constant when the pressure changes from p_1 to p_2. An adiabatic gas expansion is considered to take place. Since the density changes with pressure, it must be specified at one particular pressure value, say at p_1. Equation (8.12) now becomes

$$Q_v = EA_2\phi \sqrt{\frac{2gp_d}{\rho_1}} \tag{8.13}$$

where ϕ is the expansion factor and ρ_1 is the density at pressure p_1.

On the basis of Eqs. (8.12) and (8.13), the main problem to be solved is to determine how the alteration of area can be made. In practice, such an alteration can be made abruptly as in the case of an orifice plate or gradually as in a venturi tube or nozzle.

8.3.1 Orifice Meter

The orifice meter is the most common type of head flow measuring device for medium and large-pipe sizes. The orifice plate inserted in a pipe line causes an increase in the flow velocity and a corresponding decrease in the pressure. The flow pattern shows an effective decrease in the cross-section of flow beyond the orifice plate with the maximum velocity and minimum pressure. The particular position where the velocity is maximum and static pressure is minimum is known as vena contracta.

The orifice plate inserted in the line is basically a thin plate of metal with a circular opening. The orifice configurations may be concentric, eccentric, or segmented, as shown in Fig. 8.2. The concentric type is by far the most widely used and will be described here in detail.

The concentric orifice plate consists of a central hole in a metal plate concentric with the circumference of the plate, as shown in Fig. 8.2(a). The effect of the orifice plate on the flow pattern in a pipe is shown in Fig. 8.3. Suppose that the manometer tubes are inserted along the pipe wall at the positions shown in the figure, then the liquid in these tubes will rise until the pressure due to column of liquid in each tube is equal to the static pressure at that position. Observing the different pressure values, the pattern of the pressure changes can be traced along the pipe length, as shown in Fig. 8.3. It may be noted that at the points 5 and

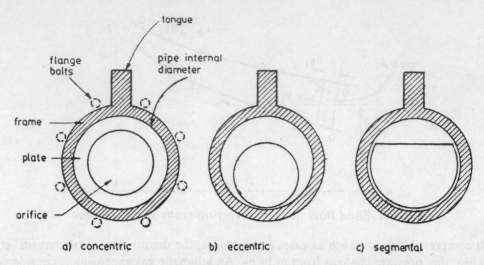

Fig. 8.2 Orifice plate configurations: (a) concentric; (b) eccentric;
(c) segmental

6 the pressure is lower than the upstream pressure, due to the increase in the velocity of the fluid passing through the smaller area. The stream or jet cross-section decreases in area after leaving the orifice until it reaches the point 7, where the pressure is minimum and the velocity is maximum. This is mainly due to the liquid being directed inward as it approaches the orifice and also due to inertia effects persisting in this direction for a distance after it leaves the orifice.

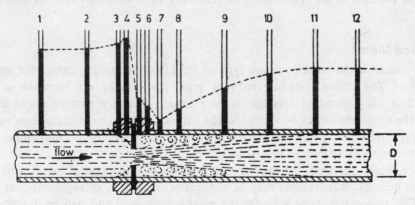

Fig. 8.3 Pressure profile in a pipe with orifice plate

Further, the static pressure also reaches its minimum value at the "vena contracta". The distance from the orifice to this position varies with the ratio of the orifice diameter to pipe diameter, but an average value would be half the pipe diameter. From the vena contracta, the stream section expands until it reaches the pipe diameter at the position 11 where it recovers to its upstream value. This would appear to be caused by the velocity change being accompanied by considerable turbulence with the resulting dissipation of energy involving a pressure loss. For a typical value of 0.6 for the orifice to the pipe diameter ratio, the percentage loss works out at 65% of the differential pressure. Where such a pressure loss is a critical consideration, this point should be borne in mind.

The pressure tappings for flow rate measurements can be taken out by a variety of methods. For pipe sizes of 0.05 m or greater in diameter, the usual practice is to locate tappings at distances D and $D/2$ in the upstream and downstream respectively, where D is the diameter of the pipe, as shown in Fig. 8.4.

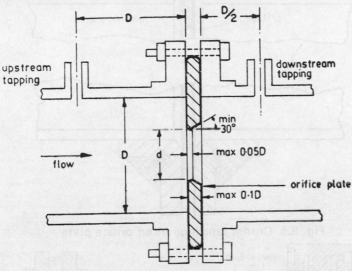

Fig. 8.4 Location of tappings near an orifice plate

Another type of tapping is the so-called corner tapping, where holes are cut obliquely through the flange or the pipe base bringing the inside openings of the holes adjacent to the orifice, as illustrated in Fig. 8.5. In this configuration, the discharge coefficient is less influenced by irregularities on the upstream side of the orifice than with the previous type. They can however present some difficulty in drilling if carried out on site.

In cases where it is not desirable to drill or tap the pipes, bosses, or flanges, a self-contained orifice assembly can be inserted between pipe flanges, as shown in Fig. 8.6(a). The assembly consists of a metal ring, holding the orifice plate with tappings drilled through the ring to communicate with the upstream and downstream sides of the orifice. The main advantages of this type are that the accuracy is maintained as obtained at the manufacturer's works itself and the discharge coefficient is less influenced by any irregularities. Figure 8.6(b) illustrates an alternative method of locating the taps in the orifice plate itself, wherein the tappings are drilled on each face of the plates directly.

Corrections for Friction and Velocity Distribution
Equation (8.11) cannot be applied directly to all the orifice plate configurations, as practical flow figures do not agree with the theoretical ones, due to friction and velocity distributions. Further, the stream area contracts after leaving the orifice to the vena contracta position. The cross-sectional area at the vena contracta may be about 0.6 of that of the orifice; since Eqs. (8.12) and (8.13) have been derived for the stream area, these equations must include

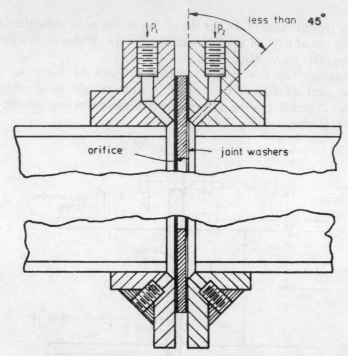

Fig. 8.5 Corner tappings in an orifice plate

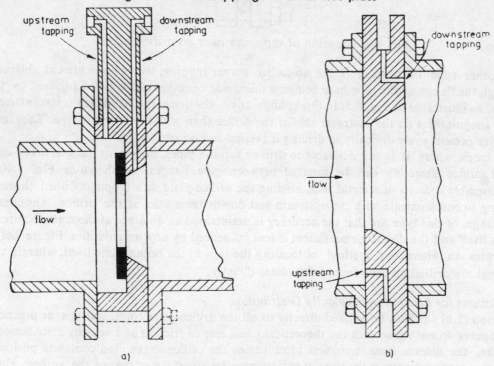

Fig. 8.6 Orifice plate assembly: (a) self-contained;
(b) with alternative locations for tappings

correction factors for friction and contraction effects. It is customary to incorporate these two effects into one constant known as the discharge coefficient c. The discharge coefficient varies with Reynold's number at the orifice and is obtained experimentally for each orifice. The calibration done for one fluid can be used for any other fluid, as long as their Reynold's numbers are the same. The variation of the discharge coefficient with Reynold's number has a typical trend as shown in Fig. 8.7. It may appear that each installation should be calibrated individually, but in practice this may not be required if the orifice is fabricated according to standard dimensions and pressure taps are located at specific points. Accurate values of discharge coefficients may be obtained from compiled tables and charts, for various values of pipe diameter, ratio of the orifice diameter to pipe diameter, and Reynold's number.

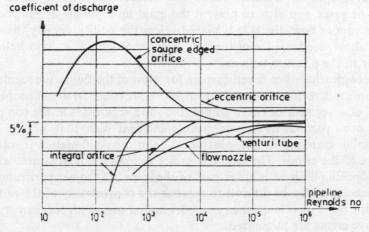

Fig. 8.7 Variations of discharge coefficients with Reynold's number

Taking the discharge coefficient into account, Eq. (8.12) becomes,

$$Q_v = cEA_2 \sqrt{\frac{2gp_d}{\rho}} \qquad (8.14)$$

Equation (8.14) can be written as

$$Q_v = 2.354 \times 10^{-3} cd^2 E \sqrt{\frac{p_d}{\rho}} \qquad (8.15)$$

where c is the discharge coefficient, d is the orifice diameter in meters, E is the velocity approach factor $(= 1/\sqrt{1-m^2})$, and p_d is the differential pressure in pascals and ρ is the density in kg/m³ at 288.7 K, and Q_v is in m³/s.

All liquids are viscous in nature, and the viscosity is a factor to be taken into account while calculating flow constants, particularly the discharge coefficient. As described earlier, the discharge coefficient varies with Reynold's number, the latter being a function of the viscosity of the fluid. Reynold's number, R_e is a dimensionless factor and is a useful criterion for comparing the flows in geometrically similar installations but with differing flow conditions. At very low values of R_e, viscous flow conditions predominate and inertial forces have little effect; the converse is true at high R_e values.

Construction of Orifice Plates

Some general rules relating to the construction of concentric orifice plates may be noted. First, the thickness of the orifice plate should be suitably chosen to prevent distortion by the differential pressure across it. The normal thickness employed is 0.0015 m for pipes up to 0.15 m diameter and 0.003 m for larger diameters. If the plate thickness exceeds 0.05 d, where d is the orifice diameter, the orifice bore is chamfered on the downstream side, as indicated in Fig. 8.4. Secondly, the upstream edge of the orifice must be quite sharp, and the bore should form a right angle with the face of the plate. Any alteration in this will affect the discharge coefficient. The orifice plates can be provided with identification tongues as indicated in Fig. 8.2. Thirdly, in the case of liquid flow, the orifice plate must have a small hole drilled in it, situated above the orifice opening, to allow the passage of trapped air or gases, and also, to prevent the build up of an air or gas pocket. In the case of air, gas or vapour flow, the hole is placed below the orifice, nearly flush with the pipe bottom, to allow condensed moisture to drain through. The drain hole must be located perpendicular to the pressure tapping.

While the concentric orifice is satisfactory for most of the fluids, the segment type or eccentric type of orifice is preferable when suspended solids (slurries) are encountered in the fluid. In the case of a segment or chord orifice, the solid segment is at the top part of the orifice plate and the open part has its circumference coincident with that of the pipe; hence the passage of solid material is not obstructed, and no solid matter is collected against the upstream face of the orifice. The eccentric orifice follows a similar course with the lower part of its orifice opening flush with lower part of the pipe. In some particular instances with concentric orifices, it may be difficult to arrange the concentricity of the orifice opening relative to the pipe bore, especially when $m = 0.7$ and above. With segment type and eccentric type, the above errors are minimized.

The materials used for orifice plates are mild steel, stainless steel, phosphor bronze, or gun metal, depending upon the application. A rough classification would be to use gun metal, bronze, or stainless steel for water metering, gun metal or mild steel for air metering, and stainless steel for steam, sewage, fuel oils, coal gas, and corrosive gases. The main advantages of an orifice meter are its simple construction and high reliability. The limitations are its poor accuracy, calibration which changes appreciably with wear, high pressure loss, and possible maintenance problems with blocked tapping. Since the pressure losses are high, the device is not recommended for high velocities.

It has been observed that the effect of inserting an orifice plate in a fluid stream causes an abrupt change in the stream area accompanied by a fairly high pressure loss. In cases where such pressure loss is not acceptable, it is preferable to use an element possessing a gradual stream area change, such as the venturi tube, which is described below.

8.3.2 Venturi Tube

The basic design of a venturi tube comprises three sections, viz., the converging conical section at the upstream, cylindrical throat, and the diverging recovery outlet cone at the downstream. Figure 8.8 illustrates a standard configuration of a venturi tube. The inlet cone tapers down from the pipe area to the throat section of a smaller area to produce the necessary increase in velocity and decrease in pressure. The cylindrical throat provides a point of measurement of this decrease in pressure where the flow rate is steady. The diverging outlet cone expands from the throat to the pipe area resulting in pressure recovery. Pressure measurements are carried out at the upstream entrance to the cone and at the throat. Tappings take the shape of annular chambers, and the inside surfaces are smoothly machined with holes drilled around the circumference at regular intervals. This enables the pressure to be averaged before transmission to the measuring instruments. The construction of the outlet cone is important. The pressure loss due to the turbulent eddies caused by the increasing diameter and due to the friction between the fluid and the wall of the cone, affects the measurement. The pressure loss due to turbulent eddies can be reduced by gradual expansion, while the frictional loss can be reduced by using a sharper cone. The result is a compromise between the two requirements. In practice, two conical angles of 5-7° and 14-15°, with pressure losses of 11 to 18% respectively are used, which is much lower than that of the orifice plate.

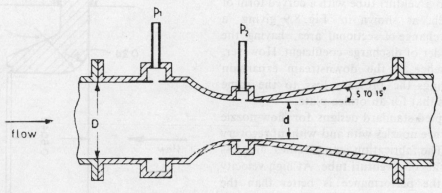

Fig. 8.8 Venturi tube

The discharge coefficient of a standard type of venturi tube is about 0.99, and this remains substantially constant for all values of throat-pipe diameter ratios between 0.25 and 0.75 ($m = 0.05$ to 0.55). In practice, the approach to the throat is given a curved profile by means of a lining, to maintain constant discharge coefficient.

The effect of a high discharge coefficient is apparent, if Eq. (8.15) is examined, which applies only to orifice plates, venturi tubes and nozzles. For the same flow in a given pipe, and with the throat diameter the same as that of an orifice, a much smaller pressure differential is needed resulting in a decrease in pressure loss. Alternatively, with the same pressure differential and throat diameter, a considerably larger flow is achieved than with an orifice. Equation (8.15) is also applicable for venturi-tube calculations, when the orifice diameter now becomes the throat diameter and m is the throat area ratio for determining the value of E in the equation. It would appear that the venturi tube seems to possess an immense advantage over the orifice plate. From a purely measurement point of view, this is probably correct, but its use is justified only when the orifice plate cannot be used. The dimensions of venturi tube are relatively large, and its cost is also high. Since the device is sufficiently resistant to abrasion, it is well suited for suspended fluids.

Constructional Features

The construction of the venturi tube is often dictated by its application. For normal uses, sections are made out of gun metal, stainless steel, and cast iron. The use of gun metal and stainless steel reduces the risk of corrosion. One advantage of the venturi tube is that the section need not be circular—square or rectangular shapes have also been used for many applications.

8.3.3 Flow Nozzles

The flow nozzle is a primary flow-metering device wherein a pressure difference is created during the flow. Flow nozzles combine the simplicity of the orifice plate with the low losses of the venturi tube, and hence are preferred in many applications. It approximates to a venturi tube with a curved form of approach, as shown in Fig. 8.9 giving a gradual change of sectional area, having the same order of discharge coefficient. However, the absence of the downstream expansion cone brings the pressure loss to the same order as that for an orifice plate.

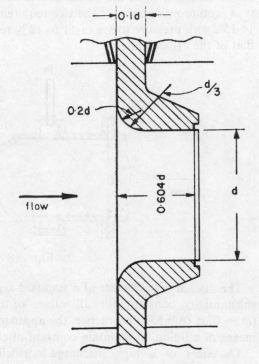

Accepted standard designs for flow-nozzle devices are nozzles with and without recovery cones. The fabrication complexities are less than that of a venturi tube. At high velocity flows, the performance is better than the orifice device. The curved profile of the nozzle renders its usefulness whenever fluids with suspended solid matter are encountered.

So far three main flow-determining elements, producing differential pressures by area changes have been discussed. A totally different system particularly convenient for airflow measurements is the pitot tube, which is described below.

Fig. 8.9 Flow nozzle

8.3.4 Pitot Tube

The pitot tube is one of the earliest devices developed for flow measurement. It consists of a cylindrical probe inserted into the fluid stream. In this device, the velocity head is converted into an impact pressure, and the difference between the static pressure and the impact pressure is a measure of the flow rate. Pitot tubes are widely used for air-speed measurements on board an aircraft.

Consider a blunt object placed in a fluid stream as an obstruction to the flow, as shown in Fig. 8.10. As the fluid approaches the object, the velocity will decrease until it reaches zero at the point where it impinges on it. A deceleration results in an increase in pressure, which follows from Bernoulli's theorem. From Eq. (8.2),

$$\frac{p_1}{\rho_1} + \frac{v_1^2}{2g} = \frac{p_2}{\rho_2} + \frac{v_2^2}{2g} \tag{8.16}$$

where p_1, v_1 and ρ_1 are the respective pressure, velocity, and density of the upstream from the object, and p_2, v_2 and ρ_2 are the respective pressure, velocity, and density in the neighbourhood of the object. At the point of impact, v_2 is zero. In other words, the kinetic energy has been converted into potential energy, and the result is reflected in the value of p_2 at the impact point. This new pressure, known as the total pressure, comprises the normal static pressure and the pressure component produced as a result of energy conversion.

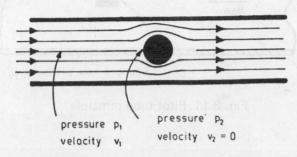

pressure p_1
velocity v_1

pressure p_2
velocity $v_2 = 0$

Fig. 8.10 Effect of a blunt object on a flow stream

For incompressible fluids, $\rho_1 = \rho_2 = \rho$. When $v_2 = 0$, Eq. (8.16) becomes,

$$\frac{p_1}{\rho} + \frac{v_1^2}{2g} = \frac{p_2}{\rho} \tag{8.17}$$

or

$$v_1 = \sqrt{\frac{2g(p_2 - p_1)}{\rho}} \tag{8.18}$$

Consider a case when the blunt object is replaced with a tube having a small opening, facing the direction of the fluid flow, connected to a differential pressure gauge as shown in Fig. 8.11. As there is no through flow in the tube, and since the flow is brought to rest, the new pressure developed and sensed is the impact pressure. This corresponds to p_2 in Eq. (8.17). A static pressure reading p_1 is taken upstream, a little away from the tube. By measuring the differential pressure $(p_2 - p_1)$, the velocity can be computed by knowing the density of the fluid.

However, it is very convenient to measure the static pressure in the close neighbourhood of the tube. A standard pitot tube consisting of an inner and outer concentric tube are designed for the purpose. The inner one connects the impact hole to one part of a differential pressure gauge, and the outer one referred to as the static tube, has a series of holes bored into it to sense the static pressure. Two typical models, one with a hemispherical head and the other with a sharp end are illustrated in Fig. 8.12. The essential drawback with the pitot tube is that it can measure velocity at only one position in the cross-section of the pipe. To

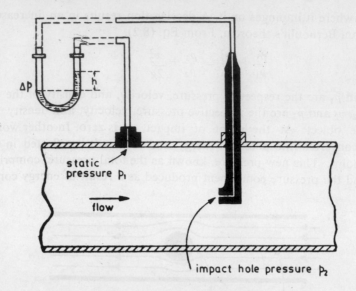

Fig. 8.11 Pitot tube principle

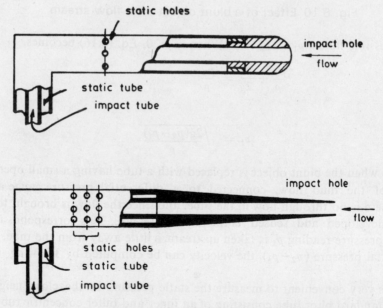

Fig. 8.12 Two types of pitot tube construction

find the mean velocity, it is necessary to traverse the tube along the diameter of the pipe, taking the differential pressure at certain specified positions. The pitot tube may be placed at the pipe, centre, and the instrument calibrated in terms of average velocity.

Expressed in appropriate units, the velocity can be computed from

$$v = 5.5748 \sqrt{\frac{p_d}{\rho}} \qquad (8.19)$$

where v = velocity of the fluid in m/s, p_d = the differential pressure produced in Pa at 288.7 K, and ρ = density of the fluid in kg/m³. For higher accuracy, compressibility effects should be taken into account, and the following formula can be employed

$$p_d = k_1 v^2 \rho (1 + k_2 v^2) \qquad (8.20)$$

where k_1 and k_2 are appropriate constants depending upon the design. The axis of the head may not be always aligned with flow direction, and hence the errors due to yaw may be present. The effect of yaw on standard pitot tubes is very small for any normal misalignment. At about 20° yaw, the error in velocity determination reaches 2%.

Any differential pressure instrument is suitable to use as a detecting element with the orifice, venturi tube, nozzle, or pitot tube. Even U-type manometers are popularly used in laboratory applications.

8.4 ROTAMETERS

A rotameter consists of a vertical tube with a tapered cone in which a float assumes a vertical position corresponding to each flow rate through the tube. The conical tube is made of glass, stainless steel, or monel, and the floats are made of brass, stainless steel, monel, or special plastics. The rotameters are sometimes referred as constant pressure drop, variable area or variable aperture meters.

The fundamental equation for an incompressible flow through a tube is, as derived earlier, given by

$$Q_v = cEA_2 \sqrt{\frac{2g p_d}{\rho}} \qquad (8.21)$$

Based on this equation, it has been so far assumed that the orifice area A_2 is fixed and the pressure difference p_d varies with flow rate Q_v, as in the case of the orifice, nozzle and venturi tube. In Eq. (8.21), if p_d is held constant, the orifice area A_2 is directly proportional to the flow rate Q_v when there is no restriction on the shape of the orifice. For example, we can have an annular pattern formed by the space between a solid disc and a conical pipe of variable diameter. The discharge coefficient c and the approach factor E may be appreciably different from the values

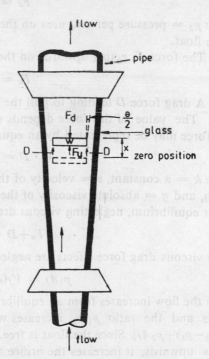

Fig. 8.13 Forces acting on a float in a rotameter

of concentric orifice. Developing the idea still further, consider a vertical tube of conical shape, the area gradually expanding from bottom to top. The fluid is allowed to flow in an upward direction in the tube. If a disc is placed which is free to move in the fluid path, it acts as a float in the fluid. An orifice is set up between the perimeter of the disc and the inside surface of the tube with a corresponding pressure drop, as shown in Fig. 8.13. Forces acting or either side of the disc keep it in equilibrium at a particular velocity. A change in flow rate will affect the pressure drop, altering the relation between the inlet and outlet pressure, thus upsetting the equilibrium of forces acting on the disc. The disc will then move up or down the tube, thereby creating variable area of the orifice (due to the conical shape of the tube) until the pressure drop is at the original value when the forces are again at equilibrium. The position of the float in the tube is then a measure of the rate of flow.

The variable area meter is analysed as follows. Consider the forces acting on the float in the vertical column of liquid, as shown in Fig. 8.13. These are:

(a) The effective weight W acting on the float,

$$W = V_f(\rho_2 - \rho_1) \tag{8.22}$$

where V_f = volume of the float, ρ_2 = material density of the float, and ρ_1 = density of the liquid.

(b) Force F_d acting in a downward direction on the upper surface of the float,

$$F_d = p_2 A_f \tag{8.23}$$

where p_2 = pressure per unit area on the upper surface of the float, and A_f = surface area of the float.

(c) The force F_u acting upwards on the lower surface of the float,

$$F_u = p_1 A_f \tag{8.24}$$

(d) A drag force D tending to pull the float in an upward direction (in the direction of flow). The value of this force depends on the float design and the conditions of fluid flow. This force may be represented by an equation of the form

$$D = kvl_f\eta \tag{8.25}$$

where k = a constant, v = velocity of the fluid, l_f = a dimensional function equivalent to length, and η = absolute viscosity of the fluid.
Under equilibrium, neglecting viscous drag effects,

$$F_u + D = W + F_d \tag{8.26}$$

If the viscous drag force effects are neglected, $D = 0$ and

$$p_1 A_f = V_f(\rho_2 - \rho_1) + p_2 A_f \tag{8.27}$$

When the flow increases from an equilibrium value, an increased differential pressure $(p_1 - p_2)$ results and the ratio p_1/p_2 increases which means that the force $p_1 A_f$ is now greater than $[V_f(\rho_2 - \rho_1) + p_2 A_f]$. Since the float is free, it will be moved in the direction of flow. As it moves upwards, it increases the orifice area due to the expanding sectional area of the tube and the pressure differential falls proportionately. The operation continues until $(p_1 - p_2)$ reaches its original value, when the forces as indicated in Eq. (8.27) are in equilibrium again. The new float position is the measure of the new flow rate. The operation is reversed when the flow rate decreases. From Eq. (8.27),

$$(p_1 - p_2) = \frac{V_f}{A_f}(\rho_2 - \rho_1) \tag{8.28}$$

Substituting this in Eq. (8.21),

$$Q_v = cEA_2 \sqrt{2g\frac{V_f}{A_f}\left(\frac{\rho_2 - \rho_1}{\rho_1}\right)} \tag{8.29}$$

where A_2 is the gap area between the float and the tube. If the displacement of the float is x and the cone angle is θ,

$$d_x = d_i\left(1 + \frac{2x}{d_i}\tan\frac{\theta}{2}\right) \tag{8.30}$$

where d_x = tube diameter at a distance x from the inlet of the tube, and d_i = diameter of the float.
Equation (8.29) can be rewritten as

$$Q_v = KcxE \sqrt{2g\frac{V_f}{A_f}\left(\frac{\rho_2 - \rho_1}{\rho_1}\right)} \tag{8.31}$$

where $K = \frac{A_2}{x}$, is a proportionality constant.

In rotameters, the velocity approach factor E is of no significance. Hence,

$$Q_v = Kcx \sqrt{2g\frac{V_f}{A_f}\left(\frac{\rho_2 - \rho_1}{\rho_1}\right)} \tag{8.32}$$

If it is desired to obtain the mass flow Q_m in gravimetric units (kg/s) instead of volume flow, Eq. (8.32) can be rewritten as

$$Q_m = Kcx\rho_1 \sqrt{2g\frac{V_f}{A_f}\left(\frac{\rho_2 - \rho_1}{\rho_1}\right)} \tag{8.33}$$

Compensation for Density Variations
In a fluid-flow system, the density of a fluid can vary with a change in temperature, and can introduce some errors in the measurement, since the equilibrium force W (Eq. (8.22)) is a function of fluid density.

The equilibrium position of the float will be upset, and it will change to a new position corresponding to the new value of W.

To minimize the errors, the change in the rate of flow with density should be minimum. It can be expressed mathematically as

$$\frac{dQ_v}{d\rho_1} = 0 \tag{8.34}$$

or

$$\frac{dQ_m}{d\rho_1} = 0 \tag{8.35}$$

Differentiating Eq. (8.32) with respect to ρ_1 and equating the result to zero, the necessary condition obtained is that for complete immunity from density change, the density of the float ρ_2 must be infinite. In practice, the density of the float is chosen to be much larger than that of the fluid, to reduce these errors to reasonable proportions.

Differentiating Eq. (8.33) with respect to ρ_1 and equating the result to zero, the following condition may be obtained

$$\rho_2 = 2\rho_1 \tag{8.36}$$

For liquids, this condition is achieved practically by making the body of the float either hollow or with solid plastic material. Usually, 10% density variations from a mean value does not introduce any significant errors into the flow measurement. From the above, it is apparent that two separate density correction requirements arise, one for volume and the other for mass flow rates.

Viscous Flow

At low flow rates, laminar or viscous flow conditions can exist. The force of viscous drag must now be taken into account, since this is a function of length l_f of the float along the direction of flow and viscosity η of the fluid.

Theoretical equations explaining the action of rotameters under viscous-flow conditions can be written as[1]

$$Q_v = \frac{V_f g(\rho_2 - \rho_1)(D_x - D_f)^3(D_x + D_f)}{24(D_x^2 + D_f^2)l_f \eta} \tag{8.37}$$

and

$$Q_m = Q_v \rho_1 \tag{8.38}$$

where D_x is the inner diameter of the rotameter tube at a distance x from the inlet point and D_f is the diameter of the float.

From the above equations, it may be noted that the flow rate under viscous flow conditions is dependent on the value of η, the viscosity of the fluid, in addition to the density ρ_1. For minimum error, it is equally important to render the instrument immune from viscosity changes. In other words, the effect of the drag force D should be reduced to a minimum. Since this is dependent on the effective length l_f of the float, the reduction of this length should result in reducing the effect of viscosity. This can be achieved by a suitable design of the float, as shown in Fig. 8.14(a) and (b). In either case, the effective orifice part of the float has been reduced due to the sharp-edged disc, i.e. with minimum length along the direction of flow. A further improvement in the design of float can be achieved by having the "body" away in a position above the float out of the main flow stream.

The rotameter is an inexpensive flow meter for gas and liquid flow in the range of 0.1×10^{-8} to 0.1 m³/s for a wide range of liquids. The pressure drop across the meter is essentially constant over the full operating range, with accuracies achievable from 0.5 to 3% F.S. The device tends to be self-cleaning, even if the liquid is contaminated, and it is relatively insensitive to viscosity changes with an appropriate design. Considering these advantages, it finds wide applications in the laboratory, testing, and production lines. The device can be easily integrated for instrumentation with alarms, indicators, controllers, and recorders.

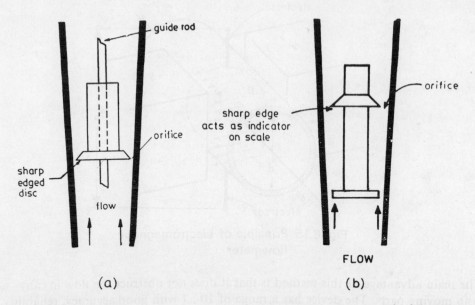

FLOW

(a)   (b)

Fig. 8.14 Rotameter principle: (a) sharp-edge configuration; (b) alternative arrangement

8.5 ELECTROMAGNETIC FLOW METERS

The operation of this type of flow meters are based on Faraday's law of electromagnetic induction. The law states that the relative motion of a medium flowing at right angles to a pair of electrodes and a magnetic field will develop an emf across the electrodes. In this device, the fluid itself should be conductive and should have a minimum conductivity value of the order of 10^{-3} ohm^{-1} m^{-1}. A schematic arrangement of this type of flow meter is given in Fig. 8.15. The flow tube lies in a magnetic field of uniform flux density B. Two electrodes are inserted in the tube, their surfaces being flush with the inner surface of the tube and in contact with the liquids. As the conductive liquid flows through the insulated tube with an average velocity (over the cross-section of the tube) v, it may be considered as a series of flat conductor discs passing through the magnetic field, inducing an emf e across the electrodes. This may be expressed by the relation,

$$e = Bdv \times 10^{-8} \text{ V} \tag{8.39}$$

where e is the induced voltage, B is the flux density in tesla, d is the distance between the electrodes in m, and v is the average velocity of the liquid expressed in m/s. The voltage is generated in a direction mutually perpendicular to both the velocity plane of the conducting liquid and the plane of the magnetic field independent of Reynold's number, viscosity, and density of the liquid. This value, multiplied by the cross-sectional area of the pipe gives the volume flow rate. In principle, both dc and ac magnetic fields can be used, but dc method has the danger of electrolytic polarisation at the electrodes. The magnetic field is usually of the order of 75×10^4 ampere/m, and flow rates as low as 10^{-6} m/s can be measured.

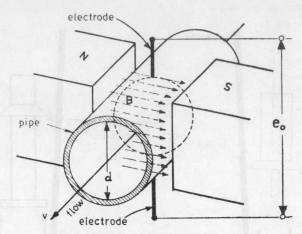

Fig. 8.15 Principle of electromagnetic
flowmeter

The main advantage of this method is that it does not obstruct the flow in any way and
has no moving parts. The device has a range of 10 : 1 with good accuracy, reliability, simplicity, and ruggedness. Its response is fast and is independent of the properties of the fluid
except for the electrical conductivity. The only condition is that the pipe should always be
full. The output signal is usually in the microvolt level and needs large amplification. The
device is ideal for bidirectional measurements and is especially suited for slurries, and
corrosive and solid contaminated liquids. The device tends to be expensive, especially for
smaller pipe sizes.

8.6 MECHANICAL FLOW METERS

Mechanical flow meters rely on the flow to induce a mechanical motion of elements within
the flow path. The magnitude of the motion is taken as a measure of the flow volume or
flow rate. Numerous designs have been evolved, and two of the most popular configurations
are the positive displacement meters and turbine meters.

8.6.1 Positive-Displacement Meters

Positive-displacement flow meters are primarily designed as quantity meters for the measurement of volume flow, incorporating pistons, sliding vanes, or meshing elements. They all
constrain the flow path, preventing leakage past the moving elements and the body of the
flow meter. The meters are self-powered and drive mechanical counters. The upstream flow
conditions are of no importance, and these can be used for viscous fluids. One of the most
popular types is the rotary piston meter which has a large flow range (50 : 1), long life, low
frictional loss, and an accuracy of 1% of the reading. Being a precision device, the cost is
high. Also, the fluid should be clean. The pressure drop in the meter is high.

8.6.2 Turbine-Type Flow Meter

The turbine-type flow meter derives its name from the operating principle used, and is perhaps the most highly developed non-friction displacement-type of mechanical flow meter. When an axially-mounted freely rotating turbine wheel (rotor) is placed in the path of a fluid stream, the flowing fluid impinging on the turbine blades imparts a force on the blade surfaces and sets the rotor in motion with an angular velocity proportional to the fluid velocity as a function of the blade angle. When a steady rotational speed is reached, the rotary speed attained is proportional to the volumetric flow rate of the fluid. By minimizing the bearing friction and other losses, the device can be so designed as to produce a linear output.

The rotor with multiple blades, mounted across the axis of the flowing fluid, is supported by ball or sleeve bearings on a shaft which is retained in the flow-meter housing by a shaft support section. Flow straighteners (straightening vanes) are added before the device to obtain laminar flow. The rotor speed is measured with a mechanical counter or with an electromagnetic pickup and associated counter. The instantaneous frequency is a measure of the flow rate, and the total number of pulses over a period of time is a measure of the total flow.

The theory of operation of the turbine transmitter is extremely complex, if a full analysis under all flow conditions is required, but for operation under laminar flow conditions, the analysis is simple, and is given below.

The turbine may be considered as a screw which is rotated by the fluid flow. Referring to Fig. 8.16, the pitch of the blade P may be written as

$$P = \frac{\pi D}{\tan \alpha} \tag{8.40}$$

where D = outer diameter of the turbine, and α = tip-blade angle.

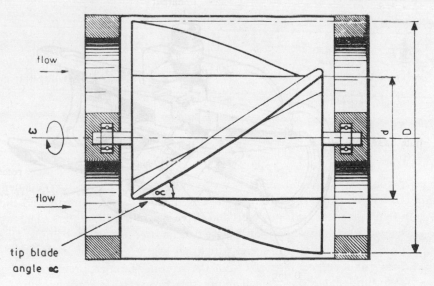

Fig. 8.16 Principle of turbine type flowmeter

The velocity v of the fluid is given by

$$v = \frac{Q_v}{A} \qquad (8.41)$$

where Q_v = volumetric flow rate, and $\qquad A$ = annular area through which fuel flows

$$= \frac{\pi}{4}(D^2 - d^2) \text{ where } d \text{ is the hub diameter.}$$

The turbine will complete one revolution as the fluid stream moves through a distance equal to the blade pitch. The rotational velocity ω is given by

$$\omega = \frac{v}{P} \qquad (8.42)$$

Substituting Eqs. (8.40) and (8.41) in Eq. (8.42), we get

$$\omega = \frac{4Q_v \tan \alpha}{\pi^2 D(D^2 - d^2)}$$

or

$$Q_v = \frac{\pi^2 D(D^2 - d^2)}{4 \tan \alpha} \omega \qquad (8.43)$$

This expression can be used to estimate the flow rates to accuracies better than $\pm 2\%$ F.S. The flowmeter consists of a tubular pipe section of light alloy within which a three-blade rotor of magnetic stainless steel is concentrically mounted, as shown in Fig. 8.17. The rotor revolves freely in two miniature stainless steel ball bearings housed in identical hub assemblies. In a typical design four electrical pick-off coils with their associated soft iron pole

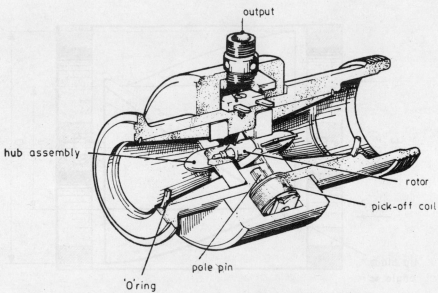

Fig. 8.17 Construction of turbine type flowmeter

pieces and a permanent magnet are mounted around the periphery of the pipe section and in the same plane as the rotor, although only one is shown in the figure. As the rotor revolves, the reluctance of the magnetic circuit is changed and a sinusoidal signal is induced, the frequency of which is equal to the speed of rotation of the rotor multiplied by the number of blades. Typical frequencies of the order of 1 kHz are obtained for full scale flow rates in these devices.

The linearity of the turbine-type flow meters is generally very good, and a value of $\pm$ 0.25% F.S. can be normally obtained. From run to run, excellent repeatabilities, better than 0.1% F.S., can be obtained as long as the maximum flow rate does not exceed a set value, and the bearings have not been disturbed. Calibration gets affected due to variations in viscosity at low flow rates, but this can be compensated, if required. Calibration can also change due to changes in fluid temperature. The pressure drop of the turbine-type flow meters will depend on the diameter of the turbine and the dimensions of the diverging outlet section provided to aid pressure recovery. This drop is normally low, and as such the device is suitable for low-pressure lines also. The dynamic response of the device is good and can be approximated to a first order system with a typical time constant of about 10 m.s. Full-scale flow rates from 0.01×10^{-4} to 1.2 m³/s can be obtained with liquids and gases. The most serious disadvantage of these meters is their susceptibility to damage with particles suspended in the fluid, and any damage to the blade requires recalibration. Also, there should be at least a 15-diameter length straight pipe upstream to the meter, to obtain the required flow pattern. These are expensive and useful for fluids in a limited viscosity range.

8.7 ANEMOMETERS

Anemometers are basically velocity-measuring devices for obtaining the velocity of a fluid stream, such as air flow in a ventilating duct or wind tunnel or water flow in a closed channel, or the wind speed as in meteorology. The design is based on a simple mechanical system as in cup anemometers or on heat-transfer principles as in hot-wire anemometers.

8.7.1 Cup-Type Anemometer

Cup anemometers consist of a vertical spindle rotating freely about the vertical axis mounted on bearings. The spindle is coupled to three equally-spaced horizontal arms. A hemispherically-shaped cup is mounted at the end of each arm with the meridian plane vertical. When placed in an airstream, a difference of pressure is set up between the concave and convex sides of the cups, resulting in a rotational torque at the vertical spindle. The spindle is coupled to a mechanical or electrical counter, calibrated in units of velocity, i.e. in m/s. The readings on the counter integrated over a specified period gives an indication of the wind speed. In the electrical type, the pickup may be a magnetic or capacitive device. Velocities up to 3000 m/s can be measured by this device. Owing to frictional losses, the device is not very accurate and needs calibration periodically.

8.7.2 Hot-Wire/Hot-Film Anemometer

The measurement of mean velocity and velocity fluctuations are important in aerodynamic research and allied fields. On account of high-frequency response requirements, hot-wire hot-film anemometers are able to give the most satisfactory results for fluid-flow measurement; the fluid can even be gases at high speeds or non-conductive liquids at low speeds. Latest devices involve laser techniques also for the purpose.

A hot-wire anemometer consists of a small length of very fine-heated metal wire supported on a probe, as shown in Fig. 8.18, which is exposed to the fluid flow whose velocity is to be measured. The wire is heated by the passage of current through it. When the device is exposed to the flow of the fluid (usually air), heat is dissipated by the wire through convection, in addition to other losses due to radiation and conduction along the wire supports, thus causing a drop in temperature, and consequently, a diminishing change in resistance. The wire attains an equilibrium temperature when I^2R heat generated in it is just balanced by the heat loss from its surface. The wire can be operated in constant current or constant temperature modes. For flow and turbulence measurements, wires of 2 to 5 microns dia., length 2 to 5 mm and resistance 2 to 5 ohms are used. The usual materials are platinum, platinum-iridium or tungsten. In the first mode, the change in resistance needed to attain equilibrium is a measure of the velocity; in the second type, the change in current required to bring the wire to the initial temperature becomes a measure of the flow velocity.

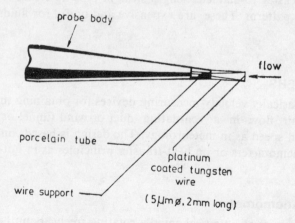

Fig. 8.18 Hot-wire anemometer probe

The anemometer electrical-output signal is related to the rate of heat loss from the probe, which is a scalar quantity, while the information required is normally the instantaneous velocity, which is a vector quantity. Therefore, not only does the anemometer require careful calibration for a specific set of flow conditions, but can also involve special considerations for meaningful interpretation of the measurements in terms of the required properties. It is possible to calculate a theoretical calibration curve for a hot-wire anemometer, once the geometry and material properties of the probe and properties of the flow are known. From a practical point of view, it is far simpler to calibrate a given probe in a known flow, as this involves fewer uncertainties. For example, the resistivity and temperature coefficient of resistivity of a set of short samples taken from a length of a very uniform wire can each vary by as much as 10% from the average value.

However, by understanding the details of the heat-transfer process, calibration procedures can be simplified. A rigorous analysis of the hot wire anemometer is beyond the scope of the book, as it involves a multidisciplinary approach. However, an analysis of the constant temperature operating hot wire anemometer is presented below, considering its many advantages.

Practical Anemometer Cooling Laws

The heat loss occurring from the heated wire comprises the convective loss due to the flow and the conductive loss due to the supports. In normal constant temperature operation, the probe resistance is maintained substantially constant. The probe forms one arm of a Wheatstone bridge which is automatically balanced by an appropriate feedback amplifier. The heat supplied to the wire is proportional to E^2, where E is the input voltage to the bridge circuit of the anemometer. If the input voltage corresponding to zero flow is E_0, the heat lost due to forced convection can be expressed as a function of $(E^2 - E_0^2)$.

One satisfactory practical correlation between the flow velocity u and convective heat loss can be expressed by King's empirical law

$$(E^2 - E_0^2) = Ku^n \tag{8.44}$$

where the constant K and index n are both functions of the flow speed. The numerical value of K depends on the probe-operating resistance and flow temperature. The index n is almost independent of modest changes in probe geometry. Above a particular lower velocity limit, typically 1 m/s, and for a practical range of aspect ratio $150 < l/d < 450$, where l and d are the length and diameter of the probe, it can be shown that

$$E^2 - E_0^2 = K_1 K_2 u^n \tag{8.45}$$

where K_1 is an experimentally determined constant which varies from probe to probe and takes account of flow temperature, resistivity, and geometrical changes of the probe wire, and K_2 is a universal constant with fixed geometry. The above relations hold good for flow normal to the probe wire. When the probe is yawed at some angle to the flow, the readings are to be corrected. The interpretation of the change in the output voltage in terms of the flow velocity u is exhaustively treated in text-books on fluid mechanics and heat transfer[2,3].

Constant Temperature Anemometer

A general arrangement of the hot-wire anemometer system in constant temperature operation is illustrated in Fig. 8.19. The amplifier used for the purpose has a gain K and has the following ideal static behaviour.

$$E_o = K(E_i + E_{qi}) \tag{8.46a}$$

where E_{qi} is any offset voltage present at the input to the amplifier. The output current from the amplifier will then be

$$I_o = K(E_i + E_{qi})/R_T \tag{8.46b}$$

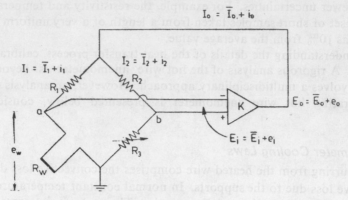

Fig. 8.19 Schematic of constant temperature hot-wire
anemometer bridge

where R_T is the static resistance of the bridge.

The current I_1 which passes through the hotwire can be expressed in terms of I_0 as

$$I_1 = \frac{I_0(R_2+R_3)}{\sum R} \tag{8.46c}$$

where

$$\sum R = R_1+R_2+R_3+R_w$$

R_1, R_2 and R_3 are fixed resistances and R_w is the resistance of the heated wire. The input
voltage E_i to the amplifier is given by

$$E_i = I_1R_1-I_2R_2 \tag{8.46d}$$

$$= \frac{-I_0R_x}{\sum R}$$

where

$$R_x^2 = R_wR_2-R_1R_3$$

Combining Eqs. (8.46 b), (c) and (d),

$$I_1 = \frac{K.E_{qi}(R_2+R_3)}{(R_1+R_w)(R_2+R_3)+KR_x^2} \tag{8.47}$$

The static behaviour of the hotwire element is described by the balance equation

$$I_1^2R_w = f(u)(R_w-R_g) \tag{8.48}$$

where R_g is the resistance of the probe wire at the ambient temperature and $f(u)$ is a function of fluid flow velocity u. Equation 8.47 also shows that an input offset voltage E_{qi} is
essential to start the operation of the bridge.

The operation of the bridge can be analysed as follows. The probe wire is assumed to
have a resistance R_g at ambient room temperature when there is a static current I_1 flowing
through it and the wire is exposed to a steady velocity $\overline{U}$. The static current I is obtained
through the initial offset voltage E_{qi} at the input of the amplifier. Under this condition the
bridge is balanced. With perturbations in flow velocity u', the wire resistance changes to R_w
whose magnitude depends upon the flow-changes and the current changes in the wire. This

change in resistance causes a bridge unbalance which is amplified by the amplifier and fed back to the bridge with proper sign. The change in bridge excitation so obtained tries to balance the bridge by producing appropriate current changes through the wire. The change in output voltage required to balance the bridge is a measure of the velocity perturbation u'. Thus at the balance point

$$E_t \simeq 0 \text{ and } R_x \simeq 0 \qquad (8.49)$$

As indicated in Fig. 8.19, all the variables expressed in small letters (such as e_o etc.) represent the perturbation values of the static quantities denoted by capital letters with a bar (such as $\bar{E}_o$ etc.), and the capital letters (such as E_o, etc.) indicate the instantaneous values.

The voltage perturbation e_w, across the wire due to a velocity perturbation u' and a current perturbation i is given by

$$e_w = u' \left.\frac{\partial E_w}{\partial U}\right|_{i_1 = 0} + i_1 \left.\frac{\partial E_w}{\partial I_t}\right|_{u' = 0} \qquad (8.50)$$

where $E_w = I_1 R_w$. The second term in Eq. (8.50) represents the effect of current changes generated by the feedback system attempting to maintain the bridge in balance condition (i.e. constant resistance of the wire and hence constant temperature) R_1, R_2, and R_3 are assumed to be constant.

The equilibrium relation for resistance-changes is obtained from the energy balance condition given by Eq. (8.48). To this equation an additional term should also be added to allow for heat accumulation in the wire. Hence Eq. (8.48) gets modified to the form

$$I_1^2 R_w = f(u)(R_w - R_g) + C\frac{dR_w}{dt} \qquad (8.51)$$

where C is the thermal capacity of the wire. The wire sensitivity to current perturbations when the velocity U is constant may be written as

$$\left.\frac{\partial E_w}{\partial I_1}\right|_{u' = 0} = Z_w \qquad (8.52)$$

From Fig. 8.19, the following equations may be formulated

$$e_o = i_1 R_1 + e_w$$
$$e_o = i_2(R_2 + R_3)$$
$$e_t = i_1 R_1 - i_2 R_2$$
$$i_o = i_1 + i_2$$

Using the above equations, and assuming

$$f(u) = p + q\sqrt{u} \qquad (8.53)$$

where p and q are constants depending upon the wire and fluid properties, determined experimentally, the output voltage e_o may be expressed as

$$e_o = i_1 \left(R_1 + \bar{R}_w + sL_w + \frac{\alpha}{\tau s + 1} \right) \qquad (8.54)$$

where $\alpha = \dfrac{2\bar{R}_w(R_w - R_g)}{R_g}$, $\tau = \dfrac{C(R_w - R_g)}{I_1^2 R_g}$, $L_w =$ inductance of the probe wire, and

$s =$ Laplace operator.

The complete closed-loop transfer function of the system can be expressed as[4]

$$\frac{e_o}{u'} = \frac{K_1}{\left(\frac{s}{\omega_n}\right)^2 + \frac{2\xi}{\omega_n}s + 1} \tag{8.55}$$

where

$$K_1 = \frac{q(R_w - R_g)^2}{2\sqrt{u}\,R_g I_1}\quad\frac{KR_1(R_2+R_3)}{[(R_2+R_3)(R_1\bar{R}_w+\alpha)+K(R_x+R_2\alpha)]} \tag{8.56}$$

$$\omega_n = \sqrt{\frac{(R_2+R_3)(R_1+R_w+\alpha)+K(R_x+R_2\alpha)}{(R_2+R_3)L_w\tau+KR_2L_w\tau}} \tag{8.57}$$

$$\frac{2\xi}{\omega_n} = \frac{(R_1+R_w)(R_2+R_3)\tau+(R_2+R_3)L_w+K(R\tau+R_2L_w)}{(R_2+R_3)(R_1+R_w+\alpha)+K(R_x+R_2\alpha)} \tag{8.58}$$

It may be noted from the above analysis that the frequency response can be improved by having a higher loop gain. If the self-inductance of the probe is negligible, then the response becomes a first-order type with a time constant, depending upon the selected overheat ratio $\bar{R}_w/R_g$ and the loop gain. For the given wire dimensions and selected overheat ratio, the time constant of the wire can be made as low as possible subject to the stability limitation.

It was shown that the response of the anemometer is non-linear with respect to flow. Hence the anemometer outputs are linearized using electronic linearizers which are discussed in Chapter 13.

Another version of the hot-wire anemometer is the hot film transducer. Here, the sensor is a thin film of platinum deposited on a glass or quartz substrate. The film takes the place of the hot wire, and the required circuitry remains basically the same. The film transducers possess great mechanical strength and can also be used at very high temperatures, using adequate cooling arrangements. An important application of this device is in the measurement of the propagation velocity of the shock in shock-tube experiments.

An important feature of the hot-wire/hot-film anemometers is the directional sensitivity of the probe, being maximum at right angles to the flow. In the angle $45° < \theta < 135°$, the effective velocity $u_{rms} = u\sin\theta$. This property can be directly utilized in flow-direction measurements in steady-flow conditions by rotating the probe until a sharply-defined null is obtained.

The frequency response of the overall system in the constant-temperature operation depends upon the amplifier gain, overheat ratio, and the basic time constant of the hot-wire element. In a typical case, an amplifier having a gain in the range 150 to 5000 gives a frequency response of 400 kHz with an overheat ratio of $1:1$, and 150 kHz when the overheat ratio is $1:20$. The hot-wire probes are mainly used for flow measurements in gases with flow rates up to 500 m/s and in non-conducting liquids with flow rates up to 5 m/s. On the other hand, hot-film probes are used for measurements in liquids for flow-rates up to 25 m/s, and these have a frequency response extending up to about 150 kHz.

8.8 ULTRASONIC FLOW METERS

Ultrasonic flow meters use two distinct measurement principles, viz., Doppler frequency shift and transit time.

In the Doppler method, an ultrasonic transducer is bonded to a pipe wall to transmit an ultrasonic signal into the flow. Particles suspended in the fluid impart a frequency shift proportional to the particle velocity, which can be measured with a suitable electronic counter. The transducers are basically piezoelectric crystals with a heavy backing to attenuate the unwanted rear movement. The fundamental frequency is determined by the thickness of the crystal. Probes of different frequencies are used for different groups of fluids, the normal values being in the range of 0.2 to 5 MHz.

In the transit time flow meter, an ultrasonic transducer is mounted at an angle or parallel to the pipe wall. When ultrasonic waves pulsed for a very short duration are transmitted across the fluid, the velocity of the ultrasonic waves is increased or decreased by the fluid velocity depending upon the direction of the fluid flow. A schematic diagram of such a device is shown in Fig. 8.20. A and B are piezoelectric devices transmitting the short duration ultrasonic signals through the fluid that is flowing through the pipe at a velocity v. Similar type of crystals are used as receivers to respond to the pressure fluctuations.

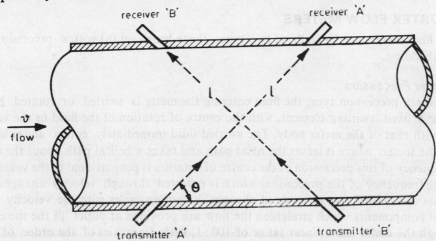

Fig. 8.20 Schematic arrangement of ultrasonic flow meter

Due to the fluid velocity v aiding the transmission, the velocity of the ultrasonic signal from the transmitter A to the receiver A is increased to a value $c + v \cos \theta$, where c is the velocity of sound through the fluid in the pipe, and θ is the angle between the path of sound and the pipe wall. The repetition frequency of the received pulse f_A will be

$$f_A = \frac{c + v \cos \theta}{l} \qquad (8.59)$$

where l is the distance between the transmitter and receiver. On the other hand, the velocity of the ultrasonic signal transmitted by the transmitter B and received by the receiver B will be reduced by the fluid velocity causing a retardation of $v \cos \theta$, and its pulse repetition frequency f_B will be

$$f_B = \frac{c - v \cos \theta}{l} \qquad (8.60)$$

The difference in frequency is given by

$$\Delta f = f_A - f_B = \frac{2v \cos \theta}{l} \qquad (8.61)$$

Expressing in terms of time duration, $\varDelta T = \dfrac{l}{2v \cos \theta}$, where $\varDelta T = \dfrac{1}{\varDelta f}$. Since the measurement is independent of the velocity of sound c through the fluid, the effects of pressure and temperature are avoided. By measuring the difference in the repetition frequency $\varDelta f$, and knowing the values of θ and l, the velocity of the fluid can be computed. Such a system is termed as a leading-edge meter. Alternatively, the flow velocity can be computed by measuring the time difference between the two pulse trains in either direction.

Ultrasonic flow meters are used mostly for liquids without any pressure loss. The measurement is insensitive to viscosity, pressure, and temperature variations. The other advantages are bidirectional measuring capability, good accuracy, fast response, wide frequency range, and its versatility in that it can be used for any pipe size; but the cost is relatively high.

8.9 VORTEX FLOW METERS

Vortex flow meters are basically of two types, those based on (a) vortex precession and (b) vortex shedding.

(a) Vortex Precession

In the vortex precession type, the fluid entering the meter is swirled or rotated by passing through a fixed swirling element, with the centre of rotation of the fluid or the vortex coinciding with that of the meter body. The swirled fluid immediately enters an enlarged area within the meter, where it leaves the axial path and takes a helical path about the centre line. The frequency of this precession of the centre of rotation is proportional to the volumetric flow rate. The frequency of the precession, which is reflected through velocity changes is sensed by means of a thermistor, in terms of changes in cooling cycles with the velocity variations. De-swirl components which straighten the flow are provided at outlet of the meter.

Though the meter has a linear range of $100:1$, with linearities of the order of $\pm 1\%$ of the reading, pressure and temperature variations necessitate constant corrections of the output. The pressure loss is typically twice the mean dynamic pressure in the pipe, which is somewhat better than most orifice devices. The minimum linear flow limit is determined by viscosity and occurs at a Reynolds number of 10^4, whereas the maximum linear limit is dictated by the compressibility effects as indicated by the flow Mach number. The main advantages are that it has no moving parts, sufficiently good linearity and repeatability, and is useful over wide temperature ranges.

(b) Vortex Shedding

Vortex shedding is the name given to a natural effect that occurs when a gas or liquid flows around a blunt or non-streamlined object. The flow, unable to follow the shape on the downstream side of the object, separates from the surface of the object, leaving a highly turbulent wake that takes the form of a continuous series of eddies that are being swept downstream. Each eddy or vortex first grows and then becomes detached or shed from the object; this phenomenon is called vortex shedding. This type of vortex shedding can be seen around and behind a rock in the bed of a water stream, or in the fluttering of a flag in the wake generated by the wind and the flagpole.

In this flow meter the vortex-generating object, which should be correctly shaped, is placed in a pipe line with correct relative dimensions. It gives pulse signals over wide flow ranges at a frequency proportional to the approaching fluid's volumetric flow rate. Triangular-shaped vortex-generating objects are found to give highly reproducible frequencies with various flow rates. The approaching flow separates from the flow element, and the vortices form and shed alternatively on either side of the triangular shape as shown in Fig. 8.21. As the flow rate increases, the speed with which each vortex forms and sheds increases at the same rate. Thermistors are employed to sense the vortices which detect the velocity fluctuations associated with the vortex shedding. Two glass coated sensors are bonded into the front face of the flow element, as illustrated in Fig. 8.21. The vortex shedding behind the flow element affects the direction of flow impinging on the face, causing out-of-phase velocity variations at the sensors. Alternatively, the sensor can be located on the side of the body.

In another design, a cantilever supported by the non-stream-lined object itself from behind and having a mass at its other end can be used to detect the frequency by using strain gauges fixed on the cantilever.

The main advantage of this type of flow meter is that the calibration in terms of the number of vortices per second per m/s is determined by the dimensions of the flow element and pipe line only. It does not depend on the fluid gravity, viscosity, or temperature; neither does it depend on whether the fluid is gas or liquid. The unique features of this flow meter are that it has no moving parts, same calibration factor for all liquids and gases, very low pressure loss, no upper flow limit other than those imposed by the electronics associated with the sensors or limitations from other sources, and fixed calibration factor based on the dimensions of the flow element. These meters can be used with many corrosive liquids or gases, slurries and cryogenic liquids. Linearities of the order of $\pm 0.5\%$ of the reading above Reynolds numbers 10^4 excellent repeatability of the order of $\pm 0.1\%$ of the reading, and good dynamic response can be obtained. The flow meter is made in the form of an integral piece, consisting of body and sensors, and should be inserted within the pipe line of the actual flow.

8.10 OTHER FLOW METERS

8.10.1 Thermal Flow Meters

Another type of flow meter which has no restrictive orifice or moving parts and is useful even for corrosive liquids is the thermal flow meter, as illustrated in Fig. 8.22. The

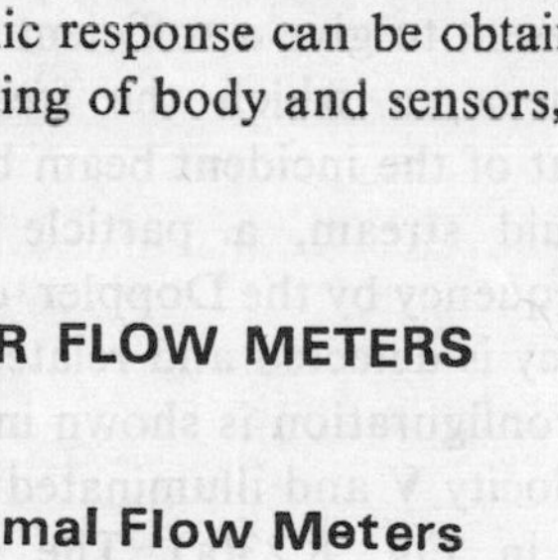

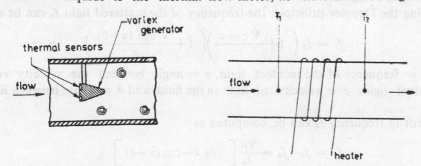

Fig. 8.21 Principle of vortex shedding

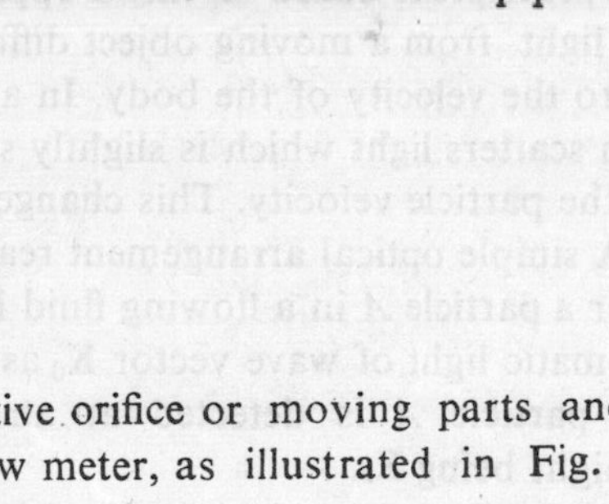

Fig. 8.22 Principle of thermal flow meter

device consists of a heater placed in the fluid stream, with two temperature sensors, such as thermocouples or resistance thermometers. The temperature sensors are located symmetrically with respect to the heater, one at the upstream side and the other at the downstream side, at a short distance from the heater. Under no flow conditions, the temperatures T_1 and T_2 of the sensors will be the same, and the differential signal measured on a detector will be zero. As the flow increases, T_1 will fall and T_2 will rise until a steady state is reached. The heat transferred to the liquid by the heater is given by

$$Q = WC_p(T_2 - T_1) \tag{8.62}$$

where Q = heat transferred, W = mass flow rate of the fluid, C_p = specific heat of the fluid, T_1 = temperature of the fluid before heat is transferred to it, and T_2 = temperature of the fluid after heat has been supplied to it.

From the above equation, the mass flow rate W can be obtained by measuring the temperature difference $(T_2 - T_1)$ and the heat transferred to the fluid Q in terms of the power input to the heater, and knowing the specific heat C_p of the fluid. Thus, under constant power input to the heater, for a given fluid, the temperature difference $(T_2 - T_1)$ is inversely proportional to the mass flow rate. The dynamic response of this type of flow meter is dependent on the flow conditions, and is generally poor.

8.10.2 Laser Anemometers

One promising system of recent origin for velocity measurements in single- and two-phase flows is the laser Doppler anemometer. However, this system can be employed only where adequate transmission of the coherent laser light through the fluid is possible, and also sufficient concentration of scattering particles are present to give a sufficient signal to noise ratio. The principle is based on the Doppler phenomena in which the frequency of the scattered light from a moving object differs from that of the incident beam by a value proportional to the velocity of the body. In a moving fluid stream, a particle intercepting a laser beam scatters light which is slightly shifted in frequency by the Doppler effect, depending upon the particle velocity. This change in frequency is detected and related to the flow velocity. A simple optical arrangement realizing this configuration is shown in Fig. 8.23.

Consider a particle A in a flowing fluid having a velocity $\mathbf{V}$ and illuminated by an incident monochromatic light of wave vector $\mathbf{K_0}$ as illustrated in Fig. 8.23(a). The scattered light from the particle A is detected at an angle to the incident light, the wave vector of the scattered light being $\mathbf{K_s}$.

Applying the Doppler principle, the frequency of the scattered light f_s can be expressed as

$$f_s = f_0 \left(1 + \frac{V \cos \alpha}{c} \right)\left(1 + \frac{V \cos (\alpha + \theta)}{c} \right) \tag{8.63}$$

where f_0 = frequency of the incident light, α = angle between the velocity vector $\mathbf{V}$ and the incident light, c = velocity of light in the fluid, and θ = angle between $\mathbf{K_0}$ and $\mathbf{K_s}$ as shown.

The shift in frequency f_d can be computed as

$$f_d = f_0 - f_s = \frac{V\mu}{\lambda_o}\left[\cos \alpha - \cos (\alpha + \theta) \right] \tag{8.64}$$

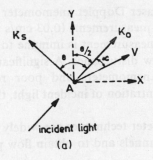

incident light
(a)

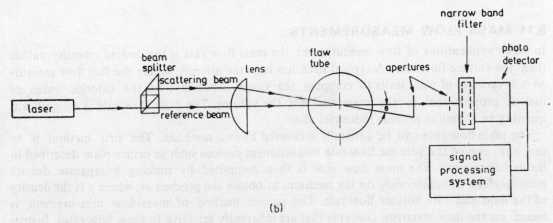

(b)

Fig. 8.23 Laser anemometer: (a) principle of optical scattering; (b) simplified measurement system

where λ_o is the wavelength of the incident light in vacuum and μ is the refractive index of the fluid. Equation (8.64) can be reduced to

$$f_d = \frac{2\mu}{\lambda_o} \mathbf{V}_x \sin(\theta/2) \qquad (8.65)$$

where $\mathbf{V}_x$ is the velocity component of $\mathbf{V}$ in the x direction. Knowing μ and λ_o for the medium, and measuring f_d and θ, the component of velocity in a particular direction can be determined.

Since the laser Doppler signal corresponds to the instantaneous velocity component of the particle, it contains information on the mean and turbulent velocities of the fluid. A simplified schematic arrangement of the measurement system, as illustrated in Fig. 8.23(b), comprises the He-Ne or argon-ion laser source, transmitting and receiving optics (focussing and light collimating), a photo detector, and a signal processor converting the frequency shift to corresponding voltage variations. Elaborate signal-processing circuits are employed to obtain sufficient accuracy and resolution, by considering the random nature of the detected signal associated with noise, maximum Doppler frequency, and the signal bandwidth. Special techniques are used to compute the mean and velocity fluctuations. The quality of measurement and subsequent data analysis depend very much upon the size, concentration and refractive index of the particle in the flow, and the intensity of the scattered light.

The main advantages of a laser Doppler anemometer are that the system can be used over a wide range of flow measurements (0.03 cm/s to 120 m/s) with good precision and high resolution in time. The measurement is immune to environmental effects with absolutely no pressure loss or flow disturbance. A significant disadvantage is the low sensitivity compared to other thermo-anemometers and poor resolution in distinguishing velocity fluctuations. At a higher concentration of incident light, the readings get very much dispersed, with a high noise content.

The laser Doppler anemometer techniques are widely used for the measurement of velocity and turbulence in wind tunnels and to obtain flow profiles in oscillating flows in ducts.

8.11 MASS FLOW MEASUREMENTS

In many applications of flow measurement, the mass flow rate is the desired quantity, rather than the volume flow rate. A typical situation is in the aircraft, where the fuel flow measured is invariably in mass units to compute the range capability, as the calorific value of fuel is proportional to the mass and not the volume. The mass flow rate is a significant quantity in chemical process industries also.

The mass flow rate can be generally measured by two methods. The first method is to use any one of the volume flow-rate measurement devices such as orifice plate described in the earlier sections. The mass flow rate is then computed by making a separate density measurement simultaneously on the medium, to obtain the product ρv, where ρ is the density of the fluid and v its volume flow rate. The second method of mass-flow measurement is based on the flow-metering concepts that are inherently sensitive to mass flow rates. Instruments based on both these principles are currently used for various applications.

The true mass flow meter concept is based on Newton's second law of motion, wherein the force required to alter the velocity of the fluid stream in a known manner is taken as a measure. In this device the fluid is accelerated in a direction normal to the inlet flow to a constant velocity v_y by external means, independent of the magnitude of the inlet velocity v_1, as shown in Fig. 8.24. The force F_y acting on the fluid stream is given by

$$F_y = \frac{d}{dt}(Mv_y) \tag{8.66}$$

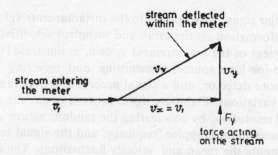

Fig. 8.24 Vector notation in a mass flow meter

where M = mass of the fluid and v_y = component of the velocity of fluid within the meter, normal to the direction of entry.

If v_y is constant, then

$$F_y = v_y \dot{M} \qquad (8.67)$$

The angular momentum can be measured using the stator torque or rotor torque principles. In both types, the fluid is given a constant rotational velocity v_y, in a direction normal to the direction of flow. In the stator torque flow meter, the fuel flows through a rotating vane, moving at a constant speed which imparts a constant angular rotation (swirl). The fuel is then passed through a turbine, designed to eliminate the angular momentum imparted earlier. In this process, a torque is exerted on the turbine proportional to the mass flow rate of the fluid. In the rotor torque type flow meter, the fluid is first passed through straightening vanes to remove all angular rotations (swirl) and then allowed to flow through a measurement assembly which consists of a set of vanes rotating at constant speed about an axis coincident with the axis of the flow meter. The torque required to drive the rotating vanes is proportional to the magnitude of the angular momentum applied to the fluid, which is in turn proportional to the mass of the fluid passing through the assembly. This device is described below considering its many advantages over the stator type, even though both involve torque measurements.

8.11.1 Rotor Torque Mass Flow Meter

The principle of operation of the rotor torque mass flow meter is described schematically in Fig. 8.25. The fluid flow is first smoothened by passing through straightening vanes fitted into an annular space, as shown in the diagram. The axially-flowing fluid is then passed through the measurement assembly, comprising an impeller driven at a constant speed, typically at 100 rpm, by an electric motor or a hydraulic turbine. The impeller is basically a set of axial vanes spaced around an annular gap with similar dimensions to that of the straightening vanes. The shaft of the impeller is free to rotate on low friction bearings. The angular torque is imparted to the impeller by the shaft, by means of a torsion spring whose linear torque/rotation characteristic is known *a priori*. This torque is proportional to the mass flow rate.

Two pairs of magnets, one pair fixed on the periphery of the rotating drum and the other on the impeller, induce voltage pulses in the two pick-off coils mounted on the case, one above each magnet. The time interval measured between the pulses is proportional to the spring deflection, and hence the mass flow rate. In case of any changes in the speed of rotation during the measurement, suitable corrections can be made. Referring to Fig. 8.25 by applying Newton's second law of motion, the torque T transmitted to the impeller can be expressed as

$$T \propto \frac{d}{dt}(I\omega) \qquad (8.68)$$

where I is the mass moment of inertia and ω is the angular velocity of the drum. Since $I = MK^2$, where K is radius of gyration,

$$T \propto \frac{d}{dt}(MK^2\omega) \qquad (8.69)$$

$$\propto \dot{M}K^2\omega \qquad (8.70)$$

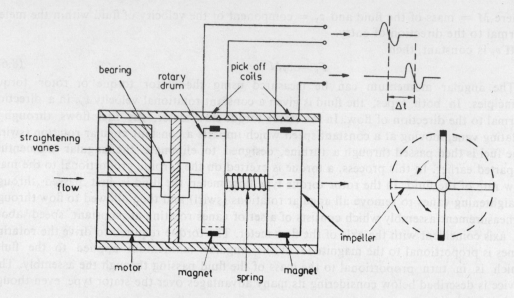

Fig. 8.25 Rotor torque mass flow meter

If $K^2 = \dfrac{R_1^2 + R_2^2}{2}$, where R_1 and R_2 are the inner and outer radii of the annular fluid chamber in the assembly,

$$T \propto \dot{M}\omega \left(\frac{R_1^2 + R_2^2}{2} \right) \tag{8.71}$$

As R_1 and R_2 are constants fixed by the physical design of the flow meter, $T = K_1 \dot{M}\omega$ where K_1 includes constants of proportionality.

If K_2 is the spring constant, the spring deflection θ can be written as

$$K_2\theta = K_1 \dot{M}\omega \tag{8.72}$$

Substituting $\theta = \omega t$, where t is the time delay between two consecutive pulses from the drum and impeller, Equation (8.72) can be written as

$$\dot{M} = \frac{K_2}{K_1} t \tag{8.73}$$

Thus, the time interval t is a direct measure of the mass flow rate M and is independent of the rotational speed ω.

Flow meters of this type can be designed to have an accuracy better than 0.5%. As the device measures the mass flow directly, no allowance is needed for ancillary-sensing equipment, such as density correctors or temperature probes. However, two significant sources of error are present, which are to be minimized during design. They are: (a) all the fluid may not pass through the measurement assembly, due to leakage through clearances, and (b) under low-flow conditions, the fluid may pass through the measurement assembly more than once. Changes can also occur in the torque/deflection curve of the impeller drive spring. Pressure drops can be reduced down to less than 14 kPa by proper design.

EXERCISES

8.1 A rotameter uses a cylindrical float 0.02 m in height and 0.02 m in diameter, with proper density to give density compensation. If the discharge coefficient is 0.5 and the maximum inside diameter of the tube is 0.04 m, calculate the maximum flow rate in m^3/s.

8.2 Discuss the suitability of the various pressure transducers in measuring the pressure difference in venturi meters, orifice meters, and pitot tubes.

8.3 The density of air in a duct is 1.2 kg/m^3 and its maximum velocity 20 m/s. The duct is of 100 mm diameter and is provided with a 80 mm diameter orifice plate. Assuming that the coefficient of discharge is 0.5, calculate the necessary range of pressure transducer needed for flow measurement.

8.4 In a constant temperature hot-wire anemometer, discuss the influence of the loop gain and current through the wire on the system performance.

8.5 In a turbine-flow meter, calculate the percentage error introduced due to 1% change in the angle of the blade tip.

8.6 Dry air at atmospheric pressure and room temperature flows through a thermally-insulated pipe having a flow area 64.5 cm^2. An electric heater mounted inside the pipe dissipates 0.1 kW. A differential thermocouple measuring the temperature ahead of the heater (cold air) as well as in the downstream (hot air) indicates a temperature difference of 4°C. Estimate the average flow velocity.

8.7 A venturi meter is to be fitted in the horizontal section of a 0.15 m pipe line. Calculate the cylindrical throat diameter, if the maximum differential pressure obtained is 0.5 cm for a maximum flow rate of 5.0 kg/s for water at 20°C. Assume a discharge coefficient of 0.99.

8.8 Derive the relevant equation for a pitot-static tube for air speed measurements.

A pitot-static tube is used on an aircraft cruising at a speed of 200 km per hour at an altitude of 3 km above mean sea level. Calculate the differential pressure, at that speed and altitude. (Note: The static pressure at 3 km altitude is 700 mb, and density is 0.9 kg/m^3.)

REFERENCES

1. Miller, J.T., "Area meters", *Instrument Practices*, Vol. 5, No. 11, 1957.
2. Hinze, J.O., *Turbulence*, McGraw-Hill, New York, 1975.
3. Lowel, H.J., "Design and application of hot wire anemometers for steady state measurements at transonic and supersonic speeds", *NACA Tech Note 2117*, 1950.
4. Perry, A.E. and Morrison, G.L., "A study of the constant temperature hot-wire amenometer", *Journal of Fluid Mechanics*, Vol. 47, Part 3, pp. 577-599, 1971.

BIBLIOGRAPHY

Arora, Y.L., *Flow Measurement Techniques*, Universal Book Corp. Bombay, 1978.

Baker, R.C., "On the electromagnetic vortex probe", *Scientific Instruments*, Vol. 4, No. 2, pp. 99-101, February 1971.

Belchman, S., "Techniques for measuring low flows", *Instruments and Control Systems*, Vol. 36, No. 10, pp. 82-85, October 1963.

Benson, J.M., "Thermal flow sensors", *Instr. Tech.*, Vol. 18, No. 7, pp. 39-43, July 1971.

Brain, T.J.S., "Reference standards for gas flow measurement", *Measurement and Control*, Vol., 11, No. 8, pp. 283-288, Aug. 1978

Consindine, D.M., *Process Instruments and Controls Handbook*, McGraw-Hill, New York, 1974.

Cook, P.P. and Grady, R.A., "Analysis of flow sensor calibration data", *Instruments and Control Systems*, Vol. 44, No. 4, pp. 101-102, April 1971.

Dijstelbergen, H.H., "Performance of a swirl flow meter", *Scientific Instruments*, Vol. 3, No. 11, pp. 886-888, Nov. 1970.

Doebelin, E.O., *Measurement Systems, Application and Design*, McGraw-Hill, New York, 1966.

Dowdell, R.B., Ed., *Flow, Its Measurement and Control in Science and Industry*, Vol. I, Part II, ISA Publication, Pittsburg, 1974.

Dowdell, R.B. and Yu-Lin Chen, "A statistical approach to the prediction of discharge coefficients for concentric orifice plates", *J. of Basic Engineering*, Vol. 92D, No. 4, pp. 752-765, December 1972.

Evans, G.W., "Signal conditioning for gas flow computation", *Instrument Technology*, Vol. 20, No. 6, pp. 38-42, June 1973.

Farmer, W.M. and Hornkohl, J.O., "Two component self aligning laser velocimeter", *Appl. Opt.*, Vol. 12, No. 11, pp. 2636-2640, Nov. 1973.

Ferris, S.A. and Blanchard, J., "A rotating cup anemometer with digital output", *Scientific Instruments*, Vol. 3, No. 12, pp. 1012-1013, December 1970.

Goodman, C.H., and Sogin, H.H., "A generalised King's law of a conical hot film anemometer", *Trans. ASME, Ser C*, Vol. 95, No. 3, pp. 429-431, Aug. 1973.

Hinze, J.O., *Turbulence*, McGraw-Hill, N.Y., 1975.

Hoffmann de Visme, G.F.A. and Singh, H., "Operation of a thermal flow meter from a super imposed DC and pulse heat injection", *J. Phys. E.*, Vol. 6, No. 6, pp. 521-522, June 1973.

Jespersen, K.I., "Measuring flow, time to reconsider ultrasonic methods", *Control and Instr.*, Vol. 5, No. 10, pp. 38-39, Nov. 1973.

Kwok, C.K. et al., "An experimental investigation of the vortex flowmeter", *Advances in Instrumentation*, Vol. 27, Part 4, paper 825, 1972.

L.D.A. Symposium, "The accuracy of flow measurements by Laser Doppler methods", *Proceedings of the Laser Anemometer Symposium*, L.D.A. Symposium, Copenhagen, 1975.

Liptak, B.G., *Instrument Engineers Handbook*, Vol. I, Chilton Book Co., N.Y., 1970.

McShane, J.L., "Ultrasonic flow meter basics", *Instrumentation Technology*, Vol. 18, No. 7, pp. 44-48, July 1971.

Norton, H.N., *Handbook of Transducers for Electronic Measuring Systems*, Prentice-Hall, Princeton, New Jersey, 1968.

Ower, E. and Pankhrust, R.C., *The Measurement of Air Flow*, Pergamon Press Ltd, London U.K., 1966.

Potter, R.C., "Technique for dynamic calibration of hot wire anemometers", *NASA CR 82591*, 1960.

Rosemary Dowden, R., *Fluid Flow Measurements—A Bibliography*, British hydromechanics research association, Cranfield, England, 1972.

Sarma, T.S. and Sarma, G.R., "A low velocity hot-wire anemometer", *Instruments and Control Systems*, Vol. 46, No. 4, pp. 62-63, April 1973.

Shercliff, J.A., *The Theory of Electromagnetic Flow Measurement*, Cambridge University Press, New York, 1962.

Spiller, R.L., "The art and practice of orifice flow metering", *Inst. Tech.*, Vol. 18, No. 7, pp. 52-56, July 1971.

Spink, L.K., *Principles and Practice of Flow meter engineering*, Foxboro Co., Massachusetts, 1967.

Thompson, R.E. and Grey, J., "Turbine flow-meter performance model", *Journal of Basic Engineering*, Vol. 92D, No. 4, pp. 712-723, December 1970.

Wilmshrust, T.H. et al., "A laser fluid flow velocimeter of wide dynamic range", *Scientific Instruments*, Vol. 4, No. 2, pp. 81-85, Feb. 1971.

9

TEMPERATURE

9.1 INTRODUCTION

The temperature of a substance or medium is a phenomenon expressing its degree of hotness or coldness, and is related with reference to its power of communicating heat to the surroundings. It is one of the fundamental parameters, denoting a physical condition of matter, similar to mass, length, and time. However, temperature denotes basically an intensive property of the matter. It is a measure of the mean kinetic energy of the molecules of the substance and represents the potential of heat flow. This phenomenon is not measurable by use of the basic standards for direct comparison purposes.

When a body is heated or cooled, various primary effects can result, and one of these effects can be employed for measurement purposes. They include: (a) change in the physical or chemical state, (b) change in physical dimensions, (c) variation in electrical properties, (d) generation of an emf at the junction of two dissimilar metals, and (e) change in the intensity of the total radiation emitted. Changes in the physical or chemical state are seldom employed for direct temperature measurements even though this property is a basic reference as a temperature standard, e.g. freezing, melting, boiling, or condensation of solids, liquids, or gases throughout the temperature ranges. The temperature at which a change in chemical state occurs, such as the ignition temperature of combustible materials can be utilized to determine the order of magnitude of the temperature scale, but even this is not a very practical method. The change in dimensions accompanying a temperature change forms the basis of operation of the common liquid in glass thermometers and bimetal thermometers. Electrical methods are by far the most convenient and accurate way of temperature measurement. They include methods based on change in resistance and generation of thermo emf. Temperature sensing, based on the method of measuring energy radiation from a hot body, is also a standard optical method of measurement, especially at very high temperatures. A comparison table surveying the characteristics of various temperature-measuring devices is given in Table 9.1.

9.2 TEMPERATURE SCALES

The establishment of a temperature scale might seem somewhat arbitrary, but its basis lies in the second law of thermodynamics and the concept of an ideal reversible Carnot cycle. It

TABLE 9.1 SURVEY OF TEMPERATURE-MEASURING DEVICES

Measuring device	Temperature range, K	Error limits % or K	Remote indication	Remarks
1	2	3	4	5
1. Mechanical Sensors				
(a) Liquid in glass thermometers				
(i) With non-wetting thermometric liquid (mercury)	235 to 903	1 to 2% F.S.	No	Direct reading
(ii) With wetting (organic) thermometric liquid (mixtures of pentanes, alcohol or toluene)	73 to 473	2% F.S.	No	—
(b) Liquid filled thermometers	238 to 773	1 to 2% F.S.	Yes	Conversion to electrical output feasible
(c) Vapour pressure thermometer	233 to 623	1 to 2% F.S.	Yes	-do-
2. Electrical Sensors				
(a) Thermoelectric thermocouples				
(i) Cu-constantan	73 to 673	0.75% of true value	Yes	Remote indication possible; multiplexing feasible; lead compensation and cold junction compensation necessary
(ii) Fe-constantan	73 to 973	—do—	Yes	
(iii) NiCr-Ni (Chromel-Alumel)	273 to 1273	—do—	Yes	
(iv) $PtRh_{13}$-Pt	273 to 1573	0.5% of true value	Yes	
(v) $PtRh_{30}$-$PtRh_6$	273 to 1773	—do—	Yes	
(vi) Tungsten-Rhenium	273 to 3033	1.0% of true value	Yes	
(b) Resistance thermometers				
(i) Platinum resistance thermometer	91 to 903	0.3% to 0.5% F.S.	Yes	Bridge measurement and lead compensation essential; multiplexing feasible; self heating to be kept minimum
(ii) Nickel resistance thermometer	213 to 423	0.2° to 2.0° according to range	Yes	
(iii) Thermistors	173 to 573	0.2°	Yes	High sensitivity, small size, but poor linearity
(iv) Semiconductor resistance thermometer	173 to 453	0.5°—1.5°	Yes	High sensitivity, small size, and good linearity
(c) Others				
(i) Crystal transducer	223 to 573	0.03° to 0.1°	Yes	High sensitivity, high resolution, digital output, complex signal conditioning, and excellent linearity. Cable capacitance problems.

(Contd.)

1	2	3	4	5
(ii) Semiconductor junction voltage variation	223 to 423	0.1° to 0.5°	Yes	Inexpensive and small size; requires individual calibration. Good linearity with appropriate signal conditioning
3. Optical Sensors				
(i) Spectral pyrometers	823 to 3773	5°—35°	Yes	Indirect method of measurement; only high temperature measurements and emission property of the body should be known
(ii) Band-radiation pyrometer	773 to 2273	1 to 1.5% F.S.	No	
(iii) Total radiation pyrometer	233 to 2273	—do—	No	
4. Distribution Pyrometers				
(a) Colour-comparison	1423 to 2073	10° to 25°	No	—do—
(b) Ratio-pyrometer	973 to 2973	1° to 1.5% F.S.	Yes	—do—

can be shown that the efficiency of the Carnot cycle is independent of the working substance and depends only on the temperatures between which it operates. The efficiency η is given by

$$\eta = \frac{Q_2 - Q_1}{Q_1} = \frac{T_2 - T_1}{T_1} \tag{9.1}$$

where Q_2 is the heat absorbed from a higher temperature reservoir at temperature T_2 and Q_1 is the heat rejected to a lower temperature reservoir at temperature T_1.

Rearranging Eq. (9.1)

$$\frac{Q_2}{Q_1} = \frac{T_2}{T_1} \tag{9.2}$$

In practice, all measurements are ultimately referred to the thermodynamic Kelvin temperature scale. Using an ideal gas as a thermometric substance, Eq. (9.2) can be rewritten as,

$$\frac{T_2}{T_1} = \lim_{F \to 0} \left[\frac{P}{P_{273 \cdot 15}} \right]_{\text{constant } V} \tag{9.3}$$

where T_1 is the triple point of water (273.15 K), P is the pressure at temperature T_2, and $P_{273 \cdot 15}$ is the pressure at triple point of water.

The measurement of thermodynamic temperatures are difficult and time-consuming. International Practical Temperature Scale (IPTS) provides convenient, precise, and reproducible measurements by the use of uniform and self-consistent methods. Basically, nine reproducible fixed points, assigned as temperature standards, are available, as shown in Table 9.2, at standard pressures. Interpolating instruments have been developed to establish temperatures on the IPTS between these fixed points.

TABLE 9.2 FIXED POINTS OF THE IPTS AT STANDARD PRESSURE

Temperature K (IPTS-68)	Temperature °C	Temperature reproduce-ability	Accuracy of realisation of thermo-dynamic temperature	Defining fixed point	Interpolating instrument
13.81	−259.34	0.001 K	0.01 K	Triple point of equilibrium hydrogen	PRT
27.102	−246.048	0.001 K	0.01 K	Boiling point of neon	-do-
54.361	−218.789	0.001 K	0.01 K	Triple point of oxygen	-do-
90.188	−182.962	0.001 K	0.01 K	Boiling point of oxygen	-do-
273.15	0.01	0.0001 K	Exact	Triple point of water	-do-
373.15	100	0.0005 K	0.0025 K	Boiling point of water	-do-
672.73	419.58	0.0005 K	0.03 K	Freezing point of zinc	-do-
1235.08	961.93	0.05 K	0.2 K	Freezing point of silver	Thermo-couple
1337.58	1064.43	0.05 K	0.2 K	Freezing point of gold	Radiation pyrometer

9.3 MECHANICAL TEMPERATURE SENSORS

Temperature measurements can be carried out with a variety of mechanically operated elements sensitive to temperature. A majority of such devices consists of a sensor bulb filled with a liquid sensitive to temperature or an enclosed volume sensitive to pressure or volume changes. They are termed as filled system thermometers and have the advantages of simple, inexpensive design, rugged construction, self-contained operation, and remote indication in special cases. However, in modern instrumentation schemes, it finds limited use because of its limited temperature coverage, large size, incompatability to electrical systems, and poor dynamic response.

Filled-system thermometers may be classified under two fundamental heads, viz., those responding to volume changes, such as mercury or alcohol in glass thermometer, and those responding to pressure changes, such as vapour pressure thermometers.

9.3.1 Liquid in Glass Thermometers

Liquid in glass thermometers make use of the thermal expansion of a thermometric liquid enclosed in a bulb exposed to the medium. The change in temperature is determined in terms of the level of the liquid in the glass capillary attached to the bulb. Mercury and alcohol are some of the liquids used, depending on the range required. A typical example is the standard clinical thermometer. Remote indication is feasible only with some special modifications.

9.3.2 Liquid-filled Systems

Liquid-filled system thermometers consist of a temperature sensor in the form of an immersible bulb, an elastic-measuring element (tube or spiral spring) coupled to the bulb through a capillary tube, and an indicating or recording attachment, as shown in Fig. 9.1(a). On exposure to the thermal medium, the liquid enclosed in the bulb expands and the change in volume drives the elastic-measuring element through a capillary link. The indicator coupled to this element deflects as a function of temperature.

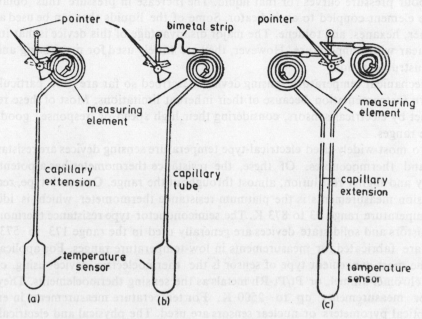

Fig. 9.1 Liquid filled mechanical thermometers: (a) basic sensor; (b) partially-compensated sensor; (c) fully compensated sensor

Mercury under a pressure of 100-150 kPa or organic liquids such as toluene under a pressure of 5-50 kPa are used as filling liquids. Filled-system thermometers using mercury have practically uniform scale divisions. They can be employed in the ranges shown in Table 9.1.

Liquid-filled system thermometers, in their simplest form, have an error in the reading, if the temperature surrounding the capillary tubing and elastic-measuring element is different from the temperature under which they are calibrated. The resultant error in indication can be partially or completely compensated by a suitable design. In a partially-compensated version, filled-system thermometers are compensated for ambient temperature variations by incorporating a temperature sensing bimetal which is located between the elastic measuring element and the indicating part of the instrument, as shown in Fig. 9.1(b).

In a fully-compensated version of the device, compensation is incorporated for both the indicating element and capillary tubing, as shown in Fig. 9.1(c). A similar sealed length of tubing without a sensor bulb is run along the main capillary tubing and is coupled to a second elastic-measuring element in the indicating part of the instrument. The two measuring elements are mechanically mounted together to operate in opposition to each other, thus compensating for temperature difference.

9.3.3 Vapour Pressure Thermometers

Vapour pressure thermometers are similar in design and construction to the liquid-filled systems, except that the bulb is replaced with an immersion tube partially filled with a low boiling point liquid and the rest of the tube filled with its vapour. The change in vapour pressure in the tube over the liquid column is a function of the temperature, as determined from vapour pressure curves for that liquid. The increase in pressure thus obtained drives an elastic element coupled to an indicator. Some of the liquids that can be used are ethylene, ethyl, ether, hexanes, and toluene. The major disadvantage of this device is that its indication is non-linear with temperature. However, they are widely used for monitoring and control in process instrumentation.

The mechanical temperature sensing devices described so far are not particularly useful in modern instrumentation because of their inherent limitations. Most of these requirements can be met by electrical sensors, considering their high speed of response, good sensitivity and wide ranges.

The two most widely-used electrical-type temperature sensing devices are resistance thermometers and thermocouples. Of these, the resistance thermometer has a potentially higher sensitivity and higher resolution, almost throughout the range. One such type, recommended for precision measurements is the platinum resistance thermometer which is ideally suited in the temperature range 93 to 873 K. The semiconductor-type resistance thermometers, such as thermistors and solid-state devices are generally used in the range 173 to 573 K. Special devices are fabricated for measurements in low-temperature ranges. For applications above 873 K, the most convenient type of sensor is the thermoelectric device using copper-constantan, chromel-alumel, or Pt/Pt-Rh metals as the sensing thermoelements. They are ideally suited for measurements up to 2500 K. For temperature measurements in excess of this value, optical pyrometers or nuclear sensors are used. The physical and electrical properties of all these devices are discussed in detail in the following pages.

In all the above mentioned electrical devices, the output (change in resistance or emf) with changes in temperature is not perfectly linear in the true sense. The response characteristics differ very much in each case and sometimes even among the devices of the same type, as well as with temperature ranges. In the measurement system, this non-linearity is overcome by incorporating analog- or digital-type linearizers. These are discussed separately in Chapter 13.

9.4 RESISTANCE-TYPE TEMPERATURE SENSORS

Metals are basically crystalline in structure comprising metal ions and free electrons in equilibrium. The application of a dc potential across the metallic element results in a directional flow of these electrons. During their movement they collide with themselves and with the ions comprising the crystat lattice, thus restricting its flow, which results in an electrical resistance. As the metal is heated, the temperature rises and the mean free path length between collisions decreases due to the increase in the amplitude of oscillation, resulting in an increase in the electrical resistance.

The range of temperature over which this phenomenon is valid is decided by the temperature coefficient of resistance, chemical inertness, and its crystal structure which should not undergo permanent changes within this range. In general, the resistivity of metals increases with an increase in temperature (i.e. the temperature coefficient is positive), whereas in some semiconductors the resistance decreases with an increase in temperature (i.e. the temperature coefficient is negative). Such variations in resistance are measured precisely with suitable electrical circuits.

The resistance thermometer based on the above phenomenon is one of the most accurately reproducible temperature-sensing device. In the vicinity of 273.15 K (0°C) and at room temperature, measurements with an accuracy of 0.0001 K can be attained. At 700 K, the accuracy attainable is 0.01 K, and at 1200 K it can be 0.1 K. The precision in resistance measurements required to obtain an accuracy of 0.001 K is of the order of 2 to 4 parts per million.

The resistance thermometer is applicable for measurements of small temperature differences as well as for wide ranges of temperature. The main disadvantage lies in its large size and sophisticated instrumentation.

Within narrow ranges of temperature, the temperature coefficient of resistance is constant. The resistance value R_t at any temperature T can be expressed as

$$R_i = R_0[1+a(T-T_0)] = R_0(1+at) \tag{9.4}$$

where R_0 is the resistance of the conductor at temperature T_0, a is a constant standing for the temperature coefficient of resistance for that material, and t is the difference in temperature.

For larger temperature ranges, the resistance value follows more accurately the polynomial relation,

$$R_t = R_0(1+at+bt^2) \tag{9.5}$$

where a and b are constants; a and b can be computed for different materials at room temperature. The value of a is usually determined from the measurements of resistance values at two temperatures, using the relation,

$$a = \frac{R_2-R_1}{R_1T_2-R_2T_1} \tag{9.6}$$

where R_1 is the resistance at temperature T_1, and R_2 is the resistance at temperature T_2. It may be noted that a depends to a large extent upon the purity of the metal and its heat treatment. The resistance material may be pure metals or alloys, but the pure metals possess relatively high temperature coefficients. This coefficient can be either positive or negative, depending upon the material as given in Table 9.3.

TABLE 9.3 TEMPERATURE COEFFICIENT OF RESISTANCE OF SOME
SELECTED MATERIALS AT ROOM TEMPERATURE

Material	Temperature coefficient in ohm/ohm/K
Nickel	0.0067
Iron (alloy)	0.002 to 0.006
Tungsten	0.0048
Aluminium	0.0045
Copper	0.0043
Lead	0.0042
Silver	0.0041
Gold	0.004
Platinum	0.00392
Manganese	0.00002
Thermistors	−0.068 to +0.14

Although a is usually treated as a constant over a small temperature range, in reality, it has a non-linear relationship with respect to temperature.

Most of the metals show an increase in resistivity with temperature, which is first linear and then increases in an accelerated fashion, as shown in Fig. 9.2. The metals that exhibit good sensitivity and reproducibility for temperature measurement purposes are copper, nickel, and platinum.

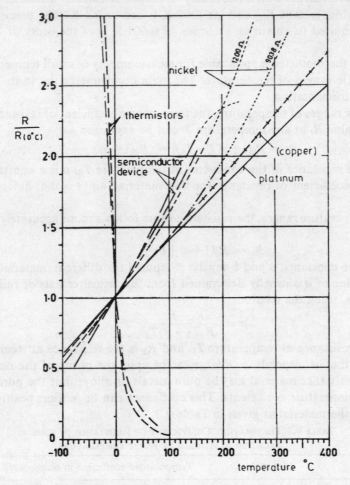

Fig. 9.2 Resistance variation with temperature for different materials

Among the base metals, copper has the highest temperature coefficient with the best linearity. However, copper is seldom used, due to certain practical problems. Because of its low resistivity, the size of the resistance element goes up to obtain reasonable sensitivity. In the range below 400 K, a gold-silver alloy can be used which has the same characteristics as platinum. For low-temperature measurements, certain phosphor-bronze alloys are found satisfactory.

Temperature sensors made out of nickel wire can be used with good reliability and repeatability in the temperature range of 100 to 450 K. It is less expensive than platinum and has a somewhat higher temperature coefficient which increases with temperature and is also less stable. Above 450 K, it changes its internal structure as it approaches the curie point, so that the resistance versus temperature curve can no longer be reproduced.

The platinum resistance element is the best choice for many applications, because of its inherent reproducibility and accuracy. Since the resistance to temperature ratio for a high purity platinum wire in its annealed and strain free state is extremely stable and reproducible, the sensor is recommended as the international standard for temperature measurements between the boiling point of liquid oxygen and the melting point of antimony. The temperature coefficient increases rapidly from zero at approximately 10 K ($-263°C$), reaches a maximum ($0.42\%/°C$) at approximately 30 K($-243°C$), and then gradually decreases as the temperature is further increased. The upper temperature limit for continuous operation is approximately 1000 K. Tabulated data for the resistance values of coiled platinum wire elements as a function of temperature can be obtained from standard resistance tables.

9.5 PLATINUM RESISTANCE THERMOMETER

The equation for pure, strain-free, annealed platinum, which also applies approximately to metals in general, for temperature from 273 K to 930 K is given by the Callender's equation[1]

$$t = 100\left[\frac{R_t - R_0}{R_{100} - R_0}\right] + \delta\left(\frac{t}{100} - 1\right)\frac{t}{100}$$

or

$$t = \frac{1}{\alpha}\left[\frac{R_t}{R_0} - 1\right] + \delta\left[\frac{t}{100} - 1\right]\frac{t}{100} \tag{9.7}$$

where t is the temperature in °C and R_t, R_0, and R_{100} are the resistance values measured at temperatures t, 0 and 100°C respectively; α and δ are constants for each sensitive element derived from resistance measurements at tin and zinc points. For platinum, $\alpha = 0.00392$ and $\delta = 1.49$ to 1.5.

For the temperature measurements below 273.15 K, the equation takes the Callender-Van Dusen form with an additional term containing constant β [termed as Van-Dusen constant] which is expressed as

$$t = \frac{R_t - R_0}{\alpha R_0} + \delta\left[\frac{t}{100} - 1\right]\frac{t}{100} + \beta\left(\frac{t}{100} - 1\right)\left(\frac{t}{100}\right)^3 \tag{9.8}$$

Constant β is determined by calibrating at boiling point of oxygen ($-182.962°C$). Equation (9.7) can be expressed in the form of a polynomial as

$$\frac{R_t}{R_0} = 1 + At + Bt^2 \tag{9.9}$$

The constants A and B are related to α and δ by

$$A = \alpha\left(1 + \frac{\delta}{100}\right) \tag{9.10}$$

$$B = -10^{-4}\alpha\delta \tag{9.11}$$

Also

$$\alpha = A + 100B \qquad (9.12)$$

$$\delta = -10^{-4}\frac{B}{A+100B} \qquad (9.13)$$

Value of t obtained from Eqs. (9.7) or (9.9) may be considered to be a first approximation to the actual temperature t' on the International Practical Temperature Scale, 1968; the actual temperature is given by

$$t' = t + M(t) \qquad (9.14)$$

and $M(t)$ is given by,

$$M(t) = 0.045\left(\frac{t}{100}\right)\left(\frac{t}{100}-1\right)^2\left(\frac{t}{419.58}-1\right)\left(\frac{t}{630.74}-1\right) \qquad (9.15)$$

The addition of $M(t)$ is to obtain the actual temperature in the IPTS to make it closer to the thermodynamic scale.

9.5.1 Construction of Platinum Resistance Thermometer Elements

Several forms of resistance thermometers have been developed for temperature measurements, depending upon their requirement, such as speed of response, environmental conditions, and ability to withstand vibration or corrosion. Figure 9.3 shows the common openwire element in which the platinum wire is wound in the form of a free spiral or held in place by an insulated carrier, such as mica or ceramic, in the form of a perforated-coil former. The wire is in direct contact with the gas or liquid whose temperature is to be measured. Such an element has an excellent response time, small conduction errors, and small self-heating errors. The gases or liquids must not be corrosive or conductive nor leave sediments behind.

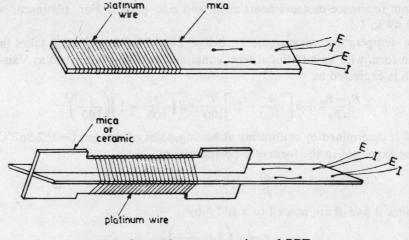

Fig. 9.3 Openwire construction of PRT

The diameter of the wire varies from 0.02 to 0.2 mm, and the preferred value is 0.1 mm. The wire should be smooth, free from defects, and drawn from an ingot which has been completely fused. The ratio of resistance at 373.15 K to the resistance at 273.15 K should be larger than 1.391 conforming to the purity tests. Annealing is recommended for preventing resistance changes due to dimensional changes. For many applications, the resistance wire is enclosed in a protective tube made of glass, quartz, porcelain, or metal for protection from mechanical damages and chemical reactions as shown in Fig. 9.4(a). The probe is suitably mounted to withstand high pressures, fluid speeds, vibrations, and damage from foreign bodies. In the more sophisticated types the wire is hermetically sealed between two platinum tubes and filled with dry air at 1/3 atmosphere. In some models, the wire is coated with an organic material and is embedded in ceramic. Since both the inside and outside of the tube are exposed to the medium, a fast response and good protection of the resistance wire is obtained.

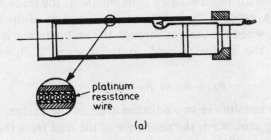

platinum
resistance
wire

(a)

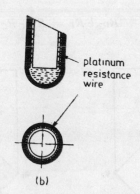

platinum
resistance
wire

(b)

Fig. 9.4 Construction of closed-type PRT:
(a) shielded probe; (b) liquid filled probe

The well type with the resistance element enclosed in a stainless steel or platinum tube is one of the most common types of construction as shown in Fig. 9.4(b). They are excellent for measurements in high-speed, electrically-conductive or corrosive liquids. For use below 80 K, the tube is filled with helium to avoid conduction of air. The resistance element is housed in a rod-shaped protective tube and is so constructed that the temperature changes on the surface of the cylinder have more effect than those at the upper end (stem-sensitive type). Longer tubes are used when the device is intended for measurement in liquids and gases.

The widely different types of element construction result, among other things, due to the fact that the thermal expansion of the resistance wire, insulation, coil formers, and chambers must be as equal as possible in order to prevent changes in resistance by elongation of the resistance wire.

9.5.2 Resistance Thermometer Circuits

Modified versions of the conventional four-arm Wheatstone's bridge circuits are widely employed for temperature measurements using platinum resistance thermometers. The Mueller bridge configuration as shown in Fig. 9.5 is one such circuit. It is basically an equal-ratio-arm bridge with provision for interchanging (commutating) the leads of the four resistors in such a way that the average of the balances is independent of the resistance of the leads. Referring to Fig. 9.5(a), when the current through the null detector is zero, the voltages e_1 and e_2 are equal and the bridge is said to be balanced. If $R_1 = R_2$, the condition for balance is

$$R_{D1} + R_C = R_X + R_T \tag{9.16}$$

where R_1 and R_2 are the resistors in two adjacent arms of the bridge, R_{D1} is the resistance of the variable balancing arm, R_C is the resistance of the lead from the bridge to the sensing element, R_X is the resistance of the sensing element (resistance thermometer), and R_T is the resistance of the lead from the element to the bridge having almost same value as R_C. If the leads marked C, T, c, and t are commutated to the position as shown in Fig. 9.5(b), the equation of balance is

$$R_{D2} + R_T = R_X + R_C \tag{9.17}$$

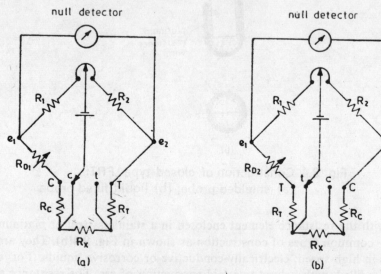

Fig. 9.5 Mueller Bridge configuration: (a) initial balance;
(b) commutated position

where R_{D2} is the resistance of the balancing arm.

Addition of Eqs. (9.16) and (9.17) yields the value of R_X in terms of R_{D1} and R_{D2}

$$R_{D1} + R_{D2} = 2R_X$$

or

$$R_X = \frac{R_{D1} + R_{D2}}{2} \tag{9.18}$$

An assumption made in the above equations is that R_T and R_C are constant during the time required for making the two balances. But this may not be the case in practice. Equations (9.16) and (9.17) may be rewritten for each case as

$$R_{D1} + R_{C1} = R_X + R_{T1} \tag{9.19}$$

$$R_{D2} + R_{T2} = R_X + R_{C2} \tag{9.20}$$

where suffixes 1, 2 correspond to each measurement.

Now, adding Eqs. (9.19) and (9.20),

$$R_{D1} + R_{D2} + (R_{C1} - R_{T1}) - (R_{C2} - R_{T2}) = 2R_X \tag{9.21}$$

Or

$$R_X = \frac{R_{D1} + R_{D2}}{2} + \frac{(R_{C1} - R_{T1}) - (R_{C2} - R_{T2})}{2} \tag{9.22}$$

Thus, a sufficient condition for the measured resistance to be independent of the lead resistance is that the difference in the resistance of the two leads be constant during the period of observation. Equation (9.22) shows that experimental emphasis can be placed in ensuring that the leads are of equal length and cross-section, and that the temperature gradients between the leads are nearly constant, rather than the more difficult option of maintaining the temperature of the leads constant.

Platinum resistance elements, fabricated with high purity wires or foils are excellent for high-precision temperature measurements. Coiled platinum wire elements are used on board aircraft for outside air-temperature measurements. For measuring surface temperatures, elements are made in the form of coated platinum foil. However, the resistance-temperature curve for the platinum foil is less predictable and is dependent on the thickness of the foil; it must be determined by individual calibration. High dynamic response can be attained by exposing the bare wire directly to the temperature.

9.6 THERMISTORS

Thermistors are essentially semiconductor devices which behave as thermal resistors having a high negative temperature coefficient of resistance. The sensors are made of sintered ceramics, usually from mixtures of oxides of iron, manganese, nickel, cobalt, and copper in the form of beads or discs. The resistance value at the ambient temperature may range from 100 ohms to 100 kohms. The variation of resistance with temperature is non-linear, decreasing with temperature, as shown in Fig. 9.2. Being a semiconductor device, each probe will have its own characteristic temperature coefficient and as such requires individual calibration. However, there are selected types available with very close tolerances and probe assemblies that are directly interchangeable. The usable range for measurement is normally between 170 to 570 K.

The resistance R_T of a thermistor at a temperature (T) can be expressed by the equation

$$R_T = a \cdot e^{b/T} \tag{9.23}$$

where a and b are constants determined by the structure and material. The variation in resistance with respect to temperature is as shown in Fig. (9.2). Rewriting Eqn. (9.23) for temperatures T_1 and T_2,

$$R_{T1} = R_{T2}e^{b(1/T_1 - 1/T_2)}$$

where R_{T1} and R_{T2} are resistances measured at temperatures T_1 and T_2 respectively.

If T_2, b, and R_{T2} are known, T_1 can be computed from the measured value of R_{T1}. By differentiating Eq. (9.23), the expression for the temperature coefficient can be written as

$$\alpha = \frac{1}{R_T}\frac{dR}{dT} = -\frac{b}{T^2} \tag{9.24}$$

The resistance temperature behaviour is usually specified by the ratio of the resistance at 0°C to the resistance at 50°C. As temperature sensors, thermistors normally operate as externally heated devices, wherein the changes in ambient or contact temperatures can be directly converted to corresponding changes in voltage or current. They are well-suited for precision temperature measurement, temperature control, and temperature compensation, because of their very large change in resistance with temperature. The resolution obtainable is higher than that of other types of temperature transducers. They are widely used for measurements in the range 170 to 470 K. A typical 2000-ohm thermistor with a temperature coefficient of 4%/°C at 25°C will exhibit a change of 80 ohms/°C change in temperature, as compared to only 7 ohm/°C of a platinum resistance sensor with the same basic resistance. Because of its smaller size, the device is ideally suited for measuring temperature distributions or gradients. The measurement of the change in resistance is carried out with a standard Wheatstone bridge network.

9.7 THERMOCOUPLES

Thermocouples are perhaps the most commonly-used electrical devices for temperature measurement. The sensing is based on the principle that a current flows in a closed circuit made up of two dissimilar metals if the junctions of the two metals are kept at different temperatures. In each lead, the concentration of valence electrons is proportional to the temperature, and at the point of contact, the electrons diffuse through the boundary layer between the two leads, resulting in one lead becoming positive and the other becoming negative. Thus the emf generated is proportional to the temperature difference in a predictable manner. This phenomenon is known as Seebeck effect.

The Seebeck coefficient or sensitivity S of a thermal element is given by,

$$S = e/t = a + bt + ct^2$$

where e is the emf generated from the junction, t is the change in temperature, and a, b, and c are constants determined by measuring the value of e at three standard reference temperatures. The magnitude of S depends upon the chemical composition and the physical treatment of the materials used. Table 9.4 gives nominal sensitivities at 273.15 K for various materials when compared with platinum. The output voltage for any two given materials, compared with each other, is obtained from the difference of the S values, e.g. the output voltage for a chromel vs alumel junction $= +25-(-15) = 40\ \mu V/°C$.

TABLE 9.4 SENSITIVITY OF THERMOCOUPLE MATERIALS VS PLATINUM

Material	$S,\ \mu V/°C$
Bismuth	−72
Constantan	−35
Alumel (nickel)	−15
Platinum	0
Aluminium	3.5
Rhodium	6
Copper	6.5
Gold	6.5
Iron	18.5
Chromel	25
Silicon	440

Certain combinations of materials also give thermal emfs proportional to the temperature differences between their junctions. In practice, the temperature measurement is carried out with two junctions. One of them, the reference junction, is kept at a constant temperature (usually 273.15 K), and the other is exposed to the medium whose temperature is to be measured. The properties of a few standard thermocouples are given in Table 9.5. The

TABLE 9.5 PROPERTIES OF THERMOCOUPLES

Type (ISA Standard)	Metal alloys used	Composition	Sensitivity $\mu V/°C$	Accuracy °C	Range °C	Remarks
Type E	Chromel (+)/ constantan (−)	90% Ni 10% Cr/ 57% Cr 43% Ni	40 to 55	± 1.8° ± 0.5%	−18 to +315 315 to 870	High sensitivity
Type K	Chromel (+)/ alumel (−)	90% Ni 10% Cr/ 94% Ni 3% Mn 2% Al 1% Sr	40 to 55	± 2.2° ± 0.5%	−18 to +276 276 to 1000	Long life and low thermal conductivity most popular for many applications
Type	Iron (+)/ constantan (−)	Fe/57% Cr 43% Ni	45 to 57	± 2.2° ± 0.5%	−18 to +276 276 to 760	Inexpensive, rapid deterioration above 560°C, mechanically strong
Type R	Platinum (−)/ platinum (−) rhodium (+)	Pt/ 87% Pt 13% Rh	5 to 12	± 0.25%	0 to 1000	Susceptible to corrosion; to be protected
Type S	Platinum (−)/ platinum (−) rhodium (+)	Pt/ 90% Pt 10% Rh	5 to 12	± 0.25%	450 to 1500	Low sensitivity, high stability, free from parasitic emf
Type T	Copper (+)/ constantan	Cu/57% Cu 43% Ni	15 to 60	± 0.8°	−200 to +93	Especially suitable for measurement below 0°C; high reliability
	Indium/ rhodium	In/ 40% Ir 60% Rh	5	± 1.0°	1200 to 2000	High stability; low sensitivity; requires careful handling

limiting temperatures indicate the temperature at which oxidation or reduction occurs. Figure 9.6 gives representative values for the thermoelectric voltage as a function of temperature difference for some popular thermocouples over the range where they are primarily used.

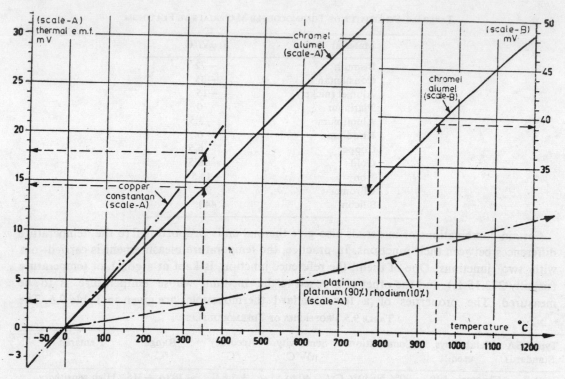

Fig. 9.6 Thermal emf's of some popular types of thermocouples

9.7.1 Construction of Thermocouple Probes

Different construction techniques for thermocouple probes are adopted to cater to the requirements of various applications depending upon the time constant, vibration insensitivity, and corrosion resistance needed. Figure 9.7 shows a few types of thermocouple probe constructions normally employed. In Fig. 9.7, the first two [(a) and (b)] are of "open" element types where the hot junctions are exposed directly to the medium. The probe consists of two insulated wires of dissimilar metals joined together at the hot junction by twisting, welding, or silver soldering as illustrated in Fig. 9.7(a) and (b). For use in media which are at high pressures, corrosive, or electrically conductive, the junction is enclosed in sealed bulbs, as shown in Fig. 9.7(c) and (d). In the former configuration, the elements are often welded to the bulb and hence grounded at the contact point. Such an arrangement normally excludes the use of several elements in parallel, but yields smaller time constants than those with an ungrounded junction. It may be noted that the time constants of the bare junctions are usually small, as the junction mass is not large. For measurements in a moving fluid medium, the open-element type is usually protected with a shield, as shown in Fig. 9.7(e).

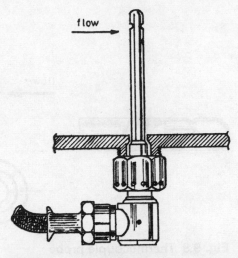

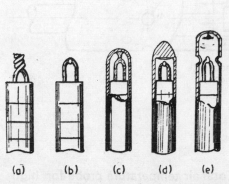

Fig. 9.7 Construction of thermocouple probes: (a) open element twisted; (b) open element welded; (c) closed grounded element; (d) closed ungrounded element; (e) protected open element

Fig. 9.8 Thermocouple probe for measurements in liquids and gases

A thermoelement when enclosed in a housing assembly is usually termed as a thermocouple probe. In contrast to the resistance probes, the thermocouple probes have lead wires without terminals, or else connectors with pins made out of the same thermoelement material. Depending on the application, numerous types of probe assemblies are available. Probes for measurement in liquids and gases are usually cylindrical in shape, and the threaded fitting is often manufactured with a clamp, so that the immersion depth of the element can be adjusted, as shown in Fig. 9.8.

For measurements in rapidly-moving gas streams, gas temperature probes (or stagnation probes) are used, as shown in Figs. 9.9 and 9.10. These are open elements with large intake openings but small exhaust openings in the housing, so that the entering gas stream is adiabatically compressed. The construction, as shown in Fig. 9.9 is better suited for measurements in high-speed gases, such as exhaust gas temperatures. In cases where the stagnation temperature is $+150°C$ or higher, as in the case of measurement of the outside air temperature in supersonic aircraft, total air temperature probes with concentric radiation shields are used, as shown in Fig. 9.10. The shields significantly reduce the otherwise large radiation errors.

9.7.2 Thermocouple Circuits

Consider the circuit shown in Fig. 9.11(a) where two dissimilar metals x and y are joined together to form the junctions J_1 and J_2. If J_1 and J_2 are kept at temperatures T_1 and T_2,

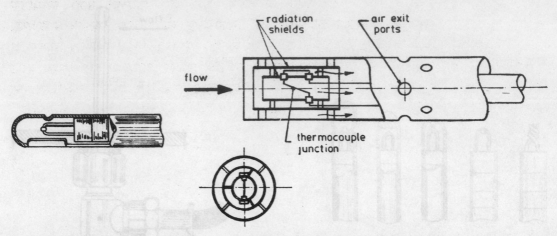

Fig. 9.9 Thermocouple probe
for high speed gases

Fig. 9.10 Total air temperature probe for high
temperature applications

a thermal emf is produced in the circuit, to a first approximation, this potential is a linear function of the temperature difference $\Delta T = T_1 - T_2$. The generated voltage is independent of the temperature and temperature gradient of the lead wires themselves. In a measurement system, one of the junctions can be maintained as a reference junction of known temperature; this junction is usually termed as the cold junction, since 273.15 K is often used as the reference temperature. The thermal emf is usually measured with a millivolt meter or potentiometer, both of which can be directly calibrated in terms of temperature.

In thermocouple circuits, symmetrical connection points (or even lines) of a different material can be arranged differentially without any consequences, as long as these points (or lines) are at the same temperature, as shown in Fig. 9.11(a). If one of the conductors is broken and a millivoltmeter is inserted (Fig. 9.11(b)), with leads made of material z (e.g. copper), and if both points of contact (J_3 and J_4) of the broken lead are kept at the same temperature T_3, there will be no effect on the thermal emf, although two new but differentially arranged thermocouples J_3 and J_4 are formed. However, if points J_3 and J_4 were at different temperatures, the thermoelectric voltages of the circuit would be equal to the algebraic sum of all individual voltages.

Usually, it is desirable to directly measure the temperature T_1 at point J_1, in which case the circuit shown in Fig. 9.11(b) is modified to 9.11(c). Instead of opening one lead and using two thermocouples, point J_2 is opened and the millivoltmeter is connected to points J_2 and J_3. Again, two new differentially arranged thermocouples have been formed with their temperatures being equal to T_2. If T_2 is kept constant at 0°C, the temperature difference ΔT between T_1 and T_2 could be the same as T_1. In case T_2 is kept at some other temperature, say 15°C, then

$$\Delta T = T_1 - 15°C$$

When the leads of the thermocouple are short and the temperature to be measured is relatively high, it would be difficult to maintain a constant temperature at junctions J_2 and J_3 because of the large fluctuating temperature gradients between the junction and the

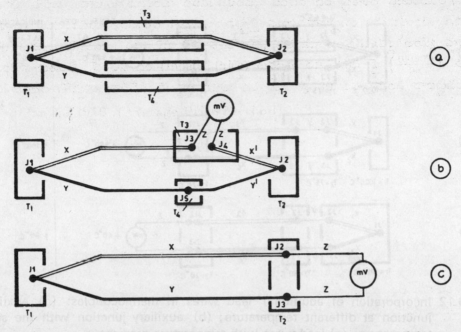

Fig. 9.11 Circuit arrangement for thermocouple measurements: (a) basic
circuit; (b) measurement with auxiliary junction; (c) alternate
circuit with the auxiliary junction

indicator. In such cases, separate reference junctions J_{12} and J_{13}, located at a more favourable position away from points J_2 and J_3 with extension leads can be employed as shown in Fig. 9.12(a) and (b). The extension leads x_3 and x_4 must however be made of the same material as x_1 and x_2. The terminal tie lugs at J_2' and J_3 can be made out of any material y, and the junctions so formed can be maintained at any temperature with respect to T_1 and T_3 (and also with respect to each other). It is essential however that the junctions $x_1 - y$ and $y - x_3$ as well as $x_2 - y$ and $y - x_4$ are at the same temperature so that there are no parasitic thermoelectric currents. This arrangement may not always hold good in plug type connectors, in which case it is advisable to use special type of inserts of thermoelectric material.

Figure 9.12(c) illustrates the effects of temperature gradients in the extension lead connections. The extension points J_2 and J_2' as well as J_3 and J_3' are assumed to be terminals that are connected with lead material y. The entire thermocouple with leads $x_1 - x_2$ is at the same temperature and hence there will be no thermoelectric emf formed between junctions J_2 and J_3, J_2 and J_2', or between J_3 and J_3', despite the large temperature difference between $J_2 J_2'$ and $J_3 J_3'$ because of the use of two similar leads y.

In measurements with chromel-alumel thermocouples, the emf generated will have a high drop if the leads are long. However, lead extensions can be carried out using copper-constantan wires to reduce the lead resistance effects. In the case of platinum/platinum-rhodium thermocouples, extension leads of copper or copper-nickel alloy are usually used for economic reasons. The thermoelectric voltage of these extension leads with respect to the thermocouple remains small within a limited temperature range.

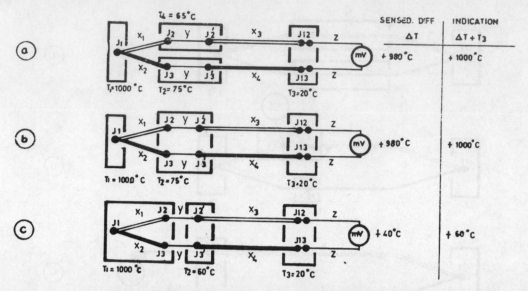

Fig. 9.12 Incorporation of additional lead wires in thermocouples: (a) auxiliary junction at different temperature; (b) auxiliary junction with the same temperature; (c) lead wires with temperature gradient

Thermocouple circuits (in contrast to those utilizing resistance elements) are characterized by measurement errors that occur as a result of parasitic voltages/currents, which often cannot be isolated from the true emf. Parasitic currents are particularly troublesome when several thermocouples are connected to a single indicator through a non-bipolar selector switch. Since the current in thermocouple circuits also depends on the resistance of all the leads, the calibration of the indicator is valid only for a particular total resistance value. The effect of lead resistance is negligible in the case of measurement with high-input impedance circuits. It may be noted that the insulation resistance of thermocouples reduces considerably at high temperatures.

9.7.3 Effect of Reference Junction

In a thermocouple measurement set-up, if the cold reference junction is kept at a temperature t_r which is different from the temperature at which it is calibrated (t_c) the measured thermoelectric voltage e_a can be corrected according to the formula,

$$e = e_a + \Delta e = e_a + k(t_r - t_c) \tag{9.25}$$

where k is the voltage change per unit temperature difference between the reference junction temperature t_r and the calibrated reference temperature t_c and e is the corrected thermoelectric voltage.

The required correction in the reference junction temperature can be electronically obtained by incorporating cold junction compensation in the circuitry, as shown in Fig. 9.13. An additional voltage is introduced into the measuring circuit, the magnitude and sign of which is a function of the reference-temperature variation.

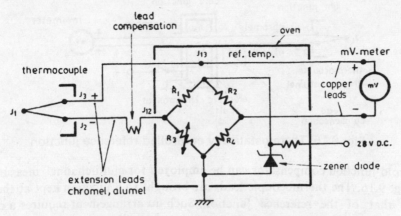

Fig. 9.13 Compensation of reference temperature variations

9.7.4 Thermocouple Indicators

The accuracy of measurement of the thermocouple emf depends very much on the circuit arrangement of the indicator. In a simple instrument using a moving-coil instrument, as shown in Fig. 9.14, the reference point is located within the compensated indicator with the thermocouple leads taken directly to the instrument. If the thermocouple is Fe−Cn, the lead wire used is made of iron for the positive line and constantan for the negative line. Compensation for the changes in the ambient temperature is achieved using a bimetallic spring mounted on the moving-coil device and a resistance R_c having a negative temperature coefficient in series with the coil. Since the indicator is a current-operated device, a trim resistance of constantan wire is added in series with the negative lead, taking care of different lengths of extension leads. A measuring device of this type has a permissible tolerance of $\pm 10°C$ in the measurement range of 0 to 1000°C. A thermostatically-controlled reference point, as shown in Fig. 9.15, gives better accuracy than the cold-junction compensator discussed earlier.

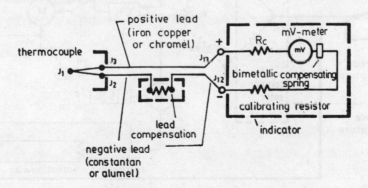

Fig. 9.14 Compensated indicator

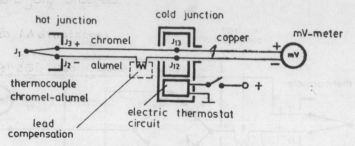

Fig. 9.15 Thermostatically controlled reference junction

A single cold-junction compensator can be employed for multi-channel measurements, as shown in Fig. 9.16. The thermocouple leads are brought to a junction kept at the same temperature as that of the reference junction. Such an arrangement requires a considerable

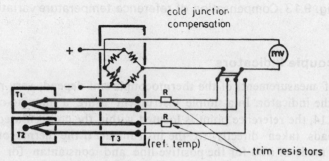

Fig. 9.16 Multiple thermocouple measurements

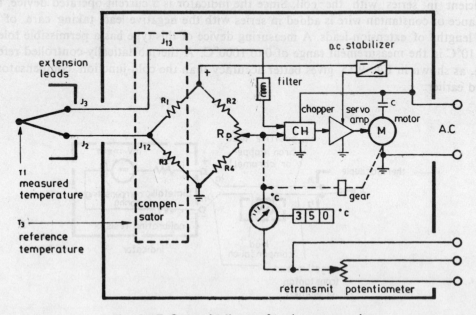

Fig. 9.17 Servo indicator for thermocouples

amount of copper wire between the junction point and the commutator. In practice, a separate trim resistance is added in series with each thermocouple lead, if exact measurements are needed. In principle, this can be extended to more number of channels for measurement of average temperatures.

Methods relying on the measurement of the current formed in the thermocouple loop have the disadvantage that any change in lead resistance due to thermocouples introduces errors. The effect of lead resistances can be eliminated, if measurements of the thermal emf are without any loading. This can be achieved by a servo-balanced potentiometer indicator, as shown in Fig. 9.17, where the thermoelectric voltage is balanced with a variable voltage across the diagonal branch of the bridge, the magnitude of which is adjusted by the potentiometer R_p.

9.8 SOLID-STATE SENSORS

The common silicon transistor normally used in electronic circuits can be employed as a high-quality temperature-sensing device with certain precautions.

The current across any *p-n* junction of a silicon transistor under forward-bias conditions consists of at least three major components, viz., diffusion current, recombination current, and leakage current.

It is well-known that the forward bias voltage of a *p-n* junction varies linearly with temperature for constant forward current. In a transistor, the collector current I_C is proportional to the emitter current I_E and is related by the equation,

$$-I_C = \alpha I_E - I_{CO} \tag{9.26}$$

where α is the short-circuit forward-transfer ratio and I_{CO} is the collector reverse current. The emitter current I_E in turn depends upon the emitter reverse current I_{EO} absolute temperature T, and the emitter-base forward bias voltage V_{BE} given by

$$I_E = I_{EO}\left(\exp\frac{qV_{BE}}{kt} - 1\right) \tag{9.27}$$

where q is the electronic charge and k is the Boltzmann's constant. This may be rewritten as

$$V_{BE} = \frac{kT}{q} \ln\left(\frac{I_E + I_{EO}}{I_{EO}}\right) \tag{9.28}$$

If the emitter current is held constant, the term in parentheses becomes a constant and the emitter base voltage is a linear function of temperature. However, in practice this linear temperature to voltage coefficient differs from transistor to transistor, as the term is also dependent on the actual value of V_{BE}. In batch production, the V_{BE} for a particular transistor can vary by as much as ± 100 mV.

In order to use the transistor with good interchangeability, the spread in V_{BE} values of individual transistors should be taken care of along with the constant current operation by having a provision to obtain same V_{BE} with different collector currents.

Another circuit technique for improving linearity and interchangeability of transistor temperature sensors is the collector current step method. If the collector current is varied between a fairly high value I_{C1} and a fairly low value I_{C2}, the corresponding change in V_{BE} is given by

$$\Delta V_{BE} = V_{BE1} - V_{BE2} = \frac{kT}{q} \ln \frac{I_{C_1}}{I_{C_2}} \tag{9.29}$$

The amplitude of the resulting voltage step is a linear function of the absolute temperature, without any offset and independent of the other properties of the semiconductor material or geometrical parameters. However, this gives rise to a reduced sensitivity apart from the fact that step-voltage amplitudes are to be measured for the temperature values.

An alternative method employs the negative feedback principle[2], where the sensor transistor is connected across the output of a self-balancing bridge and the feedback voltage is linearly proportional to the temperature.

The linear relationship between V_{BE} and T does not hold good below 170 K, due to incomplete ionization of donor or acceptor atoms. The higher limit for the sensor arises due to heat transfer characteristics and is as recommended by the transistor manufacturer.

9.9 QUARTZ THERMOMETER

A piezoelectric quartz crystal-type thermometer provides a unique method of measuring temperature with good accuracy and high stability. The principle is based upon the dominant property of a thickness-shear type LC cut crystal in which the change in the resonance frequency for a given change in temperature is highly linear with excellent repeatability in the range of 193 to 523 K. The linearity obtained is considerably better than that of the platinum resistance thermometer, thermocouple, or thermistor.

The relationship between the frequency f and temperature T of a thickness-shear resonator[3] is given by

$$f = f_0(1 + AT + BT^2 + CT^3) \tag{9.30}$$

where A, B, and C are constants and f_0 is the resonance frequency at temperature T.

In the LC cut crystal, the coefficients B and C are negligible, as such, the changes in resonance frequency versus temperature exhibit a highly linear relationship. With a resonator, operating at 28 MHz in the third overtone, the temperature sensitivity is of the order of 1000 Hz per °C, and the linearity is $\pm 0.5\%$ F.S. Being a frequency variable device, the output is in a discrete digital format and is immune to any signal-noise or cable resistance effects. A high resolution of the order of $\pm 5 \times 10^{-4}$ °C is achievable both for absolute and differential temperature measurements.

The sensor crystal is hermetically sealed in a cylindrical copper case in a helium atmosphere, and the case itself is further enclosed in a stainless steel tubular body as in thermocouples. With a suitable design of the resonator and the closely-coupled probe structure, a response time as low as 1 second is obtained. The device is normally calibrated at the ice point and boiling point of water. Considering the absolute accuracy, long-term stability, speed of response, and reliability, the quartz thermometer is ideally suited for many measurements in the limited range of 223 to 423 K in preference to thermocouples or platinum-resistance thermometers.

9.10 TEMPERATURE MEASUREMENT BY RADIATION METHODS

So far we considered methods of temperature measurement where the temperature probe is brought into contact with the medium whose temperature is being measured. The temperature sensor generally assumes the same temperature as the medium, which imposes the condition that the sensor must be capable of withstanding these temperatures. This requirement can create problems in measuring high temperatures using the sensors discussed so far. Non-contact type sensors based upon radiation methods find wide application in aerospace and industrial fields.

Any body which is above the absolute zero in temperature emits radiation, the quality being dependent on temperature. The radiation temperature sensors operate by detecting electromagnetic wave signals in the visible and infrared regions of the spectrum, mainly in the range 0.3 to 40 microns. An ideal thermal radiator is known as a black body, and such a body can completely absorb any radiation falling on it. A black body, at a given temperature, emits the maximum amount of thermal radiation possible. For a black body, the work function relationship is obtained from Planck's law and is expressed as

$$E_\lambda = \frac{c_1 \lambda^{-5}}{e^{c_2/\lambda T} - 1} \tag{9.31}$$

where E_λ is the spectral radiant intensity in W/cm^2-μ, c_1 and c_2 are the first and second radiation constants (expressed in microwatts per cm^2 per 0.01 μ zone of spectrum) λ is the wavelength of radiation in microns (μ) and T is the absolute temperature of the black body. Thus knowing the other parameters, it is possible to determine the temperature of a black body by the measurement of E_λ. For various values of T, the variation of E_λ with λ is shown in Fig. 9.18. Thus, the temperature of a medium can be interpreted in terms of spectral radi-

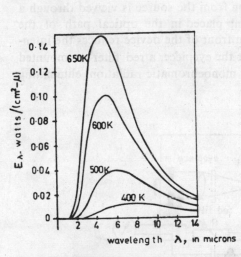

Fig. 9.18 Relation between work function of a black body and wavelengths

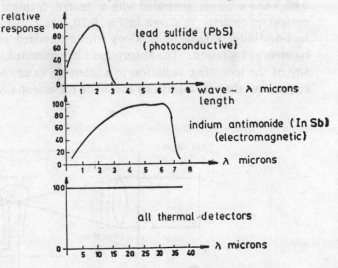

Fig. 9.19 Response of photon detectors

ance. The radiation spectrum in the range of 0.3 to 40 micron (visible and infrared) can be sensed with suitable radiation sensors with their construction approximately close to a black body.

Radiation detectors can be classified as thermal or photon detectors. Thermal detectors are blackened elements designed to absorb a maximum of the incoming radiation at all wavelengths. The absorbed radiation causes the temperature of the detector to rise until an equilibrium is reached, with heat loss to the surroundings. A resistance thermometer or a thermistor, made in the form of thin films, can be employed to measure the rise in temperature of the thermal detectors. Such thermal detectors are commonly known as bolometers.

In photon detectors, the radiation consisting of photons releases electrons in the detector structure, resulting in a change in the electrical resistance or potential. These are basically photoconductive or photovoltaic cells and possess a higher speed of response than thermal detectors. The sensitivity varies with wavelength, as shown in Fig. 9.19. Photon detectors based on the Hall effect are also employed for temperature measurements. One such popular device is the lead sulphide photoconductive cell. Typical units having areas between 1 and 35 mm^2 exhibit resistances in the range 10^5 to 2×10^6 ohms with time constants of 0.05 to 2 ms. Signal measurements can be carried out with a standard bridge, potentiometer, or chopper stabilized amplifier.

9.11 OPTICAL PYROMETERS

Optical pyrometers make use of the changes in colour of a hot body and interpret this phenomena in terms of temperature. When a body is heated, it initially becomes dark red, turns to orange, and finally attains a white colour. The actual temperature measurement is based upon the determination of the variations in colour of the object, and comparing it with known values generated with a heated filament. A schematic block diagram of the optical pyrometer is shown in Fig. 9.20. The radiation from the source is viewed through a lens-and-filter arrangement, along with a standard lamp placed in the optical path of the incoming radiation. The absorption filter mounted in front of the device reduces the intensity of the incoming radiation to a tolerable value. At the eyepiece, a red filter is mounted to ensure that comparisons are made for essentially monochromatic radiation, eliminating

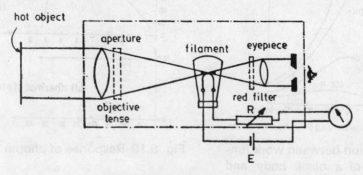

Fig. 9.20 Heated filament pyrometer

the source of the uncertainties resulting from variation of radiation properties with wavelengths. By suitable adjustment of the lamp current, the colour of the filament is made to match with the colour of the incoming radiation. When balance conditions are achieved, the filament will seem to disappear in the total incoming radiation field. Temperature calibration is then made in terms of the lamp-heating current.

9.12 CALIBRATION OF THERMOMETERS

Temperature-measuring devices should be calibrated periodically to evaluate their performance. Such calibration can be carried out either by comparison with a standard device whose accuracy is known or by the use of fixed points. The first method has the advantage that the test can be performed at any desired temperature, within the temperature range of interest, in a bath. The attainable accuracy depends on the uniformity of the temperature distribution in the test bath or oven and the quality of the reference standard used. The reference standard should possess an accuracy of at least one order higher in magnitude than that of the sensor under test. Calibration using fixed points allows the greatest possible accuracy attainable, but an elaborate measurement set-up is needed for each point.

9.12.1 Comparison Method

Both the comparison and calibration of temperature sensors can be carried out in liquid baths or in furnaces. The standard liquid-in-glass thermometers, resistance thermometers, or thermocouples whose indicating errors, resistance values, or thermal voltages as a function of temperature are known to a sufficient degree of accuracy can be used as the reference device.

For tests in the range −100 to 600°C, it is preferable to use an electrically-heated liquid bath as shown in Fig. 9.21(a). The following materials are suitable for use as bath liquids:

Material	Range
Methanol	−100 to 0°C
Water	0 to 99°C
Silicone oil	50 to 250°C
Tin	250 to 630°C

For tests below room temperature, the bath liquid can be cooled by a suitable refrigeration system or liquid nitrogen. Electrically heated furnaces, as shown in Fig. 9.21(b) can be used for temperatures up to 800°C.

The metal block which is used as a reservoir of heat with uniform temperature distribution under equilibrium conditions should be of a high heat resistance material with excellent thermal conductivity. The cylindrical block is provided with a number of equidistant holes to accommodate the sensors under test as shown in the figure. Materials used for the block are aluminium and copper up to 500°C and pure nickel up to 800°C.

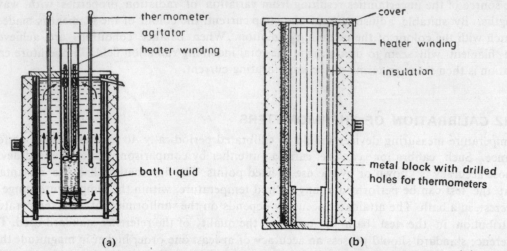

Fig. 9.21 Temperature calibration: (a) electrically heated liquid bath; (b) metal block furnace

9.12.2 Fixed Points

The various fixed points used as reference standards for temperature calibration are given in Table 9.2. Among these points, the ice point, the triple point of water, and the boiling point of water are conditions that can be attained with comparative ease. To obtain the ice point, a standard Dewar flask filled with finely-crushed ice obtained from distilled water can be utilized. The water content is kept minimum to avoid any floating of ice particles in water, thereby ensuring that the sensor is always in contact with ice only.

The triple point of water is obtained by using a glass cell filled with pure water, as shown in Fig. 9.22(a). The gases in and above the water are initially pumped out and the glass is sealed. A protective tube is provided at the centre of the water column to act as the thermo-

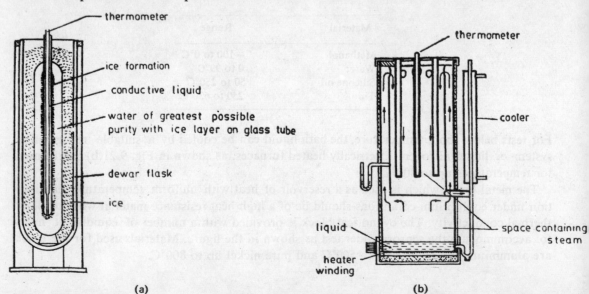

Fig. 9.22 Calibration at fixed points: (a) triple point vessel; (b) boiling point apparatus

meter well for the sensor under test. Packing the outer column with finely-crushed dry ice, a thin mantle of ice of a few millimeters thick is produced on the outside surface of the well. At this stage, the ice is taken out and replaced momentarily by water at room temperature, thereby producing a thin layer of water column between the well and the mantle of ice. The temperature of this layer will be 0.0075°C, at 4.58 mm Hg, which is termed as the triple point of water.

The boiling point temperature with any liquid is obtained with a boiler as shown in Fig. 9.22(b). The temperature at which the condensation of the liquid vapour occurs at a particular pressure is taken as the reference temperature, since this value is independent of the non-vaporized impurities present in the liquid.

EXERCISES

9.1 The resistance of a thermistor is 800 ohms at 50°C and 4 kohms at the ice point. Calculate the characteristic constants (a, b) for the thermistor and the variation in resistance between 30 and 100°C.

9.2 The resistance of a platinum resistance thermometer element at 15°C is required to be 50 ohms. Determine the length of the wire needed if the diameter of the wire is 2.5 mm. Assuming that the temperature coefficient of resistance of the wire is constant, calculate the element resistances at 0 and 100°C (use necessary tables).

9.3 The temperature of an oven is raised at the rate of 200°C per hour. For the condition that the indicating instrument must not show an error more than 5°C, what is the maximum permissible time constant?

9.4 A thermocouple bead has an approximate shape of a sphere, 1.54 mm in dia, with a density of 7360 kg/m³ and specific heat of 100 J kg⁻¹ K⁻¹. If the bead is exposed to a convection environment where the heat-transfer coefficient is 15×10^3 J h⁻¹ m⁻²×K, estimate the time constant of the thermocouple.

9.5 A 100-ohm resistance thermometer carrying a 2.0 mA current is exposed in still air with a surface area of 130 mm² whose heat-transfer coefficient is 8.5 W m⁻² K⁻¹. Find the self-heating error. (Note: See Sec. 8.7.2).

9.6 A first-order thermocouple having a time constant $\tau = 0.01$ s is to be used to measure a temperature change approximated by

$$T = 33 \times 10^3 t \text{ for } 0 \leqslant t < 0.03 \text{ s}$$
$$= 1000°C \text{ for } t \geqslant 0.03 \text{ s}$$

where T is the input temperature in °C and t is the time in seconds. (a) Plot the input and indicated temperatures. (b) Design a first-order compensating network for the thermocouple to reduce its time constant by a factor of 5. (c) What is the resultant loss in sensitivity of the thermocouple?

9.7 A thermocouple having a sensitivity of 40 µV/°C is calibrated at a reference temperature of 0°C. However, if it is actually used with a reference temperature of 40°C, what would be the output voltage at 100°C?

REFERENCES

1. Benedict, R.P., "Temperature and its measurement", *Electro-Technology*, Vol. 72, No. 3, pp. 71-74, July 1963.
2. Ruehle, R.A., "Solid-state temperature sensors out performs previous transducers", *Electronics*, Vol. 48, No. 6, pp. 127-131, March 20, 1975.
3. Karrer, H.E., "The piezoelectric resonator as a temperature sensor", *Advances in Instrumentation*, Part IV, Vol. 26, Instrument Society of America, Pittsburg, 1971.

BIBLIOGRAPHY

Aranson, M.H. (Ed.), *Temperature Measurement and Control Handbook*, I.S.A., Publication, Pittsburg, 1961.

Baker, H.D., Ryder, E.A. and Baker, N.H., *Temperature Measurement in Engineering*, Vols. I and II, John Wiley & Sons, New York, 1953.

Benedict, R.P., *Fundamentals of Temperature, Pressure and Flow Measurements*, J. Wiley and Sons, New York, 1969.

Benedict, R.P. and Russo, R.J., "Calibrating platinum resistance thermometers", *Instruments and Control Systems*, Vol. 45, No. 10, pp. 55-56, October 1972.

Bogdon, L. High, "Temperature thin film resistance thermometers", *NACA CR 26*, 1964.

Bremhorst, K., "Measurement of instantaneous fluid temperature and two fluid velocity components using hot wire anemometers", *IEEE Trans. Inst. and Meas.*, Vol. IM-23, No. 1, pp. 96-7, March 1974.

Broughton, M.B., "Analysis and design of almost linear one thermistor temperature transducers", *IEEE Trans. Instr. and Meas.*, IM-23, No. 1, pp. 1-5, March 1974.

Caldwell, F.R., "Thermocouple materials", NBS monograph, 40 and NBS Circular 561.

Consindine, D.M., *Process Instruments and Controls Handbook*, McGraw-Hill, New York, 1974.

Diamond, J.M., "Linearization of resistance thermometers and other transducers", *Rev. of Sc. Instr.*, Vol. 41, No. 1, pp. 53-60, Jan. 1970.

Ekin, J.W. and Wagner, D.K., "A simple ac bridge circuit for use in four terminal resistance thermometry", *Rev. Sci. Instr.* Vol. 41, No. 7, pp. 1109-1110, July 1970.

Freeze, P.D., "Review of recent developments of high temperature thermocouples", *ASME Paper 63*, WA 212, 1963.

Fribance, A.E., *Industrial Instrumentation, Fundamentals*, McGraw-Hill, New York, 1962.

Garelick, L. and Hamptmann, E., "Linearising thermocouple amplifiers", *Advances in Instrumentation*, Vol. 26, pt 4, paper 852, 1971.

Griffiths, E., *Methods of Measuring Temperature*, Charles Griffin & Co., Ltd., London, 1947.

Harrison, T.R., *Radiation Pyrometry and its Underlying Principles of Heat Transfer*, John Wiley & Sons Inc., New York, 1960.

Hertzfeld, Ch. M., *Temperature—its Measurement and Control in Science and Industry*, Rheinhold, New York, Vols. 1, 2, and 3, 1961.

Kadis, A.L., "Using DPMS for thermocouple readouts", *Instr. and Control Systems*, Vol. 46, No. 6, p. 43, June 1973.

Kusters, N.L. and McMartin, M.P., "Direct current comparator bridge for resistance thermometry", *IEEE Tr. Instr. and Meas.*, IM-19, No. 4, pp. 291-297, Nov. 1970.

Legan, C.A. and Cook, W.E., "A linear platinum resistance temperature circuit", *Control Engineering*, Vol. 17, No. 12, pp. 58-59, December 1970.

Lion, K.S., *Instrumentation for Scientific Research*, McGraw-Hill, New York, 1959.

Liptak, B.G., *Instrument Engineers Handbook*, Chilton Book Co., New York, 1970.

Lagan C.A. and Cook, W.E., "A linear platinum resistance temperature detection circuit", *Control Engineering*, Vol. 17, No. 12, pp. 58-59, December 1970.

Marsh, R.H., "Selecting thermocouples and platinum resistance temperature detectors", *Control Engg.*, Vol. 18, No. 11, pp. 76-77, Nov. 1971.

Moffat, "Thermocouple—theory and practice", *Fundamentals of Aerospace Instn.*, Vol. 6, pp. 111-124, 1974.

Neubert, H.K.P., *Instrument Transducers*, Oxford University Press, London, 1963.

Noakes, W., "Thermometry by radiation, Part I, Factors affecting design", *Control and Instrumentation*, Vol. 3, No. 8, pp. 45-47, Sept. 1971.

Norton, H.N., *Handbook of Transducers for Electronic System*, Prentice-Hall, N.J., 1968.

Owens, D., "The quartz crystal thermometer", *Lab. Equip. Dig.*, Vol. 11, No. 11, pp. 138-143, Nov. 1973.

Pantic D., "Application of digital linearizer with cycle counter to thermocouples", *Electronics Letter*, Vol. 10, No. 2, pp. 19-21, 24 Jan. 1974.

Paul, S.H., Hmurick, L.V., "Instantaneous temperature measurement", *Rev. Sci. Instn.*, Vol. 44, No. 9, pp. 1363-1364, Sept. 1973.

Samsonov, G.V. and Kislyi, P.S., *High Temperature Non-metallic Thermocouples and Sheaths*, Consultant Bureau, New York, 1967.

Stein, P.K., *Measurement Engineering*, Vol. I, Stein Engineering Services, Arizona, 1964.

"Temperature-measurement", British Standard Code, 1042, BSI, London.

Thompson, A.M. and Small, G.W., "AC bridge for platinum resistance thermometry", *IEE Proc.*, Vol. 118, pp. 1662-1666, 1971.

Thulin, A., "Double bridge for resistance thermometry using fixed ratio arms", *Jn. of Phy. E. Scientific Instr.*, Vol. 3, No. 10, pp. 795-797, Oct. 1970.

Trofimenkoff, F.N. and Smallwood, R.E., "JFET circuit linearizes transducers output", *IEEE Trans. Instr. and Measurement*, Vol. IM-22, No. 2, pp. 191-193, June 1973.

10

FORCE AND TORQUE

10.1 INTRODUCTION

Force is one of the major derived physical parameters having dimensions of mass, length, and time. It is a vector quantity which when applied results in a change of momentum in a body. Basically, mechanical forces are created due to the variation of stored potential energy resulting from a change in some physical dimension or by the time rate of change of momentum of a mass. Potential-energy forces are static in nature and are usually associated with elastic deformation of a material, whereas momentum-generated forces are dynamic. Included in this category are forces due to linear motion, thrust, vibratory forces, and forces in rotating components (torque). Other basic force parameters are pressure (force per unit area) and acceleration (force per unit mass being accelerated). The force applied to a body or structure is often termed as the load.

The measurement of force in a situation where a system of forces is acting is carried out either by direct measurement in which an elastic device is positioned in the line of action of a force and becomes a part of the mechanical system or by an indirect measurement in which the elastic deformation of one of the force-bearing members is measured and force deduced. The property of elasticity ensures a proportional reaction which can be measured either as displacement or strain. The direct method requires that the device intended to measure the force be capable of sustaining the full effect of the force, either in tension or in compression. Among the simplest examples are the measurement of static weight using a physical balance or the weighing of a truck with a weigh bridge. The mass in both cases is static in nature and exerts a purely vertical force due to gravity on the measuring device. Such a method of direct measurement possesses the highest inherent accuracy.

When the force is deduced from the deformation of an elastic member, the measurement accuracy depends not only on the accuracy of the sensor measuring the deformation, but also, on the theoretical interpretation of deformation. Whatever be the principle of operation of the force-measuring device, it is invariably possible to calibrate it against fundamental standards of mass.

The measurement of force can be achieved with both mechanical sensors as well as electrical sensors, but in this book, emphasis is placed more on the electrical transduction principle.

10.2 FORCE-MEASURING SENSOR—LOAD CELL

The load cell is an electromechanical sensor employed to measure static and dynamic forces. The device can be designed to handle a wide range of operating forces with high level of reliability, and hence it is one of the most popular transducer in industrial measurements. The load cell derives its output from the deformation of an elastic member having high tensile strength. The elastic member is made of homogeneous materials, preferably steel alloys, manufactured to very close tolerances. The basic design parameters include relative size and shape, material density and modulus of elasticity, strain sensitivity, deflection, and dynamic response.

Through a careful choice of the material and structural configuration, a linear relationship between a dimensional change and measured force can be achieved. The materials so chosen should possess the following properties: (a) linear stress strain relationship up to a fairly large elastic strain limit (typically 5000 micro-strains); (b) low strain hysteresis over repeated loadings (< 2 micro-strains); (c) very low creep over long periods of loading (< 5 micro-strains); and (d) very low plastic flow due to strain. In addition, many other material properties, such as the modulus of elasticity and its variation with temperature, ultimate strength, linearity of stress developed with force, and ease of fabrication are to be considered while selecting the most appropriate material for the elastic element. The various elastic materials suitable for the purpose are medium to high carbon steels of chromium molybdenum, and precipitate-hardened stainless steel (such as S_{94-98}, EN_{24} and EN_{28}). It is essential to harden the material with heat treatment to the required level for a specific application to keep the hysteresis and creep low and to obtain good repeatability.

The most popular types of configurations are analysed in the following sections.

10.2.1 Column-Type Devices

The simplest method for measuring unidirectional forces is to use a column or rod in tension or compression. The stress developed due to the force on loading is measured with electrical strain gauges attached to the body as shown in Fig. 10.1. In Fig. 10.1 the strain gauges 1 and 3, which are fixed on the opposite sides are aligned to measure axial strains only, whereas gauges 2 and 4 will measure the circumferential strains due to applied force. (Strain gauges 3 and 4 are not indicated in the figure.) The strain values can be expressed as

$$\epsilon_1 = \epsilon_3 = \frac{\sigma}{E} = \frac{F}{AE} \tag{10.1}$$

$$\epsilon_2 = \epsilon_4 = -\nu \frac{F}{AE} \tag{10.2}$$

where ϵ_1 to ϵ_4 are the strains sensed by the strain gauges, σ is the stress developed in the column, F is the axial force, A is the cross-sectional area of the column, E is the modulus of elasticity, and ν is the Poisson's ratio of the material of the rod. The strain measurement is carried out with a standard four-arm active Wheatstone's bridge as shown in Fig. 5.15. If V is the excitation voltage applied, the output voltage e is given by $e = 0.65\ VG\epsilon$, where G is the gauge factor of the strain gauges used. (See Chapter 5 for details.)

In addition to the symmetrical arrangement of the gauges and the rod, the column should be loaded as centrally as possible to avoid bending forces in the column, which can intro-

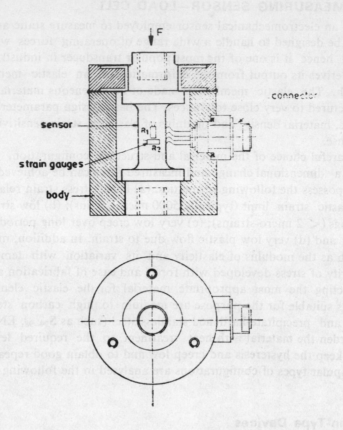

Fig. 10.1 Column type load cell assembly

duce a second-order error if the sensitivities of the longitudinal strain gauges are not identical. Similarly, rotating moments or torque should also not be transmitted. It is customary to design load cells in such a way that, at the nominal load specified, the stress levels will not exceed a particular value (about 2×10^8 N/m² for steel) which is well within safe limits.

When the load F acts on a cross-sectional area A, then the stress σ developed will be $\sigma = \dfrac{F}{A}$. To develop the same stress value at the nominal load, the cross-sectional area has to be small as the nominal load range decreases. One way of reducing the cross-sectional area is to bore a hole along the length, thus making use of a hollow cylinder. However, these slender columns are susceptible to buckling above a particular load. The limiting dimension for such load cells is the surface area required for physical bonding of the strain gauges. In general, column-type load cells are ideally suited for ranges of 2 t and above. Foil strain gauges are usually employed for strain measurements. For operation under adverse industrial conditions, the whole load cell assembly is hermetically sealed, with the joints electron beam welded.

10.2.2 Proving Rings

An alternative to the column-type load cell is the proving ring which is better suited for lower load ranges. An arrangement · of the proving ring type load cell, also known as the ring dynamometer is shown in Fig. 10.2. The forces applied across the ring, as shown in the figure, develop circumferential stresses. Such a loading causes compressive strains on the inner surfaces and tensile strains on the outer surfaces with maximum stresses occurring at 90° points of arc in either direction from the point of application of force. The strain levels are sensed by strain gauges R_1, R_2, R_3, and R_4 bonded onto the surface. Since both tensile and compressive strains are equal, a relatively higher output can result from the measuring bridge when compared to the axially-loaded columns.

Referring to Fig. 10.2 for a thin-walled ring[1], the bending couple M_θ at an angle θ from the direction of force can be expressed as

$$M_\theta = \frac{Fr}{2}\left(\sin\theta - \frac{2}{\pi}\right) \tag{10.3}$$

where r is the mean radius of the ring. The equation is valid only when the top and bottom of the ring are restrained from rotation. From Eq. (10.3) the bending couple at $\theta = 90°$ (where strain gauges are located) is

$$M = 0.182Fr \tag{10.4}$$

The maximum stress σ and maximum strain ϵ in the thin-walled ring are related by

$$\sigma = \frac{M_\theta t}{2I} \tag{10.5}$$

$$\epsilon = \frac{\sigma}{E} \tag{10.6}$$

where, M_θ — bending couple at an angle θ, $t =$ thickness of the wall, $I =$ moment of inertia about the axis of bending $=(\frac{bt^3}{12}$ for rectangular cross-section, where b is the width of the ring), and $E =$ Young's modulus of the material.

Substituting for M and I, the strain magnitude ϵ becomes[2]

$$\epsilon = \frac{1.092Fr}{Ebt^2} \ (t \ll r) \tag{10.7}$$

and the maximum stress at these points

$$\sigma_{\max} = E\epsilon = \frac{1.092\,F_{\max}r}{bt^2} \tag{10.8}$$

The values for strain ϵ and stress σ obtained from Eqs. (10.7) and (10.8) are from theoretical considerations only. However, in practice, the experimental values will be lower due to the effect of the loading attachments/couples.

As an alternative to the measurement of strain with strain gauges, the load values can be obtained from the measurement of deformation of the ring by an appropriate displacement transducer. The deflection δ_F of the ring due to load F at the maximum deflection point is given by

$$\delta_F = 1.79\frac{Fr^3}{Ebt^3} \tag{10.9}$$

The ring specimen of the type shown in Fig. 10.2(a) will sometimes have a tendency to roll if there are any horizontal components on the specimen. This tendency can be avoided by modifying the shape to that of octogonal rings, as shown in Fig. 10.2(b) where the strains due to vertical loads only are predominant. The strains and deflections developed in this case will however be lower when compared to the circular ring.

From Eq. (10.8), it can be seen that for a given material, as the nominal load reduces it is necessary either to increase the diameter or to reduce the thickness of the ring to obtain a particular stress value. It is obvious that the diameter cannot be increased beyond a practical value, and there exists a minimum below which the thickness cannot be reduced. It follows therefore that these limitations of dimensions also limit the application of the ring type of load cell to nominal loads below 50 kg. Thus, for still smaller load ranges, the alternative approach would be to use cantilever beams.

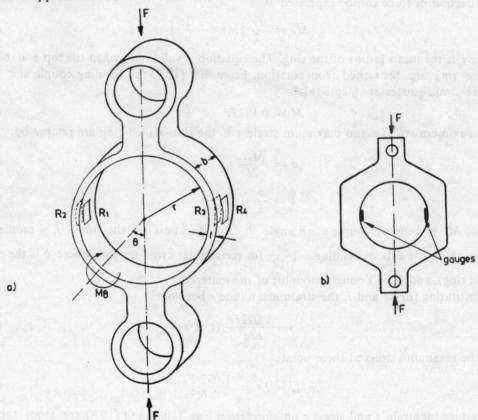

Fig. 10.2 Ring type load cells: (a) proving ring load cell; (b) octogonal ring load cell

10.2.3 Cantilever Beam

A convenient configuration that is in wide use, particularly for loads up to 10 kg is the cantilever beam, the arrangement of which is illustrated in Fig. 10.3. On the application of a force F at the end of the cantilever, a bending moment proportional to the force is developed in the beam. Strain gauges are attached to the top and bottom surfaces of the beam near the fixed end to sense the stresses so developed. With the direction of force as shown, tensile strains developed on the top surface are sensed by gauges R_1 and R_3, while compressive strains developed at the bottom surface are sensed by gauges R_2 and R_4.

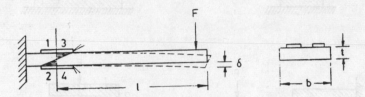

Fig. 10.3 Cantilever beam type load cell

The maximum deflection due to load will occur at the free end of the beam, while maximum strain will be developed at the fixed end. Thus, either the deflection δ or strain ϵ can be measured as a function of the applied force F. The relationship, for these quantities can be expressed as

$$\epsilon = \frac{6Fl}{Ebt^2} \text{ (at the fixed end)} \qquad (10.10)$$

$$\delta = \frac{4Fl^3}{Ebt^3} \text{ (at the free end)} \qquad (10.11)$$

Here again, to obtain a particular value of stress for a given nominal load, length l is increased or width b and thickness t are reduced. This puts a limitation on the lower nominal loads that can be measured. Conversely, for higher loads either l is decreased or b and t are increased, which again puts a limit on the higher nominal loads. In actual practice, the values are optimized for obtaining the best performance. For higher sensitivity, symmetrical double cantilever arrangements are widely employed.

10.2.4 Other Configurations

Using the same principle of measuring stresses developed due to the load applied in an elastic material with suitable strain gauges, various other design configurations[3] can also be achieved differing from those described above. Some of the practical designs are illustrated in Fig. 10.4.

It is important that in all cases the strain gauges should be suitably located so that the output strain is linearly proportional to the input force with minimum hysteresis and creep, high repeatability, and overload capability. Some of the configurations have excellent immunity to adverse side and eccentric loads. They can be designed in ranges from 1 kg to 10 t.

10.2.5 Shear-Type Load Cell

A unique method of measuring the load with the output immune to side loads and bending moments is based on the measurement of shear components. The load cell is basically a

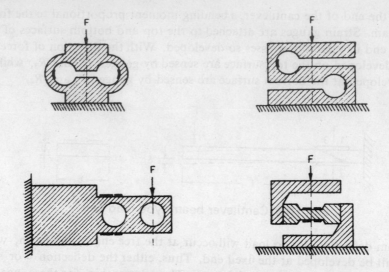

Fig. 10.4 Other practical load cell configurations

beam supported at the both ends as shown in Fig. 10.5, wherein strain gauges bonded at 45°
are employed to measure shear stresses developed on the cross members when the load is
applied. The cantilever beam is deformed into a diamond shape, causing a tensile strain at
the location T and a compressive stress at the location C, by the same amount. The resultant
output is measured with a bridge network and is linearly proportional to the applied
load. A unique feature of the device is that the sensitivity and accuracy are independent of
the point of application of the load. The cross-section of the shear web does not change
under the load condition, and overloads up to 10 times the rated load are easily handled
without any damage. As such it is ideally suited to measure shock loads also. Another
advantage of this type of cell is its capability to withstand high side loads, high bending
moments, offender loading, and low thermal gradient error. The overall linearity and repeat-

load F

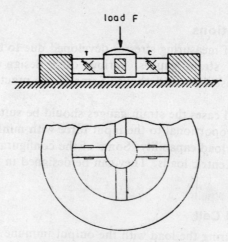

Fig. 10.5 Shear type load cell

ability are excellent. The load cell can be designed with a low profile and is easily adaptable for such applications as tank-and-bin weighing systems, portable scales, hopper scales, and in motion weighing systems. The configuration is ideally suited for the design of torque cells also.

10.2.6 Pressductor

The pressductor is basically a magneto-elastic type force transducer, wherein the permeability of a magnetic material is altered by the mechanical stress developed in it. The device consists of a number of laminated sheets of special magnetic material bonded together to form a transducer body, on which primary and secondary coils are wound and positioned perpendicular to each other and at an angle of 45° to the direction of mechanical force, as shown in Fig. 10.6. When the primary is excited with an alternating current, no magnetic induction is produced in the secondary coil under the no load condition. On the application of mechanical force on the transducer, the permeability in the direction of the force is reduced resulting in a change in shape of the magnetic field. Some of the flux lines now cut the secondary windings, thus inducing a voltage in the secondary. The output voltage is proportional to the applied force. Each lamination in the transducer assembly responds linearly and contributes independently to the total output signal. As such, the accuracy is maintained even though the load is not distributed evenly on the load cell.

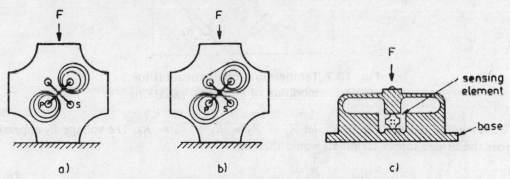

Fig. 10.6 Pressductor: (a) flux contour under no load; (b) flux contour under load; (c) transducer assembly

The load cell can be designed for load capacities ranging from 0.1 to 150 t. Some of the applications are in platform weighing, mobile scales, and batch-weighing systems. The main advantages are that it contains no moving parts, the side load effect is low, and linearity is good. A typical assembly of such a load cell is shown in Fig. 10.6(c).

10.3 EFFECT OF TEMPERATURE VARIATIONS

The elastic elements used for force measurements are affected by ambient temperature variations mainly in two ways: viz., the variation in Young's modulus and change in dimensions. Of these, the variation in Young's modulus is more important as it can contribute to more than 3% error per 100°C in normally used steels, while the other effect can contribute to about 0.1% per 100°C for the same material. Hence, for higher accuracies, it is essential to incorporate temperature compensation, particularly for varation in the Young's modulus.

10.3.1 Temperature Compensation for Young's Modulus Variations

If a load cell using resistance strain gauges is calibrated at a particular temperature, the sensitivity of the transducer increases with an increase in the ambient temperature, due to the decrease in the modulus of elasticity of the material. This particular increase in the sensitivity is separate from the effect of temperature change on the strain gauges themselves. The effect can be compensated by varying the strain gauge bridge sensitivity with appropriate magnitude and sign. In practice, this is achieved by inserting a resistance R_s, having a positive temperature coefficient of resistance, in series with the bridge supply voltage, shown in Fig. 10.7.

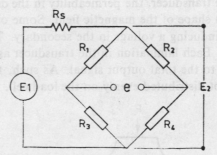

Fig. 10.7 Temperature compensation for modulus of elasticity variations

Under initial balance condition, let $R_1 = R_2 = R_3 = R_4 = R_0$. The voltage E_2 appearing across the bridge supply terminals would then be

$$E_2 = \frac{R_0}{R_0 + R_s} E_1 = \frac{1}{1 + \dfrac{R_s}{R_0}} E_1 \tag{10.12}$$

where E_1 is the supply voltage.

From the bridge sensitivity expression derived in Chapter 4 [Eq. (5.7)], the new output voltage in an equal-arm bridge with identical strain levels will be

$$e = \frac{\Delta R}{R_0} \cdot \frac{1}{1 + \dfrac{R_s}{R_0}} E_1 \tag{10.13}$$

Substituting for ϵ and also for force $F = EA\epsilon$ in Eq. (10.1) where E is the modulus of elasticity of the material, the bridge sensitivity becomes

$$\frac{e}{F} = \frac{E_1 G R_0}{AE(R_s + R_0)} \tag{10.14}$$

where G is the gauge factor of the gauges used.

To maintain the calibration sensitivity constant over a range of temperature t_1 to t_2, $\left(\dfrac{e}{F}\right)_{t_1}$ must be equal to $\left(\dfrac{e}{F}\right)_{t_2}$ i.e.,

$$\frac{E_{1_{t_1}} R_{0_{t_1}} G_{t_1}}{A_{t_1} E_{t_1} (R_{st^1} + R_{0_{t_1}})} = \frac{E_{2_{t_2}} R_{0_{t_2}} G_{t_2}}{A_{t_2} E_{t_2} (R_{s_{t_2}} + R_{0_{t_2}})} \tag{10.15}$$

where suffices t_1 and t_2 specify the values of the variables at temperatures t_1 and t_2.

If it is assumed that the bridge arms are self-compensated, and that the gauge factor, area of cross-section, and supply voltage are constant with temperature variations, then the Eq. (10.15) is satisfied when

$$E_{t_1} (R_{s_{t_1}} + R_0) = E_{t_2} (R_{s_{t_2}} + R_0) \tag{10.16}$$

However,

$$E_{t_2} = E_{t_1} [1 + a(t_2 - t_1)] \tag{10.17}$$

and

$$R_{s_{t_2}} = R_{s_{t_1}} [1 + b(t_2 - t_1)] \tag{10.18}$$

where a is the temperature coefficient of the modulus of elasticity of the material to which the gauges are attached in $N/m^2/°C$ (about 2.6×10^{-6} for nickel steel) and b is the temperature coefficient of the material of the resistance wire in ohm/ohm/°C. Hence, from Eq. (10.16),

$$E_{t_1} (R_{s_{t_1}} + R_0) = E_{t_1} [1 + a(t_2 - t_1)]\{R_{s_{t_1}} [1 + b(t_2 - t_1)] + R_0\} \tag{10.19}$$

Neglecting second-order terms, we get

$$\frac{R_{s_{t_1}}}{R_0} = -\frac{a}{a+b} \tag{10.20}$$

R_s is then computed for the required temperature range. The material for this compensating resistor is chosen on the basis of its temperature coefficient of resistance. Since R_s and R_0 are both positive quantities and a is usually negative, it follows that $|b| \gg |a|$ to make R_s/R_0 as small as possible in order not to affect the overall bridge sensitivity adversely. The material for R_s can be ascertained by knowing the resistance-temperature characteristics of various materials and the load cell material to be compensated.

The length and diameter of the wire for the compensating resistor is appropriately chosen and the compensating resistor is then connected on an unstrained portion of the load cell where it is exposed to the same temperature fluctuations as the base material itself.

10.4 DYNAMIC RESPONSE OF ELASTIC TRANSDUCERS

The idealized model of an elastic force transducer can be represented to have a mass m, spring k and damping c as shown in Fig. 10.8.

The force F acting on the mass m, spring k, and damping c causes a displacement x of the mass as shown. In elastic transducers, these components cannot be distinguished because of the distributed nature. The equation of motion under this condition is

$$m\ddot{x} + c\dot{x} + kx = F \tag{10.21}$$

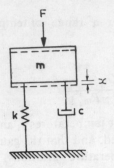

Fig. 10.8 Idealized model of an elastic force transducer

Taking Laplace transformation with zero initial conditions, the equation becomes

$$\frac{x}{F} = \frac{1}{m} \frac{1}{s^2 + 2\zeta\omega_n s + \omega_n^2} \qquad (10.22)$$

where $\omega_n = \sqrt{\dfrac{k}{m}}$, and $\zeta = \dfrac{c}{2\sqrt{km}}$.

Eq. (10.22) can be rewritten as

$$\frac{x}{F} = \frac{1}{k} \frac{1}{\dfrac{s^2}{\omega_n^2} + \dfrac{2\zeta}{\omega_n} s + 1} \qquad (10.23)$$

It may be seen that the natural frequency of the transducer should be high to obtain good dynamic response. However, since a higher natural frequency means a stiffer spring, a higher frequency response can only be obtained at the cost of sensitivity, as discussed in Chapter 3. The same argument holds good even if the strain on the member is monitored instead of the displacement. For design purposes, the natural frequency must be calculated from appropriate formulae, depending upon the geometric shape and dimensions of the cell.

10.5 DIGITAL FORCE TRANSDUCERS

The phenomenon of change in natural frequency of a vibrating string, column, or resonator on the application of a compressional or tensional load can be utilized to design load cells/force-measuring devices giving a digital output which is linearly proportional to the applied load. Some of these devices are presented in Chapters 6 and 7.

10.6 FORCE-BALANCE DEVICE

One of the most accurate methods of weighing is the force-balance system, where the applied load is transferred through a loading beam to a position-sensing device such as an LVDT or a variable capacitance, and the beam position is restored back to original position with a force generator or torque motor. The unknown force or load is then determined in terms of the restoring force. Being a closed-loop electromechanical system, high accuracy is maintained throughout the range. The system is widely used in precision-weighing balances for ranges up to about 100 g with resolutions of the order of 0.001 g. The principle of force balance devices is analysed in Chapters 6 and 7.

10.7 HYDRAULIC LOAD CELL

The limitation of the conventional load cells employing elastic members is their inability to transfer the force from the load-carrying device without restraint error. This is overcome in hydraulic load cells which are also virtually insensitive to angular loads. The inherent accuracy is maintained even when angular or horizontal load displacements occur due to bad filling, expansion, settlement, or deflection. All hydraulic load cells function on a force counterbalance principle wherein the applied load changes the pressure of the internal incompressible fluid of the cell, as shown in Fig. 10.9. This change in pressure is then measured with a wide variety of mechanical or electrical pressure gauges. The hydraulic fluid is confined within the diaphragm chamber by means of a clamped seal between the cylinder wall and the base plate. The load-bearing piston is guided within the cylinder by balls to operate it in parallel with the major axis and to limit the number of degrees of freedom to one. The leakage of the fluid is avoided with a rolling diaphragm. The capacity of the cell can be as high as 50 T. The main advantages of these cells are high capacity with high overload factor, good repeatability, absence of bearings and knife edges, and sufficiently good dynamic response.

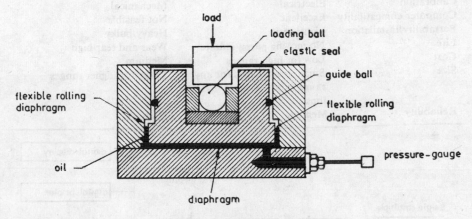

Fig. 10.9 Hydraulic load cell

10.8 ELECTRONIC WEIGHING SYSTEM

Many of the weighing problems in the industrial process as well as in general weighing are solved by incorporating an electronic system for data acquisition, processing, and control purposes. The main advantages of an electronic weighing system when compared with mechanical systems are:

(a) Compactness and small size, independent of capacity
(b) Ruggedness and high dependability, arising out of the absence of pivots, linkages, levers, etc. and of lubrication
(c) High speed of response and hence rapid weighing (useful for in-motion weighing)
(d) Good accuracy even under most adverse and hostile environmental conditions (dust, heat, and cold)
(e) Excellent flexibility to monitor multiple loads and incorporate tare facility
(f) Both analog and digital output with print-out facility, remote indication, and parallel display
(g) Computer compatibility for processing.

Table 10.1 gives a comparison of electronic and mechanical weighing systems. A typical measurement system utilized for many of the applications is shown in Fig. 10.10.

TABLE 10.1 ELECTRONIC VS MECHANICAL WEIGHING

Parameter	Electronic	Mechanical
Accuracy	High	High
Resolution	High	High
Read-out	Digital display instantaneous; no parallax	Pointer; delayed swinging
Remote reading	Excellent; telemetering easy	Difficult
Print-out	Digital printer; high speed; totalizer option	Analog readout; print-out cumbersome; single unit only
Tare capacity	100% F.S.	20% F.S.
Calibration	Electrical	Mechanical
Computer compatibility	Excellent	Not feasible
Portability/installation	Light; easy	Heavy/bulky
Life	No moving parts; infinite	Wear and tear high
Cost	Low for high ranges	Medium
Size	Small; low profiles for any range from 100 kg to 100 tons.	Large for higher ranges
Reliability	Medium	High

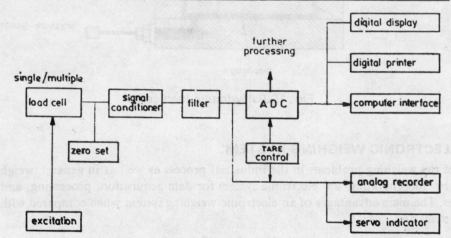

Fig. 10.10 Schematic block diagram of electronic weighing system

The system comprises the basic load cell, suitable signal conditioners, and output recorders/indicators giving both the analog and digital output for further processing. The signal from the load cells (which may be up to 4 or 8 cells) are added and amplified to give an output of 0 to 5 V or 4 to 20 mA for process instrumentation. This is further converted into a digital format with an analog to digital converter so that the output can be indicated or printed out in a digital format or used for processing. Taring facility can be provided wherever necessary.

The main applications of electronic weighing systems are in platform weighers, weighing of vehicles in motion, truck weighing, crane weighing, weigh feeders, tank-and-hopper weighing, and bulk-load sensing as encountered in steel plants, chemical plants, petrochemicals, fertilizers, textile industry, and any general purpose commodity or product weighing.

10.9 TORQUE MEASUREMENT

Torque is the tangential force required to set a body into rotation. It is represented as a moment vector of a force. For a rigid body undergoing free rotations about a single axis, the torque $T = I\alpha$, where I is the moment of inertia of the body about that axis and α is the angular acceleration. Thus, torque is the torsional twisting moment or couple which tends to twist a rigidly fixed object, such as a shaft turning about its axis of rotation. The application of a torque creates an angular displacement of the body about its axis of rotation.

The measurement of torque is often required in many engineering fields, especially in rotating machines. Mechanical, electromechanical, or electronic methods can be employed for the measurement of torque, which are presented below.

10.9.1 Absorption Type

In mechanical transmission systems, the power required to operate a machine or the power developed by the machine itself is often required to assess the efficiency of the machine. This is achieved by using dynamometers, one class of which absorbs the mechanical energy for the measurement of power generated. The input energy from the rotating shaft is dissipated by the absorbing element which tends to rotate along with the input shaft. This rotation is constrained by a force-measuring device, placed at the end of the reaction arm. By measuring the force at the known radius, the unknown torque can be computed.

In rotating machinery the power developed by the engine is determined by the torque applied to the dynamometer. The brake horsepower of the machine is given by

$$P = 2.7 \times 10^{-5} \, FRN \qquad (10.24)$$

where P is the power in brake horsepower, F is the force measured in newtons, R is the reaction arm radius in metres, and N is the driving shaft speed in rad/s.

Another form of the absorption type of torque-measuring technique involves the use of the eddy current principle. It consists of a metal wheel or disc which is rotated, cutting the flux lines in a magnetic field. The magnetic field is produced by external elements attached to the dynamometer housing and mounted on bearings. As the disc turns, the eddy currents generated develop a reaction force with a magnetic field which tend to rotate the housing in the bearings. The torque is then measured in the same manner as that of the earlier method. Ordinary electric motors or generators can also be used with suitable modification for torque measurements. However, it is considerably more difficult to obtain accurate results with these techniques.

10.9.2 Transmission Type

Torque is measured by coupling a universal strain-gauged load cell to the arm or by coupling two compression-type load cells (electrical, hydraulic, or pneumatic), one above and the other below the arm. Here the power generated by the source is measured without dissipation. In certain cases, the shaft itself can be utilized as a load cell with four active strain gauges mounted on a section of the shaft. This method is ideally suited for dynamic measurements.

10.9.3 Stress Type

For the measurement of torsional shear strain, one can take advantage of the fact that shear in a plane normal to the axis of the shaft is accompanied by tensional and compressional strains at $\pm 45°$ to the axis, as shown in Fig. 10.11. It can be shown that the two principal strains occur at $\pm 45°$ to the direction of pure shear strain (produced by the torque) and that they are opposite in polarity, though their absolute values are identical. The magnitude of shear strain at $45°$ to the axis of the shaft is given by

$$\epsilon_{45°} = \frac{16T}{\pi d^3 E}(1+\nu) \tag{10.25}$$

where E is the Young's modulus of the material of the shaft, ν is the Poisson's ratio, T is the torque developed, and d is the diameter of the shaft. For higher sensitivity, temperature compensation, and for compensation of the thrust and bending stresses possibly present in the shaft, a second pair of strain gauges can be used on the other side of the shaft. The four gauges are wired to form a full-bridge arrangement for the strain measurement. The advantage with this method is that in some cases at least, the existing shaft of the machine can be used by bonding the strain gauge on it. In other cases, a coupled shaft can be used.

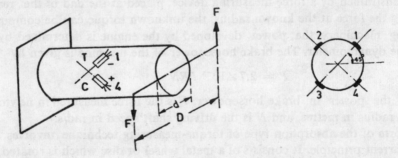

Fig. 10.11 Shear strain configuration for torque measurement

In the measurement of torque in rotating machineries, three systems are employed to feed the excitation voltage to the strain-gauge bridge network, and to take the output signal: (a) direct contact measurement through slip rings, (b) rotary transformer (non-contacting), or (c) short range telemetry (non-contacting). In all the cases, an accuracy of the order of $\pm 0.5\%$ F.S. is achievable.

(a) *Direct Measurement*

In this method, two pairs of circular slip rings are mounted on the loading shaft, one for the excitation of the bridge and the other for the output, as illustrated in Fig. 10.12(a). The dimensional tolerances, surface hardening of the slip rings and the contact resistance of the wiper are very critical to maintain high signal to noise ratios as well as accuracy. The slip ring surfaces are silver and rhodium plated, and silver graphite brushes are used as wipers. In some cases, the preamplifier of the system can be mounted on the shaft itself. Either ac or dc voltages can be used for the excitation.

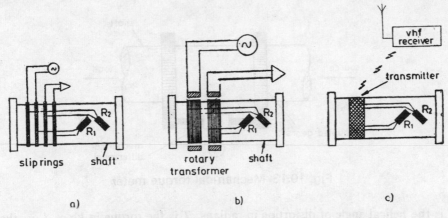

Fig. 10.12 Dynamic torque measurement: (a) slip ring; (b) rotating transformer; (c) telemetry

(b) Rotary Transformer

Instead of slip rings described above, a rotary transformer can be employed especially to avoid the noise pick-up due to contact vibrations. The system comprises two circular rotary transformers, one to induce the ac bridge supply to the strain gauge bridge and the other to pick-up the output signal, as illustrated in Fig. 10.12(b). The transformers are basically a pair of concentrically-wound coils suitably aligned for maximum mutual induction. A high permeability core is also incorporated to improve efficiency. The source signal is normally a carrier of 20 kHz. The main advantage is the elimination of contact noise, as encountered in a slip-ring system.

(c) Telemetry System

In certain cases, it may be advantageous to employ a short-range telemetry system for obtaining completely noise-free signals with good accuracy and resolution. The strain-gauge bridge network is excited with a battery strapped to the shaft itself, and the output is converted into a proportional variable-frequency signal by means of a voltage-controlled oscillator, which is then modulated and transmitted to a receiver, as shown in Fig 10.12(c). The important aspect to be considered in this method is that the system components mounted on the shaft should be able to withstand the acceleration levels experienced by the shaft.

10.9.4 Deflection Type

In the deflection-type of torque measurements, many alternatives exist according to the method used for sensing the deflection. The design features of some of them are discussed below.

(a) Mechanical Torque Measurements

These devices measure the angular deflection of the shaft by a mechanical differential, as shown in Fig. 10.13. The angular deflection of the shaft due to torsion is given by

$$\theta = \frac{0.369Tl}{\pi d^4 G} \tag{10.26}$$

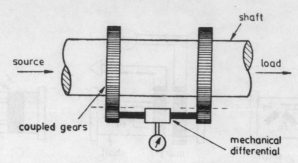

Fig. 10.13 Mechanical torque meter

where θ is the helical angle of distortion in radians, T is the torque in kg m, l is the length of the shaft in metres, d is the diameter of the shaft in metres, and G is the shear modulus of elasticity in kg/m². The accuracy of the device is not high, unless the deflection is magnified suitably by gears and levers. This design lends itself to static calibration and is insensitive to axial stress. Since any bending introduces errors, there is a definite maximum speed up to which it can be used, depending upon the shaft size. Accuracies achievable are of the order of ± 5%.

(b) Electric Torque Measurement

This method consists of two alternating current generators, coupled by spur gears to the rotating shaft, as shown in Fig. 10.14.

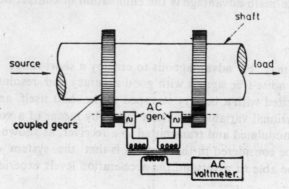

Fig. 10.14 Electrical torque measurement

A change in the originally balanced phase relationship of the ac generators caused by the torsion in the shaft results in incomplete cancellation of the transformer primary voltages. The secondary voltage induced due to unbalance is measured as a function of the torque. Torque meters of this type are satisfactory if the shaft elasticity is large enough to permit a large phase difference in generator voltages (10 to 15 degrees at the fundamental frequency). The accuracy depends upon many electrical factors and is not high unless deflections are large or multiple windings are used. Static calibration is not feasible. The main advantage of this method is its intensivity to unwanted stresses.

(c) Electronic Techniques

Torque can be precisely measured with a suitable electronic-measuring system by mounting two toothed wheels on a shaft, one located near the source and the other near the load. Two electromagnetic pick-up heads mounted close to the wheels generate voltage spikes for each tooth, as it passes over the pick-up position. The time interval or phase difference between generated pulses is precisely measured with an electronic counter and is calibrated in terms of torque. The accuracies achieved can be high and depend upon the phase-measuring circuit.

(d) Other Types

Torque can be measured by various other techniques, if the conventional methods are not convenient. The deflection of the shaft can be amplified and measured precisely with a pair of optical mirrors or an inductive-type angular displacement transducer. In some of the devices the measurement is based on the acoustic principle where the change in natural frequency of a stretched wire is the measure or on the magnetic principle wherein the change in permeability of the shaft is taken as a measure of the torque. However, all such methods are used for specialized applications only.

EXERCISES

10.1 A force transducer responds like a simple second-order system. If the natural frequency of the device is 1000 Hz and its damping is 50% of the critical value, what is the inherent error in amplitude for a sinusoidal input at 300 Hz. Determine the phase lag at this value.

10.2 A load cell consists of a solid cylinder of steel 30 mm diameter with four strain gauges bonded to it and connected in a Wheatstone's bridge arrangement. If gauges are 120 ohms each with a gauge factor of 2.0, what is the sensitivity of the load cell expressed in V/kN/V? The modulus of elasticity of steel is 200×10^9 N/m² and Poisson's ratio $= 0.3$.

10.3 A square-column type load cell is bonded with four strain gauges of 120 ohms each, along the loading direction on the four faces. All the gauges are connected in series to get the average stress and form one arm of a Wheatstone bridge.

Determine the voltage output for an applied load of 4000 kgf, if modulus of elasticity $E = 2 \times 10^6$ kgf/cm², gauge factor $G = 2.0$, cross-section of block $= 2 \times 2$ cm, and bridge excitation voltage $= 5.0$ V. Calculate the standard resistance required to be added across the active arm if the cell is to be simulated from 1000 kgf, for calibration.

10.4 Design a strain gauge load cell, axial or cantilever, capable of measuring satisfactorily a force loading F described as:

$$F = 20 \times 10^3 t \quad \text{for } 0 \leqslant t \leqslant 0.005 \text{ s}$$
$$= 100 \quad \text{for } \quad t > 0.005 \text{ s}$$

Assume a gauge factor of 2.0, supply voltage $= 5.0$ V, modulus of elasticity $E = 21.092 \times 10^9$ kg/m², density $= 7.7$ gms/cm³, and the resolution of the readout $= 10$ mV.

10.5 To obtain a sensitivity of 2 microstrain per kg load, using strain gauges of 6-mm gauge length and 6-mm gauge width, indicate which of the following configuration will be most suitable: (a) axial rod, (b) cantilever beam, and (c) proving ring.

10.6 Design a column-type load cell using nickel steel as the member and strain gauges of "advance" material to measure the stress developed, with temperature compensation for variations in Young's modulus in the range 25 to 100°C.

REFERENCES

1. Timoshenko, S., *Strength of Materials*, Chapter 12, D. Van Nostrand Co., New York, 1955.
2. Neubert, H.K.P., *Instrument Transducer*, Clarendon, Oxford, 1975.
3. Schutte, F.L., "A low profile load cell in weighing systems", *Advances in Instrumentation*, Vol. 26, Part IV, Instrument Society of America, Pittsburg, 1971.

BIBLIOGRAPHY

Cahn, L., "Electromagnetic weighing", *Instruments and Control Systems*, Vol. 35, No. 9, pp. 107, 1962.

Elias, L.F., "Electromagnetic force transducer", *Instrumentation Technology*, Vol. 18, No. 5, pp. 70-72, May 1971.

Ettleman, D. and Hoberman, M., "Torque meters", *Machine Design*. p. 134, Feb. 28, 1963.

Ferguson, A.C., "From beam to load cell", *Engineering*, Vol. 24, No. 3, pp. 202-207, March 1974.

Gates, R.L., "Review and status of inertial sensors", *Control Engg.*, Vol. 18, No. 3, pp. 54-58, March 1971.

Guthrie, J, "Lever shaft torque measurement", *Instruments and Control Systems*, Vol. 37, No. 8, pp. 116-118, Aug. 1964.

Haggstrom, R.P., "Design and application of a new shear force transducer", *Micro Technic*. Vol. 26, No. 4, pp. 240-242, May 1972.

Hughes, T.G., "Designing a shaft speed/torque pulse gating system", *Control and Instrumentation*, Vol. 4, No. 5, pp. 60-63, May 1972.

I.E.R.E., *Proceedings of the I.E.R.E. Conference on Electronic Weighing*, London, No. 13, 1968.

Johnson, C.E., "A guide to torque transducers", *Control Engg.*, Vol. 20, No. 8, pp. 47-49, Aug. 1973.

Kenner, V.K., "On the use of piezoelectric crystals in dynamic stress and force transducers", *Exp. Mech.* Vol. 13, No. 10, p. 35N, October 1973.

Lebow, M.S., "Some principles of transducer design", *Instrument Society of America Transactions*, Vol. 2, pp. 85-92, ISA, Pittsburg, 1963.

Lolley, R.A., "A review of industrial weighing systems", *Measurement and Control*, Vol. 9, No. 11, pp. 411-416, November 1976.

Michno, M.J. et al., "A two interaction tension (or compression) torsion load cell", *Rev. Sci. Instr.* Vol. 44, No. 8, p. 1148, Aug. 1973.

Potzick, J., "A method of determining the dynamic response of an elastic load cell element", *Rev. of Sc. Instr.*, Vol. 41, No. 12, pp. 1726-1731, Dec. 1971.

Reznicek, I., "Achieving precision with load cells", *Control and Instrumentation*, Vol. 5, No. 7, pp. 40-43, 1973.

Roark, R.J., *Formulas for Stress and Strain*, McGraw-Hill, New York, 1954.

Ruge, A.C., "Precision measurements of force", *Metal Progress*, Vol. 70, No. 7, pp. 92-93, July 1956.

System Engineering Division, *Proceedings of the Seminar on Electronic Weighing Systems*, N.A.L., Bangalore, 1978.

Timoshenko, S., *Theory of Elasticity*, McGraw-Hill New York, 1936.

Valentich, J., "Keeping tabs on torque using strain gauges", *Machine Design*, Vol. 44, No. 3. pp. 104-107, Feb. 3, 1972.

Van Stanten, G.W., *Electronic Weighing and Process Control*, Philips Technical Library, Eindhaven, Holland, 1968.

Vanghan, P., "Tipping the scale in favour of load cell weighing", *Engineer*, Vol. 237, No. 6136, pp. 38-41, 18 Oct. 1973.

Wyman, P.R., "A new force to frequency transducer", *Conference on Digital Instrumentation* (*London*), England, 12-14 Nov. 1973, pp. 117-123 (IEE 1973).

11

INSTRUMENTATION AMPLIFIERS

11.1 INTRODUCTION

Instrumentation amplifiers are generally required in any measurement system using electrical transducers to enhance the signal level which is often in the low level range of less than a few millivolts. They are also required in certain cases to provide impedance matching and isolation. When the desired input rides over a common mode signal, special amplifiers are required so that the differential signals can be amplified to an acceptable level while at the same time, the common mode signals are attenuated. In certain applications, a galvanic connection between the input source and the subsequent instrumentation system is avoided by using unconventional type isolation amplifiers as in biomedical instrumentation. Starting with the basic characteristics of amplifiers, the following sections briefly describe the various categories of instrumentation amplifiers and certain characteristics particular to them.

11.2 BASIC CHARACTERISTICS

The characteristics that are required of an instrumentation amplifier depend upon the system design and specific application. These are specified in terms of

(a) input impedance
(b) output impedance
(c) gain and frequency response
(d) noise.

Familiarization and a clear understanding of these terms are essential to enable optimum design of the instrumentation system.

11.2.1 Input Impedance

The input impedance required of an amplifier is often dependent on the output impedance of the source, viz., the transducer that feeds the amplifier. A thermocouple used for the measurement of temperature has an output impedance of only a few ohms, whereas that of a piezoelectric transducer used in the measurement of acceleration and force is in the range of a few hundred megaohms. Considering the transducer and the signal that it generates in terms of the equivalent Thevenin source and impedance, the effect of the input impedance of the amplifier on the source can be estimated. As an example, an electromagnetic pickup and its Thevenin equivalent circuit are illustrated in Figs. 11.1(a) and (b). Due to the loading effect of the input resistance of the amplifier (1 MΩ) on the transducer, the effective input e_I to the amplifier is obtained as

$$e_I = e_s \frac{10^6}{(2 \times 10^3 + 10^6)} \simeq 499 \ \mu\text{V/mm/s} \ \text{ for } e_s = 500 \ \mu\text{V/mm/s}$$

where e_s is the source voltage.

Though the signal itself has not been decreased significantly, it is nevertheless important to note that a 0.2% error in the overall sensitivity of the system has been introduced by the non-infinite input impedance of the amplifier. A very high input impedance amplifier can be used to reduce the error. Alternatively, it may be often simpler and economical to use an amplifier having an input impedance of ten to fifty times the source impedance and then calibrate the system sensitivity as a whole, combining the effects of the amplifier and the transducer.

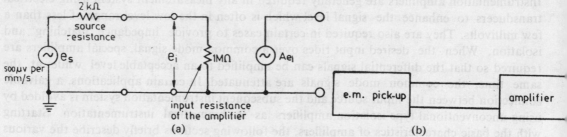

Fig. 11.1 Electromagnetic pick-up connected to an amplifier: (a) schematic; (b) equivalent circuit

A recommended practical approach is to choose the input impedance of an amplifier as approximately ten times the source impedance. The resulting loading effect which reduces the available signal by about 10% will be often permissible, since calibration can be carried out for the integrated system. In certain cases the choice might depend upon the signal to noise ratio deterioration due to loading, cost advantages obtainable by permitting more than 10% reduction in signal due to loading, and such other factors.

In certain cases, amplifiers having high input impedance are essential to prevent changes in sensitivity of the system due to changes in source impedance. A specific example is an amplifier for use with a strain gauge bridge, wherein the resistance of the strain gauges may be from 120 ohms to 600 ohms depending on the specific type used. In such cases, either the input impedance should be high enough to reduce the loading errors below a tolerable percentage, or the sensitivity of the system should be recalibrated for the particular strain gauge bridge.

EXAMPLE 11.1 Determine the input resistance desired of an amplifier so as to ensure that the linearity error of the ratio set by a 10 turn potentiometer (Fig. 11.2) is less than 0.2% for any setting. The potentiometer has a resistance of 10 kohms and a linearity of 0.1%.

Solution: The potentiometer as fed from a voltage source is shown in Fig. 11.2. The amplifier input resistance R_{in} has to be computed to ensure that the additional error created by the loading effect is no more than 0.1%, which when added to the 0.1% non-linearity of the potentiometer will give an overall linearity of less than 0.2%.

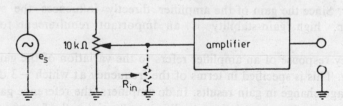

Fig. 11.2 Loading effect due to the input resistance of an amplifier

The worst case loading error occurs when the Thevenin (output) resistance of the potentiometer is at its maximum. This resistance is 2.5 kohms and occurs at a setting of 0.5. To ensure that the loading error is less than 0.1% for this setting, R_{in} should be more than 1000×2.5 kohms or 2.5 Mohms. Therefore, this is the minimum input resistance required of the following amplifier[1].

11.2.2 Output Impedance

The output impedance required of an amplifier is dependent on the input impedance of the following sub-system. If the amplifier is required to drive a meter or a recorder, the output impedance has to be such that the error due to loading (by the input impedance of the meter, recorder, etc.) is below a minimum desired limit. Alternatively, the output impedance can be a specific value so that the effect of loading can be calculated or taken care of by a calibration of the total sub-system.

When the driven device is external to the system and if the amplifier does not have a sufficiently low output impedance, it becomes necessary to have a specific input resistance for the driven device if recalibration is to be avoided. This is particularly true while using external galvanometers having arbitrary input impedance, connected to amplifiers designed for use with specific input impedance galvanometers.

The output impedance and the output drive capability of an amplifier are two independent characteristics; this is a fact which often creates confusion due to lack of proper distinction. Consider an amplifier required to drive a galvanometer having a resistance of 100 ohms. All amplifiers having an output impedance of less than an ohm are not necessarily suitable for the purpose, since the selected amplifier should also be able to provide the current drive required for the galvanometer. In this particular case, if the deflection sensitivity is 0.2 cms/mA, the selected amplifier should then possess an output voltage swing capability of ± 5 V *and* current drive capability of ± 50 mA for a span of ± 10 cm. If an error of less than 0.2% is required without recalibration, the output resistance of the amplifier should be less than 0.2 ohms.

11.2.3 Gain and Frequency Response

The gain of an amplifier is in effect the amplification that results in using the amplifier. Depending on the relative values of the output impedance of the source and the input impedance of the amplifier, a certain amount of attenuation invariably occurs at the input. The effective amplification obtained is hence a product of this attenuation and the gain factor of the amplifier. Since the gain of the amplifier directly influences the system's sensitivity and calibration, high gain-stability is an important requirement for instrumentation amplifiers.

The frequency response of an amplifier refers to the variation of the gain of the amplifier with frequency. This is specified in terms of the frequency at which -3 dB loss occurs or a certain percentage change in gain results. In dc amplfiers, the reference gain is taken as the gain at dc. In many instrumentation amplifier applications, the frequency above which the gain falls below a certain desired percentage will be more important than a -3 dB cut-off frequency. Though the typical frequency response of amplifiers tends to result in lower amplification at higher frequencies, this is not always true. The high frequency response may peak up often as a result of a deliberate attempt to enhance the frequency response. In such a case the frequency response of a system may be decided by the frequency range over which the deviation in the gain is less than $\pm x\%$ of the midband gain or a specified gain, where x is the gain error tolerable for the particular system.

The frequency response of an amplifier is often influenced by the output impedance also, which is a complex quantity dependent on frequency. When the system response is computed, it is necessary to consider the final load impedance also as a part of the system.

An additional parameter which results in different frequency cut-off values for various output swing levels is the "slew rate" capability of the amplifier. For highly capacitive loads and even for resistive loads at frequencies higher than about 10 kHz, the slew rate plays a significant role in determining the overall frequency response (see Sec. 11.4.6).

11.2.4 Noise

All amplifiers use active devices whose performance is influenced by internally-generated noise. The noise contributed by the devices is generally frequency dependent. The noise spectral density is expressed for noise voltage as $V/\sqrt{Hz}$, for noise current as $A/\sqrt{Hz}$, and for noise power as W/Hz. Over a wide range of frequencies, typically from 100 Hz to a few hundred kilohertz, the noise spectral density is constant. In this frequency span, the noise is almost entirely due to shot noise[2]. At very low frequencies, the noise spectral density increases due to the presence of flicker noise; and at high frequencies, it again increases due to the limitations in the frequency response of the amplifier, as shown in Fig. 11.3.

In operational amplifiers, the manufacturers specify the noise performance in various ways. In many cases a total noise value is given, which is the average noise referred to the input over a specified frequency band. For dc applications, the peak to peak noise for a frequency range of 0.01 to 10 Hz is often specified. For ac applications, the total noise over a frequency range of 20 Hz to 20 kHz is sometimes mentioned. In addition, a plot of the spectral density of the equivalent input noise voltage and equivalent input noise current, as a function of frequency, is provided. From these plots, the typical noise performance for any specific source resistance over a particular frequency range of interest can be estimated.

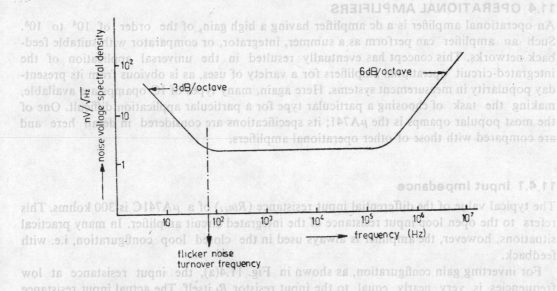

Fig. 11.3 Noise characteristics of amplifier

11.3 DC AMPLIFIERS

In dc amplifiers, the frequency response extends down to dc signals. In a practical dc amplifier, the output of the amplifier may not necessarily have a zero dc value even if the input of the amplifier is at zero potential (i.e., input is shorted). This error is expressed in terms of an average offset voltage defined as the equivalent input voltage required at the input to ensure zero output. The offset voltage referred to the input is not dependent on the gain of the amplifier. This is so because at higher gains, though the output offset is higher, the equivalent input voltage required to nullify the output offset remains the same.

The offset voltage of an amplifier may not remain constant with time and ambient temperature. The change in the offset voltage with temperature is expressed as an average temperature coefficient of the offset. This, for modern integrated circuit amplifiers, is typically between 10 μV/°C for low-cost amplifiers and 0.1 μV/°C for high-performance amplifiers.

Another source of error in dc amplifiers is the presence of finite dc current in the input leads. This is referred to as the input bias current of the amplifier. The bias current of an amplifier will produce additional offset errors depending on the dc output impedance of the source. This has to be borne in mind while using dc amplifiers for ac applications as well, since capacitive coupling of the ac source will not provide a dc path for the bias current.

The errors due to bias current again assume importance when dealing with amplifiers having high input impedance coupled to transducers having high dc output impedance. When the output impedance of the source exceeds a few megaohms, it might become necessary to use dc amplifiers having bias currents of a few nanoamperes or less. Amplifiers having very low leakage FETs in the input stages can possess bias currents of the order of a few picoamperes. Amplifiers having bias current as low as a few Femto amperes (10^{-15} A) are available commercially, such as Burr Brown 3523L and Teledyne Philbrick 1702.

11.4 OPERATIONAL AMPLIFIERS

An operational amplifier is a dc amplifier having a high gain, of the order of 10^4 to 10^8. Such an amplifier can perform as a summer, integrator, or comparator with suitable feedback networks. This concept has eventually resulted in the universal application of the integrated-circuit operational amplifiers for a variety of uses, as is obvious from its present-day popularity in measurement systems. Here again, many types of IC opamps are available, making the task of choosing a particular type for a particular application difficult. One of the most popular opamps is the μA741; its specifications are considered in detail here and are compared with those of other operational amplifiers.

11.4.1 Input Impedance

The typical value of the differential input resistance (Rin_{dd}) of a μA741C is 300 kohms. This refers to the open loop input resistance of the integrated circuit amplifier. In many practical situations, however, the amplifier is always used in the closed loop configuration, i.e. with feedback.

For inverting gain configuration, as shown in Fig. 11.4(a), the input resistance at low frequencies is very nearly equal to the input resistor R_i itself. The actual input resistance R_{in} is given by

$$R_{in} = R_i \left[1 + \frac{(R_f/R_i)}{A+1} \right] \tag{11.1}$$

where R_f is the feedback resistance and A is the open loop gain of the amplifier. R_{in} is almost equal to R_i when the open loop gain A is large. The effect of Rin_{dd} is considered separately in Appendix 1.

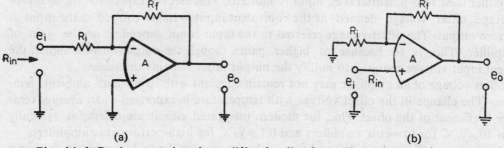

Fig. 11.4 Basic operational amplifier feedback configurations: (a) inverting amplifier; (b) non-inverting amplifier

EXAMPLE 11.2 For an amplifier having the parameters given below, evaluate the error in the closed loop gain e_o/e_i in the inverting configuration for $Rin_{dd} = 3$ kohms, 30 kohms, 300 kohms and infinity (see Appendix 1). $R_f = 100$ kohms; $R_i = 10$ kohms; $A = 10^5$; $R_o = 50$ ohms; and $R_L = 2$ kohms, where R_o is the output resistance of the amplifier and R_L is the load resistance.

Solution: Using Eq. 11A.11 in Appendix 1, the gain error can be computed by straight forward substitution. The exact gain being -10, the gain error is

    (a) 0.04546% for $Rin_{dd} = 3$ kΩ
    (b) 0.014698% for $Rin_{dd} = 30$ kΩ

(c) 0.01162% for $Rin_{dd} = 300$ kΩ
(d) 0.01128% for $Rin_{dd} = $ infinity

(Note that even with an input resistance of 3 kohms, the gain error is less than 0.05%.)

In the non-inverting input configuration, as shown in Fig. 11.4(b), the Rin_{dd} does play a more significant role. The effective input resistance R_{in} is

$$R_{in} = \left\{ Rin_{dd} \left[\frac{A}{1+(R_f/R_i)} \right] \right\} \|^l R_{cm} \tag{11.2}$$

where R_{cm} is the common mode input resistance and Rin_{dd} is the differential input resistance. Even for a nominal value of 300 kΩ for Rin_{dd}, the term in the above expression related to Rin_{dd} becomes 3 Gigaohms for a closed-loop gain of 10 and an open-loop gain of 10^5. This value is often higher than the common mode input resistance R_{cm}, the actual input resistance being decided by the parallel combination of these two terms.

11.4.2 Open-Loop Gain

The open-loop gain of a μA741C is typically 2×10^5, a value sufficiently high for a majority of practical applications. For an inverting amplifier, as shown in Fig. 11.4(a), one would expect an exact gain of $\left(-\dfrac{R_f}{R_i} \right)$ from an ideal amplifier. For a practical amplifier having a finite open-loop gain, some gain error will exist (Appendix 1).

The closed-loop gain is approximately given by

$$\frac{e_o}{e_l} = -\frac{R_f}{R_l} \left[1 + \left(\frac{1 + \dfrac{R_f}{R_l} + \dfrac{R_f}{Rin_{dd}}}{A} \right) \right]^{-1} \tag{11.3}$$

It may be noted that the gain error is significantly dependent on the closed-loop gain desired and can be reduced by having large A.

11.4.3 Average Voltage Offset

For μA741C, the typical value of the input offset is 2 mV (the maximum is 7 mV). In a practical situation, the output offset is decided by the product of gain and the input offset, and this can be corrected for by appropriate offset correction circuits (see Example 11.3).

Average Temperature Coefficient of Voltage Offset

The average temperature coefficient of offset $\dfrac{\Delta V_{os}}{\Delta T}$ for μA741C is typically about 6 μV/°C. For operation from 20 to 40°C, the total offset voltage change at the output of an inverting amplifier with gain 10 can be estimated as equal to $\Delta V = \left\{ \dfrac{\Delta V_{os}}{\Delta T} \right\} (G+1)(\Delta T) = $ (average temperature coefficient of offset)$\times(1+$gain$)\times$(temperature change) $= (6 \ \mu$V/°C$)\times(1+10) \times(40-20) \simeq 1.32$ mV.

11.4.4 Input Bias Current

The input bias current I_B of μA741C is typically 80 nA, a value which limits the usage of 741-type amplifiers to relatively low input and feedback resistances (20 kohms and below). This current is the average of the individual bias currents I_{B1} and I_{B2}, as shown in Fig. 11.5(a). The presence of the bias currents introduces an additional "offset error", depending on the input and feedback resistors used. Referring to Fig. 11.5(b), the output error voltage e_o resulting from the effect of bias current is

$$e_o = I_{B1}R_f - I_{B2}R_{i2}\left(1 + \frac{R_f}{R_{i1}}\right) \qquad (11.4)$$

This error is exclusive of any other output error resulting from the presence of the input offset voltage. For an amplifier having a typical offset voltage error V_{os} and bias current I_B, there is a critical resistance value of $R_i = \dfrac{V_{os}}{I_B}$, above which the offset error due to bias current tends to be more significant than that due to offset voltage. In the case of μA741C, this resistance is approximately equal to 25 kohms.

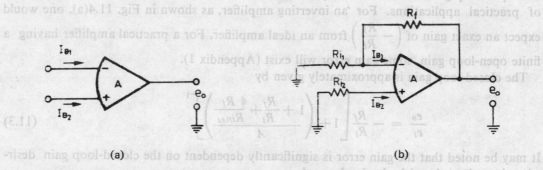

(a)   (b)

Fig. 11.5 Input bias current: (a) individual bias currents at input points; (b) compensation for offset resulting from bias current

EXAMPLE 11.3 Estimate the output offset voltage and its variation from 25°C to 45°C for a μA741C used as an inverting amplifier, as shown in Fig. 11.4(a) having a gain of -10 and input resistance R_i of (a) 10 kohms and (b) 100 kohms. Use typical values of μA741C.

Solution: Consider first (a) $R_i = 10$ kohms. For a gain of -10, $R_f = 100$ kohms. At 25°C, $V_{os} = \pm 2$ mV and $I_B = 80$ nA.

The general expression for the output voltage combining the errors due to offset voltage and bias current is

$$e_o = \pm\left[V_{os}\left(1 + \frac{R_f}{R_i}\right)\right] + I_B R_f$$

Therefore, taking into account the direction of current flow,

$$[e_o]_{25°C} = \pm[2 \times 10^{-3}(1 + 10)] + [80 \times 10^{-9} \times 100 \times 10^3]$$
$$= +30 \text{ to } -14 \text{ mV}$$

To calculate the errors at 45°C, the variation of the offset voltage and bias current with temperature has to be known.

The average temperature coefficient of the offset voltage $= \pm 6\ \mu\text{V/}°\text{C}$. The bias current typically decreases at a rate of 1% per degree celsius rise in temperature. Hence at 45°C, the offset voltage can be expected to be ± 2.12 mV and the bias current to be 60 nA, resulting in

$$[e_o]_{45°C} = +29.3 \text{ to } -17.3 \text{ mV}$$

If the offset voltage has been corrected for at 25°C, the change in output at 45°C will be

$$\Delta e_o = (\pm 1.32 - 2)\text{ mV} = +0.68 \text{ to } -3.32 \text{ mV}$$

Repeating the above calculations for (b), $R_i = 100$ kohms; $R_f = 1$ Mohm

$$[e_o]_{25°C} = +102 \text{ mV to } +58 \text{ mV}$$
$$[e_o]_{45°C} = +83.3 \text{ mV to } +36.7 \text{ mV}$$

and

$$\Delta e_o = -18.68 \text{ mV to } -21.32 \text{ mV}$$

Note that the errors due to bias current increases as R_i is increased.

Input Offset Current

The typical value of the input offset current for $\mu\text{A}741\text{C}$ is 20 nA. The input offset current I_{os} is the difference between the bias currents I_{B1} and I_{B2} [see Fig. 11.5(a)]; I_{os} is typically 20 nA for $\mu\text{A}741\text{C}$. $I_{B1} \simeq I_{B2}$ in many operational amplifiers, and they tend to track with temperature. It is hence possible to minimize the errors due to bias currents by a proper choice of the input resistors as shown in Fig. 11.5. From Eq. (11.4), if

$$R_{I2} = \frac{R_{I1}R_f}{R_{I1} + R_f} \tag{11.5}$$

then

$$e_o = (I_{B1} - I_{B2})R_f \tag{11.6}$$
$$= I_{os}R_f$$

In cases where R_{I2} cannot be selected as in Eq. (11.5), the bias current value will determine the dc output errors.

11.4.5 Frequency Response

The typical values of the parameters related to the open-loop frequency response of a $\mu\text{A}741\text{C}$ are:

Unity gain bandwidth $= 1$ MHz

DC open-loop gain $= -2 \times 10^5$

Fall-off rate $= -6$ dB/octave

Corner frequency $= 5$ Hz

The small signal bandwidth for any closed loop gain A_{CL} is given by

$$\text{Bandwidth} \simeq \frac{10^6}{A_{CL}} \text{ Hz} \tag{11.7}$$

for A_{CL} greater than about 10.

11.4.6 Slew Rate and Full Power Frequency Response

The slew rate of an operational amplifier is the maximum rate of change of output voltage at the rated output. For μA741C. this rate is about 0.5 V/μs. The slew rate is normally specified for the unity gain follower configuration, as this is often the worst case. If frequency compensation is optimized, higher closed loop gains often yield higher slew rates. The slew rates for positive and negative swings of the output need not always be the same. For any desired output swing, the slew rate can set the limit for the frequency response obtainable for that particular swing.

The full power response frequency f_p, which is the maximum frequency at which rated output can be obtained without significant distortion, is related to the slew rate of the amplifier as,

$$f_p = \frac{S_r}{2\pi E_o} \tag{11.8}$$

where S_r is the slew rate and E_a the rated output voltage.

This relationship is obtained by equating the slew rate to the maximum slope of a sinusoidal signal of peak value E_o and frequency f_p. This indicates that the effective frequency response of an amplifier for a specific output swing is often more limited by the slew rate of the amplifier than by the small signal frequency response predicted by the open-loop gain characteristics.

11.4.7 Comparison of Operational Amplifiers

Due to the continuous development in the technology, a variety of amplifiers with different specifications are available commercially. The salient features of a few of the more important types are indicated below with a view to simplify the task of proper selection of the opamp for a particular situation.

(a) μA748

This opamp is identical to μA741, the only difference being the non-inclusion of the internal phase compensation capacitor. With a 30 pF connected between the phase compensation terminals, the unity gain bandwidth is $\simeq$ 1 MHz; with a 3 pF, the effective unity gain bandwidth increases to 10 MHz. This is an advantage when a higher bandwidth is required at closed loop gains of typically 10 and more. The use of a 3 pF compensation capacitor al enhances the slew rate by a factor of 10 resulting in increased full power frequency. With controlled positive feedback, the opamps can be used as comparator without any compensation capacitor. The rate at which the output "slews" as a comparator is considerably higher than that for μA741.

(b) μA709

This is one of the early opamps to become an industry standard; this type has to be provided with suitable external compensation networks for any chosen feedback configuration. The bandwidth obtainable with a gain of 1000 often exceeds that obtainable from μA741 or μA748. The μA709 does not possess short circuit protection, but a 200Ω connected in series with the output (within the feedback loop) often provides sufficient protection. For certain gain configurations, a tendency to latch up can exist[3].

(c) LM 301

The typical offset current of this type of opamp is in the range of 3 nA, a factor of five less than that of μA741. With balanced input connections, these opamps can be used with input and feedback resistors as high as 100 kΩ. With feedforward compensation, the unity gain inverting configuration has a full power bandwidth exceeding 100 kHz.

(d) LM 308

A unique feature of the LM 308 is the very low bias current ($\simeq 2$ nA typical), and it is therefore ideally suited for many low frequency low level instrumentation system applications. The low frequency noise being low, the dc drift is much lower compared to that of μA741 or LM 301 type amplifiers. The quiescent power requirement is also typically about 15% of that needed for μA741. Flexibility of tailoring the frequency response by external compensation enhances the performance at high frequencies as well. This device is used for a variety of measurement applications.

(e) μA740

The μA740 has an FET input stage and hence has a very low input current of $\simeq 1$ nA and an offset current of 60 pA (typical). The input offset voltage is 30 mV (typical). The opamp is useful where a very high input impedance is required, provided the higher offset is tolerable.

(f) NE 536

NE 536 is basically an FET input opamp having an input current of 30 pA at 25°C and an offset current of 5 pA. The typical input offset voltage is 30 mV. Applications are similar to those for μA740.

(g) μA715

This is a very high-speed operational amplifier with a bandwidth of 65 MHz and slew rate of 100 V/μs. The setting time being very low, this device is ideally suited for D/A converters, active filters, and precision comparators.

(h) μA725

Having low offset voltage drift (0.6 μV/°C) combined with low input noise, this opamp is particularly suitable for low level dc amplification. Since the common mode rejection and loop gain are high, this amplifier is widely used in many instrumentation systems.

(i) μA791

The main advantage of this opamp is its high power-handling capability. The amplifier can provide an output voltage swing of more than ± 10 V into a 10 Ω load with a rated internal dissipation of 20 W. Applications include dc and ac servo amplifiers and power amplifiers required for galvanometer drives.

(j) Chopper Stabilized Amplifiers

For ultra low-drift performance with average temperature coefficients of offset of less than 0.5 μV/°C, chopper stabilized amplifiers are preferred. Many of them can be used in inverting configuration only. Some of the recommended types are Analog Devices AD 234 K/L and Teledyne Philbrick 1340/1701.

The suitability of the various types of amplifiers for specific applications is given in Table 11.1.

TABLE 11.1 COMPARISON OF OPERATIONAL AMPLIFIERS

Device	Offset voltage (mV) (max)	Bias current (nA) (max)	Offset current (nA) (max)	Unity gain bandwidth (MHz) (typical)	Slew rate (V/μs) (typical)	Applications
μA741C	6	500	200	1	0.5	General purpose; low frequencies
μA709C	7.5	1500	500	1	0.3	General purpose
μA748C	6	500	200	1	0.5	General purpose
μA301A	7.5	250	50	1	0.5	General purpose
μA740	100	2	0.3	3	6	High impedance; high slew rate
μA308	7.5	7	1	1	0.3	High impedance
μA725	2.5	125	35	1	—	Instrumentation
μA715	7.5	1500	250	65	100	High speed; very high slew rate
μA357A	2	0.05	0.01	25	75	High impedance; high speed
μA776	6	10	6	0.2	0.1	Multipurpose programmable
μA791	6	500	200	1	0.5	High power (one ampere output)

11.5 INSTRUMENTATION AMPLIFIERS

The low-level signal outputs of electrical transducers often need to be amplified before further processing, and this is carried out with instrumentation amplifiers. The important features of instrumentation amplifiers are:

(i) selectable gain with high "gain accuracy", and "gain linearity"
(ii) differential input capability with high common mode rejection, even with sources having unbalanced high output impedances
(iii) high stability of gain with low temperature coefficient
(iv) low dc offset and drift errors referred to input
(v) low output impedance.

Instrumentation amplifiers differ from the ordinary operational amplifier in the following respects:

(a) The instrumentation amplifier is often a package comprising operational amplifiers, wired up with accurate and stable resistive feedback network to give a desired gain. The gain is often selectable to be a precise value by a single external resistance.

(b) Due to the closed loop configuration used, the instrumentation amplifier can be directly used to amplify the signal, by a fixed amplification factor. There is no user effort required in choosing the input and feedback configurations or in selecting suitable components. The gain accuracy, gain stability, and drift performance are normally specified by the manufacturer.

(c) Resulting from the configuration employed, the instrumentation amplifier will often yield high common mode rejection even with source impedances exceeding 1 MΩ and with source unbalance of a large value (1 to 10 kΩ). The dc operational amplifier has often a common mode rejection ratio specified for it which is only applicable for very low source impedances.

In actual application an instrumentation amplifier is a specific combination of suitable dc operational amplifiers wired up with feedback, and requires very little design effort from the user.

11.5.1 The Three-Amplifier Configuration

The schematic diagram of an instrumentation amplifier possessing many of the general features described earlier and constructed with dc opamps is shown in Fig. 11.6. Many of the input specifications of the opamps employed will directly determine the input specifications of the instrumentation amplifier. The analysis of the circuit of Fig. 11.6 results in the following equations for $R_4 = R_5 = R_6 = R_7$.

$$e_3 = \left(1 + \frac{R_2}{R_1}\right)e_1 - \left(\frac{R_2}{R_1}\right)e_2 + e_{cm} \tag{11.9}$$

$$e_4 = \left(1 + \frac{R_3}{R_1}\right)e_2 - \left(\frac{R_3}{R_1}\right)e_1 + e_{cm} \tag{11.10}$$

$$e_5 = e_4 - e_3 \tag{11.11}$$

where $e_{cm} + e_1$ is the input to amplifier A_1 and $e_{cm} + e_2$ is that to A_2. If $R_2 = R_3$, the output voltage e_5 is given by

$$e_5 = \left(1 + \frac{2R_2}{R_1}\right)(e_2 - e_1) \tag{11.12}$$

The input amplifiers A_1 and A_2 act as input buffers with unity gain for common mode signals e_{cm}, and with a gain of $\left(1 + \frac{2R_2}{R_1}\right)$ for differential signals. A high input impedance is ensured due to the non-inverting configuration in which they operate. The common mode rejection is achieved in the following stage which is wired as a differential amplifier. The optimum common mode rejection can be achieved by trimming R_6 or R_7 to ensure that $\frac{R_5}{R_4}$ $\doteq \frac{R_7}{R_6}$. The amplifier A_3 can also be made to have some nominal gain for the whole amplifier by proper choice of R_4, R_5, R_6 and R_7. The drift errors of the second stage will add to the product of the drift errors of the first amplifier and first stage gain[4]. Hence, it is necessary that the gain in the first stage be adequate to prevent the overall drift performance from being significantly affected by the drift in the second stage. The drift performance of the instrumentation amplifier can be improved if the amplifiers A_1 and A_2 have offset voltages which tend to track with temperature.

The gain of the instrumentation amplifier can be varied by changing R_1 alone. A high gain accuracy can be obtained by using precision metal film resistors for all the resistances shown. Because of the large negative feedback employed, the amplifier has good linearity, typically about 0.01% for a gain of less than 10^4. The output impedance is also low, being often in the milliohm range.

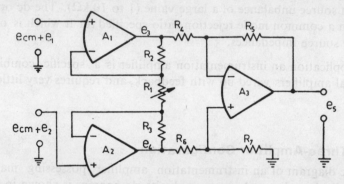

Fig. 11.6 Instrumentation amplifier

The input bias current of the instrumentation amplifier is determined by those of the input amplifiers A_1 and A_2. The use of opamp μA725 C for A_1 and A_2 gives an input bias current of typically 42 nA. As with operational amplifiers, the use of equal source resistances in the input leads, i.e., low source resistance unbalance, reduces the bias current errors to the limit set by offset current errors ($\simeq$ 2 nA for μA725C). The use of the FET opamp NE 536 for A_1 and A_2 will result in bias currents of the order of a few pA and will permit the use of sources whose impedance exceeds 1 megaohm. Typical specifications of a commercial amplifier making use of this arrangement of Fig. 11.6 are listed in Table 11.2.

EXAMPLE 11.4 A strain gauge type transducer produces a differential output of 0 to 1 mV with a common mode output of 3 V. The output impedance is in the range of 100 to 1000 ohms. Design an instrumentation amplifier suitable for amplifying this signal so that the output is 0 to 10 V as required for an 8-bit A/D converter with an input impedance of 10 kohms. The desired operating temperature range is 20 to 30°C.

Discuss the changes required to be made if the A/D converter requires only 0 to 1 V as input.

Solution: The overall gain desired is 10 V/1 mV = 10,000.

Since an 8-bit A/D converter has a quantization error of $\simeq$ 0.4% of full scale, the design should aim at less than 0.4% overall error over the temperature range desired for operation. The likely errors are due to: (i) gain variation with temperature, and (ii) input drift due to changes in offset voltage, offset current, and bias current with temperature.

The gain errors arise from (i) open-loop gain variations due to temperature and the resulting closed loop gain variations, and (ii) the temperature coefficient of gain determining resistors.

TABLE 11.2 SPECIFICATIONS FOR BURR BROWN TYPE 3620 INSTRUMENTATION AMPLIFIER

Parameter	Specifications
Gain, G	$1 + \dfrac{25}{R}$ (to within 0.2%; R is the gain determining resistance)
Gain range	1 to 1000
Gain non-linearity	$\pm 0.01\%$ at $G = 100$
Gain stability	$\pm 0.001\%$ per °C; $\pm 0.001\%$ per month
Rated output	± 10 V, ± 10 mA
Input impedance	300 MΩ differential; 1000 MΩ common mode
CMR, dc to 100 Hz: Gain of 10; (1 kΩ source unbalance)	74 dB min
Gain of 1000; 1 kohm balance source	100 dB
Input offset (can be zeroed)	± 1 mV
Output offset ($G = 1000$)	± 0.25 mV/°C; ± 3 mV/month
Bias current	± 25 nA
Bias current variation with temp.	± 0.5 nA/°C
Input noise ($G = 100$)	
Voltage (0.01 Hz to 1 Hz)	1 μVpp
Current (0.01 Hz to 10 Hz)	200 pApp
Dynamic response ($G = 100$)	
Small signal $\pm 1\%$	1.5 kHz
± 3 dB	10 kHz
Full power ($G = 10$)	5 kHz
Settling time to within ± 10 mV of output value	200 μs
Slew rate	0.3 V/μs
Power supply	± 12 V to ± 18 V
Drain	± 24 mA
Temperature range	0 to 70°C

The input drift will be mainly due to the offset voltage variation with temperature. As an initial error allotment, one can decide to limit the error due to drift to 0.2% and that due to gain variations to 0.2%. To reduce the effect of the open-loop gain, the gain per stage can be limited to 25. The required gain can be achieved by adding one more stage to the circuit of Fig. 11.6.

To limit the error due to drift to 0.2%, the average offset voltage change with temperature, for the input amplifiers, should be less than

$$\frac{0.2\% \text{ of 1 mV}}{30° - 20°} = \frac{2 \ \mu V}{10°} = 0.2 \ \mu V/°C$$

A suitable amplifier meeting this stringent specification is the Precision Monolithics OP07A which is a low-offset voltage low-drift opamp. The use of the same type of opamp for amplifier A_3 will also be necessary since the drift contribution due to that stage should not significantly change the overall drift. With a gain of 25 in the first stage, the first stage output drift would be $25 \times 0.2 \ \mu V/°C$ or 5 $\mu V/°C$. The second stage will add to this another 0.2 $\mu V/°C$ drift, which is relatively insignificant. The second and third stages can be designed to have individual gains of 20 each. The third stage can use $\mu A741$ since its contribution of about 6 $\mu V/°C$ to drift will be considerably small compared to a drift at the output of second stage of $\simeq 104 \ \mu V/°C$ ($= 5.2 \ \mu V \times 20$).

The gain-determining resistors should all possess a temperature coefficient of less than 25 ppm/°C so that their total contribution (worst case) to the gain change will be less than 0.02%/°C. Though there are about 13 resistors, the typical value of the gain error will be $\sqrt{13} \times 25$ ppm/°C or $\simeq$ 90 ppm/°C.

To obtain the specified low drift performance from the OP07A amplifiers, the amplifiers will have to be individually corrected for offset, as shown in Fig. 11.7. (R_1 to R_9: 0.5% tolerance; R_{v_1}: adjusted for optimum common mode rejection; R_{v_2}: adjusted for gain of $10,000 \pm 0.05\%$; and R_{v_1}, R_{v_2}: wire wound variable resistors.)

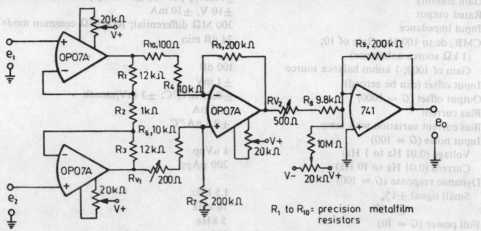

Fig. 11.7 Instrumentation amplifier for strain gauge transducer

11.5.2 Linear Gain Control

A modification of the arrangement shown in Fig. 11.6 enables one to obtain an instrumentation amplifier having continuously adjustable gain. The advantage of the modified circuit shown in Fig. 11.8 is that the gain is linearly proportional[5] to the adjustable resistance R_{v_3}. The set position of R_{v_3} provides a direct indication of the gain.

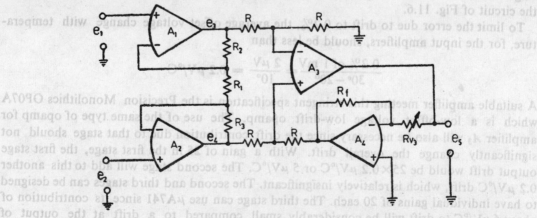

Fig. 11.8 Instrumentation amplifier with linear gain control

The gain of the amplifier circuit shown in Fig. 11.6 is

$$\frac{e_5}{e_2 - e_1} = 1 + \frac{2R_2}{R_1} \tag{11.13}$$

for $R_2 = R_3$. Though the gain can be varied by R_1 alone, its dependence on R_1 is non-linear. For the schematic shown in Fig. 11.8, the gain is given by

$$\frac{e_5}{e_2 - e_1} = \left[1 + \frac{2R_2}{R_1} \right] \frac{1}{R_f} R_x \tag{11.14}$$

where R_x is the set value of R_{v_3}. The gain is thus linearly proportional to R_x. The ratio R_2/R_1 in Fig. 11.8 can be suitably chosen to provide some nominal gain in the first stage so that additional drift errors due to the following stages are less significant.

11.5.3 Input Guarding

The instrumentation amplifier has often very high common mode rejection ratio. This ensures that the gain of the amplifier for common mode signals presented at its input is very low as compared to its gain for differential mode signals. It is often necessary to run a cable with a length of one metre or more from the transducer to the amplifier. In such cases, the common mode signals presented to the amplifier will not be the same as that existed at the transducer, because of the mismatch in cable capacitance. In the equivalent circuit of Fig. 11.9(a), if $R_{G1}C_1$ is not equal to $R_{G2}C_2$ (where R_{G1}, R_{G2} are the source resistances and C_1, C_2 are the cable capacitances), the common mode voltage gets converted to a differential mode voltage and gets amplified by the differential mode gain. Due to this, the common mode rejection ratio of the system deteriorates significantly.

In order to alleviate this problem, the cables should preferably be connected to the common mode voltage, instead of being grounded. The voltage across the cable capacitances then reduces to the differential mode signal, and the common mode voltage appears at the input of the amplifier unattenuated by the cable capacitance.

When the common mode voltage e_{cm} is high, the cables can be driven by one of the input signals itself, as shown in Fig. 11.9(b). When the common mode voltage is not large compared to the differential mode signal e_{dm}, it is necessary to derive the common mode voltage as the average of the two input signals. In the schematic shown in Fig. 11.9(c), this is achieved by the resistive summing of the outputs of amplifiers A_1 and A_2 to get $e_{cm} = \frac{1}{2}$ $(e_1 + e_2)$ where $e_1 = e_{cm} + Ge_{dm}$, $e_2 = e_{cm} - Ge_{dm}$, and G is the gain of the first stage for differential mode signals.

In situations where large shield capacitances are to be driven at high frequencies, the divider resistance has to be low or a unity gain buffer amplifier should be added[6].

11.5.4 Programmable Gain Data Amplifier

A programmable gain data amplifier (PGDA) is a low-level signal amplifier where the gain is controlled by the digital signals applied to it. When employed for multichannel measurements, the amplifier gain can be "preprogrammed" on a per channel basis or the gain can be adjusted digitally; after channel selection, the output signal is brought within a desired range. The main advantage of using the PGDA is the enhancement of the dynamic range of the system, for a specific analog-to-digital converter employed.

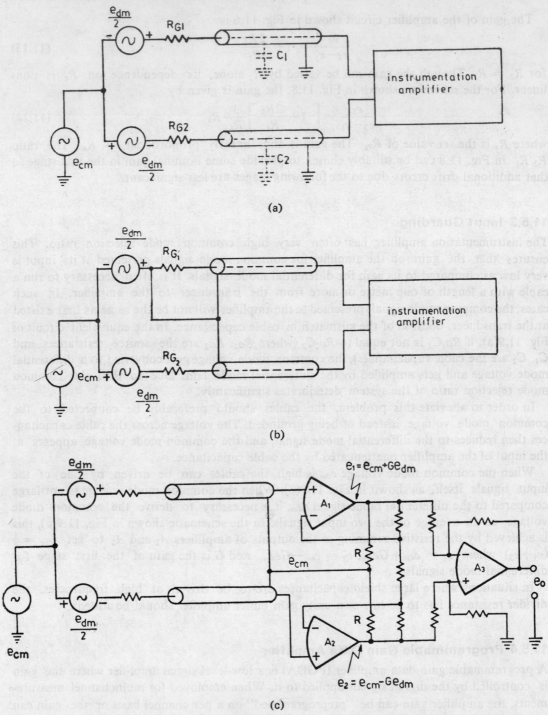

Fig. 11.9 Input guarding: (a) effect of cable capacitance; (b) driving the shield from one of the inputs to enhance CMRR; (c) deriving the e_{cm} signal to drive the shielded cable

The internal operation of a PGDA is similar to that of an instrumentation amplifier except that gain changing is performed by "switching in" appropriate resistors. These switches, typically employing MOSFETs, are operated by decoders included within the PGDA. The external digital code forms the input to these decoders. A typical programmable gain data amplifier, such as the Burr Brown 3606, has its gain selectable from 1 to 1024 in steps of 1 by the application of a 10-bit code. The gain accuracy is typically 0.02% for any selected gain. PGDA finds wide application in computer-based data acquisition systems.

11.6 ISOLATION AMPLIFIERS

In many applications in industrial and medical instrumentation, the need arises for amplifiers to have very high common mode voltage capabilities (extending to kilovolts), high isolation resistance, and high common mode rejection. The isolation characteristics are achieved in practice with a variety of signal couplers. The non-linearity of such a coupler can be overcome by linearizing the characteristics with operational amplifiers.

Isolation can be achieved by several means, such as by the use of transformers, photo-resistors, Hall-effect devices, and thermal couplers. One such example is the isolation amplifier, illustrated in Fig. 11.10(a), wherein a LED-phototransistor coupler is used in the

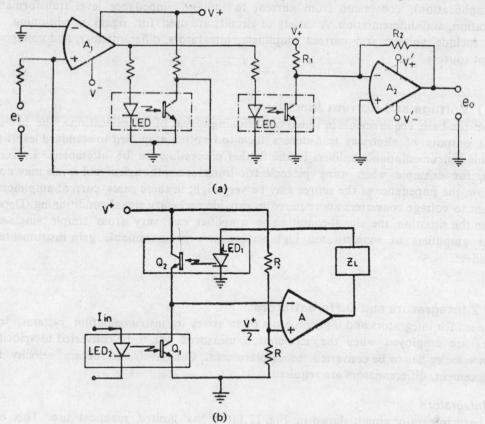

(a)

(b)

Fig. 11.10 Isolation amplifiers: (a) LED-phototransistor linearized isolation
amplifier; (b) isolated current amplifier with feedback linearization

feedback loop of amplifier A_1. A second LED-phototransistor coupler with matched characteristics, wherein the LED is driven by the same amplifier A_1, and the phototransistor is connected in the feedback loop of another amplifier A_2, provides the necessary isolation. Due to the matched characteristics of the two LED-photo-transistor pairs, the non-linear characteristics and temperature dependence get compensated.[7]

In many process-control applications, where the measurand is converted to a current, the linearized current amplifier shown in Fig. 11.10(b) is suitable for providing isolation. With equal resistors connected to the positive input of the amplifier, as shown in the figure, the amplifier gain forces a current through the load Z_L and LED$_1$, so that the currents in the transistors Q_1 and Q_2 are equal. With matched characteristics of the LED and phototransistor pairs, the load current is equal to the current I_{in} through LED$_2$. Again, the reduction of non-linearity depends on the matching of the characteristics of the LED and phototransistor pairs. The error produced by the bias current of the amplifier can be reduced by use of a low input bias current amplifier.

11.7 SIGNAL CONDITIONING

Signal conditioning involves modification of the signal and often includes scaling (attenuation or amplification), conversion from current to voltage, impedance level transformation, integration, and differentiation. A variety of circuits are used for signal conditioning, and these include voltage and current amplifiers, integrators, differentiators, and voltage and current sources.

11.7.1 Voltage and Current Amplifiers

One of the basic requirements in signal conditioning is that of amplification. The low-level signal outputs of electrical transducers have to be often amplified to standard levels with suitable instrumentation amplifiers before further processing can be attempted. In certain cases, for example when using piezoelectric transducers, though signal levels may not be too low, the impedance of the source may be very high; in these cases, current amplifiers or current to voltage converters are required to provide necessary signal conditioning. Depending on the situation, the signal-conditioning amplifier can vary from simple single-stage buffer amplifiers to sophisticated high-performance programmable gain instrumentation amplifiers.

11.7.2 Integrators and Differentiators

The need for integrators and differentiators often arises in instrumentation systems. Integrators are employed when the acceleration measured has to be converted to velocity or when velocity has to be converted to displacement. Conversely, to obtain velocity from displacement, differentiators are required.

(a) Integrators

The basic integrator circuit shown in Fig. 11.11(a) has limited practical use. This is so because the non-zero offset errors get amplified by the dc gain of the operational amplifier and produce high output offset errors. These errors can be reduced by lowering the dc gain by dc feedback, as shown in Fig. 11.11(b). Though this results in non-ideal integrator characteristics, the final-circuit is useful for many applications over a limited frequency range. For the component values indicated, the phase lag of this circuit is $\pm 270° \pm 0.5°$ (as against $+270°$ for an ideal inverting integrator) over a frequency range of 10 Hz to 10 kHz. At dc, the gain is limited to -1000, resulting in output drift of less than a few millivolts. The gain at 10 Hz is approximately -10 and that at 10 kHz is about 0.01. To ensure that the output at 10 kHz does not become comparable with the drift, the input at this frequency should be of the order of a few volts. The phase error at the high frequency end is the direct result of the limited unity gain bandwidth of the operational amplifier used. Low-frequency end phase errors are related to the basic low-pass characteristics of the configuration used with a cut-off (-3dB relative to dc gain) frequency of approximately 0.1 Hz. The useful operating range of this integrator can be shifted to a frequency range of 1 Hz to 1 kHz by increasing the feedback capacitance to 1 μF. Further reduction of dc errors can be obtained by providing higher feedback for dc and making this feedback ineffective for ac in the desired frequency range. The arrangement shown in Fig. 11.11(c) has a dc gain of 100, reducing the output dc errors by a factor of ten as compared to the performance of the integrator shown in Fig. 11.11(b)[8].

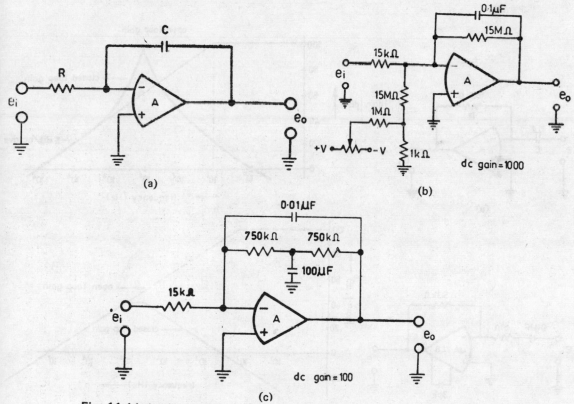

Fig. 11.11 Integrator: (a) basic configuration; (b) practical integrator circuit; (c) integrator with reduced dc error

(b) Differentiators

Differentiating action can be obtained by the straightforward arrangement shown in Fig. 11.12(a), but this has certain limitations. Due to the roll-off of the amplifier gain at high frequencies (-6 dB/octave) and the differentiating characteristics of the configuration at the operating frequency, the closed-loop gain shows a peaky response, as indicated in Fig. 11.12(b). Using a μA741 and an RC value of 0.16 s, this results in a gain of one at 1 Hz; the peak occurs at a frequency of approximately 1 kHz. The damping factor ζ is obtained from the equation

$$\frac{e_o}{e_i} = \frac{-RCs}{1 + \frac{1}{A_o}(\tau_o + RC)s + \left(\frac{RC\tau_o}{A_o}\right)s^2} \tag{11.15}$$

as

$$\zeta = \sqrt{\frac{(\tau_o + RC)^2}{RC\tau_o}\frac{1}{A_o}} \tag{11.16}$$

where A_o is the open loop gain, and τ_o is the open loop time constant of the amplifier. $\zeta = \frac{1}{1000}$ for $RC = 0.16$ s, if $A_o = 10^5$ and $\tau_o = 0.016$ s corresponding to a unity gain bandwidth of 1 MHz.

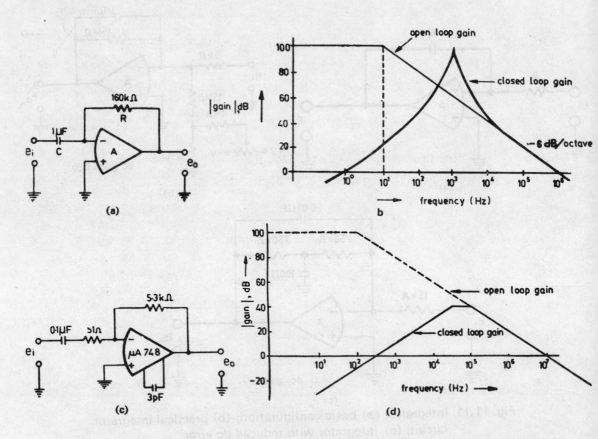

Fig. 11.12 Differentiator: (a) basic configuration; (b) frequency response of (a); (c) modified differentiator; (d) frequency response of (c)

As a result of this peaky response, the differentiator is very noisy, amplifying its own internal noise in the 1 kHz range by as much as 10^5 times. If the amplifier has a response rolling-off at more than 6 dB/octave, the circuit may even oscillate.

The modified differentiator shown in Fig. 11.12(c) can be used in practical situations. Here the closed-loop response is so shaped that the resonance peak is well-damped. For the values shown in Fig. 11.12(c), the response is shown in Fig. 11.12(d). The resistance in series with the input circuit capacitance flattens the response at about 30 kHz. At 100 kHz, the response starts falling due to the open loop gain fall-off of the opamp. For this to happen at 100 kHz, the unity gain bandwidth of the opamp should be 10 MHz and is obtained readily with a μA748 using an external compensation of 3 pF. The phase shift is 90° lead (in addition to the "inversion" of the amplifier) with less than 2° error for all frequencies less than 1 kHz. At frequencies of 0.1 Hz and below, the reduced gain for the input signal can affect the performance. A differentiator for the frequency range of 0.01 to 100 Hz is achieved by using the μA748 opamp with 30 pF compensation (or a μA741), and by changing the input circuit capacitance to 1 μF.

11.7.3 Voltage Sources

Voltage sources are required for many applications, such as for excitation of certain passive transducers and as reference sources. They are also needed to compensate the existing dc outputs so that a dc or ac change in the input can be measured differentially.

(a) DC Voltage Sources

The choice of a suitable voltage source for any particular requirement will depend on the magnitude of voltage, its adjustability, and stability. For high accuracy better than typically 0.1%, and for low-temperature coefficient requirements, a temperature-compensated zener should be used as the basic reference source. Temperature-compensated zeners with very low-temperature coefficients (as low as 10 ppm/°C) are available commercially[9]. The reference sources used in many integrated-circuit voltage regulators also yield better than 150 ppm/°C temperature coefficient (worst case) with a typical figure of $\simeq$ 20 ppm/°C. For very high-accuracy purposes (better than 0.01% accuracy), the noise of the reference and its long-term stability (variation of the reference voltage due to ageing) are additional factors that need to be considered. Due to the non-zero dynamic impedance of the reference element, an apparent change in its terminal voltage can also occur due to changes in the quiescent current of operation. Highly-regulated current sources employing operational amplifiers can be used to ensure constant current operation of the reference element. In addition, the low output impedance and ease of variability of gain offer attractive possibilities for variable reference voltage requirements.

A circuit possessing high stability and minimum sensitivity to input voltage variations is shown in Fig 11.13(a). The output voltage is

$$E_o = \left[1 + \frac{R_f}{R_i}\right]V_z \tag{11.17}$$

where V_z is the voltage across the zener. The current through the zener diode is $\frac{E_o - V_z}{R}$ (R is

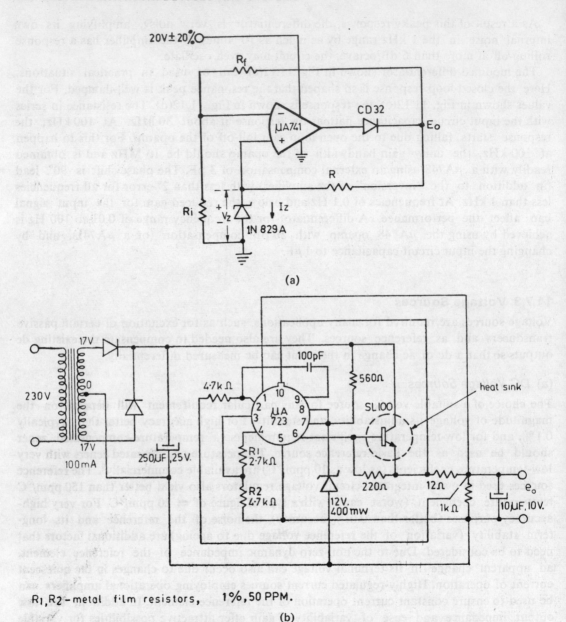

R₁,R₂—metal film resistors, 1%, 50 PPM.

(b)

Fig. 11.13 DC voltage reference circuits: (a) general purpose source; (b) excitation for strain gauge bridge

chosen to establish the required operating current). The reference diode IN829 A is a temperature-compensated zener diode having a temperature coefficient of 5 ppm/°C. Choosing the values of R_f, R_i and R as 3.8 kohms, 6.2 kohms and 1 kohm (high stability, ± 25 ppm/°C) respectively, the output voltage E_o will be approximately 10 V. The resistance R_f or R_i can be trimmed to adjust the output to exactly 10 V. The diode CD 32 has been included to provide start-up. The source meets the following brief specifications:

Output voltage	$\simeq$ 10 V (trimmable to 10 V by R_f)
Output voltage stability	$= \pm 0.01\%$ over $\pm 1°C$ ambient change
Output resistance	< 0.2 ohm
Output current	$= \pm 1$ mA max.
Output voltage sensitivity for supply changes	$< 0.005\%$ change for a supply voltage of 20 ± 4 V

The current that the source can deliver will depend upon the current capability of the amplifier, and this can be improved by suitable buffering with a high current output stage. Alternatively, IC voltage regulators can also be employed to provide the required current capability. A precision voltage drive, capable of exciting a four-arm strain gauge bridge is shown in Fig. 11.13(b). The precision voltage regulator μA723 used has a low-temperature coefficient of 0.002% (typical) for the internal reference. To ensure very good line regulation, a zener preregulator is incorporated. The use of an external-pass transistor ensures that internal reference voltage variations due to self-heating of the IC is avoided. (Care should be taken in the practical circuit to keep the regulator IC and the pass transistor away from each other.) The circuit shown in Fig. 11.13(b) is protected for short circuit and yields a stable voltage of $\simeq$ 4.5 V. Line regulation and load regulation are typically better than 0.01% for line variations from 207 to 253 V (230 V $\pm$ 10%) and for load variations from zero to 10 mA.

(b) AC Voltage Sources

In certain carrier excited systems and in precision testing of ac systems, an ac source having high amplitude stability can become necessary. A stable ac voltage can be obtained by low-pass filtering of a square wave of precise amplitude. The amplitude stability for the square wave is achieved by switching a standard dc at the desired frequency using a precision switch (e.g. CMOS switch). The low-pass filter is employed to remove the harmonic components, and it should have high stability for pass-band gain. An amplitude-stable ac voltage can also be achieved by controlled amplification of an ac voltage. Here, the output of the amplifier is sensed by a precision detector circuit and is compared with a reference dc. The difference is amplified and is used to control the amplification of the ac voltage so that the output amplitude remains constant. The typical amplitude stability obtainable is in the range of 0.01 to 0.1%.

11.7.4 Current Sources

Various types of current sources are available, and the choice of a suitable one is based on the following factors:

(i) Is the load floating?
(ii) Is bipolar capability required?
(iii) Should the current be capable of being controlled by a voltage?
(iv) What is the compliance voltage required? (Compliance voltage is the maximum voltage permissible across the current source.)

Other requirements, such as the necessity to switch the current ON and OFF can also arise. The required stability (with time and temperature), output impedance, and accuracy are the other important considerations.

One of the simplest forms of current sources is obtained using the opamp, as shown in Fig. 11.14(a). The circuit is suitable only for floating loads. The stability of the current is dependent on that of the reference voltage used. The compliance voltage is limited by the supply voltages for the opamp. The bias current of the opamp affects the accuracy of the current at very low current values; when the required current is of the order of a few microamperes, the FET input amplifier is preferred. The circuit has bipolar capability.

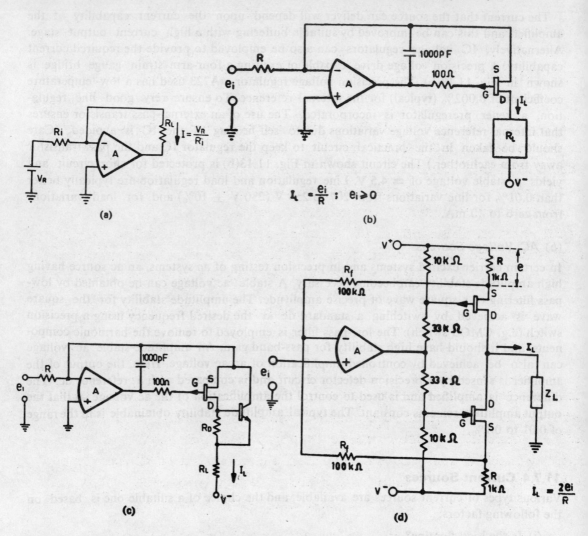

Fig. 11.14 Current sources: (a) a bipolar current source for floating loads; (ba) unipolar current source having output resistance; ($I_L < I_{DSS}$); (c) same as (b) but for $I_L > I_{DSS}$; (d) bipolar current source operated from grounded voltage source and driving grounded load

A unipolar current source capable of having an output impedance of the order of 10^{12} ohms is shown in Fig. 11.14(b). The load is connected to the "drain" lead of the FET whose source current is determined by the reference voltage and input resistor R. The load current is limited to I_{DSS} of the FET. While the output resistance is $\simeq 10^{12}$ ohms, the output capacitance (3 pF) limits the output impedance at frequencies greater than 0.05 Hz.

A modification of the arrangement shown in Fig. 11.14(b) to enable higher load currents is shown in Fig. 11.14(c). For $e_i = 10$ V, $R = 500$ ohms, and $R_D = 330$ ohms, I_L will be of the order of 20 mA while the output impedance continues to be as high as $\simeq 10^{11}$ ohms$\|$ 3 pF[10].

A most versatile current source having bipolar capacity to drive grounded loads, which is controllable with grounded sources, is shown in Fig. 11.14(d). The feedback resistors $(R_f \gg R)$ force the current through the FETs such that the voltage e across resistance R in the source circuit is twice the input voltage e_i. As a result, the output current is related to e_i as

$$I_L = \frac{2e_i}{R} \tag{11.18}$$

This current source also has an output impedance approximated by $Z_0 = 10^{12}$ ohms $\|2C_{gd}$, C_{gd} being the gate to drain capacitance of the FETs. As shown, the maximum current is limited to I_{DSS}, the saturation current of FET for zero gate to source bias voltage, but the enhancement configuration shown in Fig. 11.14(c) can be extended to this circuit as well for higher-load current requirements. Since the voltage e is influenced by the supply voltages V^+ and V^-, they should be well-regulated and so adjusted as to be equal in magnitude. Matching of source resistors and feedback resistors is also essential to equalize the output currents for equal positive and negative input voltages.

APPENDIX 11.1

Analysis of an Operational Amplifier

The analysis of the equivalent circuit of the opamp shown in Fig. 11.15 results in the following equations:

$$\frac{e_i - \epsilon}{R_i} = \frac{\epsilon}{R_{in_{dd}}} + \frac{\epsilon - e_o}{R_f} \tag{11A.1}$$

or

$$\frac{e_i}{R_i} = \epsilon \left(\frac{1}{R_i} + \frac{1}{R_{in_{dd}}} + \frac{1}{R_f} \right) - \frac{e_o}{R_f} \tag{11A.2}$$

$$\frac{-A\epsilon - e_o}{R_o} = \frac{e_o - \epsilon}{R_f} + \frac{e_o}{R_L}; \tag{11A.3}$$

or

$$-\frac{e_o}{R_o} - \frac{e_o}{R_f} - \frac{e_o}{R_L} = \epsilon \left(\frac{A}{R_o} - \frac{1}{R_f} \right) \tag{11A.4}$$

$$\epsilon = -e_o \left\{ \frac{\frac{1}{R_o} + \frac{1}{R_f} + \frac{1}{R_L}}{\frac{A}{R_o} - \frac{1}{R_f}} \right\} \tag{11A.5}$$

Substituting in (11A.2),

$$\frac{e_l}{R_i} = -e_o \left[\frac{1}{R_f} + P \left\{ \frac{\frac{1}{R_o} + \frac{1}{R_f} + \frac{1}{R_L}}{\frac{A}{R_o} - \frac{1}{R_f}} \right\} \right] \qquad (11A.6)$$

where,

$$P = \frac{1}{R_i} + \frac{1}{Rin_{dd}} + \frac{1}{R_f} \qquad (11A.7)$$

$$I_l = \frac{e_i - \epsilon}{R_i} = -l_o \left[\frac{1}{R_f} + P \left\{ \frac{\frac{1}{R_o} + \frac{1}{R_f} + \frac{1}{R_L}}{\frac{A}{R_o} - \frac{1}{R_f}} \right\} \right] - \frac{1}{R_i} \left\{ \frac{\frac{1}{R_o} + \frac{1}{R_f} + \frac{1}{R^7}}{\frac{A}{R_o} - \frac{1}{R_f}} \right\}$$

$$= -e_o \left[\frac{1}{R_f} + \left\{ \frac{\left(\frac{1}{Rin_{dd}} + \frac{1}{R_f} \right) \left(\frac{1}{R_o} + \frac{1}{R_f} + \frac{1}{R_L} \right)}{\frac{A}{R_o} - \frac{1}{R_f}} \right\} \right] \qquad (11A.8)$$

$$\frac{e_l}{I_l} = \frac{e_i}{R_i} \frac{1}{I_l} R_l$$

$$= R_i \left[1 + \frac{\frac{1}{R_l} \left\{ \frac{\frac{1}{R_o} + \frac{1}{R_f} + \frac{1}{R_L}}{\frac{A}{R_o} - \frac{1}{R_f}} \right\}}{\frac{1}{R_f} + \left[\left\{ \frac{\frac{1}{R_o} + \frac{1}{R_f} + \frac{1}{R_L}}{\frac{A}{R_o} - \frac{1}{R_f}} \right\} \left\{ \frac{1}{R_f} + \frac{1}{Rin_{dd}} \right\} \right]} \right] \qquad (11A.9)$$

If $R_o \to 0$, the above expression simplifies to

$$\frac{e_l}{I_l} = R_l \left[1 + \frac{R_f/R_l}{A + 1 + A(R_f/Rin_{dd})} \right] \qquad (11A.10)$$

From (11A.6)

$$\frac{e_o}{e_i} = - \frac{R_f/R_i}{1 + \left[\left(\frac{R_f}{R_{l}} + \frac{R_f}{Rin_{dd}} + 1 \right) \left\{ \frac{1 + \frac{R_o}{R_f} + \frac{R_o}{R_L}}{A - \frac{R_o}{R_f}} \right\} \right]} \qquad (11A.11)$$

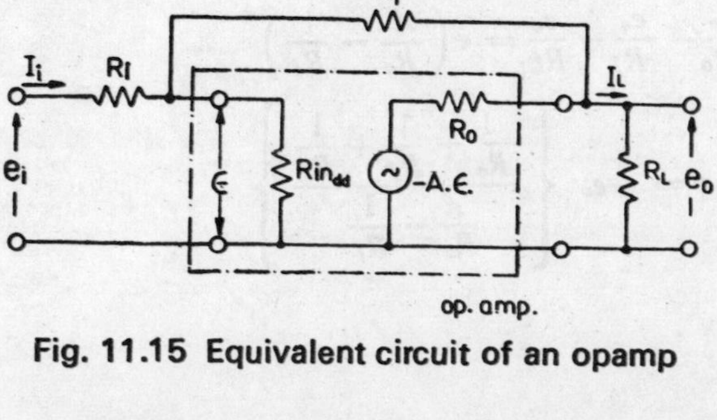

Fig. 11.15 Equivalent circuit of an opamp

EXERCISES

11.1 A standard ±10 V source is connected across a series string of ten 1 kohm resistors. A unity gain voltage follower connected to this network through a selector switch enables setting the output voltage from 0 to 10 V in 1 V steps. If a 1 Mohm resistance is shunted across the input of the voltage follower, calculate the resulting non-linearity error as the output voltage is varied from 0 to 10 V.

11.2 An amplifier having a gain of −10 is wired up as in Fig. 11.4(a) using a μA741C and R_l of 10 kohm. Calculate the typical output offset voltage that would result if the input is: (i) shorted to ground, and (ii) left floating.

11.3 An instrumentation amplifier having a gain settable in the range of 10 to 100 is desired for a certain system. Show how this can be realized using the circuit of Fig. 11.8 and a linear 10 turn potentiometer of value 100 kohm.

11.4 From the specifications given in Table 11.2, calculate the worst case output error voltage that would result when the Type 3620 amplifier is used with a gain of 100 and is operated from sources having 10 kΩ dc output resistance. (Assume common mode input and differential input as zero.)

11.5 Design an integrator to give a phase shift of 90° ±0.01°, in the frequency range 45 to 55 Hz. (Assume that a gain of 0.3 to 3 is permissible.)

11.6 Design a differentiator for operation in the range 20 Hz to 20 kHz, with the phase error not exceeding 5° and with an effective damping coefficient more than 1.

11.7 Describe a scheme that can be used to assess the output resistance of a current source of the type used in Fig. 11.14(c) over the output voltage range 0 to 5 V, at a current of 10 mA.

11.8 An amplifier having a non-inverting gain of 10 is constructed using μA748. What is the maximum frequency that can be applied to this amplifier if the phase shift should be no more than 5°? How is the compensating capacitor chosen to optimize the bandwidth?

REFERENCES

1. Korn, G.A. and Korn, T.M., *Electronic Analog and Hybrid Computers*, pp. 86-85, McGraw-Hill, New York, 1964.
2. Hamilton, T.D.S., *Handbook of Linear Integrated Electronics for Research*, pp. 143-150, McGraw-Hill, U.K., 1977.
3. Jung, W.G., *IC Op-amp Cookbook*, pp. 128-130, Howard W. Sams and Co., Indiana, 1974.
4. Ibid., 1, p. 137.
5. Graeme, J.G., *Applications of Operational Amplifiers: Third Generation Techniques*, pp. 61-62, Burr-Brown Research Corp., McGraw-Hill, New York, 1973.
6. Ibid. 5, pp. 57-59.
7. Ibid. 5, pp. 65-66.
8. Tobey, G.E. et al., *Operational Amplifiers—Design and Applications*, Burr Brown Research Corp., McGraw-Hill, New York, 1971.
9. Jung, W.G., "Voltage references determine accuracy", *Electronic Design*, Vol. 25, No. 16, pp. 84-88, Aug. 2, 1977.
10. Ibid. 5, pp. 79-89.

BIBLIOGRAPHY

Brokaw, A.P., "An IC amplifier users' guide to decoupling, grounding and making things go right for a change", *Application Note*, Analog Devices, Norwood, Massachusetts, 1977.

Clavien, M.N., "Specifying instrument cable", *Instruments and Control Systems*, Vol. 51, No. 11, pp. 47-50, November 1978.

Donn Soderquist, "Minimization of noise in operational amplifier applications", *Application Note, AN-15*, Precision Monolithics Inc., California, 1979.

Graeme, J., "Using op-amps in low noise applications", *Application Note, AN 68*, Burr Brown Res. Corp., Tucson, Arizona, 1978.

Graeme, J., "Design of unique precision controlled current source", *Application Note, AN 74*, Burr Brown Res. Corp., Tucson, Arizona, 1975.

Harper, C.A. (Ed.), *Handbook of Wiring, Cabling and Interconnecting for Electronics*, McGraw-Hill, New York, 1972.

"How to select operational amplifiers", *Application Note*, Analog Devices, Norwood, Massachusetts, 1975.

Kilpec, B.L., "How to Avoid noise pick-up on wire and cable", *Instruments and Control Systems*, Vol. 50, No. 12, pp. 27-30, Dec. 1977.

Linear Applications Vol. I and II, National Semiconductor Corp., California, 1976.

Malmstadt, H.V. et al., *Electronic Analog Measurements and Transducers, Module 1*, W.A. Benjamin Inc., California, 1973.

"Model 3620—differential input instrumentation amplifier", *Data Sheet and Applications*, Burr Brown Res. Corp., Tucson, Arizona, 1972.

Morrison, R., "Answers to grounding and shielding problems", *Instruments and Control Systems*, Vol. 52, No. 6, pp. 35-38, June 1979.

Nalle, D.H., "Kill signals that attack measurement data", *Instruments and Control Systems*, Vol. 50, No. 2, pp. 35-39, Feb. 1977.

"Optical coupling extends isolation amplifier utility", *Application Note, AN 85*, Burr Brown Res. Corp., Tucson, Arizona, 1978.

Ott, W.E.. "Instrumentation amplifiers—versatile differential input gain blocks", *Application Note, AN 75*, Burr Brown Res. Corp., Tucson, Arizona, 1978.

Prenskey, S.D., *Manual of Linear Integrated Circuits*, Reston Publishing Co., Inc., Virginia, 1974.

"Programmable data amplifiers", Burr Brown Res. Corp., Tucson, Arizona, 1973.

Solomon, J.E., "The monolithic opamp: A tutorial study", *IEEE J. Solid State Circuits*, Vol. SC-9, No. 6, pp. 314-322, Dec. 1974.

Widlar, R., et al., "Low voltage opamp breakthrough expands linear design horizons", *EDN*, Vol. 24, No. 3, pp. 91-99, Feb. 5, 1979.

12

SIGNAL GENERATION AND PROCESSING

12.1 INTRODUCTION

A complete electronic measurement system very often requires some form of excitation in a majority of cases and one or more types of processing circuits to convert the outputs of transducers into useful data. The excitation may be a constant dc voltage or current or a well-stabilized ac signal. In the case of swept measurements, the need arises for varying the excitation source frequency or amplitude in a predetermined manner with time. When the transducer characteristics are nonlinear, it may be advantageous to "linearize" the output. Some of the basic types of signal generators and processors that are often used in instrumentation systems are discussed briefly in the following sections.

12.2 SINEWAVE GENERATION

The main requirements for sinusoidal signal generators in instrumentation and measurement systems are amplitude stability and frequency stability. The accuracy to which the amplitude and frequency are to be maintained depends on the actual application. The frequency of interest can vary from 0.001 Hz to 1 MHz, and the amplitude may be in the range of 1 mV to 10 V rms.

The Wien bridge oscillator is one of the most popular types of generators used in the audio and sub-audio frequency ranges because of its simplicity, low distortion, good amplitude stability, and the relative ease with which the frequency can be varied. The oscillator is based on the Wien network as shown in Fig. 12.1(a). The transfer function of the network is

$$\frac{E_o}{E_i} = \frac{\mathcal{L}(e_o)}{\mathcal{L}(e_i)} = \frac{sRC}{s^2R^2C^2+3sRC+1} \tag{12.1}$$

where $\mathcal{L}$ represents the Laplace operator. This network exhibits zero phase at a frequency, $f_o = \frac{1}{2\pi RC}$. The gain $\frac{e_o}{e_i}$ at f_o is 1/3, and less than this value at higher and lower frequencies. As such, if sufficient positive feedback is employed around the network, oscillations can be induced. A possible scheme providing a gain of 3 in the positive feedback path is shown in Fig. 12.1(b). With $(R_f/R_i) = 2$, the non-inverting amplifier in the feedback path provides the required gain of 3. The system oscillates at a frequency of $= \dfrac{1}{2\pi RC}$.

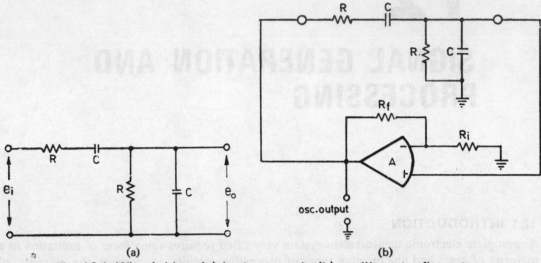

osc.output

Fig. 12.1 Wien bridge: (a) basic network; (b) oscillator configuration

(a)   (b)

Due to the sharp reduction of the closed-loop gain of the opamp near saturation, the oscillator output will almost always be clipped, and the amplitude of oscillations will be limited to the saturation level. It is rather difficult to reduce the output distortion by trimming the gain to a value just sufficient to start the oscillations. A modification of the gain characteristics can be achieved with the circuit shown in Fig. 12.2 so that a sharp change in the loop gain is avoided. When the output exceeds the zener voltage, the gain reduces to a value that prevents a further increase of the output amplitude. As a result, output distortion is reduced considerably. The peak output amplitude is also governed by the zener voltage V_z and is often only a fraction of a volt higher than V_z ($\simeq 6.8$ V).

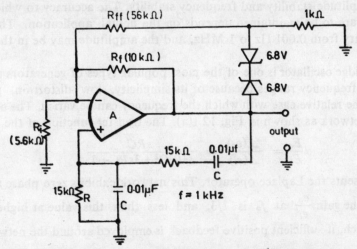

Fig. 12.2 Wien bridge oscillator with amplitude control

Table 12.1 gives the resistance and capacitance values for various frequencies of oscillation.

TABLE 12.1 COMPONENT VALUES FOR WIEN BRIDGE OSCILLATOR

f	R	C†	IC's	R_f	R_i	R_{ff}
0.01 Hz	3.3 MΩ	4.7 μF	LM 308, NE 536	100 kΩ	56 kΩ	560 kΩ
0.1 Hz	3.3 MΩ	0.47 μF	-do-	-do-	-do-	-do-
0.1 Hz	330 kΩ	4.7 μF	741, 748*	-do-	-do-	-do-
1 Hz	330 kΩ	0.47 μF	-do-	-do-	-do-	-do-
10 Hz	330 kΩ	0.047 μF	-do-	-do-	-do-	-do-
100 Hz	30 kΩ	0.047 μF	-do-	-do-	-do-	-do-
1 kHz	33 kΩ	0.0047 μF	-do-	-do-	-do-	-do-
1 kHz	15 kΩ	0.01 μF	-do-	10 kΩ	5.6 kΩ	56 kΩ
5 kHz	3.3 kΩ	0.01 μF	748+	-do-	-do-	-do-
10 kHz	3.3 kΩ	0.0047 μF	-do-	-do-	-do-	-do-
30 kHz	3.3 kΩ	0.0015 μF	-do-	-do-	-do-	-do-

†Capacitors should be low leakage type such as polycarbonate.
748* : 748 with 30 pF compensation
748+ : 748 with 5 pF compensation

The frequency stability of the oscillations is governed primarily by the stability of R and C at low frequencies. For very low frequencies, the value of R may have to be higher for practical values of C. When the value of R is more than a few hundred kilohms, amplifiers chosen should have low bias currents so that high dc offset at the output is avoided (with $R \simeq 3.3$ Mohms, output dc offset is $\simeq 0.25$ V for μA741). The capacitance used should be of a low leakage type with good stability. Recommended types are polyester, metallized polyester, and polycarbonate. In the case of large resistance values, any change in effective R due to the leakage across R in the printed circuit board should be taken care of.

At high frequencies, the slew rate of the opamp often limits the swing allowable, when an undistorted output is desired. High slew-rate opamps, such as μA715, NE 531, CA 3080, and AD 518 are possible choices.

12.2.1 Amplitude Stabilization

In situations where the frequency of the oscillator needs to be varied and the amplitude is to be kept constant, the performance of the circuit of Fig. 12.2 is not satisfactory. The basic approach employed to ensure amplitude stability is to sense the amplitude of the output and control the gain by feedback so that the amplitude remains constant. A circuit wherein an FET is used to achieve the desired control of gain[1] is shown in Fig. 12.3. The output amplitude is sensed, and a voltage is fedback to the FET so that when the output peak amplitude builds up to a fraction of a volt more than V_z, the loop gain is reduced, preventing further build-up. With this active automatic gain control loop, the amplitude is maintained constant and the distortion is reduced to below 0.2%. The frequency of oscillation is given by $f = \dfrac{1}{2\pi R_v C}$ and the corresponding period T is $2\pi R_v C$. The use of linear potentiometers for R_v variation thus results in an oscillator whose "period" is directly proportional to the setting.

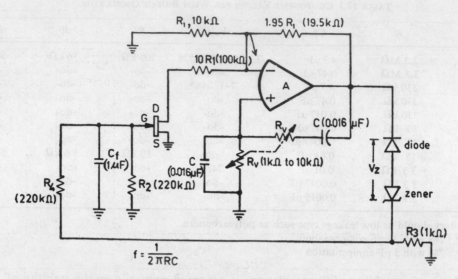

$$f = \frac{1}{2\pi RC}$$

Fig. 12.3 Variable frequency oscillator with amplitude stabilization

12.2.2 Linear Frequency Control and Quadrature Output

In situations where one would like to have linear dependence of frequency on the setting of the variable resistance, an oscillator based on the three-amplifier state-variable filter, described in Chapter 13 is useful. This type of oscillator is particularly useful for generating frequencies as low as a fraction of a hertz to a few kHz. The centre frequency of the filter in Fig. 12.4 is directly dependent on the ratio set by the potential divider R_{v_1} (ganged with R_{v_2}). As the ratio is varied from about 0.1 to 1, the frequency of the oscillations varies from 0.1 f_{max} to f_{max} where f_{max} is given by $f_{max} = \dfrac{1}{2\pi RC}$ and R and C are the constants of the integrators.

The feedback through R_1 and R_2 acts as positive damping for the oscillations and that through R_3 and R_{v_5} provides negative damping to initiate oscillations. The diodes ensure soft limiting of the oscillation amplitude. The final output e_1 has a distortion less than 0.2% for proper choice of R_{v_5}. For the circuit constants shown in the figure, the output frequency is variable from 100 Hz to 1000 Hz by varying R_{v_1} and R_{v_2} simultaneously. A unique feature of this circuit is the availability of a second output e_2 which is exactly in quadrature with e_1. Another advantage is that fine tuning of the frequency is possible by connecting additional potentiometers R_{v_3} and R_{v_4} across R_{v_1} and R_{v_2} respectively, and feeding the individual outputs through 16 MΩ to the following summing junction. By proper choice of component values, a high accuracy (better than 0.1%) in frequency can be achieved for a set value.

The circuit can also be modified by using FET-controlled negative damping to provide better amplitude stability.

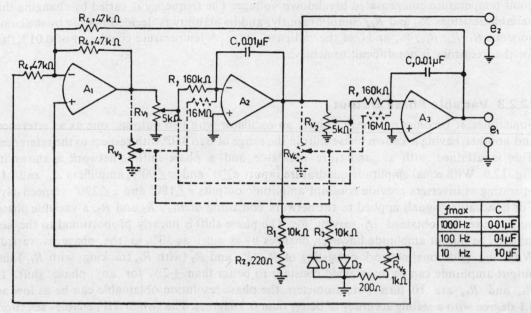

f_{max}	C
1000 Hz	0·01 µF
100 Hz	0·1 µF
10 Hz	1·0 µF

Fig. 12.4 Quadrature oscillator with linear frequency control

Another type of quadrature oscillator employs an integrator and an all-pass network in a closed loop, as shown in Fig. 12.5. The amplifier A connected as an integrator, provides a 90° lag and an inverting gain of approximately 1.05 at a frequency, $\dfrac{1}{2\pi RC}$. The following stage is an all-pass network providing unity gain and additional 90° lag. The two outputs e_1 and e_2 are in phase quadrature. Due to the overall phase shift of 360° around the loop and a gain of 1.05, oscillations start initially. When the output e_1 builds upto a little more than the voltage across the zeners (6.8+0.6 V), the loop gain falls and the amplitude stabilizes at this value. The choice of 6. 8 V for the zener enables good temperature stability to be achieved, since the combination (with the other zener conducting as a diode) yields a fairly

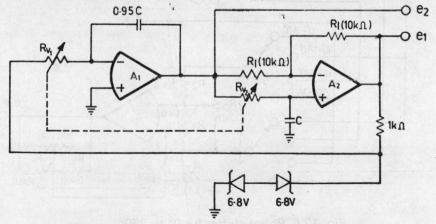

Fig. 12.5 Quadrature oscillator using an all pass network

good temperature compensated breakdown voltage. The frequency is varied by changing the variable resistors R_{v_1} and R_{v_2} simultaneously, and its stability is decided mainly by the components, R_1, R_2, R_{v_1}, R_{v_2} and C of the "all-pass" stage. A temperature coefficient of $0.01\%/°C$ for the frequency is not difficult to achieve.

12.2.3 Variable Phase Output

Sometimes, it becomes necessary to have an oscillator with two outputs, one as a reference and another having a known phase shift in the range of 0 to 360° with respect to the reference. This is attained with a quadrature oscillator and a phase-shifting network as shown in Fig. 12.6. With equal amplitude quadrature inputs $e\angle0°$ and $e\angle90°$, amplifiers A_1 and A_2 operating as inverters provide constant amplitude outputs $e\angle180°$ and $e\angle270°$ respectively. For quadrature signals applied to the network consisting of R_{v_1}, R_2 and R_3, a variable phase output can be obtained by varying R_{v_1}. The phase shift is linearly proportional to the set ratio. The output amplitude however, changes by as much as 30% as the phase is varied. With the additional network consisting of R_{v_2}, R_4, and R_5 (with R_{v_2} tracking with R_{v_1}) the output amplitude can be maintained constant to better than $\pm2\%$ for any phase shift. If R_{v_1} and R_{v_2} are 10 turn potentiometers, the phase resolution obtainable can be as low as 0.1 degree with a setting accuracy of better than 0.3 degrees. The switch SW_1 enables selection of a desired quadrant over which continuous variation is obtained using R_{v_1}.

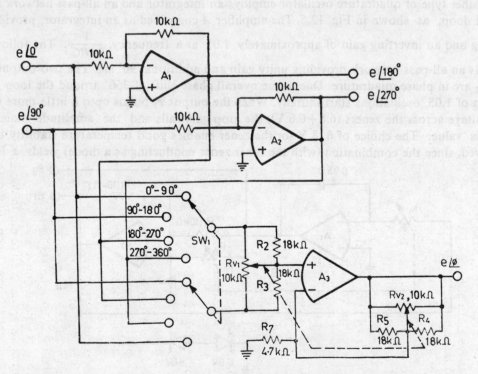

Fig. 12.6 Phase shifter for 0° to 360°

12.3 OTHER WAVEFORM GENERATORS

One of the popular methods of obtaining a sinusoidal waveform of constant amplitude is by converting the output of triangular wave generators, using triangular to sine converters. Square wave and pulse generators are useful aids in testing TTL circuits and in the measurement of step response and impulse response of analog systems. These types of waveform generators are discussed in the following sections.

12.3.1 Triangle and Square-Wave Generators

The schematic circuit diagram of a standard triangular wave generator is shown in Fig. 12.7. A capacitor C is charged at a constant rate until the voltage across it becomes just equal to a positive threshold E, after which it is charged in the reverse direction at the same rate until the voltage drops to a negative threshold $-E$, the cycle repeating itself thereafter. Such a design is widely employed in function generators and in oscillators used in phase-locked loops. With a few modifications, the same circuit can be used as a saw-tooth generator or as a voltage to frequency converter.

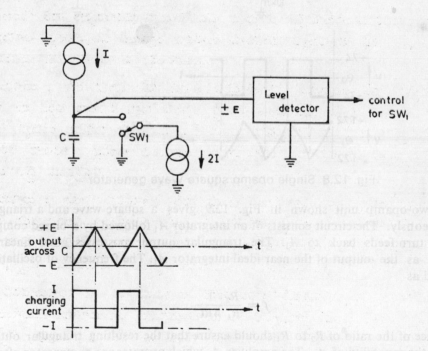

Fig. 12.7 General scheme for triangular waveform generation

The simplest version of this circuit, for frequencies below 20 kHz, is shown in Fig. 12.8, wherein the current generators are far from ideal, and a single opamp performs the task of level comparison and the control of charging and discharging currents. The resistance R in the feedback circuit in association with the capacitor C forms an integrator, and the positive feedback through R_2 and R_1 sets the comparator levels with the opamp acting as a comparator. The frequency is related to the component values as

$$f = \frac{1}{2RC \ln\left(1 + \frac{2R_1}{R_2}\right)} \tag{12.2}$$

For a limited range, the frequency is linearly related to R_2. In the circuit shown in Fig. 12.8, the variation of R_2 from 24 to 42 kohms gives a frequency variation from 800 to 1200 Hz with better than 1% linearity with respect to the value of R_2.

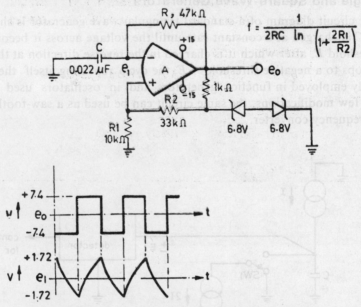

Fig. 12.8 Single opamp square wave generator

The two-opamp unit shown in Fig. 12.9 gives a square wave and a triangular wave simultaneously. The circuit consists of an integrator A_1 followed by a biased comparator A_2 which in turn feeds back to A_1. The triangular output possesses good linearity, being obtained as the output of the near ideal integrator A_1. The frequency of oscillation can be expressed as

$$f = \frac{R_2}{R_1} \frac{1}{4RC} \tag{12.3}$$

The choice of the ratio of R_2 to R_1 should ensure that the resulting triangular output swing is within the capability of A_1. The amplifier A_2 which operates as a comparator often need not necessarily be compensated, thereby enabling it to slew at a faster rate. The frequency can be made continuously variable down to almost zero by feeding R from R_{v1} as shown. In this case, at low settings of R_{v1}, asymmetry in the triangular wave can occur; this can be compensated for by an offset adjustment of amplifier A_1. Asymmetry at the highest frequency, obtained by feeding the full square wave swing to R_1 is determined by the relative matching of the zeners. The offset adjustment of A_2 shifts the average dc level of the triangular output of A_1.

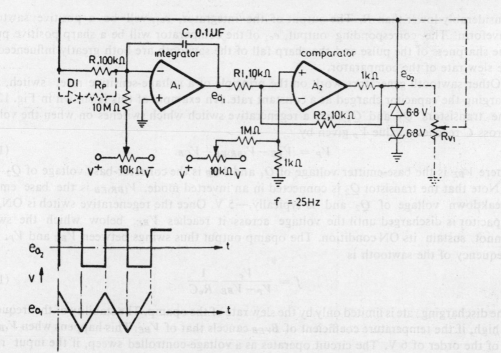

Fig. 12.9 Linear triangular wave generator

For very low frequency operation, the value of R could be made $10\ M\Omega$ or higher, if amplifier A_1 is an FET type. The capacitor should be bipolar and for good stability, should be a polycarbonate or polyester type. For a choice of $R = 10$ Mohms, $C = 1\ \mu F$, $R_1 = R_2 = 10$ kohms and R_{v1} set to give 4% of the voltage across the zeners as input to the integrator, the frequency of the generator is 10^{-3} Hz. Since the input current swings by as little as ± 30 nA, the amplifier should have an input bias current of less than a few hundred picoamperes. The offset voltage control range will also have to be reduced by proper attenuation.

For frequencies exceeding 10 kHz, the opamps used should possess high unity-gain crossover frequency and high slew rate. The latter in particular places a limit on the maximum frequency obtainable. In certain cases uncompensated amplifiers can be used for the comparator thus yielding better slew rate for this stage. It is also possible to choose the ratio of R_2 to R_1 so that the amplitude of the triangular wave is of the order of a volt. This tends to reduce slew-rate limitations for the integrator stage.

12.3.2 Sawtooth Generators

Sawtooth waveform signals can be generated by a suitable modification of the triangular waveform generator circuit. It is seen that in the triangular generator charging and discharging of the capacitor is done at equal rates. If either the charging rate or the discharging rate is enhanced considerably, the result is a sawtooth waveform. One simple method of getting this is to shunt the resistor R in Fig. 12.9 with a diode in series with a resistor R_ρ which is considerably lower than R. The output of the integrator, e_{o1}, will be a positive sawtooth waveform. The corresponding output, e_{o2} of the comparator will be a sharp positive pulse. The sharpness of the pulse and the sharp fall of the sawtooth are both greatly influenced by the slew rate of the comparator.

Other sawtooth generators work on the principle of a voltage-sensitive reset switch, discharging the capacitor charged at a constant rate. An example of this is shown in Fig. 12.10. The transistors Q_1 and Q_2 form a regenerative switch which switches on when the voltage across C reaches a value V_p given by

$$V_P = V_{BE} - V_{(BR)EB} + V_{CB} \tag{12.4}$$

where V_{BE} is the base-emitter voltage of Q_1 and V_{CB} is the collector-base voltage of Q_2.

Note that the transistor Q_2 is connected in an inverted mode. $V_{(BR)EB}$ is the base emitter breakdown voltage of Q_2 and is typically, -5 V. Once the regenerative switch is ON, the capacitor is discharged until the voltage across it reaches V_{BE}, below which the switch cannot sustain its ON condition. The opamp output thus swings between V_{BE} and V_P. The frequency of the sawtooth is

$$f = \frac{V_c}{V_P - V_{BE}} \frac{1}{R_v C} \tag{12.5}$$

The discharging rate is limited only by the slew rate of the opamp. The stability of the frequency is high, if the temperature coefficient of B_{VEB} cancels that of V_{BE}. This happens when $V_{(BR)EB}$ is of the order of 6 V. The circuit operates as a voltage-controlled sweep, if the input resistor R_v is fed from the control voltage V_C. The control voltage has to be necessarily negative

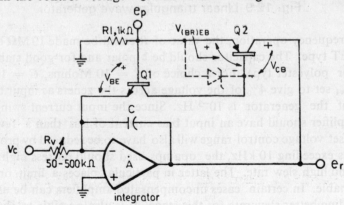

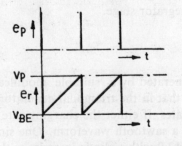

Fig. 12.10 Linear sawtooth generator

to provide a positive sawtooth. A negative sawtooth signal can be obtained by interchanging Q_1 and Q_2 and feeding a positive input control voltage.

12.3.3 Staircase Generators

If the charging current for the capacitor C_1 in Fig. 12.10 is provided in a pulsed form, the output is a staircase waveform. To achieve this, a square wave generator output (Fig. 12.8) is fed to the amplifier A_1 of Fig. 12.11. For an input e_i, the current i through the capacitor C_1 is equal to $C_1 \dfrac{de_i}{dt}$ for a value of R_1 sufficiently low. While the current resulting from the positive transition of e_i is conducted away by diode D_1, the current from the negative transition forces transistors Q_1 and Q_2 to conduct. These current pulses are integrated by A_2, producing a voltage change of

$$\Delta e_o \simeq -\frac{C_1}{C_2} \Delta e_i \tag{12.6}$$

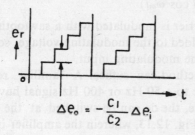

Fig. 12.11 Staircase waveform generator

corresponding to each staircase step. Δe_i is the change in e_i on the negative transition. When e_r builds up to a voltage sufficiently high to produce breakdown of base emitter junction of Q_4, the regenerative switch comprising of Q_3 and Q_4 switches on, thereby discharging the capacitor C_2. The diode D_2 biased by R_5 prevents a pedestal of V_{BE} appearing at the output. The potential divider formed by R_2 and R_3 at the input of A_1 is used to obtain proper bias for Q_1 and Q_2.[2]

A more precise but complex method to generate a staircase waveform is a clock controlled counter feeding a D/A converter. This method is particularly useful when the repetition period required is very high—of the order of a few tens of minutes to a few hours or more. If the counter used is an up-down counter, the output waveform is a staircase-type triangular waveform. This waveform can be shaped into a sinusoid using a triangular to sine converter. With a crystal-controlled clock input, the accuracy and stability of the frequency of the sinusoid can approach those of the crystal output. Such a method is employed in some "frequency synthesizers" for low and very low frequencies.

12.4 MODULATION

A "carrier" wave can be modulated by a "modulating" signal in several ways. The important of these are:

(i) Amplitude modulation—in which the amplitude of the carrier wave is made proportional to e_{in}

(ii) Frequency modulation—wherein the instantaneous frequency of the carrier wave is proportional to e_{in}

(iii) Phase modulation—in which the phase of the carrier wave is varied so that its instantaneous value is proportional to e_{in}

wherein e_{in} is the instantaneous value of the modulating signal.

Various general methods of obtaining modulation, as applied to measurement systems, are discussed in the following sections.

12.4.1 Amplitude Modulation

Amplitude modulation of any carrier wave signal can be obtained using analog multipliers, by executing the following mathematical operation

$$e_o = (A \cos \omega_c t)(1 + mB \cos \omega_m t) \tag{12.7}$$

A practical circuit wherein a sinusoidal carrier is modulated with a sawtooth voltage is shown in Fig. 12.12. Note that a "dc bias" is added to the modulating voltage so that the envelope of the output e_o is directly related to the modulating input.

There are many situations where a simpler method can suffice. A familiar requirement encountered in servo-loops is to convert a dc to a 50 Hz or 400 Hz signal having a peak voltage proportional to the input dc. In this case, the dc can be switched at the rate of 50 or 400 Hz as required, by the circuit shown in Fig. 12.13, wherein the amplifier is switched between positive and negative unity gain modes alternately at the frequency of the drive signal applied to the FET switch. When the switch is OFF the gain is $+1$, whereas when the switch is ON the gain is -1. The output is then fed to a servomotor through a suitable tuned power amplifier. The tuning of the power amplifier will aid in reducing the harmonics generated by the "switched" modulator.

Amplitude modulation can be effectively achieved by any other device as well, where the "gain" of a stage can be controlled with the voltage or current. Operational transconductance amplifiers often have such a capability and are hence suitable for amplitude

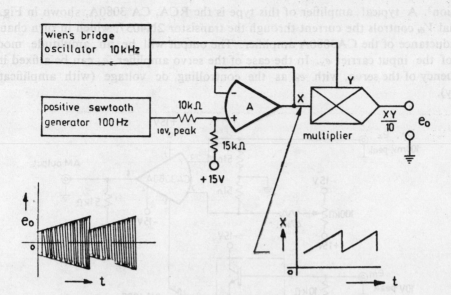

Fig. 12.12 Amplitude modulation using multiplier

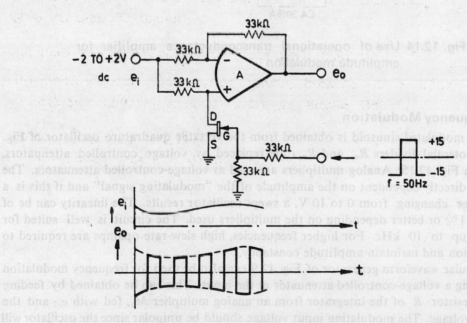

Fig. 12.13 Conversion of a dc to a 50 Hz square wave with the
peak voltage proportional to input dc

modulation[3]. A typical amplifier of this type is the RCA, CA 3080A, shown in Fig. 12.14. The signal V_m controls the current through the transistor 2N4037, which in turn changes the transconductance of the CA3080A amplifier. The output will be an amplitude modulated version of the input carrier e_x. In the case of the servo amplifier, e_x can be a fixed input at the frequency of the servo, with e_m as the controlling dc voltage (with amplification, if necessary).

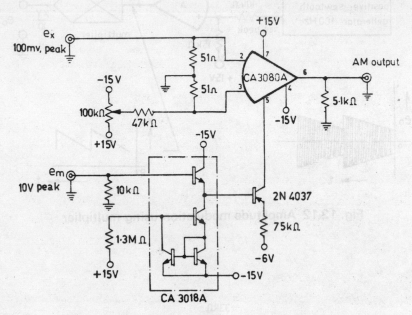

Fig. 12.14 Use of operational transconductance amplifier for amplitude modulation

12.4.2 Frequency Modulation

A frequency modulated sinusoid is obtained from the versatile quadrature oscillator of Fig. 12.4, if the potential dividers R_{v_1} and R_{v_2} are replaced by voltage controlled attenuators, as shown in Fig. 12.15. Analog multipliers are used as voltage-controlled attenuators. The frequency is directly dependent on the amplitude of the "modulating signal" and if this is a sweep voltage changing from 0 to 10 V, a swept oscillator results. The linearity can be of the order of 1% or better depending on the multipliers used. The circuit is well suited for frequencies up to 10 kHz. For higher frequencies, high slew-rate opamps are required to avoid distortion and maintain amplitude constancy.

The triangular waveform generator of Fig. 12.9 can also be used for frequency modulation by introducing a voltage-controlled attenuator at the input. This can be obtained by feeding the input resistor R of the integrator from an analog multiplier M_1, fed with e_{o2} and the modulating voltage. The modulating input voltage should be unipolar since the oscillator will cease to function for negative inputs to the multiplier.

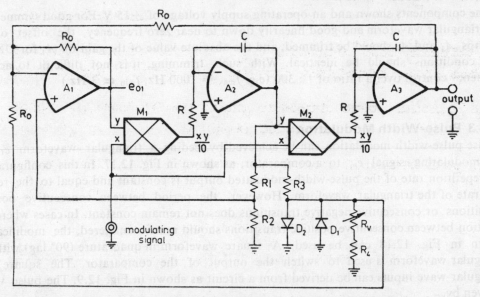

Fig. 12.15 Frequency modulated sinewave oscillator

Instead of using a multiplier as described above, it is possible to introduce a gain switched stage as in Fig. 12.16 to achieve frequency modulation. Amplifier A_1 is used as in Fig. 12.13 to obtain a square wave with an amplitude equal to the instantaneous value of the applied modulation input. The output of A_1 is integrated in A_2 and then compared with a predetermined level in A_3. The output of A_3 in turn controls the FET switch so that the direction on integration is reversed when the integrator exceeds a certain level. The circuit yields a triangular as well as square wave output, both frequency modulated. Note that the input will have to be unipolar. If the input is a slow positive sweep, the output frequency changes from near zero to the maximum frequency, determined by the components. The swept triangular output thus obtained can be converted to a swept *sinusoidal* output, with a triangular to sine converter. For an input of 2 V, the set-up shown in Fig. 12.16 gives a frequency $\simeq 200$ Hz,

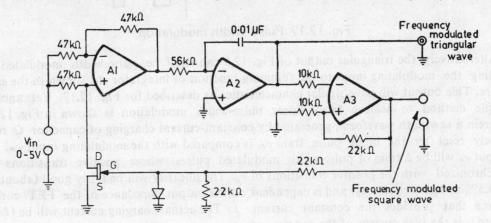

Fig. 12.16 Frequency modulation of triangular wave generator

for the components shown and an operating supply voltage of ± 15 V. For good symmetry of the triangular waveform and good linearity down to near zero frequency, the offset of the opamps A_1 and A_2 should be trimmed, and the absolute value of the gain of A_1 for ON and OFF conditions should be identical. With such trimming, it is not difficult to achieve frequency control over a ratio of $1 : 300$ (e.g. $f_{max} = 1000$ Hz, $f_{min} \simeq 3$ Hz.)

12.4.3 Pulse-Width Modulation

Precise pulse-width modulation can be achieved by feeding a triangular waveform e_t and the modulating signal e_m to a comparator, as shown in Fig. 12.17. In this configuration, the repetition rate of the pulse-width-modulated output is constant and equal to the repetition rate of the triangular waveform. However, the period between consecutive positive transitions or consecutive negative transitions does not remain constant. In cases where the duration between consecutive positive transitions should remain unaltered, the modification shown in Fig. 12.18 can be used. A square waveform in quadrature (90° lag) with the triangular waveform is used to switch the output of the comparator. The square and triangular wave inputs can be derived from a circuit as shown in Fig. 12.9. The pulse width is given by

$$\tau = \frac{T}{2} - Ke_m \tag{12.8}$$

where K is a constant and e_m is the modulating input.

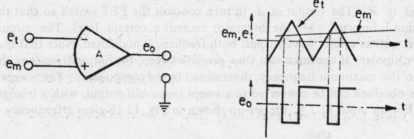

Fig. 12.17 Pulse-width modulation

Alternatively, the triangular output of Fig. 12.9 can itself be pulse-width modulated by feeding the modulating input to the summing junction of integrator A_1, shown in the same figure. This output will have similar characteristics as described for Fig. 12.17. Yet another simple method to achieve fairly linear pulse-width modulation is shown in Fig. 12.19, wherein a sawtooth waveform, generated by constant-current charging of capacitor C repetitively reset by the input pulse train e_p, is compared with the modulating input e_m. The output e_o will be a train of pulse-width modulated pulses, whose positive transitions are synchronized with the positive transitions of e_p. The linearity will be fairly good (about 0.2 to 0.5% at low frequencies) and is dependent on the output impedance of the FET current source that provides the constant current, I. The actual charging current will be $(I - i_b)$ where i_b is the bias current of the opamp.

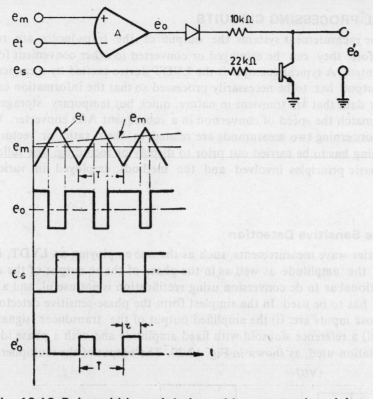

Fig. 12.18 Pulse-width modulation with constant time delay between positive transitions

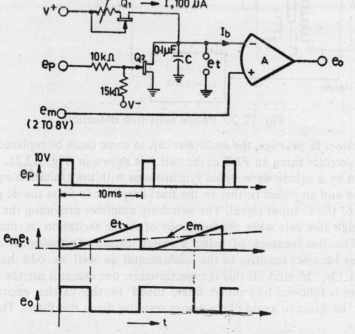

Fig. 12.19 Pulse-width modulation using sawtooth waveform

12.5 SIGNAL-PROCESSING CIRCUITS

In many of the measurement systems, the output of the transducers are required to be processed before they can be displayed or converted to other convenient forms for transmission or control. A typical example is the LVDT device excited by a carrier wave, where the signal output has to be necessarily processed so that the information can be retrieved faithfully. For data that are transient in nature, quick but temporary storage may become essential to match the speed of conversion in a subsequent A/D converter. When the final information concerning two measurands are related to their ratio or vector sum, appropriate processing has to be carried out prior to display or recording. The following sections describe the basic principles involved and the methods employed in various processing schemes.

12.5.1 Phase Sensitive Detection

In certain carrier wave measurements, such as the one employing an LVDT, information is contained in the amplitude as well as in the phase of the ac output of the device. In such cases, conventional ac to dc conversion using rectification is not useful, and a "phase-sensitive detector" has to be used. In the simplest form the phase-sensitive detector consists of a multiplier whose inputs are: (i) the amplified output of the transducer signal to be measured, and (ii) a reference sinusoid with fixed amplitude and with a phase identical to that of the ac excitation used, as shown in Fig. 12.20. The output of the multiplier is filtered and

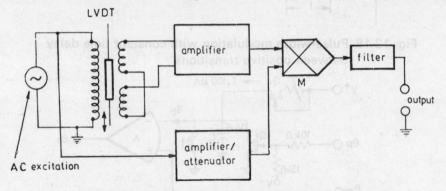

Fig. 12.20 Phase sensitive detection

fed to an indicator. In practice, the multiplier can in some cases be replaced by a switch. A phase-sensitive detector using an FET as the switch is shown in Fig. 12.21. The n-channel FET Q_1 is driven by a square wave signal synchronous with the excitation signal. The switch output is filtered and amplified further in the final amplifier to form the dc proportional to the amplitude of the ac input signal. The switching amplifier providing the drive waveform should have a high slew rate when the frequency of the ac excitation is more than a few hundred Hz. The disadvantage of using a switch instead of a multiplier is that the phase sensitive detector becomes sensitive to the fundamental as well as odd harmonics of the reference signal ($3f$, $5f$, etc.). If this is objectionable, one can still use the switch provided the first amplifier is followed by a tuned filter, tuned to the carrier excitation frequency (tuning should be exact to avoid phase errors resulting from this filter). The final filter can

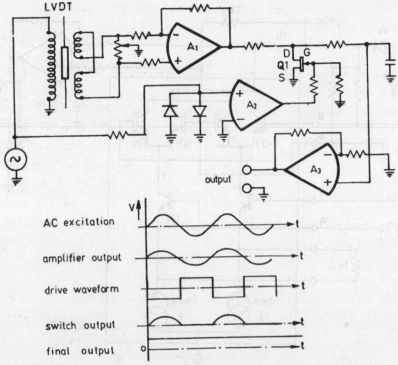

Fig. 12.21 Phase sensitive detection using FET switch

be chosen to be of a higher order, if required, to enhance the carrier frequency rejection at the output.

The integrated circuit MC 1496 is ideally suited for phase-sensitive detection. As shown in Fig. 12.22, the current in Q_1 and Q_2 is each 1 mA in the absence of modulating signal e_m. With a resistance of 1 kohm connected between the emitters of Q_1 and Q_2, the currents in them vary at the rate of the signal frequency. With no signal applied at the carrier input terminals BB, Q_3 and Q_4 share equally the current through Q_1 while Q_5 and Q_6 share the current through Q_2. When a carrier signal is fed to the terminals BB, for part of the carrier signal period, Q_4 passes full current of Q_1 while Q_3 starves; for the rest of the period, Q_4 starves with Q_3 passing the full current of Q_1. A similar action takes place in Q_5 and Q_6. By summing the currents through Q_3 and Q_5 in the collector resistance R_1 and those through Q_4 and Q_6 in resistor R_2, a balanced modulator/demodulator results; in this the differential output across R_1 and R_2 provides an output which has negligible frequency components at f_c or f_m, but has frequency components f_c+f_m (f_c and f_m being the frequency of the carrier and modulating signals respectively). The detector stage MC 1496 is followed by a differential amplifier and filter to provide the final output.

When it is necessary to measure the phase difference between two square waves A and B, the simple exclusive OR circuit shown in Fig 12.23 can be used. When B lags A by a certain phase ϕ where $\phi = 2\pi \dfrac{\tau}{T}$ the exclusive OR output has an average voltage proportional to

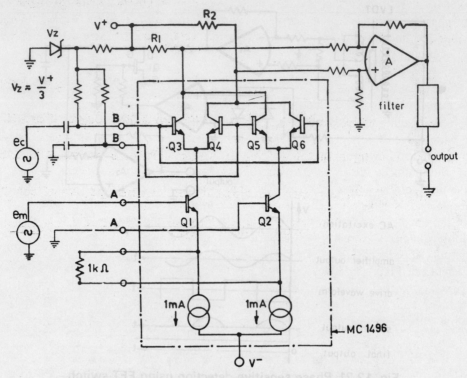

Fig. 12.22 Phase sensitive detection using MC 1496

be chosen to be of a higher order, if required, to enhance the carrier frequency rejection at the output.

The integrated circuit MC 1496 is ideally suited for phase-sensitive detection. As shown in Fig. 12.22, the current in each line is each 1 mA in the absence of modulating signal e_m. With a respective phase connected between the emitters of Q_1 and Q_2, the currents in them vary at the rate of the signal frequency. With no signal applied at the carrier input terminals BB, Q_3 and Q_6 share the current through Q_1, while Q_4 and Q_5 share the current through Q_2. When a carrier signal is fed to the terminals BB, for part of the carrier signal period, Q_3 passes full current of Q_1 while Q_6 carries for the rest of the period Q_4 starves with Q_5 passing the full current of Q_2. A similar situation applies in Q_5 and Q_6. By summing the currents in Q_3 and Q_5 in the collector resistance R_1, and those through Q_4 and Q_6 in resistance R_2, a balanced modulator/demodulator results; in this the differential output across R_1 and R_2 provides an output which has negligible frequency components at ω_c ... but is directly proportional to $e_m E_c$ (E_c and ω_c being the frequency of the carrier and modulating signal). The output of the detector stage MC 1496 is followed by a differential amplifier and filter to provide the final output.

When it is necessary to measure the phase difference between two square waves A and B, the simple exclusive OR circuit shown in Fig. 12.23 can be used. When A lags B by a certain phase ϕ where ... the circuit provides an output whose average voltage is proportional to

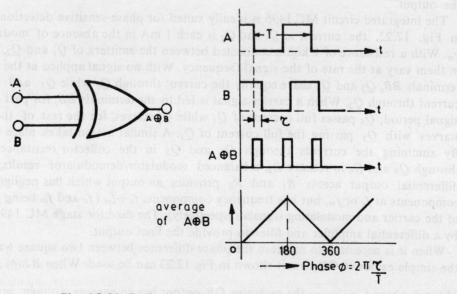

Fig. 12.23 Exclusive OR as phase detector

ϕ for $0 < \phi < 180°$ and proportional to $(360° - \phi)$ for $180° < \phi < 360°$. The range of this type of phase detectors is hence 0 to 180°. By dividing A and B by a binary divider, the range can be increased to 0 to 360°. This type of phase detectors are often used in phase locked loops and in digital systems.

12.5.2 Absolute-Value Circuit

A precision absolute-value circuit is one that provides the true absolute value of the output over a wide range of voltages. Normal diodes connected directly as in full-wave rectification fail to respond to low-level signals due to their threshold voltage limitations. To enable the use of these diodes down to a few millivolts, they are tied in with opamps such that the effective threshold is decreased to a few microvolts. The simplest form of a half-wave rectifier using this principle is shown in Fig. 12.24(a). Here the diode is within the feedback loop of the opamp, and the effective threshold referred to the input is V_d/A, where A is the open loop gain and V_d is the voltage required to forward bias the diode. It may be noted that the output impedance of this circuit is low when the diode conducts and is high when the diode is cut off. Figure 12.24(b) shows the same circuit with the necessary offset control for the opamp used. With proper adjustment of the offset, input signals as low as 1 mV peak can be half-wave rectified with this circuit. (The additional diode used prevents saturation of amplifier for negative inputs.)

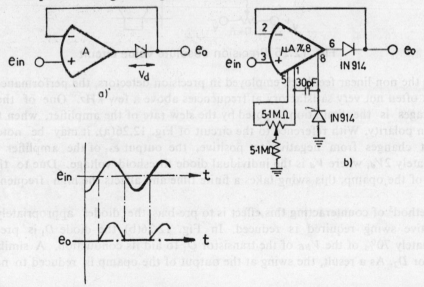

Fig. 12.24 Precision half-wave circuits: (a) basic circuit; (b) modified
form with offset control

Using the same principle, full-wave rectification can be obtained with the circuit shown in Fig. 12.25. The individual outputs of the two precision half-wave circuits, one an inverting type and the other a non-inverting type, are added by direct connection, making use of the changing output impedances for positive and negative signals. Offset-adjustment-controls have been provided in the circuit. To ensure that the gain for positive and negative signals are equal, the only trimming necessary is that of R_v in series with R_2. The circuit can handle signals from 10 V peak down to a fraction of a millivolt. The source impedance has to be kept low to avoid gain and offset errors[4].

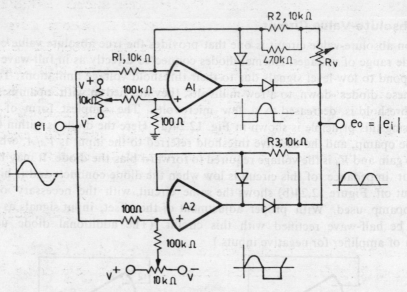

Fig. 12.25 Precision absolute value circuit

Due to the non-linear feedback employed in precision detectors, the performance of these circuits is often not very satisfactory at frequencies above a few kHz. One of the primary disadvantages is the limitation imposed by the slew rate of the amplifier, when the signal reverses in polarity. With reference to the circuit of Fig. 12.26(a), it may be noted that if the input changes from negative to positive, the output e_{o1} of the amplifier swings by approximately $2V_d$, where V_d is the individual diode threshold voltage. Due to the limited slew rate of the opamp, this swing takes a finite time and affects the high frequency performance.

One method[5] of counteracting this effect is to pre-bias the diodes appropriately so that the effective swing required is reduced. In Fig. 12.26(b), the diode D_1 is pre-biased by approximately 70% of the V_{BE} of the transistor Q_1 to aid its conduction. A similar biasing is used for D_2. As a result, the swing at the output of the opamp is reduced to nearly 30% of $2V_d$.

12.5.3 Peak Detector

A simple peak detector is obtained by connecting a capacitor at the output of the half-wave precision rectifier circuit of Fig. 12.24(a). The capacitor "holds" the peak value, subject to its discharge through the input impedance of the following stage. To achieve large hold time and low decay rate, a low bias current buffer stage (unity gain follower) should follow

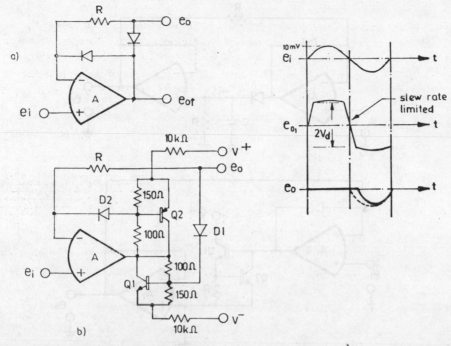

Fig. 12.26 Improving the high frequency response of precision rectifiers:
(a) unmodified circuit with $2V_d$ swing at output changes
polarity; (b) pre-biasing of diodes reduces the swing to $\simeq 0.6V_d$

this circuit. Such an arrangement, with both the stages included within the feedback loop, is shown in Fig. 12.27(a). For the hold time to be high, the amplifier A_2 should be a low-bias current type, such as an FET opamp. A controlled decay rate can be obtained by having a resistor R connected across the holding capacitor C, and the reset can be provided by placing a switch across C. When the switch employed is an electronic switch, the reset time will depend on the ON resistance of the switch. The maximum rate at which the capacitor can charge to attain the peak input voltage depends on the maximum current that the amplifier A_1 can supply. To enhance this maximum rate, the amplifier A_1 can be followed by a transistor buffer as in Fig. 12.27(b). While the transistor Q_1 provides enhanced current for charging, Q_2 in combination with R limits the peak current to a safe value that Q_1 can handle. When the input signal reduces to a value lower than the peak, the transistor Q_1 gets reverse biased and hence the capacitor holds the charge. If the reverse bias on the transistor exceeds the base emitter breakdown voltage of Q_1, it is necessary to add a protection diode in series with the opamp output.

An alternative arrangement[6] for peak detection is to incorporate an amplifier A_2, connected as an integrator with the capacitor C_1 in the feedback path as shown in Fig. 12.28, thus avoiding the necessity to drive a grounded capacitive load. The advantage is that closed-loop stability is easier to maintain than in the previous circuit. (The capacitors shown dotted are necessary to stabilize the loop.) The circuit detects positive peaks of the input e_i. The output e_o is related to e_{lp} as

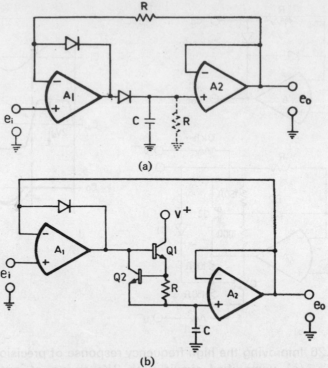

(a)

(b)

**Fig. 12.27 Peak detector: (a) low frequency; (b) modified
form for improved high frequency performance**

$$e_o = -e_{ip}(R_f/R_l) \text{ where } e_{ip} \text{ is the peak value of } e_i \qquad (12.9)$$

By reversing the direction of the diodes, the output can be made proportional to the negative peak of the input e_i. The differential output of a positive peak detector and a negative peak detector enables the determination of peak-to-peak excursions of an arbitrary input.

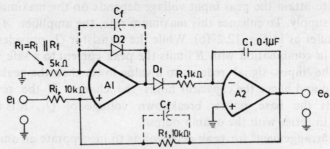

Fig. 12.28 Peak detector using integrator

12.5.4 Sample-and-Hold Circuits

The sample-and-hold circuit[7] has two modes of operation, viz., (i) the sample mode during which the output is equal to the input, and (ii) the hold mode, during which the output is held at the value of the input when the logic command changed from 'sample' to 'hold'.

"Aperture time" and "acquisition time" are two parameters of primary importance in the sample and hold (S/H) circuit. The aperture time is the delay between the transition of the command logic from "sample" to "hold" and the time at which the actual action takes place. In the simplest circuit of S/H shown in Fig. 12.29(a), the switch, if it is mechanical, can open only after a few milliseconds after the command e_c for changeover from "sample" to "hold" has taken place. As a result of this, the actual value held is not the value that the input had when the command for hold was given. The resulting error increases for rapidly-varying signal inputs. With the use of electronic switches, the aperture time can be made as low as a fraction of a microsecond. When the command changes from "hold" to sample", there is a finite delay for the capacitor to acquire the new value of the input (within a certain accuracy). This delay is termed as the "acquisition time". This is dependent on the rate at which the capacitor "slews" to finally settle at the new value of the input. The slew rate in turn depends on the current capability of the amplifier driving the capacitor.

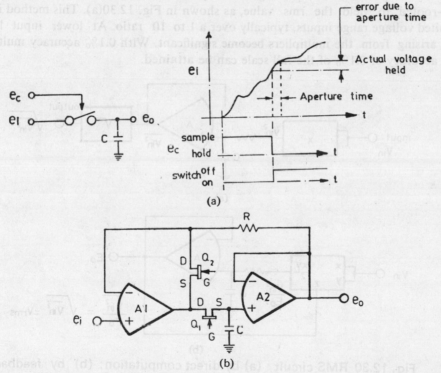

Fig. 12.29 Sample and hold circuit: (a) basic form; (b) non-inverting type

A non-inverting sample-and-hold circuit using two operational amplifiers and FET switches for the control of sample-and-hold conditions is shown in Fig. 12.29(b). In the "sample" mode, switch Q_1 is closed and Q_2 is opened. The charging rate of the capacitor is decided by the current that amplifier A_1 can provide. An acquisition time of less than 10 microseconds and an aperture time of less than one microsecond are easily achieved with a value of 0.01 microfarad for the capacitor. In the "hold" mode, Q_1 is opened and the amplifier is maintained within the linear range by the feedback provided to A_1 through Q_2. Several methods for accuracy and speed improvement of the basic sample and hold circuit are discussed in Ref. [7].

12.5.5 RMS Converters

The "root mean square" is a measure of the heating value of a voltage or current applied to a resistor. A "true-rms" meter provides an indication of the rms value of the signal that it measures, irrespective of its waveform. While conventional ac meters measure the rectified average of the input and are thus rms calibrated for sinusoidal inputs, the true rms meters often have capability to measure arbitrary waveform with crest factors (peak to rms ratio) up to 10, and sometimes, even up to 100.

The rms measurement is generally carried out by one of the following methods[8]: (i) direct computation, (ii) feedback computation, and (iii) thermal conversion.

In direct computation the input signal is squared, averaged in a low-pass filter, and square-rooted to yield the rms value, as shown in Fig. 12.30(a). This method is suitable for limited voltage range inputs, typically over a 1 to 10 ratio. At lower input levels, the errors arising from the multipliers become significant. With 0.1% accuracy multipliers, an output accuracy of 0.1% of the full scale can be attained.

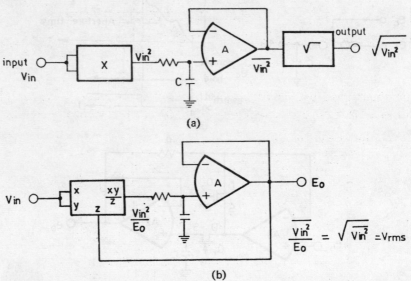

Fig. 12.30 RMS circuit : (a) by direct computation; (b) by feedback computation

The method of achieving the rms value by feedback computation is illustrated in Fig. 12.30(b). The rms value is related to the average of the square of the instantaneous value of the input voltage as

$$V_{\text{rms}} = \sqrt{\overline{V_{in}^2}} \qquad (12.10)$$

This equation is solved by indirect computation, using

$$V_{rms} = \frac{\overline{V}_{in}^2}{V_{rms}} \qquad (12.11)$$

A schematic diagram for executing this operation with a log-antilog circuit is shown in Fig. 12.31. The amplifiers A_1 and A_2 form a precision absolute-value circuit combined with

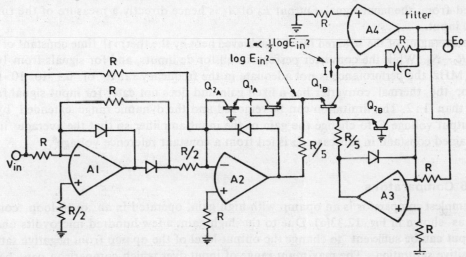

Fig. 12.31 Computation of rms value by log-antilog circuits

a logarithmic amplifier (using transistors Q_{2A} and Q_{1A} providing an output voltage proportional to twice the logarithm of the input voltage. The log of the output E_o is obtained by A_3 and the difference between this and the output of A_2 is antilogarithmically converted and averaged by A_4 to provide the output E_o. The current I through Q_{1B} is proportional to the rms value of E_{in}. The arrangement as shown enables cancellation[8] of the temperature-sensitive terms due to transistors Q_{1A}, Q_{1B}, Q_{2A} and Q_{2B}. By this scheme a large dynamic range (1000 : 1) can be obtained with an accuracy of about $\pm 0.2\%$.

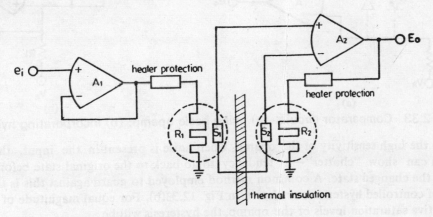

Fig. 12.32 Thermal method of rms conversion

The thermal method utilizes the heat energy derived from the signal to balance the heat energy produced from a dc circuit, resulting in a dc output which is proportional to the rms value of the signal input as illustrated in Fig. 12.32. $R_1 - S_1$ and $R_2 - S_2$ are two separate heater-sensor pairs with identical characteristics but thermally isolated. Heaters R_1 and R_2 are fed from amplifiers A_1 and A_2 respectively. The differential output of sensors S_1 and S_2 controls the output of A_2 such that the power delivered from it to R_2 equalizes that to R_1, derived from the input signal. Output E_o of A_2 is hence directly a measure of the rms value of the input.

The averaging of the squared input is achieved here by the thermal time constant of $R_1 - S_1$ and $R_2 - S_2$. While the converter performs well for dc inputs, and for signals from 10 Hz to a few MHz, the performance is not adequate in the frequency range of 0.1 to 10 Hz. As shown, the thermal converter has a fixed gain and does not cater for input signal ratios of more than 1 : 2. This limitation can be removed and the dynamic range extended by using the output voltage E_o to change the gain of the input amplifier so that the average in R_1 is maintained constant. In this case R_2 is fed from a constant reference voltage[8].

12.5.6 Comparators

The simplest comparator is an opamp with high gain, operated in an open-loop configuration, as shown in Fig. 12.33(a). Due to the high gain, a few hundred microvolts change in the input can be sufficient to change the output level of the opamp from negative saturation to positive saturation. The maximum range of input over which comparison can be made is limited by the allowable common mode voltage range. Additional input protection can be provided for inputs exceeding the differential input voltage limitations. The transition of the output from low to high and vice versa will take a finite time depending on the slew rate of the opamp. Since operation in the linear region is not envisaged, the compensation capacitance can be altogether removed when using certain types of opamps (μA 748, LM 308).

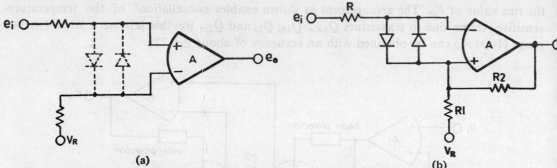

(a)   (b)

Fig. 12.33 Comparator circuit: (a) using basic opamp; (b) incorporating hysteresis

Due to the high sensitivity of the opamp, when noise is present in the input, the output transition can show "chatter"—a tendency to go back to the original state before settling finally in the changed state. A common method employed to guard against this is the introduction of controlled hysteresis, as shown in Fig. 12.33(b). For equal magnitude of positive and negative saturation levels of the opamp, the hysteresis will be

$$\frac{2R_1}{R_1 + R_2} \times V_s \tag{12.12}$$

where V_s is the saturation level on either side.

Window Comparators

In cases where an indication is to be provided when an input lies between two voltage levels $(V+\Delta V)$ and $(V-\Delta V)$, a window comparator is useful. The arrangement shown in Fig. 12.34 enables independent control of V and ΔV. The input voltage e_i and the reference voltage V_R are summed and detected using the precision detector A_1. This output is then compared with ΔV in A_2, the output of which then stays in positive saturation except for the condition $|e_i + V_R| < \Delta V$. When V_R is equal to $-V$, this becomes $|e_i - V| < \Delta V$, the

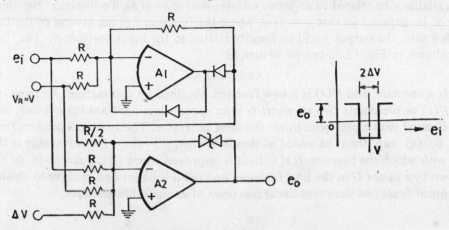

Fig. 12.34 Window comparator circuit

relation to be satisfied for the output to be in negative saturation. For $V_R = -5$ V, and $\Delta V = 1$ V, the output is in negative saturation for $4\,\text{V} < e_i < 6\,\text{V}$. The transfer characteristic is shown in Fig. 12.34.

12.5.7 Linearization

Any arbitrary function can be linearized within limits by passing it through a function generator which has the inverse relationship. For example, just as a linear input (from a triangle wave generator) can be converted to an S-shaped output (see transfer curve in Fig. 12.35(a)), the reverse is also true, namely, that the S-shaped input can be converted to an approximate linear output in a function generator having the transfer curve shown in Fig. 12.35(b). Function generators of this type can be built by piecewise linear approximation of the required transfer curve. The accuracy of the transfer curve is about 0.2% to 1% depending on the number of segments used. For the higher accuracy stated, precision

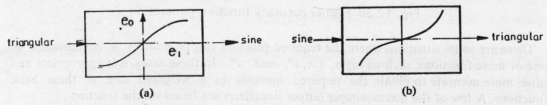

Fig. 12.35 Triangle to sine converter characteristics: (a) direct relationship;
(b) inverse function

rectifiers have to be necessarily employed. Amplifier frequency limitations and the diode capacitance set an upper limit for the highest frequency at which the transfer curve accuracy can be retained.

In cases where the deviation from a linear relationship is not very large, some improvement can be achieved by generating an amplified version of the function corresponding to the "deviation from the linear output", rather than the actual output itself and adding this difference suitably to the linear part.

Let a variable x be related to an input variable p as $x = h(p)$. To linearize the output a function y is required so that $y = f(x)$, where the function f is the inverse of the function h. In such a case, the output y will be linearly related to the input variable p. The function $y = f(x)$ shown in Fig. 12.36 can be written as

$$y = kx + f'(x) \qquad (12.13)$$

where K is a constant and $f'(x)$ is a new function obtained by subtracting Kx from y. The function $f'(x)$ or preferably $Gf'(x)$, where G is an appropriate constant scale factor, can then be approximated with a piecewise linear function generator. The two independent functions Kx and $Gf'(x)$ can then be added as shown to yield $y = f(x)$. The advantage is that the accuracy with which the function $f(x)$ is built is improved, since (i) the errors in $Gf'(x)$ are scaled down by a factor G in the final function, and (ii) it is easier and cheaper to obtain more accurate linear functions than non-linear functions of comparable accuracy.

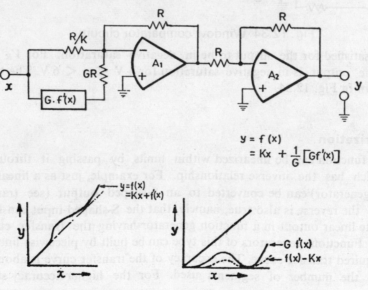

Fig. 12.36 Higher accuracy function generation

There are some situations where the required function can be built by a combination of one or more functions, such as $\log x$, $1/x$, e^x, and x^m. In these cases, it is appropriate and often more accurate to obtain the required function as a weighted sum of these basic functions. A few of the thermocouple output linearizers are based on the function

$$T = 1 + K \log x \qquad (12.14)$$

A generalized but complex approach to obtain a function $y = f(x)$ is to apply the power series expansion yielding,

$$y = K + Ax + Bx^2 + Cx^3 + \cdots \qquad (12.15)$$

The 'powers' of x can be obtained using multipliers and other non-linear function modules. However, when "implicit" feedback is used, often a greatly improved theoretical fit can be obtained. For example, $y = \sin x$ can be approximated by an explicit function,

$$y = Ax + Cx^3 \qquad (12.16)$$

and can be realized with the circuit shown in Fig. 12.37(a), with $\pm 0.6\%$ error (with respect to full scale from $\pi/2$ to $-\pi/2$ only. However, the same function may be realized with implicit feedback, as shown in Fig. 12.37(b), in which theoretical error can be kept to within $\pm 0.01\%$ of full scale[9].

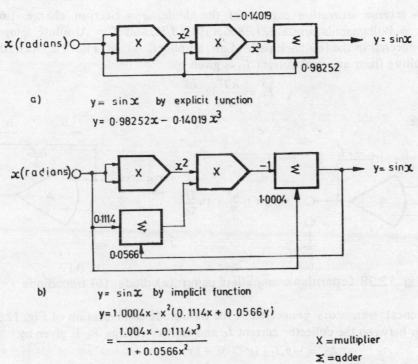

a) $y = \sin x$ by explicit function
$$y = 0.98252x - 0.14019\,x^3$$

b) $y = \sin x$ by implicit function

$$y = 1.0004x - x^2(0.1114x + 0.0566y)$$

$$= \frac{1.004x - 0.1114x^3}{1 + 0.0566x^2}$$

X = multiplier
Σ = adder

Fig. 12.37 Generation of $y = \sin x$: (a) by explicit function;
(b) by implicit function

The digital method of linearizing is carried out by either storing the values in an ROM which is then used as look-up table, or by more or less a parallel approach to piecewise linearization in which the slope of the curve is altered by changing the counting rate of a counter over selected spans of the input variable and by later D/A conversion of the output of the counter.

The abovementioned techniques are widely used in measurement systems, such as temperature measurements with thermocouples and resistance thermometers, and flow measurements with hot-wire anemometers.

12.5.8 Logarithmic Amplifier

The inherent logarithmic properties of silicon-junction devices can be usefully utilized to obtain the logarithmic output in many applications. General-purpose diodes do not exhibit a logarithmic relationship for more than one or two decades of current due to the bulk resistance at currents higher than about 1 mA and due to the deviation from the true logarithmic response at currents lower than 1 μA. A transistor having high h_{FE} over wide range of emitter currents can be used as a log diode by connecting the base and collector together. Such a transistor connected as a diode termed transdiode, often exhibits log characteristics over 5 or 6 decades of the operating current in the range 10^{-10} A to 10^{-5} A.

The ideal logarithmic diode has the $V-I$ characteristic given by

$$I = I_o(e^{qV/kT} - 1) \tag{12.17}$$

where I_o = reverse saturation current of the diode, q = electron charge, 1.602×10^{-19} coulomb, k = Boltzmann's constant, 1.3806×10^{-23} J/K, and T = Absolute temperature.

When connected in the feedback path of an amplifier, as in Fig. 12.38(a), the output voltage resulting from an input current I_{in} is given by

$$E_o = \frac{kT}{q} \ln \frac{I_{in}}{I_o} \tag{12.18}$$

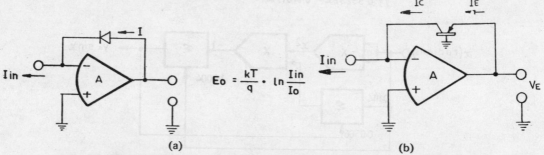

Fig. 12.38 Logarithmic amplifiers using: (a) diode; (b) transdiode

For practical transistors connected in the transdiode configuration of Fig. 12.38(b), the relationship between the collector current I_C and emitter voltage V_E is given by

$$I_C = -\alpha_n I_{ES} (e^{qV_E/kT} - 1) \tag{12.19}$$

where α_n = forward current transfer ratio, I_{ES} = emitter saturation current, and V_E = emitter base voltage.

The resulting output voltage V_E is given by

$$V_E = \left[\frac{kT}{q} \ln \frac{I_{in}}{I_{ES}}\right] - \left[\frac{kT}{q} \ln \alpha_n\right] \tag{12.20}$$

for $I_{in} \gg I_{ES}$. The typical value of I_{ES} is $\simeq 10^{-13}$ A, and α_n is very nearly unity[10]. Due to the temperature dependence of I_{ES}, however, practical log amplifiers invariably use dual transistors since their I_{ES} values tend to track with each other. Such a temperature compensated log circuit is shown in Fig. 12.39.

For an input voltage E_i, a current I_{in} equal to E_i/R_1 flows through Q_1. The output E_o is controlled by A_1 such that the voltage across R_T is equal to the difference between the V_{BE} of

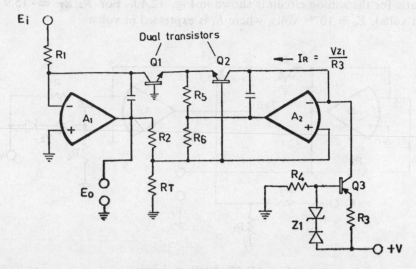

Fig. 12.39 A practical logarithmic amplifier

Q_1 (through which a current I_{in} is flowing) and that of Q_2 (the current through which is set by the current source transistor Q_3 at a reference value I_R). Since the value of kT/q at 25°C is 0.0257 mV, if the ratio of R_2 to R_T is

$$\frac{R_2}{R_T} = \left[\frac{1}{0.0257 \times \ln 10} \right] - 1 = 15.9 \qquad (12.21)$$

the output E_0 of the log amplifier becomes

$$E_o = -K \log_{10} \frac{I_{in}}{I_R} = -K \log_{10} \frac{E_l}{V_R} \qquad (12.22)$$

where,

$$V_R = V_{z_1} \frac{R_1}{R_3}$$

and

$$K = \left[1 + \frac{R_2}{R_{TC}} \right] \frac{kT}{q} \ln 10$$

or

$$E_o = -[\log_{10} E_i] \text{ V} \qquad (12.23)$$

for $R_3 = V_{z_1}$ (in volts)R_1.

The resistance R_T is chosen to have a temperature coefficient of $\simeq 0.35\%/°C$ in order that the resulting temperature coefficient of 0.33%/°C for the gain factor $(1 + R_2/R_T)$ cancels the equivalent negative temperature coefficient of the term (kT/q). The resistor R_6 introduces a controlled amount of positive feedback so as to cancel the effect of bulk resistance R_B of Q_1. The value of R_6 should be such that

$$R_6 = \frac{R_5}{R_B} \frac{R_T \cdot R_2}{R_T + R_2} \qquad (12.24)$$

The schematic for the antilog circuit is shown in Fig. 12.40. For $R_2/R_T \simeq 15.9$ and $R_1 = R_3 \times V_{z_1}$ (in volts), $E_0 = 10^{-E_i}$ volts, where E_i is expressed in volts.

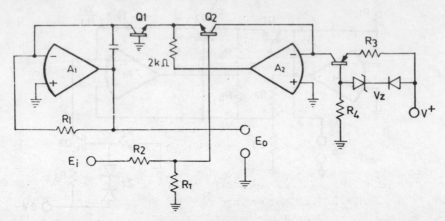

Fig. 12.40 Antilog circuit

12.5.9 Frequency to Voltage and Voltage to Frequency Converters

A frequency to voltage converter provides an analog output voltage proportional to the frequency of the input signal. The circuit employed is often a precision charge dispenser wherein a capacitor is charged to a predetermined level and the stored charge is discharged into an integrator or low-pass circuit for every cycle of the input waveform. In the circuit of Fig. 12.41, the monostable together with the precision switch that follows it, generates a

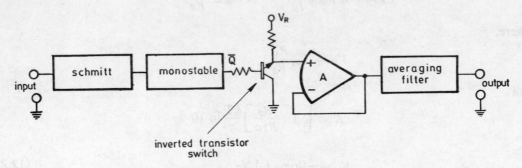

Fig. 12.41 Frequency to voltage converter

pulse of precise amplitude (V_R) and precise period (T, period of monostable) feeding into an averaging network. The final output is a dc voltage (with low ripple), proportional to the average of the input frequency. A frequency to voltage converter based on this scheme is shown in Fig. 12.42. The input signal which can be a sinusoidal, triangular, or rectangular pulse is converted to a TTL compatible trigger waveform using a Schmitt trigger circuit. The signal is then fed to a 74121 monostable multivibrator (IC_2) to obtain a pulse of width approximately equal to 35 μs. The p channel FET, Q_1 is driven OFF by the monostable output to deliver a pulse of constant amplitude and constant pulse width as the input to the following averaging stage, which is a Butterworth third order LP filter (IC$_3$ and IC$_4$). To maintain a constant output pulse width from 74121, its power supply should be stable to better than 0.02%. With the output adjusted to zero for zero frequency input to the F/V converter, the linearity is typically better than 0.1% full scale. The output for an input frequency of 10 kHz is about 10 V (adjusted by R_v).

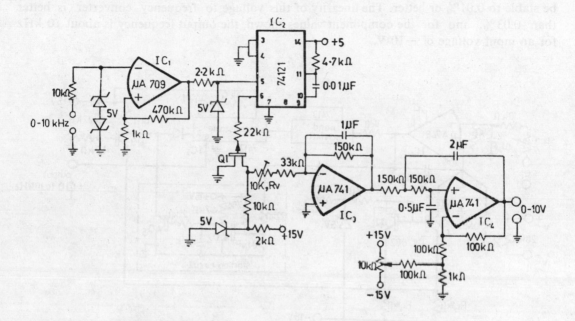

Fig. 12.42   0 to 10 kHz frequency to voltage converter

Due to the high linearity obtainable from F/V converters, they are often used in a feedback configuration to realize linear voltage to frequency converters. This type of V to F converters produce an output pulse train of constant pulse width and variable frequency. A typical circuit shown in Fig. 12.43 performs as follows. A constant current I_{ref} is maintained in the transistor Q_2. Due to the matched characteristics of transistors Q_1 and Q_2 which form a dual transistor pair, the current through the transistor Q_1 is also equal to that in the transistor Q_2 whenever the transistor Q_3 is cut-off. If the transistor Q_3 conducts the transistor Q_1 turns off since the current provided by the transistor Q_3 maintains a voltage across the emitter resistor R_1 of the transistor Q_1 to reverse bias it. The amplifier IC$_1$ is an integrator; the current through the capacitor C is equal to e_i/R when transistor Q_1 is OFF and equal to $(e_i/R - I_R)$, when the transistor Q_1 is conducting. The output of amplifier IC$_1$ feeds to an inverting NAND schmitt trigger IC$_2$ which in turn triggers the monostable multivibrator IC$_3$, whenever the input falls below its lower tripping level. For an input voltage e_i (negative) such that e_i/R is approximately one-eighth of I_R, the waveforms obtained at various points are shown in Fig. 12.43. At any time when the transistor Q_1 is OFF, the output of amplifier IC_1 falls at a rate proportional to e_i/R. When its output reaches the lower tripping point of the schmitt trigger, the latter changes state, simultaneously triggering the monostable multivibrator. During the period τ of the monostable multivibrator, the transistor Q_3 is turned OFF and the integrator output starts rising at a rate proportional to $(I_R - e_i/R)$. After the period τ, the integrator output starts falling again, repeating the earlier cycle. For an input e_i such that $e_i = (I_R \times R)$, the output waveform of the amplifier IC_1 is near triangular. For high stability of the pulse width τ, the power supply of the monostable multivibrator IC_3 should be stable to 0.01% or better. The linearity of this voltage to frequency converter is better than 0.03%, and for the component values shown, the output frequency is about 10 kHz for an input voltage of -10 V.

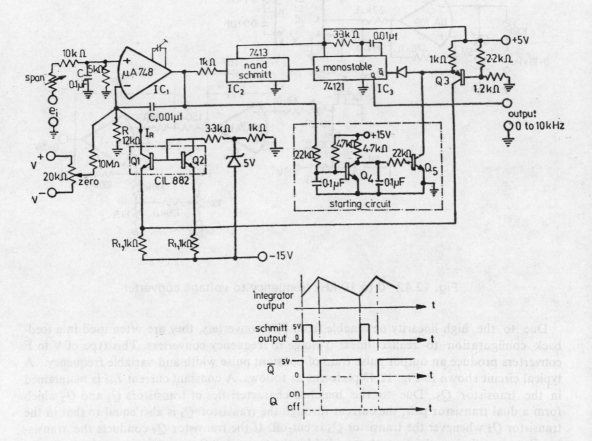

Fig. 12.43   0 to 10 kHz voltage to frequency converter

A large variety of V/F, F/V and V/F/V converters are available commercially. The V/F/V module enables one to use it as a V/F or F/V converter depending upon the external connections. A few F/V converters are also available in IC form (e.g. Burr Brown VFC 32). The V/F converter can be used for the transmission of data through a pair of wires over long distances with high-noise immunity. They are well suited for isolation in data transmission through opto-isolators, and for recording very low frequency data in the converted frequency format, in analog tape recorders[11].

12.5.10 Analog Computing Circuits

An insight into the operation of many physical systems can be obtained by simulation of the systems in an analog computer. In addition, the influence of various factors, coefficients, and time constants on the system performance can also be studied so that the system performance can be optimized.

A typical analog computer consists of 20 to 40 operational amplifiers, four multipliers, and two function generators. An oscilloscope or an X-Y plotter is used for display of the various time functions. Precision 10-turn potentiometers, usually one per amplifier, but often uncommitted to any part of the system, are also incorporated for use in coefficient setting and input parameter control. Precision reference voltages and an analog or digital voltmeter also often form part of the analog computer.

The operational amplifiers are used as "adders", "inverters', or "integrators". Since, in the case of integrators, some form of "resetting" is essential, the number of opamps that can be used as integrators is restricted to 8 or 10. The resetting is carried out using reed-relays in "slow computers" and using semiconductor-switches in "fast" computers.

Precision components, such as accurate resistances and capacitances are provided as moulded components in mounting plugs, so that they can be inserted into suitable locations on a "patch bay". Typically, the input points provided enable summation of at least three separate inputs.

One of the concepts of importance in simulating any system in an analog computer is that of scaling. In a practical set-up, both amplitude scaling and time scaling are involved. The "variables" of a given problem are represented by voltages in an analog computer. Hence it is necessary to speak in terms of a specified voltage per unit of the problem variable. Typical amplitude scale factors may be 1 N/V when the problem variable is force, or 10°C/V when the problem variable is temperature. The scale factors in amplitude scaling are so chosen as to ensure operation of the opamps in the set-up at 50 to 80% of their maximum swing, in order to achieve near optimum signal to noise ratios at the output[12]. Time scaling refers to the choice of a suitable time ratio wherein the unit time interval in the simulated problem is equated to a fraction or a multiple of unit computer time. Consider a problem relating to the study of transient behaviour of a mechanical system having a natural resonance of 500 Hz and a damping factor of 0.1. Typically, the transient in this case dies out to insignificant values in a short period of 25 ms or less. When this system is simulated in an analog computer having an RC time constant of 1 s for the integrators, for best results 1 s of computer time should be made equivalent to say, 20 or 50 ms of problem time. By this, inconveniently long or short runs can be avoided; further, opamps having practically possible frequency capabilities can be used to simulate systems where problem-times vary from a few hundred hours or even longer, to a few nanoseconds and shorter.

Linear and non-linear differential equations, such as the Mathieu's equation and Van-der Pol's equation can be solved using analog computers by appropriate "scaled" set-ups.

The ease of solving non-linear differential equations is one of the most attractive features of an analog computer. Feedback control systems can also be often simulated retaining a one-to-one correspondence between a section of the simulated set-up and the actual feedback system. Hybrid computers in which digital devices, such as comparators, logic gates, and other digital elements are used in association with analog elements offer advantages of speed and performance and are widely used in instrumentation, control, and data-handling systems[13].

EXERCISES

12.1 Design a sinewave oscillator to generate frequency in the range of 10 Hz to 10 kHz and amplitude variable from 0.1 V rms to 5 V rms. The oscillator should have an output impedance of 600 ohms.

12.2 Design a voltage controlled oscillator providing triangular output and having frequency variation from 100 Hz to 1 kHz for corresponding input voltage variation of 1 V to 10 V.

12.3 Design a simple power factor meter to operate from 230 V mains. Current range = 1 to 10 amps; Power factor range: 0.4 to 1.

12.4 An experimental radio telephone requires an amplitude modulator so that a 100 mV rms signal from a crystal oscillator can be modulated by a 10 mV rms audio signal, so as to achieve 30% modulation ratio. Design a suitable modulation system, using MC 1496.

12.5 A certain crystal has a temperature coefficient of −0.5 pp m/°C (parts per million per degree centigrade) in the temperature range, 0 to 60°C. If the oscillator frequency is calibrated to 10 MHz at 25°C, what will be the frequency of the oscillator at 45°C?

12.6 An aerodynamic model used for simulation studies on wind tunnel has a natural resonance at 3 Hz and a damping coefficient of 0.02. When the horizontally mounted model is displaced by an angle of 30°, and allowed to freely oscillate, the output of 4.5 V excited strain gauge bridge located at the root of the model decays from 10 mV peak, max. Design a suitable amplifier, precision absolute value detector and log amplifier required to facilitate recording of the log of the envelope of the decaying oscillations, in a fast recorder having 1 V full scale sensitivity and 10 kΩ input impedance.

12.7 Find the optimum value of R_7 in Fig. 12.6 so that the output amplitude variation at $e \angle \phi$ is the minimum, as the phase shift is varied from 0° to 90°.

12.8 Using the circuit of Fig. 12.8, calculate the component values required so that a frequency variation from 5 Hz to 8 Hz is achieved, as a 100 kΩ potentiometer connected in series with R_1 is varied from maximum to minimum.

12.9 Construct the circuit of the V/F converter of Fig. 12.43 and study the functioning of the circuit. Explain the necessity for the inclusion of the 'starting circuit'. By feeding inputs from a standard DC source and monitoring the output frequency in a counter, calculate the linearity of the V/F converter for 0 to −1 V, 0 to −3 V, and 0 to −10 V.

REFERENCES

1. Graeme, J.G., *Applications of Operational Amplifiers*: *Third Generation Techniques*, p. 147, McGraw-Hill, New York, 1963.
2. Ibid 1, p. 170.
3. Wittlinger, H.A., "Applications of the CA 3080 and CA 3080A high performance operational transconductance amplifiers", *RCA Application Note ICAN 6668*, RCA Solid State Div., Somerville, N.J., 1971.
4. Ibid 1, p. 124.
5. Ibid 1, p. 131.

6. Tobey, G.E., et al., *Operational Amplifiers: Design and Applications*, p. 356, McGraw-Hill, Kogakusha, Tokyo, 1971.
7. Ibid 1, pp. 132-138.
8. Sheingold, D.H. (Ed), *Nonlinear Circuits Handbook*, Part 3, Ch. VII, Analog. Devices Inc., Massachusetts, 1974.
9. Ibid 8, pp. 60-61.
10. Ibid 8, pp. 168-169.
11. "V-F's, F-V's and audio tape recorders", *Applications Bulletin AN-11*, Teledyne Philbrick, Massachusetts, 1974.
12. Rubin, A.I., "Analog computer programming, scaling and problem preparation", in Huskey, H.D. and G.A. Korn, *Computer Handbook*, McGraw-Hill, New York, 1962.
13. Housner, C., *Analog and Analog/Hybrid Computer Programming*, Ch. 18, 19, and 20, Prentice Hall Inc., Englewood Cliffs, New Jersey, 1971.

BIBLIOGRAPHY

Applications Manual for Operational Amplifiers, Philbrick/Nexus Research Dedham, Massachusetts, 1965.

Bell, J.F.W., et al., "A digitally controlled sinusoidal signal generator", in *IERE Conference Proceedings No. 38, on Programmable Instruments*, Institution of Electronic and Radio Engineers, 1977.

Counts, L., "Reduce multiplier errors by upto an order of magnitude", *EDN*, Vol. 19, No. 6, pp. 65-68, March 20, 1974.

Function Generator Data Book, EXAR Integrated Systems, California, 1979.

Gibbons, J.G. and Horn, H.S., "A circuit with logarithmic transfer response over 9 decades", *IEEE Trans. Circ. Theory*, Vol. CT-11, No. 3, p. 378, Sept. 1964.

Graeme, J.G., "Controlled current source is versatile and precise", in Weber, S., *Circuits for Electronics Engineers*, p. 96, McGraw-Hill, New York, 1977.

Hnatek, E.R., *Applications of Linear Integrated Circuits*, John Wiley and Sons, New York, 1975.

Jenks, E. and Powner, E.T., "Digital waveform synthesis", in *Conference Publication No. 106 on Digital Instrumentation*, Inst. of Electrical Engineers, London, 1973.

Jung, W.G., "Precision voltage to frequency converter uses only single supply voltage", *Electron Des.* Vol. 24, No. 21, p. 82, Oct. 11, 1976.

Jung, W.G., *IC Op Amp Cookbook*, Howard W. Sams and Co., Indiana, 1974.

Korn, G.A. and Korn, T.M.. *Electronic Analog and Hybrid Computers*, McGraw-Hill, New York, 1964.

"Linear Integrated circuits and MOS devices", RCA Corpn., *Application Notes, SSD-202*, New Jersey, 1972.

Pease, R.A., "V/F Converter ICs Handle Frequency to Voltage Needs", *EDN*, Vol. 24, No. 6, pp. 109-116, March 20, 1979.

Product Guide, Teledyne Philbrick, Massachusetts, 1979.

Sheingold, D., and Pouliot, F., "The hows and whys of log amps", *Electronic Design*, Vol. 22, No. 3, pp. 52-59, Feb. 1, 1974.

Specifications and Applications Information—MC 1495 L., MC 1595 L., Motorola Semiconductors, Phoenix, Arizona, 1975.

Wong, Y.J. and Ott, W.E., *Function Circuits, Design and Applications*, McGraw-Hill, New York, 1976.

13

FILTERING AND SIGNAL ANALYSIS

13.1 INTRODUCTION

In a measurement system, it is seldom that the transducer used measures the measurand precisely and presents the information in a standard form eliminating the need for further filtering and analysis. Excepting for simple measurements, the measurement engineer soon finds that for high accuracy, the main factors that must be considered are signal-to-noise ratio, response time, and the bandwidth over which the measurements are desired. Among these, the signal-to-noise ratio is perhaps the most important parameter that needs to be considered, and the use of signal filters becomes a necessity when low-level measurements or high-resolution measurements are attempted. Consider, for example, a requirement as simple as having to monitor the ac mains line voltage. Though an analog ac voltmeter connected across the line is sufficient for requirements where accuracy does not exceed 3 to 5%, the moment the accuracy requirements are increased to even 0.2 to 0.5%, several additional factors become significant, viz., (i) the rate at which the measurements are to be carried out, (ii) the stability of the line voltage during the period of measurements, (iii) the parameter to be measured (average, rms, or peak), (iv) harmonic content of the waveform, and (v) line transients and their effects. Going one step further, if it is sought to control other generating equipment to correct for changes in the line voltage so that the line voltage is maintained within a certain limit, then the situation becomes even more complex with the necessity of having to consider the effect of the delay and overshoot arising in the monitor so that a stable control action is effected.

In order to solve these and many other such problems satisfactorily, it therefore becomes necessary for the instrumentation engineer to have a clear understanding of the various types of filters and their characteristics, and the more sophisticated equipment available for use in signal analysis based on them.

13.2 PASSIVE AND ACTIVE FILTERS

Prior to the advent of integrated circuits, the filters that were being used were mainly passive networks using inductance, capacitance, and resistance. The classical theory employed therein was the "image parameter theory", based on which the filter characteristics, performance. and component values were calculated for operation from a source having a specified source resistance and feeding into a constant load resistane known as the "termination resistance". The "constant k type" filters evolved were often modified with "m derived" end sections to obtain better impedance matching between the source and filter network on the input side, and the filter and load on the output side.

With these passive filters, one of the serious constraints was the necessity to always use the specified source and termination impedances. Cascading of the filters was also not straightforward—in spite of designing the filters so that their source and termination resistances were equal, additional isolation amplifiers had to be often interposed between cascaded sections. This was to prevent severe distortion of the filter characteristics due to non-ideal matching between the filter end sections and the source and terminating load. Another main drawback was the necessity to use bulky and often non-linear inductances for low and very low frequency filters. Due to the relatively low value of the inductive reactance at low frequencies in addition to the non-linearity problems at high current levels (due to saturation of cores), the circuit designer was constrained to keep the signal levels low.

The availability of operational amplifiers in the integrated form has changed the situation significantly, leading to the emergence of "active filters". Today, a majority of low frequency filters are necessarily of this type, particularly for frequencies below about 100 kHz. The special advantage of the active circuitry for use in low-frequency filters is the interesting fact that inductors can be totally avoided. In addition, active capacitance multiplication enables use of capacitors of low practical values to be used even for cut-off frequencies down to a fraction of one hertz. However, due to the limited gain bandwidth product of ICs and their effect on the filter characteristics, and due to the advantages of the inductor in the high frequency range, passive filters are preferred for frequencies above a few hundred kilohertz.

13.2.1 First-Order Filters

While the simple RC arrangement shown in Fig. 13.1(a) can be used in many practical situations, it suffers from certain drawbacks, such as dependence of the cut-off frequency and the pass-band gain on source and load impedances. A suitable addition of buffer stages at the input and output of this filter, as in Fig. 13.1(b), enables cascading similar sections without interaction, operation from sources having high output impedance, and feeding to any load resistance without a change in the characteristics.

The transfer function of the filter is expressed as

$$\frac{E_o}{E_l} = \frac{\mathcal{L}[e_o]}{\mathcal{L}[e_l]} = \frac{1}{1+sCR} \tag{13.1}$$

where $\mathcal{L}$ indicates Laplace transformation. A plot of $\left|\dfrac{E_o}{E_l}\right|$ shown in Fig. 13.2(a) indicates a -3 dB (-3.010 dB, to be exact) "gain" or 3 dB "attenuation" at a frequency f_c termed as the "cut-off frequency", where

$$f_c = \frac{1}{2\pi RC}$$

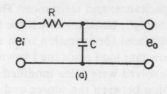

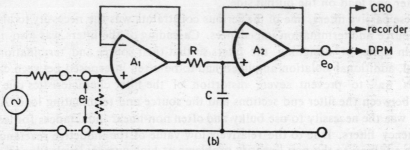

Fig. 13.1 First order low-pass sections: (a) basic network; (b) with isolation at input and output

At frequencies very much higher than f_c, the attenuation increases at a slope of 6.02 dB/octave or 20 dB/decade. The "slope" of the attenuation curve at the frequency f_c is about 3.01 dB/octave. The phase characteristics (Fig. 13.2 (b)) show a phase difference of 0° at dc, decreasing to −45° at f_c, and settling at −90° (90° lag) at frequencies very much higher than f_c

A first-order high-pass filter is shown in Fig. 13.3. Its transfer function is given by

$$\frac{E_o}{E_i} = \frac{sCR}{1 + sCR} \tag{13.2}$$

where E_o and E_i are the Laplace transforms of the output e_o and input e_i respectively.

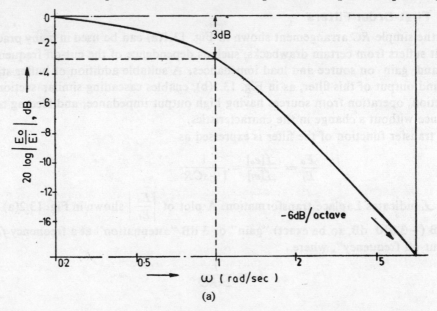

(a)

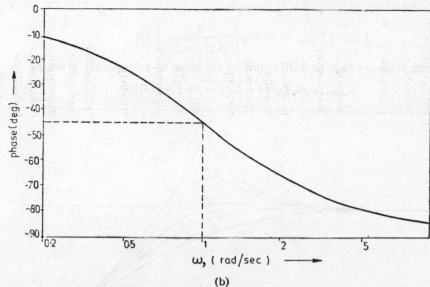

(b)

Fig. 13.2 Frequency response of first order low-pass filter: (a) magnitude response; (b) phase response

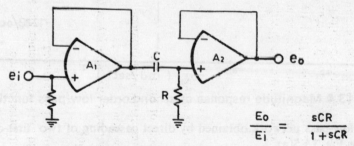

$$\frac{E_o}{E_i} = \frac{sCR}{1+sCR}$$

Fig. 13.3 First order high-pass filter

13.2.2 Second-Order Filters

The transfer function for a second-order low-pass filter is

$$H(\omega) = \frac{\omega_n^2}{s^2+2\zeta\omega_n s+\omega_n^2} \qquad (13.3)$$

where ω_n is the undamped natural resonance frequency and ζ is the damping coefficient. The frequency response of $|H(\omega)|$ (the magnitude function) is dependent on ζ and is as shown in Fig. 13.4, for various values of ζ. For $\zeta = \dfrac{1}{\sqrt{2}}$, the response is "maximally flat". For lesser values of ζ, a peak occurs in the magnitude response at a frequency given by

$$\omega_{peak} = \omega_n\sqrt{1-2\zeta^2} \qquad (13.4)$$

At this peak, the value of $|H(\omega)|$ is given by

$$|H(\omega)|_{max} = 20 \log\left[\frac{1}{2\zeta\sqrt{1-\zeta^2}}\right] dB \qquad (13.5)$$

The magnitude response falls to 3 dB below its dc value at a frequency given by

$$\omega_{-3dB} = \omega_n\{\sqrt{(1-2\zeta^2)^2+1}+1-2\zeta^2\}^{1/2} \qquad (13.6,$$

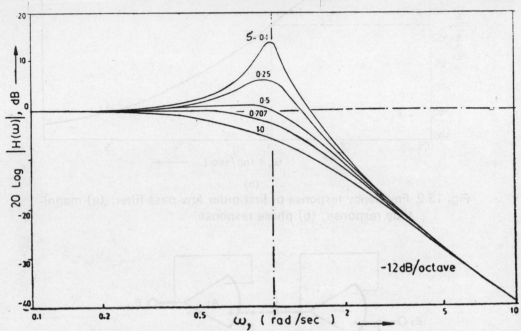

Fig. 13.4 Magnitude response of second order low-pass function

A second-order low-pass network obtained by direct cascading of two first-order LP networks is shown in Fig. 13.5(a).

The transfer function in this case is

$$\frac{E_o}{E_i} = \frac{1}{s^2R_1C_1R_2C_2+s(R_1C_1+R_2C_2+R_1C_2)+1} \qquad (13.7)$$

For the special case $R_1 = R_2$ and $C_1 = C_2$, the transfer function becomes

$$\frac{E_o}{E_i} = \frac{1}{s^2R_1^2C_1^2+3sR_1C_1+1} \qquad (13.8)$$

resulting in a damping factor ζ of 1.5.

For $R_2 = 10\,R_1$ and $C_2 = \dfrac{C_1}{10}$,

$$\frac{E_o}{E_i} = \frac{1}{s^2R_1^2C_1^2+2.1\,sR_1C_1+1} \qquad (13.9)$$

giving a damping factor of $\zeta = 1.05$.

It may be noted that the relatively low loading of R_2 and C_2 on R_1 and C_1 in the latter case has resulted in a reduced damping factor.

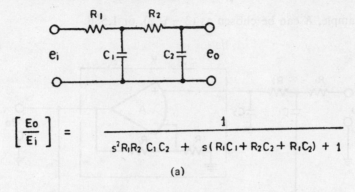

$$\left[\frac{E_o}{E_i}\right] = \frac{1}{s^2R_1R_2\,C_1C_2 + s(R_1C_1 + R_2C_2 + R_1C_2) + 1}$$

(a)

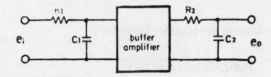

(b)

Fig. 13.5 Second order low-pass filter: (a) cascaded RC sections;
(b) cascade with buffer amplifier

The loading error of R_2 and C_2 can be removed completely if one interposes a buffer stage between the two sections as shown in Fig. 13.5(b). The transfer function then becomes

$$\frac{E_o}{E_i} = \frac{1}{s^2R_1C_1R_2C_2 + s(R_1C_1 + R_2C_2) + 1} \tag{13.10}$$

For the case $R_1C_1 = R_2C_2$,

$$\frac{E_o}{E_i} = \frac{1}{s^2R_1^2C_1^2 + 2sR_1C_1 + 1}, \tag{13.11}$$

the damping factor ζ being equal to 1.

If the isolator has a positive gain $K = 1 + \dfrac{R_f}{R_i}$, and if C_1 is returned to the output, as shown in Fig. 13.6 instead of being grounded, the transfer function becomes

$$\frac{E_o}{E_i} = \frac{K}{s^2R_1C_1R_2C_2 + s(R_1C_1 + R_2C_2 + R_1C_2 - KR_1C_1) + 1} \tag{13.12}$$

For $R_1 = R_2 = R$ and $C_1 = C_2 = C$, this reduces to

$$\frac{E_o}{E_i} = \frac{K}{s^2R^2C^2 + (3-K)sRC + 1} \tag{13.13}$$

The damping factor ζ is now $\dfrac{3-K}{2}$ and is determined by the value of K chosen. To obtain $\zeta = \dfrac{1}{\sqrt{2}}$, for example, K can be chosen as $(3-\sqrt{2})$, or 1.586.

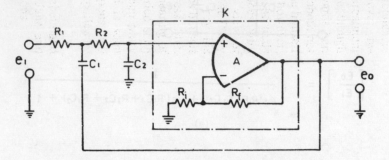

Fig. 13.6 Butterworth second-order LP filter

This second-order filter possessing the transfer function

$$\frac{E_o}{E_i} = \frac{1}{s^2 R^2 C^2 + 1.414 s RC + 1} \tag{13.14}$$

is of particular interest since the frequency response of this filter exhibits maximally-flat characteristics in the pass-band.

13.3 TYPES OF FILTERS

The general classification of fiters, viz., low-pass, high-pass, band-pass, and band-rejection (or band-elimination) types lend themselves to several subclasses, depending on the order of the filter. In addition, filters of the same order can also differ from one another in the type of characteristics they possess. Based on the characteristics, the filters may be grouped as Butterworth, Tchebychev, Bessel, or Elliptic. Many other combinations of characteristics also exist[1]. The choice of a filter for a particular situation is by no means simple, and a fuller understanding of the topic will prove useful for choosing a near optimum filter for a specific application.

13.3.1 Butterworth Filters

Butterworth filters are a class of filters optimized for maximal flatness of their frequency-response characteristics in the pass-band. Their attenuation monotonically increases within the pass-band, reaches 3.01 dB at the cut-off frequency and further increases at a rate of $(n \times 6)$ dB/octave ultimately at higher frequencies for an nth order filter. The magnitude function for this class of filters is given by

$$|H(\omega)| = \left\{ 1 + \left(\frac{\omega}{\omega_0} \right)^{2n} \right\}^{-1/2} \tag{13.15}$$

For any order n, the magnitude becomes $\dfrac{1}{\sqrt{2}}$ corresponding to -3.01 dB at a frequency $\omega = \omega_0$. The relative frequency response of the nth-order Butterworth low-pass filter for $n = 2$ 3 and 4 are shown in Fig. 13.7.

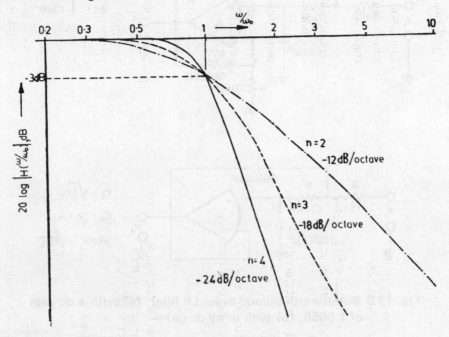

Fig. 13.7 Response of Butterworth LP filter

The transfer function for the Butterworth second-order, third-order, and fourth-order filters, are expressed as

Second order: $\dfrac{1}{s^2 + 1.4142s + 1}$ (13.16)

Third order: $\dfrac{1}{s^3 + 2s^2 + 2s + 1} = \dfrac{1}{(s+1)} \cdot \dfrac{1}{(s+0.5)^2 + 0.866^2}$ (13.17)

Fourth order: $\dfrac{1}{s^4 + 2.6131s^3 + 3.4142s^2 + 2.6131s + 1}$

$$= \dfrac{1}{(s+0.3827)^2 + .9239^2} \cdot \dfrac{1}{(s+0.9239)^2 + 0.3827^2}$$ (13.18)

The circuit of a practical filter having a cut-off frequency of 1 kHz and possessing Butterworth second order low-pass characteristics is shown in Fig. 13.8(a). The cut-off frequency f_c is given by

$$f_c = \dfrac{1}{2\pi RC}$$ (13.19)

For $f_c = 1$ kHz, if $C = 0.01 \ \mu$F, $R \simeq 15.9$ kΩ.

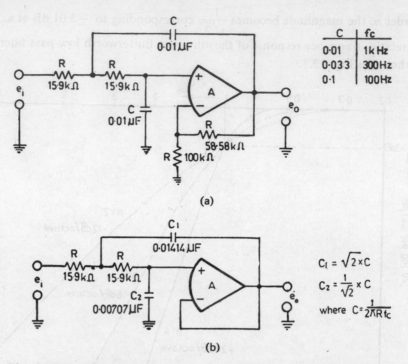

C	fc
0·01	1k Hz
0·033	300Hz
0·1	100Hz

(a)

(b)

Fig. 13.8 Butterworth second order LP filter: (a) with a dc gain of 1.5858; (b) with unity dc gain

The operational amplifier is used in the positive gain configuration, with a gain of $(1+0.5858)$, to realize the required ζ. Note that a dc gain of 1.5858 results due to this. To obtain a different cut-off frequency, C required can be calculated from Eq. (13.19).

The above realization is based on the voltage controlled voltage source (VCVS) type of realization evolved by Sallen and Key[2]. Other methods of realizing this transfer function exist, but the VCVS realization is by far the simplest. A modified circuit to realize the same transfer function using a unity gain voltage follower is given in Fig. 13.8(b). The advantage of this circuit is that the dc gain is exactly one.

In order to realize the third-order and fourth-order low-pass filters of the Butterworth type, it is easier to split the transfer function into a combination of equivalent first-order and second-order sections. For the third-order filter, this results in

$$\frac{E_o}{E_i} = \left[\frac{1}{s+1}\right]\left[\frac{1}{s^2+s+1}\right] \tag{13.20}$$

The first-order section is easy to realize. The second-order section has a ζ of 0.5 as realized by the circuit shown in Fig. 13.9(a). The filter has a dc gain of unity, and the component values shown are for $f_c = 1$ kHz.

The practical circuit for a fourth-order LP Butterworth filter, realized as the cascade of two second-order sections, is shown in Fig. 13.9(b). The cut-off frequency is 1 kHz and gain at dc is unity. Higher order filters of this type can also be realized in a similar way[3].

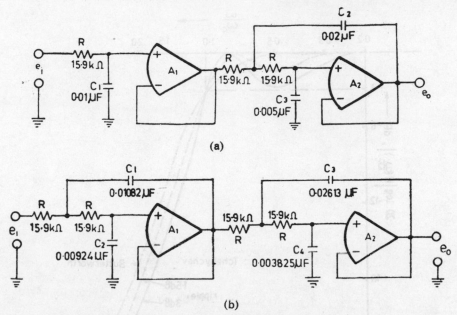

Fig. 13.9 Butterworth LP filter: (a) third-order; (b) fourth-order

13.3.2 Tchebychev Filters

A second class of filters, providing a higher rate of attenuation near the cut-off frequency than that available from Butterworth filters, is the Tchebychev filters. The pass-band regions of the frequency response of Tchebychev filters do not show a monotonic increase in attenuation as exhibited by Butterworth filters. Instead, the attenuation can increase, decrease, and increase again, depending on the order. Beyond the cut-off frequency, the attenuation increases monotonically, as illustrated in Fig. 13.10, wherein the response of a third-order Tchebychev LP filter is compared with that of a Butterworth third-order filter. It may be noted that the ultimate attenuation rate is the same in both the cases. However, the rate of attenuation at the cut-off frequency is higher for the Tchebychev filter. The Tchebychev filter also shows an attenuation in the pass-band which changes non-monotonically with frequency. Depending on the amount of ripple, the characteristics of two third-order Tchebychev filters will differ. The one possessing a higher ripple in the pass-band will also show a higher attenuation rate at the cut-off frequency. The number of peaks and valleys in the attenuation curve in the pass-band depends on the order of the filter.

Even order Tchebychev filters are normalized, conventionally, with the ripple value of the attenuation at low frequencies. From Fig. 13.11, which is a plot of the frequency response of a fourth-order Tchebychev filter, it is seen that the gain starts at -1.5 dB for the fourth-order 1.5 dB ripple filter, increases to zero dB at a certain frequency, and decreases later to -1.5 dB. For higher frequencies, the gain again increases to 0 dB, decreases to -1.5 dB at a frequency ω_b, and falls to -3.01 dB at ω_c. The frequency ω_b is referred to as the band-edge frequency and is in general different from ω_c. The relationship between ω_b and ω_c is complex and has been numerically evaluated in Ref. 4. For the special case of 3.01 dB ripple, the two frequencies are the same.

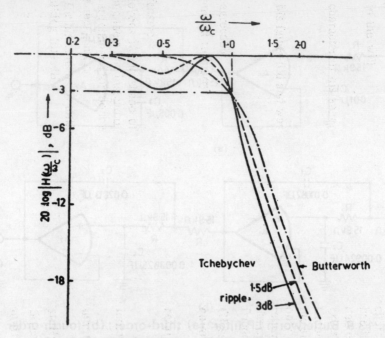

Fig. 13.10 Butterworth vs Tchebychev response

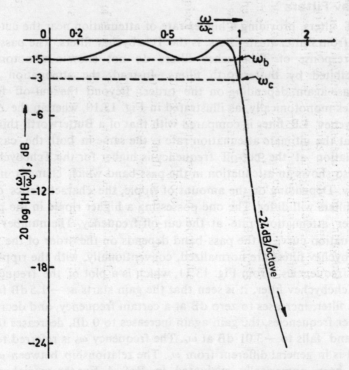

Fig. 13.11 Tchebychev fourth-order LP filter response

The transfer function for the Tchebychev filters of various ripple values and of different order are well tabulated in literature[3,5]. As an example, the normalized transfer function of a third-order Tchebychev filter having a ripple of 0.5 dB is

$$\frac{E_o}{E_i} = \left[\frac{0.83813}{s^2+0.5366s+0.83813}\right]\left[\frac{0.5366}{s+0.5366}\right] \tag{13.21}$$

The practical circuit of a low-pass filter having this characteristic and -3 dB frequency of 250 Hz is shown in Fig. 13.12(a).

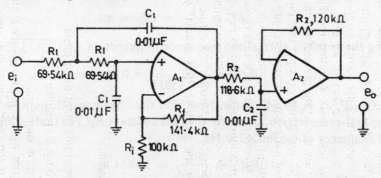

(a)

(b)

Fig. 13.12 Tchebychev third-order filter: (a) dc gain $= 2.414$;
(b) dc gain $= 1$

Design of the Practical Circuit
(a) For the second-order section, calculate ζ.

$$\zeta = \frac{1}{2}\left[\frac{0.5366}{\sqrt{0.83813}}\right] = 0.2931$$

For realization of this ζ with positive gain configuration, calculate the positive gain required as

$$K = 3-2\zeta = 2.414$$

Hence the ratio of the feedback resistor to the input resistor is

$$\frac{R_f}{R_i} = K-1 = 1.414$$

For 250 Hz (-3 dB frequency), obtain normalized value of RC from

$$RC = \frac{1}{2\pi f} = 0.6366 \text{ ms}$$

For obtaining the required normalized resonance frequency of $\sqrt{0.83813}$, calculate

$$R_1 C_1 = \frac{RC}{\sqrt{0.83813}} = 0.6954 \text{ ms}$$

For $C_1 = 0.01$ μF, $R_1 = 69.54$ kohms. Note that the stage has a dc gain $= K$.

(b) For the first-order section, calculate the time constant $R_2 C_2$ so that -3.01 dB attenuation occurs for a frequency of 0.5366×250 Hz.

$$R_2 C_2 = \frac{RC}{0.5366} = 1.1864 \text{ ms}$$

For $C_2 = 0.01$ μF, $R_2 = 118.64$ kΩ.

The resulting circuit for the filter is as shown in Fig. 13.12(a). Note again that this filter has a dc gain $= K = 2.414$. The filter can be modified as in Fig. 13.12(b) to provide unity dc gain by choosing R_3 and R_4 as:

$$R_3 = KR_2 = 286.4 \text{ k}\Omega$$

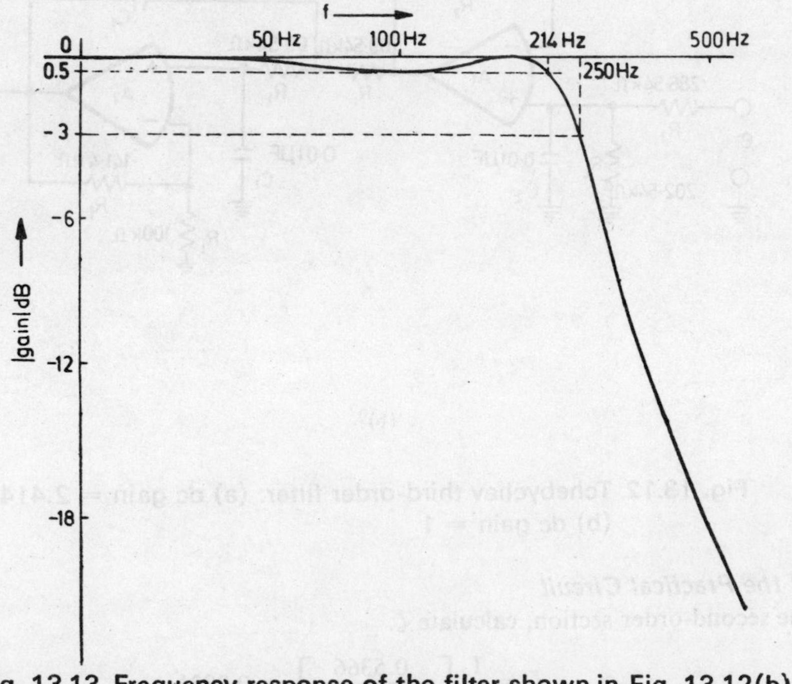

Fig. 13.13 Frequency response of the filter shown in Fig. 13.12(b)

$$R_4 = \frac{K}{K-1} R_2 = 202.54 \text{ k}\Omega$$

The frequency-response characteristic of this filter is shown in Fig. 13.13. Note that while the -3 dB frequency is 250 Hz, the band-edge frequency is $\simeq 214$ Hz.

It is important to note that the normalized coefficients tabulated in literature often corresponds to normalization with respect to the band-edge frequency and less often to the -3 dB frequency. (Tables in Ref. 5 are normalized for band-edge frequency while those in Ref. 3, pp. 175-176, are normalized for -3 dB frequency.)

13.3.3 Elliptic Filters

Elliptic filters are distinguished by ripple in the attenuation characteristics, both in the pass-band and in the stop-band. The magnitude plot in Fig. 13.14(a) exemplifies this type of characteristics. The transfer function of this third-order LP filter has the following form:

$$H(\omega) = \left[\frac{0.7801}{s+.7801} \right] \left[\frac{s^2+3.35^2}{3.35^2} \right] \left[\frac{1.298}{(s^2+.6898s+1.298)} \right] \tag{13.22}$$

with $\omega_s/\omega_b = 2.9238$ (Table 7.2 of Ref. [3]), where ω_s/ω_b is the lowest frequency at which the attenuation of the filter is at least 39.48 dB and ω_b is the band-edge frequency. This transfer function yields an LP response with a pass-band ripple of 0.28 dB and a stop-band attenuation of 39.48 dB. The stop-band response has, in addition, one zero, i.e., a frequency at which transmission is zero or attenuation is infinite.

In general, for the same pass-band ripple, the higher the stop-band attenuation desired, the higher will be the relative value of ω_s/ω_b. Similarly, for the same stop-band attenuation, if less pass-band ripple is permitted, ω_s/ω_b increases again. As expected, the transition-band range of frequencies between ω/ω_b and ω_s/ω_b can be reduced in any application by allowing the pass-band ripple to be as much as can be tolerated and by seeking a stop-band attenuation as much as is just necessary.

While the stop-band attenuation increases at the rate of 6 dB per octave for odd order filters, the even-order filters exhibit an increase at the rate of 12 dB per octave [curve A in Fig. 13.14(b) for fourth-order filter] in cases where the number of pole pairs is one more than the number of zero pairs. In certain designs wherein the transfer function has as many number of pole pairs as zero pairs, the high frequency attenuation stabilizes at a particular value and does not increase for further increase in frequency (curve B in Fig. 13.14(b) for a fourth-order filter). A circuit to realize the transfer function given by Eq. (13.22) is shown in Fig. 13.15.

The use of the transmission zeroes in elliptic filters enables a steep rate of descent in the transmission curve as the stop-band approaches. Consequently, when the application demands a short transition-band, the use of the elliptic filter becomes mandatory.

EXAMPLE 13.1 Design a low-pass filter with a ripple band-edge frequency of 380 Hz and having the normalized transfer function given by Eq. (13.22).

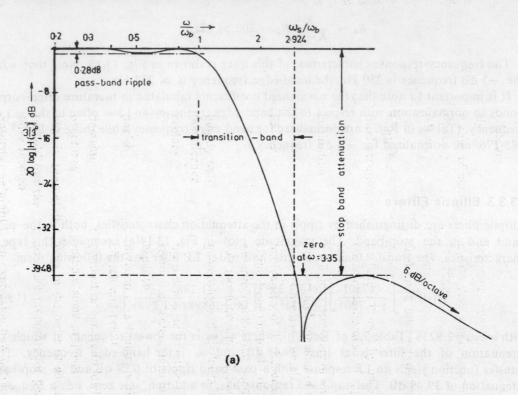

(a)

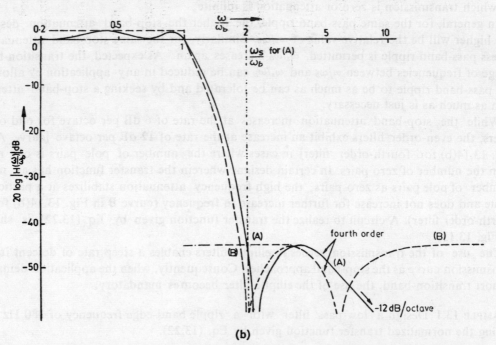

(b)

Fig. 13.14 Frequency response of elliptic filters: (a) odd-order; (b) even-order

Solution: For the elliptic filter realization, a generally favoured method is one using cascaded second-order sections using state-variable techniques. Such a realization of the complex pole pair in Eq. (13.22) is obtained by the amplifiers A_1, A_2 and A_3 of Fig. 13.15(a). The

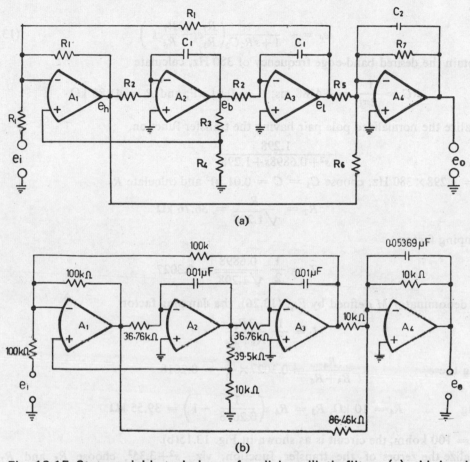

(a)

(b)

Fig. 13.15 State variable technique of realising elliptic filters: (a) third-order elliptic-filter; (b) elliptic LP filter for 380 Hz

amplifier A_4 enables the zero to be realized by the summing process on its inputs and the real pole to be realized by the feedback RC combination. For a simpler design, certain resistors and capacitors are taken as being equal in the realization. The circuit has the following relationships.

$$\frac{e_h}{e_i} = \frac{-s^2 R_2^2 C_1^2}{M} \tag{13.23}$$

$$\frac{e_b}{e_i} = \frac{sR^2C_1}{M} \tag{13.24}$$

and

$$\frac{e_l}{e_i} = -\frac{1}{M} \tag{13.25}$$

where

$$M = s^2 R_2^2 C_1^2 + 3 \frac{R_4}{R_3 + R_4} s R_2 C_1 + 1 \tag{13.26}$$

Further,

$$e_o = - \frac{1}{1 + s R_7 C_2} \left(\frac{R_7}{R_5} e_l + \frac{R_7}{R_6} e_h \right) \tag{13.27}$$

To obtain the desired band-edge frequency of 380 Hz, calculate

$$RC = \frac{1}{2\pi f} = 0.4188 \text{ ms}; \; C = 0.01 \; \mu\text{F}; \text{ and } R = 41.88 \text{ k}\Omega$$

To realize the normalized pole pair having the transfer function,

$$\frac{1.298}{s^2 + 0.6898s + 1.298}$$

and $f_c = 1.298 \times 380$ Hz, choose $C_1 = C = 0.01 \; \mu$F and calculate R_2.

$$R_2 = \frac{R}{\sqrt{1.298}} = 36.76 \text{ k}\Omega$$

The damping factor,

$$\zeta = \frac{1}{2} \frac{0.6898}{\sqrt{1.298}} = 0.3027$$

For the denominator M defined by Eq. (13.26), the damping factor

$$\zeta = \frac{1}{2} \frac{3R_4}{R_3 + R_4}$$

Equating these,
$$\frac{R_4}{R_3 + R_4} = 0.3027 \times \frac{2}{3} = 0.2018$$

Choosing
$$R_4 = 10 \text{ k}\Omega, \; R_3 = R_4 \left(\frac{1}{0.2018} - 1 \right) = 39.55 \text{ k}\Omega$$

For $R_1 = 100$ kohm, the circuit is as shown in Fig. 13.15(b).

To realize the zeroes of the transfer function, viz., $s^2 + 3.35^2$, choose R_5 and R_7 as 10 kohm and calculate R_6 from

$$\frac{R_6}{R_5} = \frac{3.35^2}{1.298} = 8.646; \text{ i.e., } R_6 = 86.46 \text{ k}\Omega$$

Finally, to realize the normalized real pole at 0.7801, calculate

$$R_7 C_2 \text{ as } \frac{1}{2\pi \times 380 \times 0.7801} = 0.5369 \text{ ms}$$

For
$$R_7 = 10 \text{ k}\Omega, \; C_2 = 0.05369 \; \mu\text{F}$$

13.3.4 Bessel Filters

While Butterworth, Tchebychev, and Elliptic filters are suitable for operation with continuous signals, their transient response show considerable overshoot[6]. When handling pulse trains and signal bursts, it might be favourable to use filters which have negligible over-shoot in the step response. A class of filters particularly suitable for such signals is the Bessel filter. The phase characteristics of this class of filters exhibit a linear increase with frequency. The group delay, defined as the derivative of the phase with respect to frequency, is hence extremely flat over a wide range of frequencies. The normalized delay responses of Bessel filters, shown in Fig. 13.16, indicate the advantage achieved in providing constant delay over a wide frequency range, as the order of the filter increases. As a penalty for the

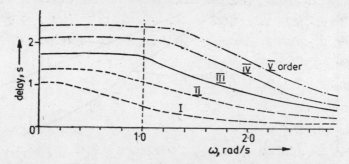

Fig. 13.16 Normalized delay response of Bessel filters

linear phase characteristics achieved, frequency domain characteristics are relatively poorer for this class of filters, particularly near the cut-off frequency. The relative attenuation characteristics for Butterworth and Bessel fourth-order LP filters having the same nor-malized —3 dB frequency are compared in Fig. 13.17.

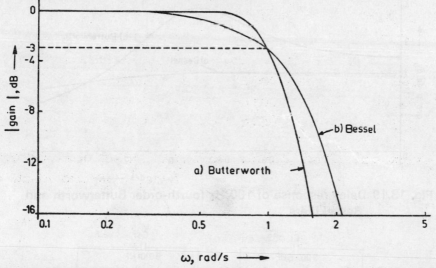

Fig. 13.17 Magnitude response of fourth-order Butterworth and Bessel filters

The Bessel filter of fourth-order, normalized for unity — 3 dB frequency, has the following transfer function

$$\frac{E_o}{E_i} = \frac{5.1}{(s^2+2.7192s+2.0142)(s^2+1.9754s+2.5321)}$$

The attenuation characteristic is shown in curve *B* of Fig. 13.17. The phase characteristic of the Bessel filter in comparison with that of a Butterworth filter of the same order is illus-

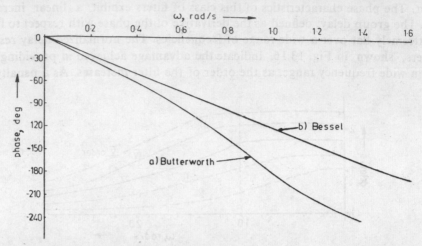

Fig. 13.18 Phase characteristics of fourth-order Butterworth and Bessel filters

trated in Fig. 13.18. The delay provided by the Bessel filter is $\simeq 2.13$ s constant to within -5% up to a frequency of 1.13 rad/sec. The filter has a -3 dB cut-off at $\omega = 1$ rad/s cor-

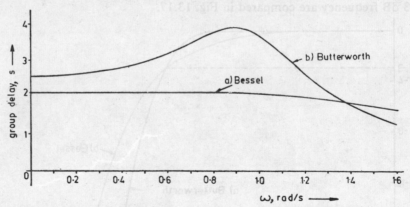

Fig. 13.19 Delay response of 100 Hz fourth-order Butterworth and Bessel fiters

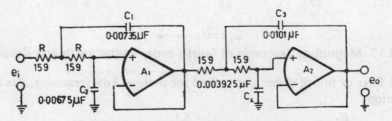

Fig. 13.20 Fourth-order Bessel Filter for 100 Hz

responding to 0.159 Hz. The delay characteristic of this filter is shown in Fig. 13.19. The practical circuit for a 100 Hz, − 3 dB Bessel filter of fourth-order, is shown in Fig. 13.20. This filter provides a delay of ≃ 3.4 ms constant to within −5% up to a frequency of about 113 Hz.

13.3.5 All-Pass Filters

All-pass filters are characterized by the phase shift they produce on the signal while the magnitude of the signal is left unaffected. The first-order all-pass network has the transfer function

$$\frac{E_o}{E_i} = \frac{1-s}{1+s}$$

The gain of the network, a practical example of which is shown in Fig. 13.21(a), is unity at all frequencies. However, the phase shift varies from 0° to 180° lag as the input frequency

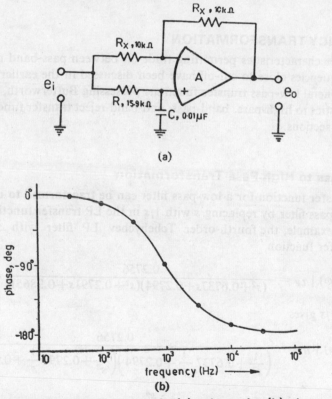

(a)

(b)

Fig. 13.21 First-order all-pass network: (a) schematic; (b) phase response

varies from zero to infinity, as shown in Fig. 13.21(b). The second-order, all-pass network has as its transfer function

$$\frac{E_o}{E_i} = \frac{s^2 - \dfrac{s}{Q} + 1}{s^2 + \dfrac{s}{Q} + 1}$$

where $$Q = \frac{1}{2\zeta} \quad (\zeta \text{ is damping factor})$$

Here the phase shift varies from 0 to 360° for frequencies from 0 to ∞. The rate of change of phase shift is high at the normalized value of $\omega = 1$, the slope of the phase shift curve at this point being dependent on the value of Q. The unique phase characteristics of this type of filters enable their use in "phase equalizers" wherein the phase shift arising from other networks is corrected by addition of all-pass networks. Another particularly important use is as "delay equalizers" in MODEMS and other data transmission networks[7]. All-pass networks are also used in wide-band phase shifters that are needed in the generation of single side-band systems and in tracking filters. Here the signal input passes through two parallel networks, each being a cascaded set of first order all-phase filters with optimized RC values. While the outputs of the networks are equal in amplitude to each other and to the input, the phase shift between the two outputs is a constant 90° over a wide range of frequencies[8].

13.4 FREQUENCY TRANSFORMATION

A variety of filter characteristics permitting trade-off between pass-band ripple and attenuation rate at frequencies close to cut-off have been discussed in the earlier sections. Methods to convert the general low-pass transfer functions possessing Butterworth, Tchebychev, and other characteristics to high-pass, band-pass, and band-reject transfer functions are discussed in the following sections.

13.4.1 Low-Pass to High-Pass Transformation

The general transfer function for a low-pass filter can be transformed to obtain that of the equivalent high-pass filter by replacing s with $1/s$ in the LP transfer function.

Consider, for example, the fourth-order Tchebychev LP filter with a ripple of 1 dB, having the transfer function

$$H(\omega) \mid _{LP} = \frac{0.2756}{(s^2 + 0.6737s + 0.2794)(s^2 + 0.2791s + 0.9865)}$$

Replacing s by $1/s$ gives

$$H(\omega) \mid _{HP} = \frac{0.2756}{\left(\frac{1}{s^2} + 0.6737\frac{1}{s} + 0.2794\right)\left(\frac{1}{s^2} + 0.2791\frac{1}{s} + 0.9865\right)}$$

$$= \frac{s^4}{(s^2 + 2.4112s + 3.579)(s^2 + 0.2829s + 1.0137)}$$

It may be noted that the frequency corresponding to 0.2794 in LP becomes equivalent to 3.579 (= 0.2794^{-1}) in the HP transformed relationship. This is a direct result of the transformation used. Extending this further, if X dB of attenuation results for a frequency of ω_x in the low-pass, the same attenuation is achieved in the high-pass at a frequency of $1/\omega_x$.

13.4.2 Low-Pass to Band-Pass Transformation

The transformation is obtained by replacing s with $\left(Qs + \dfrac{Q}{s}\right)$ in the normalized low-pass transfer function. The value of Q to be used is the ratio of the centre frequency of the desired band-pass filter to its bandwidth. For example, for a centre frequency of 480 Hz and a bandwidth of 24 Hz, the Q is 20. If the desired response is that of a two pole band-pass filter, starting with the normalized low-pass transfer function of

$$H(\omega)\mid_{LP} = \frac{1}{1+s}$$

the normalized transfer function of the band-pass filter is

$$H(\omega)\mid_{BP} = \frac{1}{1 + \left(Qs + \dfrac{Q}{s}\right)}$$

$$= \frac{s/Q}{s^2 + s/Q + 1} \tag{13.28}$$

The -3.01 dB response of this filter occurs at the normalized frequencies given by

$$\omega = \pm\frac{1}{2Q} + \sqrt{\frac{1}{4Q^2} + 1} \tag{13.29}$$

It may be noted that the real pole of a low-pass function at $s = P$, on transformation results in a band-pass function having a resonance frequency f_0 and a bandwidth equal to $P\varDelta f$ where $f_0/\varDelta f$ is the Q used for the transformation.

Consider, for example, the transformation of the real pole at $s = -0.7801$ in the low-pass elliptic function of Eq. (13.22).

The low-pass function $\dfrac{0.7801}{s + 0.7801}$ becomes, on transformation,

$$\frac{0.7801}{Q_{BP} \cdot s + \dfrac{Q_{BP}}{s} + 0.7801} \quad \text{or} \quad \frac{0.7801\,\dfrac{s}{Q_{BP}}}{s^2 + 0.7801\,\dfrac{s}{Q_{BP}} + 1}$$

where Q_{BP} is the desired Q of the band-pass filter. The final transfer function can be written in the standard form as $\dfrac{\dfrac{s}{Q_0}}{s^2 + \dfrac{s}{Q_0} + 1}$ where Q_0 is the effective Q which in this case is related to Q_{BP} as

$$Q_0 = \frac{Q_{BP}}{0.7801} = 6.409 \quad \text{for } Q_{BP} = 5$$

The complex pair of poles in the LP function of Eq. (13.22) transforms to two pairs of poles in the BP function. The procedure to obtain these is rather complicated and starts with the roots $s = -\alpha + j\beta$, and $s = -\alpha - j\beta$, of the LP function.

Let the Q for the desired BP filter be Q_{BP} (Ref. 7). Then,

$$s = -\alpha \pm j\beta \qquad = -.3449 \pm j1.0858$$

$$C = \alpha^2 + \beta^2 \qquad = 1.298$$

$$D = \frac{2\alpha}{Q_{BP}} \qquad = 0.13796 \text{ for } Q_{BP} = 5$$

$$E = \frac{C}{Q_{BP}^2} + 4 \qquad = 4.05192$$

$$G = \sqrt{E^2 - 4D^2} \qquad = 4.0425$$

$$Q_0 = \sqrt{\frac{E+G}{2D^2}} \qquad = 14.582$$

$$K = \frac{\alpha Q_0}{Q_{BP}} \qquad = 1.00588$$

$$\omega_0 = K + \sqrt{K^2 - 1} = 1.11453$$

From this, the desired transfer function of the two pole pair can be written as

$$\left[\frac{\frac{s}{Q_{BP}}}{\left(s^2 + \frac{\omega_0}{Q_0}s + \omega_0^2\right)}\right]\left[\frac{\frac{s}{Q_{BP}}}{\left(s^2 + \frac{1}{\omega_0 Q_0}s + \frac{1}{\omega_0^2}\right)}\right] \tag{13.30}$$

where ω_0 and Q_0 are calculated as above. For a $Q_{BP} = 5$, the relevant values obtained while transforming the pole pair of Eq. (13.22) are also shown above.

The zeroes at $s = \pm j\omega_z$ in the LP function can be transformed to BP using the following relationships:

$$\omega_{zBP} = \pm\frac{\omega_z}{2Q_{BP}} + \sqrt{\left(\frac{\omega_z}{2Q_{BP}}\right)^2 + 1} \tag{13.31}$$

where ω_{zBP} refers to the zeroes in the BP transfer function. The transfer function for BP becomes

$$\frac{\left(s^2 + \omega_{zBP}^2\right)\left\{s^2 + \frac{1}{\omega_{zBP}^2}\right\}}{\left(s^2/Q_{BP}^2\right)} \tag{13.32}$$

For the specific case of $Q_{BP} = 5$, the zeroes at $s = \pm j3.35$ in Eq. (13.22) transform to the following transfer function:

$$\frac{(s^2 + 1.3896^2)(s^2 + 0.7196^2)}{(s^2/5^2)}$$

The overall normalized transfer function for the band-pass filter thus obtained by transforming LP function of Eq. (13.22) with a $Q_{BP} = 5$ is

$H(\omega) \mid _{BP}$

$$= \left[\frac{\dfrac{s}{6.409}}{s^2 + \dfrac{s}{6.409} + 1} \right] \left[\frac{(s^2 + 1.3896^2)(s^2 + 0.7196^2)\left(\dfrac{1.298}{3.35^2}\right)}{\left(s^2 + \dfrac{1.11453}{14.582}s + 1.11453^2\right)\left(s^2 + \dfrac{1}{1.11453 \times 14.582}s + \dfrac{1}{1.11453^2}\right)} \right]$$

(Since the bandwidth of the LP function in Eq. (13.22) is normalized for ripple band-edge, the bandwidth corresponding to $Q_{BP} = 5$ in the transformed filter will also refer to the ripple band-edge frequencies[9].)

13.4.3 Low-Pass to Band-Reject Transformation

The 's' terms in the LP function are replaced with $(Qs + Q/s)^{-1}$ to yield the band-reject (BR) transfer function. Alternatively, it is possible to obtain the HP transfer function by replacing s with $1/s$. In the resulting HP transfer function replacing s with $Qs + Q/s$ yields the BR transfer function. When this method is adopted, the procedure listed already for transforming real poles, pole pairs, and zeroes hold good.

EXAMPLE 13.2 Obtain the BR transfer function for a Tchebychev LP filter of second order having 1 dB ripple. The band-reject Q required is 8.

Solution: The normalized LP transfer function is

$$H(\omega) \mid _{LP} = \frac{1.05^2}{s^2 + (1.045 \times 1.05)s + 1.05^2}$$

The normalized *HP* function is obtained by replacing s with $\dfrac{1}{s}$ as follows:

$$H(\omega) \mid _{HP} = \frac{1.05^2}{\left(\dfrac{1}{s}\right)^2 + (1.045 \times 1.05)\dfrac{1}{s} + 1.05^2}$$

$$= \frac{1.05^2 s^2}{1.05^2 s^2 + (1.045 \times 1.05)s + 1}$$

For $Q_{BR} = 8$, the BR transformation is obtained by replacing s by $8s + \dfrac{8}{s}$ in the above expression, yielding

$$H(\omega) \mid _{BR} = \frac{1.05^2(s^2 + 1)^2\left(\dfrac{8}{s}\right)^2}{1.05^2(s^2 + 1)^2\left(\dfrac{8}{s}\right)^2 + (1.045 \times 1.05)(s^2 + 1)\left(\dfrac{8}{s}\right) + 1}$$

This transfer function has two pairs of zero and two pairs of poles. The pole pairs are obtained by the following procedure:

The HP poles are at $\qquad s = -.4976 + j0.8120 = -\alpha + j\beta$

and at $\qquad s = -.4976 - j0.8120 = -\alpha - j\beta$

Let

$$C = \alpha^2 + \beta^2 = 0.9070$$

$$D = \frac{2\alpha}{Q_{BR}} \qquad = 0.1244 \text{ for } Q_{BR} = 8$$

$$E = \frac{C}{Q_{BR}^2} + 4 \qquad = 4.01417$$

$$G = \sqrt{E^2 - 4D^2} \qquad = 4.00645$$

$$Q_0 = \sqrt{\frac{E+G}{2D^2}} \qquad = 16.098$$

$$K = \frac{\alpha Q_0}{Q_{BR}} \qquad = 1.001288$$

$$\omega_0 = K + \sqrt{K^2 - 1} = 1.05206, \qquad \frac{1}{\omega_0} = 0.9505$$

Then the BR transfer function becomes

$$H(\omega)|_{BR} = \left[\frac{(s^2+1)}{\left[s^2 + \left(\frac{1.05206}{16.098} \right)s + 1.05206^2 \right]} \right] \left[\frac{(s^2+1)}{\left[s^2 + \left(\frac{1}{1.05206 \times 16.098} \right)s + \frac{1}{1.05206^2} \right]} \right] \tag{13.33}$$

13.5 REALIZATION OF PRACTICAL FILTERS

The theoretical transfer functions can be realized as practical circuits using more than one approach. The voltage controlled voltage source (VCVS), multiple feedback method, state variable techniques, Biquad, and Gyrator are some of the more popular approaches. As has already been shown in Figs. 13.8, 13.9, and 13.12, the VCVS approach can be used when the Q factors involved are less than about 10. When zeroes and poles are required, the three amplifier state variable technique can be used with advantage[10]. Tuning-up procedures are simple in this case and are relatively free of interaction. The use of gyrator in the realization of high Q filters yields configurations possessing low Q sensitivity. The circuit of Fig. 13.15 is a typical application of the state-variable technique which can be used in realization of low-pass and high-pass elliptic filters and band-pass filters of a higher order.

The practical circuit for the band-reject filter having the transfer function given by Eq. (13.33) and providing rejection at 800 Hz is shown in Fig. 13.22(a). The amplifiers A_1, A_2, and A_3 form a resonator block having an undamped resonance at a frequency of 1.05206×800 Hz = 841.6 Hz. Input resistors R of the integrators A_2 and A_3 are chosen so that

$$R = \frac{1}{2\pi \times 841.6 \times 0.01 \times 10^6} = 18.91 \text{ k}\Omega$$

[See Example 13.1]. The Q of the circuit is made 16.098, as required, by the feedback attenuator connected to A_2 output. Since $Q = \frac{1}{2\zeta}$, referring to Eq. (13.26),

$$Q = \frac{R_3 + R_4}{3R_4} = 16.098$$

For $R_4 = 1$ kΩ, $R_3 = (16.098 \times 3 - 1)$ kΩ = 47.29 kΩ

The summing amplifier A_4 provides a zero at a frequency of 800 Hz. The resistor from A_1 output to the summing junction is calculated as being equal to

$$\frac{1}{1.05206} \times 100 \text{ k}\Omega = 90.348 \text{ k}\Omega$$

In much the same way, the input resistors of the integrators A_6 and A_7 are calculated to yield an undamped resonance at $\frac{800}{1.05206} = 760.41$ Hz. For a feedback capacitance of 0.01 μF,

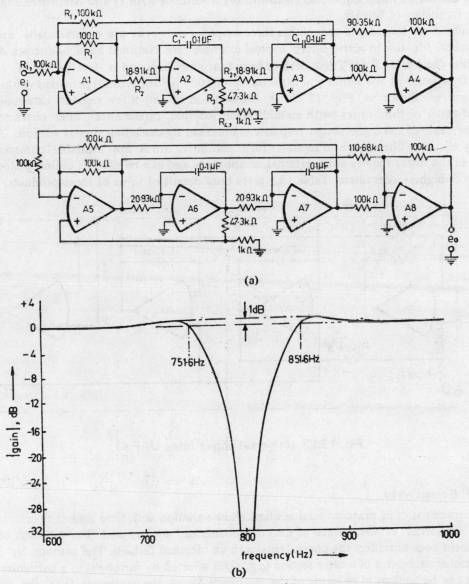

(a)

(b)

Fig. 13.22 Band reject filter for 800 Hz: (a) circuit schematic; (b) frequency response

the input resistance is obtained as

$$\frac{1}{2\pi \times 760.41 \times 0.01 \times 10^6} = 20.93 \text{ k}\Omega$$

In order to provide a zero at 800 Hz, i.e., at 1.05206 times the undamped resonance frequency, the resistor from A_5 output to the summing junction of A_8 is chosen as $100 \text{ k}\Omega \times 1.05206^2 = 110.68 \text{ k}\Omega$. The filter response shown in Fig. 13.22(b) indicates a ripple of 1 dB in the pass-band and band-edge frequencies of 751.6 and 851.6 Hz. These frequencies can be calculated using Eq. (13.29), substituting a value of 8 for Q and denormalizing for a centre frequency of 800 Hz.

A number of hybrid and monolithic three amplifier networks are commercially available at present for use in active filters. Typical examples are National Semiconductors AF 100 and Burr Brown UAF 41. These devices have four amplifiers and a few precision components (resistance of 500 kohm and capacitance of 1000 pF are typical) provided within the package, as shown in Fig. 13.23. By the addition of only a few resistors externally, any second-order or third-order (with an additional external capacitance) filter characteristics can be realized. A higher-order response is obtained by cascading similar sections. A wide variety of active filters, both in modular form and in IC form are available commercially. Some of the filters require some external components and can be used as building blocks to construct higher-order filters. Table 13.1 gives brief details of some of these products.

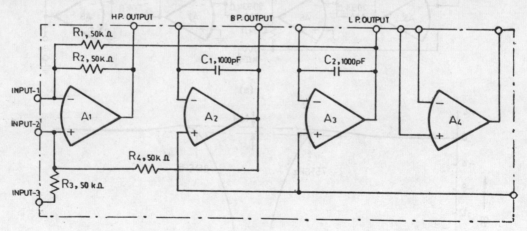

Fig. 13.23 Universal active filter, UAF 41

13.5.1. Sensitivity

The characteristics of practical analog filters show variation with time and temperature due to the variation of the values of the components and devices used. The variation of each component does not affect the characteristics in an identical fashion. The amount by which a particular parameter of a filter section (e.g. Q) is affected by variations in a particular component can be spoken of in terms of the sensitivity $S_{R_1}^Q$ on the parameter Q of the selected component R_1. Similarly, $S_{C_1}^{\omega_0}$ indicates the sensitivity on ω_0 of the capacitor C_1. Consider

TABLE 13.1 SOME COMMERCIALLY AVAILABLE FILTERS

Type No. and make	Order	Characteristics and type	Comments
ATF 76, Burr Brown	2, 4 6, 8	Butterworth, Bessel, or Tchebychev; low-pass band-pass, high-pass, and band-reject	Factory tuned, no external components required.
UAF 11, 21, 31, 41 Burr Brown	2	Three amplifier network, configurable as low-pass, high-pass, band-pass, band-reject, or all-pass	Building block for higher order filters; external components required; externally tuned.
AF 100, National Semi-conductors	2	—do—	—do—
AF 120 —do—	2		Usable as gyrators or as negative immittance converters.
FLT series, Datel	4, 6	Butterworth, Bessel, tunable band-pass, low-pass	A few external components required.
EF 40, 41, Burr Brown	2	Three amplifier network configurable as low-pass, high-pass, band-pass, band-reject, and all-pass	Building block for higher-order filters.
300 series, Frequency Devices	2	Low-pass, high-pass, band-pass	Voltage tunable.
FS 60, Kinetic Technology	2	Low-pass, high-pass, band-pass, band-reject or all-pass	Three amplifier configuration.
AF 300, Multi-metrics	2	Butterworth, Bessel, Tchebychev, low-pass, high-pass, band-pass, and band-reject	Factory tuned, no external components required.
A 251, ITHACO Inc.		High-pass, low-pass, variable electronic filter	General-purpose active filter with variable cut-off frequency.
AF 100 m Multimetrics	4	High-pass, low-pass, variable electronic filter	General-purpose active filter with variable cut-off frequency.
852, Rockland	4	—do—	—do—
1471 A, Dawe	4	—do—	—do—
EF 2, Barr & Stroud	4	—do—	—do—
615, Precision Filters	7	Elliptic, low-pass/high-pass	124 programmable cut-off frequencies, digitally programmable.
531 A, National Aeronautical Laboratory	4	Butterworth, low-pass/high-pass	General-purpose variable cut-off frequency.

for example, a second-order LP Butterworth filter having a cut-off frequency of 300 Hz. The normalized transfer function for the filter is

$$H(\omega) = \frac{1}{s^2 + 1.414s + 1}$$

For a choice of R as 47 kohm, the value of the capacitance C can be calculated as

$$C = \frac{1}{2\pi \times 300 \times 47 \times 10^3} = 0.01129 \ \mu F$$

Using a VCVS configuration, one method of realizing the transfer function is as shown in Fig. 13.24, where $C_1 = 1.414, C = 0.01596 \ \mu F$ and $C_2 = 0.707, C = 0.00798 \ \mu F$. Since these values are not standard values, the effect of using a 0.015 μF for C_1 and 0.0082 μF for C_2 can be evaluated using the sensitivity function. The transfer function of the circuit of Fig. 13.24 is

$$H(\omega) = \frac{1}{s^2 C_1 C_2 R_1 R_2 + s(C_2 R_1 + C_2 R_2) + 1} \qquad (13.34)$$

$$= \frac{\omega_n^2}{s^2 + 2\zeta\omega_n s + \omega_n^2} \qquad (13.35)$$

where,

$$\omega_n = \frac{1}{\sqrt{C_1 C_2 R_1 R_2}}$$

and,

$$\zeta = \frac{C_2 R_1 + C_2 R_2}{2\sqrt{C_1 C_2 R_1 R_2}}$$

For the special case $R_1 = R_2 = R$,

$$\omega_n = \frac{1}{R\sqrt{C_1 C_2}}$$

and,

$$\zeta = \sqrt{\frac{C_2}{C_1}}.$$

$$S_{C_1}^{\omega_n} = \frac{\dfrac{d}{dC_1}(\omega_n)}{\omega_n/C_1} = \frac{\Delta\omega_n}{\omega_n} \div \frac{\Delta C_1}{C_1}, \text{ as } \Delta\omega_n \text{ and } \Delta C_1 \to 0$$

$$= \frac{\text{percentage change in } \omega_n}{\text{percentage change in } C_1} = -\frac{1}{2}$$

Similarly, $S_{C_2}^{\omega_n} = -\dfrac{1}{2}$, $S_{C_1}^{\zeta} = -\dfrac{1}{2}$, and $S_{C_2}^{\zeta} = +\dfrac{1}{2}$

With these relationships, the effect of using $C_1 = 0.015 \mu$F and $C_2 = 0.0082 \mu$F can be evaluated.

(a) Due to C_1 being 6% low, ω_n increases by $\dfrac{1}{2} \times 6\% = 3\%$.

(b) Due to C_2 being 2.1% high, ω_n decreases by $\dfrac{1}{2} \times 2.8\% = 1.4\%$.

(c) Net effect is such that ω_n increases by $(3 - 1.4)\% = 1.6\%$.

(d) Net effect on ζ is $\left(-\dfrac{1}{2}\right) \times (-6\%) + \left(+\dfrac{1}{2}\right) \times (+2.8\%) = 4.4\%$ increase; i.e.,

$\zeta = 0.738$ instead of 0.707.

Hence the circuit of Fig. 13.24 will yield a normalized transfer function of

$$\frac{1}{s^2 + 1.476s + 1.032}$$

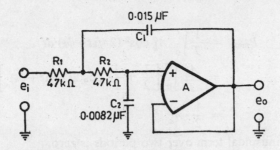

Fig. 13.24 Second-order Butterworth LP
filter for 150 Hz

Whether the resulting changes in the response can be tolerated or not depends on the application. When realizing elliptic filters with complex zeroes and poles, it is seldom that variations of this order can be tolerated. As a result, typically a minimum of two adjustments can become necessary for each complex pole pair, viz., one for frequency and another for ζ. Depending on the circuit, these adjustments will have to be carried out in sequences decided judiciously. Repeated adjustments can then converge to yield the desired transfer function. A third adjustment might be required when complex zeroes are also involved.

In spite of such "tweaking" of the circuit to provide the required response at the time of adjustment, the changes in the response due to temperature dependence of components and ageing still remain. The sensitivity functions can again be used to assess the resulting changes in the performance. The use of components with low-temperature coefficients (e.g., metal-film resistors and polycarbonate or NPO ceramic capacitors) reduces the effects due to temperature. In spite of this, high-Q high-order band-pass and band-reject filters may still require periodic retuning to ensure that they meet certain stipulated stringent specifications.

13.6 SIGNAL ANALYSERS

The mathematical basis of signal analysis is the "Fourier Transform" which takes different forms depending on the type of signal analysed[11]. All have a common feature in that the signal is assumed to be composed of sinusoidal components at various frequencies, each having a given amplitude and initial phase.

A signal which is "periodic" in the time domain has a spectrum which is "discrete" and in which all components fall at frequencies that are integral multiples of the fundamental frequency.

An arbitrary time signal $g(t)$ has an instantaneous power equal to $\{g(t)\}^2$, and the mean power P_{mean} over one period T is

$$P_{mean} = \frac{1}{T} \int_0^T \{g(t)\}^2 \, dt \qquad (13.36)$$

For the typical sinusoidal component, if

$$g(t) = A_k \cos\left(2\pi f_k t + \phi^k\right)$$

then,

$$P_{\text{mean}} = \frac{1}{T} \int_0^T A_k^2 \cos^2 (2\pi f_k t + \phi_k) \, dt$$

$$= \frac{A_k^2}{T} \int_0^T \left\{ \frac{1}{2} + \frac{1}{2} \cos 2(2\pi f_k t + \phi_k) \right\} dt$$

$$= \frac{1}{2} \cdot A_k^2$$

since the integral of a sinusoidal term over two periods is zero.

The root-mean-square value is thus $\dfrac{1}{\sqrt{2}} A_k$. The peak and rms values of the harmonic components of a periodic waveform can be obtained from Fourier analysis.

Consider a periodic function, $g(t)$ having a periodicity T.

$$g(t) = g(t + nT)$$

where n is any integer. $G(f_k)$, the amplitude of the kth harmonic of the function $g(t)$ is then given by

$$G(f_k) = \frac{1}{T} \int_{-T/2}^{T/2} g(t) e^{-j2\pi f_k t} \, dt \tag{13.37}$$

where $f_k = k f_1 = \dfrac{k}{T}$, is the kth harmonic of the fundamental frequency f_1, having a period T.

The function $g(t)$ is the sum of such individual components and is related as

$$g(t) = \sum_{k=-\infty}^{\infty} G(f_k) e^{j2\pi f_k t} \tag{13.38}$$

The series of values $G(f_k)$ are known as the spectral components of $g(t)$ and since there is an amplitude and phase (or equivalently, real and imaginary parts) associated with each one, a full description of the spectrum should include both the amplitude spectrum as well as the phase spectrum. If the function $g(t)$ is real-valued (as is generally so in the case of real-time signals), the harmonic components $g(f_k)$ are such that

$$G(f_k) = G^*(-f_k)$$

where G^* is the complex conjugate of G. The spectrum of a real-valued function is thus "conjugate-éven".

Figure 13.25 illustrates the power spectrum of a symmetric square wave. This is the one-sided [power spectrum obtained by adding the negative frequency components $(-f_k)$ to their positive counterparts (f_k). This is the normal representation of the power spectrum and directly corresponds to the measurements with practical filters, since both positive and negative frequency components are passed equally. The phase spectrum is not usually obtained in the practical case, and hence the input function $g(t)$ cannot be reconstructed solely from the amplitude components obtained after an analysis in the absence of this phase information.

13.6.1 Classification of Signals

In frequency analysis, the type of signal to be analysed influences the choice of the analysis parameters. A broad classification of the signal types normally encountered is illustrated in Fig. 13.26.

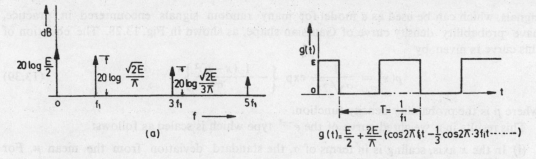

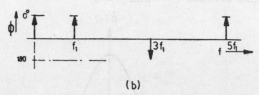

$$g(t) = \frac{E}{2} + \frac{2E}{\pi} \left(\cos 2\pi f_1 t - \frac{1}{3} \cos 2\pi \cdot 3 f_1 t \cdots \cdots \right)$$

Fig. 13.25 Power spectrum of symmetric square wave: (a) amplitude; (b) phase

Signals may be stationary or non-stationary. The stationary signals are those whose average properties do not vary with time and are thus independent of the sample record used to determine them. Stationary, deterministic signals are made up of entirely sinusoidal com-

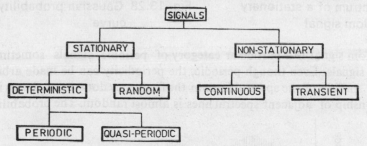

Fig. 13.26 Classification of signals

ponents at discrete frequencies. For periodic, stationary, deterministic signals, such as a distorted sinewave, the various discrete frequencies that it comprises are harmonically related to the fundamental frequency. In quasi-periodic signals, the various sinusoidal components are not harmonically related. Examples of this type of signal are: (i) a combination of two or more independent distorted sine waves, and (ii) vibration spectra from an engine having two independently rotating shafts.

A stationary random signal has a spectrum which is continuous in the frequency domain, as shown in Fig. 13.27. When analysing this type of signals, the power transmitted by a filter depends on its bandwidth. For a random signal having relatively constant "power spectral density" (i.e., power per unit Hz, expressed in W/Hz), the power transmitted by a filter is proportional to its bandwidth. Even though their instantaneous values cannot be predicted, the random signals can be characterized by their probability-density curves. Gaussian random signals, which can be used as a model for many random signals encountered in practice, have probability density curve of Gaussian shape, as shown in Fig. 13.28. The equation of this curve is given by

$$p(x) = \frac{1}{\sigma\sqrt{2\pi}} \exp\left\{-\frac{1}{2}\frac{(x-\mu)^2}{\sigma^2}\right\} \tag{13.39}$$

where p is the probability density function.

This results in a weighted curve of the e^{-x^2} type which is scaled as follows:

(i) In the x axis, scaling is in terms of σ, the standard deviation from the mean μ. For $\mu = 0$, σ is the rms level and σ^2 is the variance or power.

(ii) In the y axis, scaling is such that the area under the curve is unity, this being the total probability that the value of x is anywhere between $-\infty$ and $+\infty$.

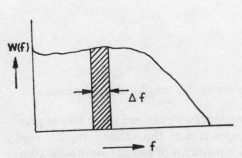

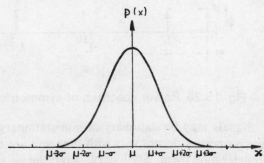

Fig. 13.27 Spectrum of a stationary random signal

Fig. 13.28 Gaussian probability density curve

A pseudo-random signal is a particular category of periodic signals sometimes used to simulate random signals. Even though periodic, the periodicity can be made arbitrarily large, resulting in close spacing of the spectral lines in the frequency domain, as shown in Fig. 13.29. The phase relationship of adjacent spectral lines is almost random. The probability density of

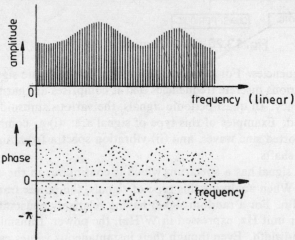

Fig. 13.29 Spectrum of pseudo-random signal

the pseudo-random signals may be made very close to Gaussian. A distinguishing feature is that the pseudo random signal can be reproduced exactly, a characteristic that can be of use in the standardization of testing.

Non-stationary signals may be roughly divided into continuous non-stationary signals and transient signals. These are often analysed over short intervals during which they can be considered quasi-stationary. The process of dividing up a continuous signal into short intervals is called "time windowing". A simple time window is a rectangular weighting function wherein the signal is cut off at each end as indicated in Fig. 13.30. While this window gives uni-

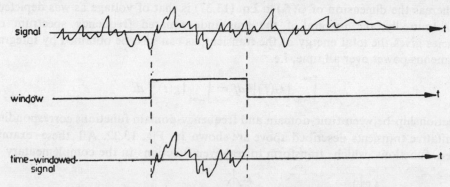

Fig. 13.30 Rectangular time window

form weighting along the selected sample, the effect that it produces on the frequency domain is that of filtering the original spectrum by a filter characteristic corresponding to the Fourier transform of the rectangular weighting function. A more desirable filtering effect is sometimes obtained by choosing a non-uniform weighting function such as the Gaussian curve as shown in Fig 13.31.

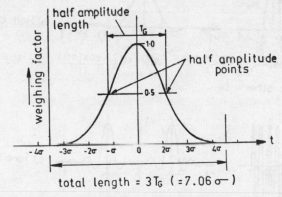

Fig. 13.31 Gaussian time window

A host of signals that need to be analysed in practice are transient in nature. Examples are: sonic boom, vibration resulting from a hammer hit, and current pulse used for welding.

Simpler transient signals that can be conceived of are: a rectangular pulse, a half-cosine pulse, and a tone burst.

In these cases when the signal exists only for a finite duration of time, the distribution of the components in the frequency domain becomes continuous, and the continuous spectrum $G(f)$ is given by

$$G(f) = \int_{-\infty}^{\infty} g(t)e^{-j2\pi ft}\, dt \tag{13.40}$$

This is in contrast to Eq. (13.37) which gives the time-averaged value of the discrete frequency components for a periodic signal. The dimension of $G(f)$ in Eq. (13.40) is voltage $\times$ time whereas the dimension of $G(f_k)$ in Eq. (13.37) is that of voltage as was depicted in Fig. 13.25. Admittedly, the integral of the amplitude squared frequency spectrum over all frequencies gives the total energy of the transient, as can also be obtained by integrating the instantaneous power over all time, i.e.

$$\int_{-\infty}^{\infty} |G(f)|^2\, df = \int_{-\infty}^{\infty} |g(t)|^2\, dt \tag{13.41}$$

The relationship between time-domain and frequency-domain functions corresponding to the representative transients described above are shown in Fig. 13.32. All these examples are real-even functions which transform to real-even functions in the complementary domain.

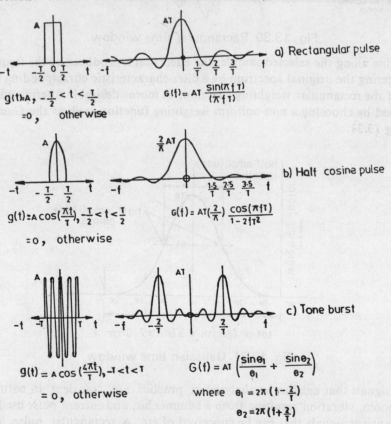

a) Rectangular pulse

$$g(t) = A, \quad -\frac{T}{2} < t < \frac{T}{2}$$
$$= 0, \quad \text{otherwise}$$

$$G(f) = AT\,\frac{\sin(\pi f T)}{(\pi f T)}$$

b) Half cosine pulse

$$g(t) = A\cos\left(\frac{\pi t}{T}\right), \quad -\frac{T}{2} < t < \frac{T}{2}$$
$$= 0, \quad \text{otherwise}$$

$$G(f) = AT\left(\frac{2}{\pi}\right)\frac{\cos(\pi f T)}{1 - 2f\, T^2}$$

c) Tone burst

$$g(t) = A\cos\left(\frac{4\pi t}{T}\right), \quad -T < t < T$$
$$= 0, \quad \text{otherwise}$$

$$G(f) = AT\left(\frac{\sin\theta_1}{\theta_1} + \frac{\sin\theta_2}{\theta_2}\right)$$

$$\text{where} \quad \theta_1 = 2\pi\left(f - \frac{2}{T}\right)$$
$$\theta_2 = 2\pi\left(f + \frac{2}{T}\right)$$

Fig. 13.32 Transient signal characteristics of: (a) rectangular pulse; (b) half-cosine pulse; (c) tone burst

In a general case, description of the overall spectrum is not complete without the phase spectrum. The complete spectrum is illustrated in Fig. 13.33 for a rectangular pulse starting at zero time. (Compare this with Fig. 13.32(a).)

Analysis of a transient is usually performed by treating it either directly or implicitly as though it were repeated periodically with repetition time T. Because of the periodicity artificially introduced, the measured spectrum becomes a line spectrum with line spacing $1/T$; but

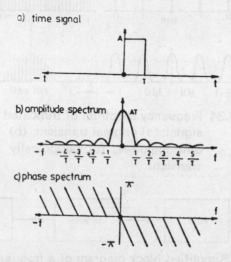

a) time signal

b) amplitude spectrum

c) phase spectrum

Fig. 13.33 Spectrum of a rectangular pulse

the individual lines can be considered as samples of the true continuous spectrum with a line spacing that can be made arbitrarily small by increasing T as indicated in Fig. 13.34(b). The spectrum of the periodic signal will normally be represented on an amplitude scale instead of the energy spectral density scale that should have been used to appropriately depict the frequency spectrum of the transient. However, scaling of the results is not difficult[12].

13.7 FREQUENCY ANALYSIS

The conventional method of obtaining the frequency spectrum of an electrical signal is to pass it through: (i) a number of analog filters with different centre frequencies and record the output of a detector connected sequentially to these filter outputs, or (ii) a single tunable filter and record the output of a detector connected to this filter while the filter centre frequency is continuously swept over the desired frequency range, or (iii) a number of analog filters as in (i) above but with individual detectors and scan the outputs of the detectors sequentially to result in the spectrum output.

A simplified block diagram of the analog analyser is shown in Fig. 13.35. The filter transmits a particular band of frequency in the input while attenuating the rest. The detector enables measurement of the power content in the selected bandwidth. Since the average power is measured in general, the detector has, incorporated within it, an averager which can be a linear type or, more commonly an RC type. To obtain the complete frequency spectrum of

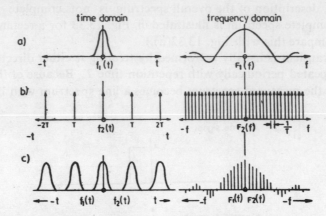

Fig. 13.34 Frequency spectrum of truncated transient signal: (a) original transient; (b) train of unit impulses; (c) periodically repeated transient

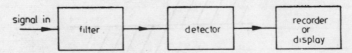

Fig. 13.35 Simplified block diagram of a frequency analyser

the input, the filter centre frequency should be either changed discretely or swept continuously. The rate at which this can be done is determined by the delays which arise in each of the sections, viz., filter, detector, and recorder.

The resolution of the final spectrum will be principally decided by the bandwidth of the filter used in the analysis. Two specific types of filters are available: (i) constant bandwidth, and (ii) relative bandwidth or constant Q. In the former, the bandwidth is independent of the selected centre frequency. For example, if the centre frequency is chosen as 100, 500, or 1000 Hz, the bandwidth might be a constant, say 3.16 Hz. In the constant Q type, the bandwidth is related to the centre frequency f_0 as

$$\text{Bandwidth} = \frac{1}{Q} \times \text{centre frequency}$$

If the Q is 20, then the bandwidth is 5 Hz at $f_0 = 100$ Hz and 25 Hz at $f_0 = 500$ Hz.

The use of constant bandwidth filters gives uniform resolution on a *linear* frequency scale, and this, for example, can facilitate detection of a harmonic pattern in the input analysed as illustrated in Fig. 13.36. However, when a linear frequency scale is used, one is restricted to, at best, about 2 decades of frequency range, because the lower decades tend to be crowded and the higher decades are vastly expanded.

Constant percentage bandwidth analysis gives uniform resolution on a logarithmic frequency scale and thus can be often meaningfully used over a wide frequency range of 3 to 6 decades. Spectra dominated by structural resonances are often best analysed in this way. The octave and one-third octave filters which are widely used fall under this category.

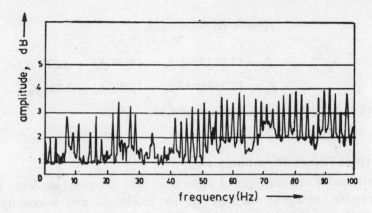

Fig. 13.36 Spectrum output of a constant bandwidth analyser

The octave filters have a bandwidth of one octave, i.e., the upper -3 dB frequency is twice (i.e. one octave above) the lower -3 dB frequency.

If $f_1 =$ lower -3 dB frequency, $f_0 =$ centre frequency, and, $f_2 =$ upper -3 dB frequency

then
$$f_2 = 2f_1$$

and
$$f_0 = \sqrt{f_2 f_1} = \sqrt{2f_1^2} = \sqrt{2}f_1$$

Hence,
$$f_1 = \frac{f_0}{\sqrt{2}}$$

and
$$f_2 = 2f_1 = \sqrt{2}f_0$$

The bandwidth,
$$(f_2 - f_1) = \frac{f_0}{\sqrt{2}}$$

Specifically, for a centre frequency of 1000 Hz, $f_1 = 0.707 \times 1000 = 707$ Hz and $f_2 = 1414$ Hz, giving a bandwidth of 707 Hz. This is equivalent to a Q of only 1.414, and octave filters are often used for only a very coarse analysis. Typical applications include noise analysis as applied to industrial-noise monitoring, industrial-vibration monitoring, and airport-noise monitoring.

In contrast, the one-third octave filter has a bandwidth of one-third of an octave. Here, the upper -3 dB frequency is one-third of an octave higher than the lower -3 dB frequency. The factor corresponding to one-third octave is $2^{1/3} = 1.2589$. Expressing in dB, this corresponds to 2.007 dB $\left(= \frac{1}{3} \times 6.02 \text{ dB} \right)$.

In contrast, the factor corresponding to one-tenth decade is
$$10^{1/10} = 1.2589 = 2.00 \text{ dB}$$

Since ten filters having one-tenth decade bandwidth will exactly cover one decade of the frequency span ($10 \times 2.00 = 20$ dB corresponding to one decade) this set of filters continue to be called one-third octave filters though their exact bandwidth is one-tenth of a decade. Hence, for one-third octave filters

$$f_2 = 1.2589 f_1$$

and
$$f_0 = \sqrt{f_1 f_2} = \frac{f_2}{\sqrt{1.2589}}$$

Hence,
$$f_2 = (1.2589)^{1/2}\, f_0 = 10^{1/20}\, f_0 = 1.122\, f_0$$

and
$$f_1 = (1.2589)^{-1/2}\, f_0 = 10^{-1/20}\, f_0 = 0.891\, f_0$$

The bandwidth is $0.231\, f_0$, resulting in a Q of 4.33.

13.7.1 Practical Filters for Analysis

The characteristics of various types of filters have been described in Secs. 13.3.1 to 13.3.4. The main parameters of a practical filter are its bandwidth and selectivity, provided the "ripple" within the pass band is kept within acceptable limits. The "bandwidth" normally refers to the -3 dB bandwidth. However, in many filters used for noise and vibration analysis, the bandwidth referred to is the "noise bandwidth" of the filter. The noise bandwidth of a filter is the equivalent bandwidth of an ideal filter which transmits the same power, from a white noise source, as the practical filter, for the same reference transmission level in the pass-band. When dealing with random signals, it is more relevant to use the noise bandwidth, since results derived for ideal filters can then be generally applied to practical filters with the same noise bandwidth. Higher-order filters which approximate ideal filters to a closer extent than lower-orders filter have values for the noise bandwidth which are closer to the -3 dB bandwidth. For the standard six-pole one-third octave filters, where the noise bandwidth is one-third octave, the -3 dB bandwidth is approximately 95% of the noise bandwidth.

While the bandwidth of a filter gives information as regards its ability to separate frequency components of approximately the same level, the selectivity indicates the ability to separate components of widely different levels. The basic parameter indicating selectivity is the "shape factor" defined as the ratio of the -60 dB bandwidth to the -3 dB bandwidth of a filter, illustrated in Fig. 13.37(a). A four-pole Butterworth BP filter has a shape factor of 31.6 as against a shape factor of 10 for a six-pole Butterworth filter. For filters with lesser dynamic range, the 40 dB shape factor or the 30 dB shape factor can also be referred to, to indicate the selectivity. Another conventional practice is to refer to the "octave selectivity" for a filter, which gives the relative attenuation of the filter at one octave frequency on either side of the centre frequency as shown in Fig. 13.37(b). A six-pole one-third octave filter has an octave selectivity of about 50 dB.

13.7.2 Filter Response Time

When a signal burst is applied to a filter, the filter takes some finite time before it responds to this signal. The envelope response of a BP filter (obtained by transforming a low-pass filter) for a signal burst having a frequency corresponding to the centre frequency of the BP filter, has the same shape as the step response of the untransformed low-pass filter. The response of a one-third octave filter for a signal burst having a frequency equal to the centre frequency of the filter is indicated in Fig. 13.38. The time taken for the output of the filter

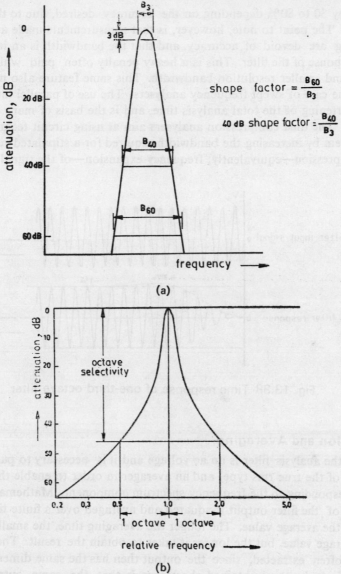

$$\text{shape factor} = \frac{B_{60}}{B_3}$$

$$\text{shape factor} = \frac{B_{40}}{B_3}$$

Fig. 13.37 Selectivity of filters: (a) shape factor; (b) octave selectivity

to approach its final value is of the order of $1/B$ where B is the filter bandwidth. If t_R represents this time, then

$$B \cdot t_R \simeq 1$$

or

$$f \cdot t_R = \frac{f}{B} = Q$$

i.e.,

$$n_R = Q$$

where n_R is the number of periods of centre frequency f in the time t_R. Since these equations are only expected to yield the order of magnitude of t_R and n_R, the values for these in practice may be higher by 30 to 80% depending on the accuracy desired, due to the inclusion of the "settling time". The point to note, however, is that measurements made at the output prior to such settling are devoid of accuracy, and that the bandwidth is an important criterion deciding the response of the filter. This is a heavy penalty often paid while doing analysis with smaller and smaller resolution bandwidth. This same feature also naturally limits the sweep rate in the case of swept frequency analysers. The use of parallel filters hence enables appreciable shortening of the total analysis time, and is the basis of many of the older real-time analysers. The time compression analysers aim at using circuit techniques to mitigate the above problem by increasing the bandwidth required for a stipulated resolution in analysis by time compression—equivalently, frequency expansion—of the signal.

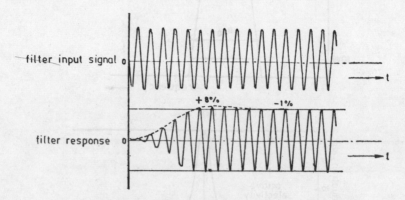

Fig. 13.38 Time response of one-third octave filter

13.7.3 Detection and Averaging

The output of the analysis filter is an ac voltage and it is necessary to pass this through a detector (often of the true rms type) and an averager in order to enable the measurement of the power corresponding to the frequency spectrum component. Mathematically, the instantaneous value of the filter output is squared and averaged over a finite time (the averaging time) to obtain the average value. The longer the averaging time, the smaller are the variations in the average value, but the longer it takes to obtain the result. The square root of this value is often extracted, since the output then has the same dimensions as the input signal. A practical advantage obtained therefrom is that the same output voltage range represents twice the dB range, and thus gives a wider dynamic range in general. In addition, it may be often required to convert the average values to equivalent dB values by a logarithmic conversion.

The detector that gives the true rms output irrespective of the input waveform, is termed a "true rms" detector. Many so-called rms indicators often use rectification followed by averaging as a substitute for true rms detection and calibrate the output in terms of the rms value using the known relationship between the rms and the rectified average values for sinusoidal signals. For random signals and other complex signal inputs, inaccuracies far exceeding ±0.5 dB result unless true rms detectors are used for the rms estimation. Thus all high quality detectors square the input signal in one way or another.

The purpose of averaging is to suppress the fluctuations in the squared rectified signal from the squaring circuit, thereby obtaining a value representing the mean square spectral estimate. Though the Fourier analysis implies integration over all time, in practice this cannot be done due to the necessity to limit the averaging time to a finite value. As a result, a ripple at twice the frequency of analysis is often present in the averaged value. An RC filter having a time constant equal to three times the period of the ripple (1.5 times the period corresponding to the frequency of analysis) can be shown to result in reduction of the ripple to within ± 0.5 dB.[11] Such a filter requires a time of approximately 2.85 RC to settle to within 0.5 dB of the final value. Hence the averaging filter should have a time constant of at least about 4.3 times the period of the analysis frequency for an accuracy of $\pm$ 0.5 dB.

While the above is true for single-frequency components being passed by the analysis filter, this is not the case in general. When a narrow band noise of bandwidth B is applied to a detector with averaging time t_a, the relative standard deviation ϵ of the measured level is expressed by the equation,

$$\epsilon = \frac{1}{2\sqrt{Bt_a}}, \quad \text{for } Bt_a \gg 1 \tag{13.42}$$

$$\simeq \frac{4.34}{\sqrt{Bt_a}} \text{ dB}$$

Referring to Fig. 13.39, where μ refers to the variance, it may be noted that the result itself is a random variable with a probability-distribution curve that gets closer to the true value as the averaging time is increased. For a single estimate there is 68.3% chance of the estimate being within $\pm\epsilon$ of the true value, 95.5% chance of being within $\pm 2\epsilon$, and 99.7% of being within $\pm 3\epsilon$.

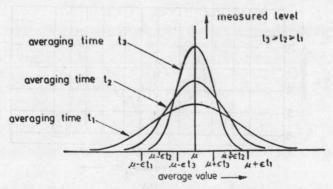

Fig. 13.39 Effect of averaging time on error distribution

13.8 METHODS OF ANALYSIS

Several methods employed for spectral analysis of signals have been mentioned in Sec. 13.7. In a particular situation, the method to be used depends on many factors such as the resolution required, total time available for analysis, stationarity of the process being analysed, and equipment available. Some of the normally-used methods and modern trends are described in the following sections.

13.8.1 Discrete Stepped Filter Analysis

Figure 13.40(a) shows a simple block diagram of a typical stepped-filter analyser. The signal, after necessary preamplification, is applied to a parallel bank of filters which together cover the frequency range of interest (e.g., 31 third octave filters cover the frequency range of 10 Hz to 10 kHz). A detector followed by an averager is connected sequentially to the various filter outputs and thus measures successively the output power in each frequency band. A typical spectrum obtained by synchronizing the scanning rate of the filters with the speed of a level recorder is shown in Fig. 13.40(b).

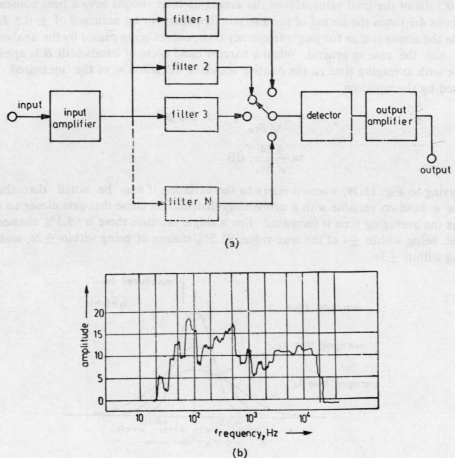

(b)

Fig. 13.40 Stepped filter analyser: (a) block diagram; (b) spectrum output

13.8.2 Swept Filter Analysers

When a higher resolution of analysis is needed, it is more convenient to use a single tunable filter, as illustrated in Fig. 13.41. The filter can be a constant bandwidth or a constant Q type. Instead of a number of spectrum estimates at discrete frequencies, the resulting spectrum is now continuous in frequency. Necessarily, the sweep speed will have to be decided upon based on the resolution bandwidth and the accuracy desired.

resolution can be now achieved with 100 Hz resolution analysis and a consequent analysis time of only 100 ms. Hence a frequency expansion (or time compression) of 10 times directly reduces the analysis time required to analyse. In a heterodyne frequency analysers use this basic principle and expand the analysis time to speed up the analysis. and more. Normally, a hybrid technique which enables the incoming signal analysis stored in digital memories and recirculated. These memories have the recirculated signal which is then analysed in an analog subsystem. The resulting spectrum can often be displayed in a linear frequency scale with a constant bandwidth analysis done by the heterodyne analyser. As many as 400 lines can be obtained in the displayed spectrum amounting to a resolution of as low as 2.5 Hz in a 1 kHz spectrum.

Another mathematical technique which has revolutionized the spectrum display is the FFT (Fast Fourier Transform) analysis. While the normal direct Fourier transform requires N^2 complex multiplications to provide a spectrum display ....

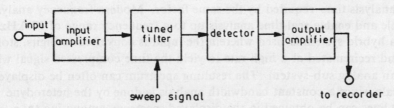

                         input

Fig. 13.41 Swept filter analyser

13.8.3 Real-Time Parallel Analysers

By connecting an individual detector and averager to each one of the set of parallel filters as was used in stepped-filter analysers, one can reduce the time required to obtain the frequency spectrum considerably. As indicated in Fig. 13.42, the detector/averager outputs are multiplexed and are presented as the spectrum display. The display is continuously updated so that the spectrum that is displayed represents the input information immediately preceding the updating of the display. A typical example of this type of analyser is the Bruel & Kjaer type 3347 1/3 octave analyser.

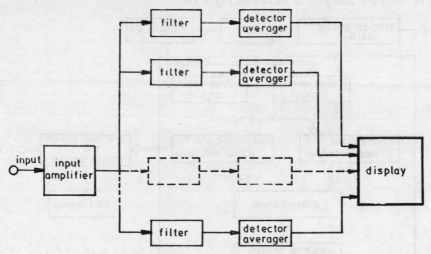

Fig. 13.42 Parallel filter analysers

13.8.4 Time Compression and FFT Techniques

Noting that the time required for analysis is severely limited by the response time of the filters when narrow band analysis is to be carried out, methods were attempted to reduce this time artificially. If a 1 kHz band limited spectrum is to be analysed with 10 Hz resolution and if a limitation of 1 s minimum analysis time results thereby, it is obvious that if the frequency range of 0—1 kHz is expanded to 0—10 kHz, then the same equivalent 10 Hz resolution can be now achieved with 100 Hz resolution analysis and a consequent analysis time of only 100 ms. Hence a frequency expansion (or time compression) of 10 times directly reduces the analysis time required by the same factor. Modern frequency analysers use this basic principle and enable real-time analysis up to a frequency range of 10 kHz and more. Normally, a hybrid system is used wherein the input is converted to digits, stored in digital memories, and recirculated at a high rate to yield the time compressed signal which is then analysed in an analog sub-system. The resulting spectrum can often be displayed in a linear frequency scale, since a constant bandwidth analysis is done by the heterodyne analyser. As many as 400 lines can be obtained in the displayed spectrum amounting to a resolution of as low as 2.5 Hz in a 1 kHz max. display.

Another mathematical technique which has revolutionized the spectrum display is the FFT (Fast Fourier Transform) analysis. While the normal direct Fourier transform requires N^2 complex multiplications to provide a spectrum with N discrete lines, the FFT permits reduction in the number of multiplications to only $N \log_2 N$. A "factor of 100" improvement is obtained for the case of $N = 1024$. This is achieved by factorizing the multiplication matrix to various submatrices which by proper manipulation turn out to be simple 2×2 matrices. The multiplication can now be carried out easily with digital circuits and dedicated hardware. The presentation of the spectrum is much the same as in time compression analysers, i.e., the spectrum comprises 400 equally-spaced lines. The bandwidth of analysis is thus 0.25% of the maximum frequency corresponding to the range. The block schematic of the FFT analyser is shown in Fig. 13.43.

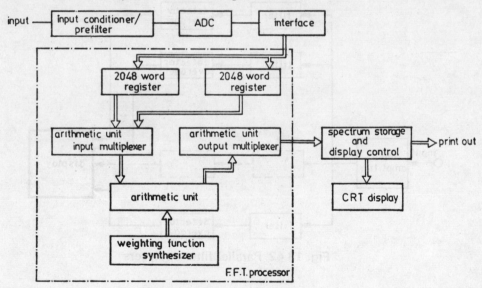

Fig. 13.43 FFT analysers

In both the above cases, prefiltering is necessitated to avoid aliasing errors and this is internally done for each selected range. These spectrum analysers can also store transients and analyse them by repeating the transient effectively by internal recirculation. A typical dynamic range of 72 dB is achievable in a FFT analyser having a 12 bit A/D converter and an internal circulation accuracy of 16 bits.

13.9 APPLICATIONS OF SIGNAL ANALYSIS

The fields of applications of signal analysis encompass almost all known fields where electrical measurements are made. A short list of specific applications [13,14,15] is as follows:

1. Machinery health monitoring and preventive maintenance;
2. Analysis of flutter in turbo engines;
3. Identification of loose shafts;
4. Identification of resonance in gear box assemblies;
5. Identification of whirl modes of vibration in crankshaft;
6. Rotor transient analysis;
7. Identification of cracked shafts;
8. Impact testing of quality control tools;
9. Noise signature analysis of structural vibrations; and
10. Acoustic monitoring of breeder reactors.

One can extend this list indefinitely as newer methods of applications of signal analysis continually get added to this list.

A typical application of signal analysis can be considered in more detail, for the sake of completeness. For the evaluation and surveillance of compressor performance at a gaseous diffusion plant, signal analysis has been used to study: (i) new blade design and prototype compressor evaluation, (ii) corrective and preventive maintenance of machinery components, and (iii) evaluation of machinery health.

The system used monitors signals from accelerometers mounted on the load bearing housings of sixteen on-line compressors. These signals are transmitted by hard-wire to the analyser for daily monitoring. The accelerometer signals are analysed over the full-scale range of 5 kHz with a resolution of 5 Hz. The total g forces are measured to obtain the severity level of surges. The surges in g are caused by the application of pressure surges to evaluate the condition of the compressor. Velocity is analysed over a frequency range of 2 kHz with a resolution of 1 Hz. Blade resonance frequencies for each row of blades in the shaft are stored, and the total energy dissipated in each range is measured. Displacement analysis extends over a frequency range of 100 Hz with a resolution of 0.05 Hz. The fundamental rotor frequency and its first two harmonics are measured. The analysis also provides means to measure the change of rotor speed during surges.

After analysis of a prototype compressor free of defects, information obtained therefrom is stored and used to compare the analysis results from new compressors erected or on reassembly of disassembled compressors. A similar procedure is adopted for the identification of defects due to faulty lubrication, and to monitor the presence of fatigue cracks in blades.

EXERCISES

13.1 Calculate the "peak" frequency and the gain at the "peak" frequency for networks having the following second-order transfer functions:

(i) $\dfrac{5}{s^2 + 0.3s + 5}$

(ii) $\dfrac{64}{s^2+8s+64}$

(iii) $\dfrac{s^2}{s^2+3s+100}$

13.2 A multiplier providing the product of a 10 V peak 1 kHz carrier and a 30% modulated carrier (1 kHz with modulation at 100 Hz) provides an output voltage of 1 V peak at the modulating frequency and 3.33 V peak at twice the carrier frequency. Design a suitable filter so that the ratio of the modulating signal to the carrier signal after filtering is 50 : 1 and the phase shift introduced by the filter on the modulating signal is less than 10°.

13.3 A second-order Butterworth LP filter is required to filter a signal. For a cut-off frequency of 100 Hz, the phase shift introduced by the filter is 30° at a frequency of 29 Hz. Design a phase equalizer that would cancel this phase shift so that the phase shift of the overall system is 0° at 29 Hz.

13.4 Design a Tchebychev third-order LP transformed band-reject filter for 50 Hz, meeting the following specifications:

pass-band gain	: 0 dB
pass-band ripple	: 0.5 dB
minimum attenuation required	: 40 dB from 45 to 55 Hz

13.5 Design a third-order Butterworth high-pass filter for 100 Hz. Estimate the worst case error in the −3dB frequency, if the components used have a tolerance of ±5%.

13.6 Based on the tables given in Ref. 17, design a wideband phase shifter that provides two outputs that have a phase difference of 90° ± 3° between them over the frequency range 100 Hz to 10 kHz.

13.7 Using Eqn. (13.42), estimate the averaging time required to provide an indication having an error less than 0.5 dB for the measured rms level if the bandwidth of the noise is : (a) 10 Hz and (b) 1 Hz.

13.8 In a swept filter analyser a filter of bandwidth 2 Hz is swept from 10 Hz to 1 kHz. With a sweep rate of 2 Hz/s, calculate the time required to sweep over the desired frequency range.

REFERENCES

1. Zverev, A.I., *Handbook of Filter Synthesis*, Ch. III, John Wiley and Sons, N.Y., 1967.
2. Sallen, R.P. and E.L. Key, "A practical method of designing RC active filters", *IRE Trans. Circuit Theory*, Vol. CT-2, pp. 74-85, March, 1955.
3. Williams, A.B., *Active Filter Design*, Ch. III, Artech House Inc., Massachusetts, 1975.
4. Blinchikoff, H.J. and Zverev, A.I., *Filtering in the Time and Frequency Domain*, pp. 120-121, John Wiley and Sons, N.Y., 1976.
5. Tobey, G.E., et. al., *Operational Amplifiers—Design and Applications*, pp. 322-325, Burr/Brown Research Corporation, McGraw-Hill, N.Y., 1971.
6. Ibid. 1, p. 407.
7. Ibid. 3, Ch. V.
8. Dickey, R.K., "Outputs of op amp networks have fixed phase difference", p. 278 in Weber S. (Ed), *Circuits for Electronics Engineers*, Electronics Magazine Books Series, McGraw-Hill, N.Y., 1977.
9. Ibid. 3, pp. 111-114.
10. Ibid. 5, pp. 303-308.
11. Randall, R.B., *Application of B & K Equipment to Frequency Analysis*, Ch. II, Bruel and Kjaer, Denmark, 1977.
12. Ibid. 11, p.38.
13. Cole, S.S. (Conference Director), "Application of signature analysis to machinery reliability and performance", *Conference Proceedings*, Engineering Foundation Conferences, Inc., New York, 1975.
14. "Vibrations in rotating machinery", *I. Mech E. Conference Publications 1976-79*, Institution of Mechanical Engineers, London.
15. Randall, R.B., "Vibration signature analysis techniques and instrumentation systems", *Noise, Shock and Vibration Conference*, Manash University, Melbourne, 1974.

16. Harbarger, "Vibration signature analysis of compressors in the gaseous diffusion process for uranium enrichment", pp. 159 to 176, in Cole, S.S. (Conference Director), "Application of signature analysis to machinery reliability and performance", *Conference Proceedings*, Engg. Foundation Conferences, Inc., N.Y., 1975.

17. Bedrosian, S.D., "Normalized design of 90° phase difference network", *IRE Trans. on Circuit Theory*, Vol. CT-7, No. 2, pp. 128-136, June 1960.

BIBLIOGRAPHY

Berlin, H.M., *The Design of Active Filters, with Experiments*, E & L Instruments, Inc., Connecticut, 1977.

Betts, *Signal Processing, Modulatian and Noise*, The English Universities Press Ltd., London, 1970.

Blackman, R.B. and Tukey, J.W., *The Measurement of Power Spectra*, Dover Publications, Inc., N.Y., 1958.

Broach, J.T., *Acoustic Noise Measurements*, Bruel & Kjaer, Denmark, 1971.

Budak, A., *Passive and Active Network Analysis and Synthesis*, Houghton, Mifflin Col, Boston, 1974.

Collacott, R.A., *Vibration Monitoring and Diagnosis*, George Godwin Ltd., London, 1979.

Comer, D.J., "The utility of the all pass filters", *IEEE Trans. on Instr. and Meas.*, Vol. IM-28, No, 2, pp. 164-167, June 1979.

Crandall, S.H. (Ed), *Random Vibration*, Vol. 2, The MIT Press, Cambridge, Massachusetts, 1963.

Crothers, M.H., "Tuning an RC tee notch filter", *Proceedings of IEEE* (Letters), Vol. 64, No. 5, p. 819, May 1976.

Daniels, R.W., *Approximation Methods for Electronics Filter Design*, McGraw-Hill, N.Y., 1974.

Daryanani, G., *Principles of Active Network Synthesis and Design*, John Wiley and Sons, N.Y., 1976.

Girling, F.E.J. and Good, E.F., "Active filters: 12, the leap-frog or active ladder synthesis", *Wireless World*, Vol. 76, No. 1417, pp. 341-345, July 1970.

Griffiths, J.W.R. and Stocklin, P.L. (Ed.), *Signal Processing*, Academic Press, London, 1973.

Harris, C.M. and Crede, C.E. (Ed.), *Shock and Vibration Handbook*, McGraw-Hill, N.Y., 1976.

Hines, G.E., "Predicting failures with vibration analysis", *Instruments and Control Systems*, Vol. 51, No. 7, pp. 31-35, July, 1978.

Huelsman, L.P. (Ed.), *Active RC Filters: Theory and Applications*, Dowden Hutchinson and Ross, Inc., Pennsylvania, 1976.

Hurtig, G. III, "Voltage tunable multiple bandpass active filters", *IEEE International Symp. on Circuits and Systems*, pp. 569-572, California, 1974.

Laker, K.R. and Chausi, M.S., "A comparison of active multiple loop feedback techniques for realizing high order band pass filters", *IEEE Trans. Circuits and Systems*, Vol. CAS 21, pp. 774-783, Nov. 1974.

Lam, H.Y.F., *Analog and Digital Filters: Design and Realization*, Prentice Hall, Inc. Englewood Cliffs, New Jersey, 1979.

Lubkin, Y.L., *Filter Systems and Design*, Addison Wesley Publishing Co., Massachusetts, 1970.

Mitra, S.K., *Active Inductorless Filters*, IEEE Press, N.Y., 1971.

Papoulis, *Signal Analysis*, McGraw-Hill, New York, 1977.

Petrusewicz, *Noise and Vibration Control for Industrialists*,, Elek Science, London, 1974.

Rhodes, J.D., *Theory of Electrical Filters*, John Wiley and Sons, London, 1976.

Sedra, A.S. and Bracket, P.O., *Filter Theory and Design: Active and Passive*, Matrix Publishers Inc., Illinois, 1978.

Skwirzynski, J.K., *Design Theory and Data for Electrical Filters*, D Van Nostrand Co., London, 1965.

Special Function Data Book, National Semiconductor Corporation, Sunnyvale, California, 1976.

Tarmy, R. and Chausi, M.S., "Very high Q insensitive active RC networks", *IEEE Trans. Circuit Theory*, CT-17, No. 3, pp. 358-366, Aug. 1970.

Van Vanlkenburg, M.E. (Ed.), *Circuit Theory, Foundations and Classical Contributions*, Benchmark Papers in Electrical Engg. and Computer Science, Dowden Hutchins and Ross Inc., Pennsylvania, 1974.

14

DATA ACQUISITION AND CONVERSION

14.1 INTRODUCTION

A typical data acquisition system consists of individual sensors with necessary signal conditioning, multiplexing, data conversion, data processing, data handling and associated transmission, storage, and display systems. In order to optimize the characteristics of a system in terms of performance, handling capability, and cost, the relevant sub-systems may often be combined. The analog data is generally *acquired* and converted to digital form for the purposes of processing, transmission, display and storage.

Processing may consist of a large variety of operations from simple comparison to complicated mathematical manipulations. It can be for such purposes as collecting information (averages, statistics, etc.), converting the data into a useful form (e.g., calculation of efficiency of a prime mover from speed, power input and torque developed), using data for controlling a process, performing repeated calculations to separate out signals buried in noise, generating information for displays, and a variety of other goals. Data may be transmitted over long distances (from one location to another) or short distances (from a test centre to a nearby computer). The data may be displayed on a digital panel meter or as a part of a cathode ray tube (CRT) presentation. The same may be stored in either raw or processed form, temporarily (for immediate use) or permanently (for ready reference later).

Data acquisition generally relates to the process of collecting the input data in digital form, as rapidly, accurately, completely, and economically as necessary. The basic instrumentation used may be a standard digital panel meter (DPM) with digital outputs, a shaft digitizer or a sophisticated high-speed high-resolution device. To match the input requirement of the converter with the output available from the sensor, some form of scaling and offsetting is necessary and is performed with an amplifier/attenuator. For converting analog information from more than one source, either additional converters or a multiplexer may be required; to increase the speed with which information is to be accurately converted, a sample and hold circuit may be desired or become a necessity. In the case of extra-wide range analog signals, logarithmic conversion have to be resorted to. A schematic block diagram of a general data acquisition system is shown in Fig. 14.1.

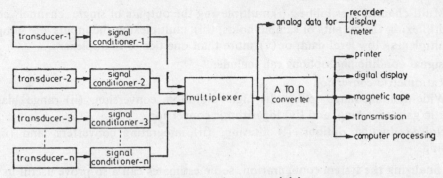

Fig. 14.1 Generalized data acquisition system

The characteristics of data acquisition systems depend both on the properties of the analog data itself and on the processing to be carried out. Based on the environment, a broad classification divides data acquisition systems into two categories[1], viz., those suited to favourable environments (minimum Radio Frequency Interference and Electromagnetic Induction) and those intended for hostile environments. The former category may include, among others, laboratory instrument applications, test systems for gathering long-term drift information on zeners, high-sensitivity calibration tests, and research or routine investigations, such as ones using mass spectrometers and lock-in amplifiers. In these the system designers' tasks are oriented more towards making sensitive measurements rather than to the problems of protecting the integrity of the analog data. The second category specifically includes measurements protecting the integrity of the analog data under the hostile conditions present. Situations of this nature arise in industrial process control systems, aircraft control systems, turbovisory instrumentation in electrical power stations, and a host of other measurements to be carried out under industrial environments.

Measurements under hostile conditions often require devices capable of wide temperature range operation, excellent shielding, redundant paths for critical measurements, and considerable processing of the digital data. In addition, digital conversion of the signal at early stages, thus making full use of high noise immunity of digital signals, as well as considerable design effort in order to reduce common mode errors and avoidable interferences can also enhance performance and increase reliability. On the other hand, laboratory measurements are conducted over narrower temperature ranges, with much less ambient electrical noise, employing high sensitivity and precision devices for higher accuracies and resolution. The preservation of an appropriate signal-to-noise ratio may still have to be achieved with due emphasis on design and measurement techniques.

The important factors that decide the configuration and the sub-systems of the data acquisition system are: (i) resolution and accuracy, (ii) the number of channels to be monitored, (iii) sampling rate per channel, (iv) signal conditioning requirement of each channel, and (iv) cost.

The various general configurations include:

(a) Single channel possibilities: (i) direct conversion, (ii) preamplification and direct conversion, (iii) sample and hold, and conversion, (iv) preamplification, sample and hold, and conversion, or (v) preamplification, signal conditioning, and any of the above.

(b) Multi-channel possibilities: (i) multiplexing the outputs of single channel converters, (ii) multiplexing the outputs of sample-holds, (iii) multiplexing the inputs of sample-holds, (iv) multiplexing low level data, or (v) more than one tier of multiplexers.

The signal conditioning options can include:

(a) Ratiometric conversion

(b) Wide-dynamic-range options: (i) high resolution conversion, (ii) range biasing, (iii) automatic gain switching, and (iv) logarithmic conversion.

(c) Noise-reduction options: (i) filtering, (ii) integrating converters, and (iii) digital processing.

Before finalizing the system configuration, some estimates can also prove useful in deciding the final configuration, viz., system measurement time, error, and cost.

14.1.1 Resolution and Accuracy

The resolution desired for a measurement is often governed by the overall accuracy required from the system and is typically three to five times better than the desired accuracy figure. When difference measurements are envisaged. the effect on the overall accuracy of the difference quantity, imposed by the resolution of the individual measurements should be carefully considered. The resolution obtainable from a measurement is not only dependent on the resolution that the measuring device is capable of, but also on the relative time stability of the measurand itself. When a time-varying stationary parameter is under observation, improvement in stability and hence resolution is possible by statistical averaging of the measured values. Accuracy being the closeness with which a measured value agrees with a specified standard, absolute accuracy can always be brought into a system which has sufficient stability and linearity, by providing a calibration facility. Once the system has been calibrated, accuracy impairments will depend on the stability of the system variants, such as gain stability and reference stability. Since the resolution with which a measurement can be made often decreases for higher measurement rates, for the same cost, the need for a specific resolution desired has to be examined with great care and full understanding of the requirement. An error budget should necessarily be prepared, and an optimum distribution of errors should be made to match with the cost of the sub-systems involved.

14.1.2 Number of Channels and the Sampling Rate

The number of channels on which measurements are to be carried out and the desired rate at which each channel should be measured decide the overall bit rate of the converters necessary to be used. If N channels need to be monitored with a rate less than K readings (measured value) per second in any of the channels, the bit rate of the converter should be, as a guideline, approximately $3NKP$ bits/s, where P refers to the resolution in bits for the readings desired to be taken. It is evident that increasing the bit resolution increases the overall speed requirement of the converter. When the sample rate desired from a specific number of channels are lesser by a factor of two or more, it may be possible to employ sub-commutation[2] in order to reduce the effective number of channels that have to be scanned at the highest rate.

14.2 SIGNAL CONDITIONING OF THE INPUTS

Since all the data that have to be acquired do not in general originate from identical sources, signal conditioning becomes necessary in some cases. The scaling of input gains to match the input signal to the converter's full scale range is a simple and obvious example. Linearization of data from thermocouples and Wheatstone bridges are performed by analog techniques using either piece-wise linear approximations or smooth series approximations using low cost IC multipliers. Alternatively, they can be performed digitally, after data acquisition and conversion, by using a Read-Only-Memory (storing a suitable linearization table or programme). Analog differentiation, precision rectification and averaging, phase detection, log conversion, ratio computation using dividers, and many other such types of processors are employed, where necessary, prior to data acquisition.

Two methods of signal conditioning which are particularly applicable, with advantage, to data acquisition are: (i) ratiometric conversion, and (ii) logarithmic compression.

14.2.1 Ratiometric Conversion

Consider a transducer using four strain gauges in a Wheatstone bridge network. The output voltage is a function of the change in resistance of each arm and the excitation voltage of the bridge. When the strain gauges are under maximum but constant unbalance, and if the excitation voltage varies by $\pm X\%$, the output of the bridge also varies by $\pm X\%$. However, if the bridge output is conditioned in such a way that the output of the signal amplifier is a voltage proportional to the strain only and independent of the excitation voltage, the system accuracies improve since the fluctuations in the excitation voltage do not affect the sensitivity of the system. The analog method of achieving this is to incorporate an analog divider to which the amplifier output and the excitation voltage are fed so that the output of the divider is a ratio of the amplifier output voltage to the excitation voltage. An alternative method, as shown in Fig. 14.2, is to feed the bridge-excitation voltage as an external reference voltage for the analog to digital (A/D) converter, in which the conversion factor is proportional to the reference voltage. The system sensitivity is then independent of the fluctuations in the bridge-excitation voltage.

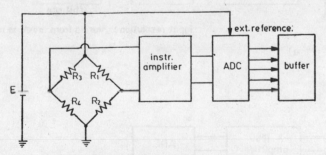

Fig. 14.2 Ratiometric conversion

14.2.2 Logarithmic Compression

A logarithmic compression circuit enables the measurement of a fractional change in the input as a percentage of the input magnitude rather than as a percentage of a range. For an input in the range of 100 μV to 100 mV, the output may correspond to zero volt for 100 μV input and 3 V for 100 mV input, if the logarithmic conversion gain is 1 V per decade (*see* Sec. 5.8, Chapter 12). Consider now a 1% change in the input from 100 to 101 mV. The output of the log amplifier would change by

$$\Delta V = \left(\log \frac{101}{100} \right) \times 1 \text{ V} = 4.3 \text{ mV}$$

Since the output change is related to the ratio of the inputs, it is evident that the change in the output is the same, viz., 4.3 mV, whether the input changes from 10.0 to 10.1 mV or from 100 to 101 μV. If the log amplifier output is converted into a digital output using a 12-bit BCD converter, the resolution of the converter would be $\dfrac{3 \text{ V}}{10^3} = 3$ mV, for a 3 V full-scale, provided the output of the log amplifier is scaled up appropriately. With this resolution of the converter, it is possible to monitor and record changes as low as 1 μV for an input of 100 μV, or 10 μV for an input of 1 mV. In the absence of log conversion, if the 100 mV input were scaled up to yield the full scale input of the 12 bit converter, the resulting resolution would have been only 100 μV $\left(= \dfrac{100 \text{ mV}}{100^3} \right)$. Thus a 100 to 1 improvement in resolution can be effected by logarithmic compression.

Admittedly, as indicated in Fig. 14.3(a) and (b), this cannot be achieved without loss of performance elsewhere. For example, while the log amplifier can enhance the resolution at low inputs, the effective resolution at high inputs (99.9 mV) is definitely poorer. At this input, one least significant bit (LSB) change in the output of the ADC can occur only if the input is decreased to 92.2 mV, i.e., an equivalent resolution of only 700 μV. (This would have been uniformly 100 μV without log conversion.) The log conversion in effect thus distributes the resolution on a "percentage of reading" basis as against a "percentage of full scale" as with A/D conversion.

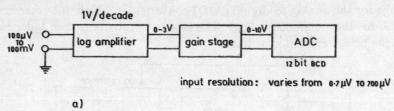

input resolution: varies from 0·7 μV to 700 μV

a)

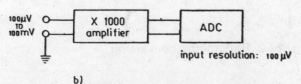

input resolution: 100 μV

b)

Fig. 14.3 (a) Signal conditioning: logarithmic compression of input;
(b) direct conversion without log operation

Such conditioning can be advantageous in systems possessing an output relationship involving the logarithm of the measurand or where a moderate accuracy measurement ($\simeq 1\%$) is desired over a wide range ($1 : 10^5$).

Since the log function is inherently unipolar, other types of compression can be employed when handling bipolar inputs. A particular case of interest is the $\sinh^{-1}$ function which can be obtained using complementary logarithmic transconductors[3].

14.3 SINGLE CHANNEL DATA ACQUISITION SYSTEM

A single channel data acquisition system consists of a signal conditioner followed by an analog to digital (A/D) converter, performing repetitive conversions at a free-running, internally-determined rate. The outputs are in digital code words, including "over-range" indication, polarity information, and a "status" output to indicate when the output digits are valid. As shown in Fig. 14.4, the digital outputs are further fed to a storage or print-out device, or to a digital computer for analysis.

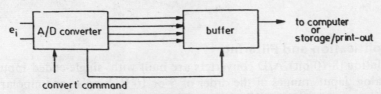

Fig. 14.4 Single channel data acquisition system

The popular digital panel meter (DPM) is a well-known example of this kind, though the sole purpose of digitizing in this case may be only to provide a numerical display. However, two major drawbacks exist in using them for data acquisition. The first is that it is slow and the binary coded decimal (BCD) digital coding has to be changed to binary, if the output is to be processed by a binary equipment. The second is that, while free-running, the data from the A/D converter is transferred to the interface register at a rate determined by the DPM itself, rather than by a command originating from the external interface.

A/D converters intended for data system applications are usually designed to receive external commands to convert and hold. For dc and low frequency signals, the converter is often a dual-slope type. This technique inherently has linear averaging capability and has null response for frequencies harmonically related to the integrating period. Generally, the integrating time is chosen to be equal to the period of the line frequency, since the major portion of system interference occurs at this frequency and its harmonics. For a 50 Hz line supply, the integrating period will be typically 20 ms and the maximum coversion rate achievable is about 20 to 30 conversions per second. For a 0.1% resolution, individual samples are valid to within 1 LSB (least significant bit) only when the maximum change in the average input is less than $\dfrac{dV}{dt}\Big|_{\max}$ where,

$$\frac{dV}{dt}\Big|_{\max} = \frac{(0.1\%)V_0}{20\ \text{ms}} = 0.5\ \text{V/s} \tag{14.1}$$

if the full-scale voltage V_0 is 10 V and the integration time is 20 ms.

While the A/D converters based on dual-slope techniques are useful for conversion of low-frequency data, such as from thermocouples, especially in the presence of noise, the most popular type of converter for data system applications is the "successive approximation" type since it is capable of high resolution and high speed at moderate cost. In this case, for a conversion time of 10 μs, the maximum dV/dt for 10 V full scale and 0.1% resolution is about 1 V/ms, which is a considerable improvement. Higher speeds are obtained by preceding the A/D converter with a sample-hold. The sample-hold is particularly required with successive approximation type A/D converters, since at higher rates of input change it generates substantial non-linearity errors because it cannot tolerate changes during the conversion process.

Direct digital conversion, carried out near the signal source is very advantageous in cases where the data needs to be transmitted through a noisy environment. Even with a high-level signal of 10 V, an 8-bit converter (1/256 resolution) can produce 1-bit ambiguity when affected by noise of the order of 40 mV (i.e., 10 V/256), whereas the TTL digital noise immunity is about 1.2 V($= 2$ V $- 0.8$ V). This amounts to a signal-to-noise ratio improvement of about 30:1.

14.3.1 Preamplification and Filtering

Many low resolution (8-10 bit) A/D converters are built with single-ended input, and have normalized analog input ranges of the order of 5 or 10 V, bipolar or unipolar. For signal levels which are low compared to the input requirements, amplification should be resorted to in order to bring up the level of the input to match the converter input requirements so that optimum use can be made of the capability of the A/D converter in terms of accuracy and resolution. The amplifier used has either a single-ended input or a differential input, as shown in Fig. 14.5. If the signal levels are below a few tens of millivolts, or when resolutions of 14 bit or 16 bit are sought, the use of differential amplifiers can become a necessity. When differential outputs have to be handled as from a bridge network, the use of three amplifier type differential input instrumentation amplifiers can become mandatory. The accuracy and linearity as well as gain stability specifications should be carefully considered to confirm that the system performance is not impaired because of these limitations.

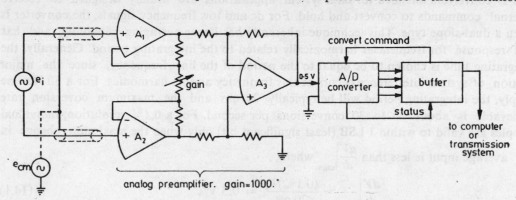

Fig. 14.5 DAS with preamplification

If input signals must be galvanically isolated from the system, the conductive paths are broken by using a transformer coupled or an optocoupled isolation amplifier (*see* Sec. 6. Chapter 11). These techniques offer advantages in handling signals from high-voltage sources and transmission towers. In biomedical applications, such isolation becomes essential.

Preamplifiers can be coupled with active filters before the process of data acquisition, in order to minimize the effect of noise, carriers, and interfering high-frequency components and for avoiding aliasing on conversion. They effectively compensate for transducer-sensitivity loss at high frequencies and thus enable measurements over an enhanced dynamic frequency range. Special-purpose filters, such as tracking filters are used for preserving phase-dependent data. In short, in system design, all data processing need not be digital. Analog circuits can perform data reduction effectively, reliably, and economically and should be considered as an alternative way for reducing the number of transmission channels, software complexity, noise, and perhaps the most important factor, cost.

14.4 MULTI-CHANNEL DATA ACQUISITION SYSTEM

The various sub-systems of the data-acquisition system can be time-shared by two or more input sources. Depending on the desired properties of the multiplexed system, a number of techniques are employed for such time-shared measurements. Large systems can combine several kinds of multiplexing and utilize, in addition, cascaded tiers of the same kind.

14.4.1 Multi-Channel Analog Multiplexed System

The conventional multi-channel data system has a single A/D converter preceded by a multiplexer, as shown in Fig. 14.6. The individual analog signals are applied directly, or after preamplification and/or signal-conditioning wherever necessary, to the multiplexer;

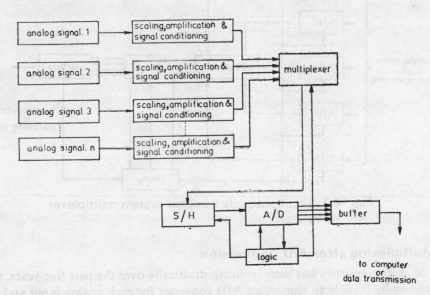

Fig. 14.6 Multi-channel data acquisition system using single A/D converter

these are further converted to digital signals by the A/D converter, sequentially. For most efficient utilization of time, the multiplexer is made to seek the next channel to be converted while the previous data stored in the sample-hold (S/H) is converted to digital form. When the conversion is complete, the status line from the converter causes the S/H to return to the sample mode and acquires the signal of the next channel. On completion of acquisition, either immediately or upon command, the S/H is switched to the hold mode; a conversion begins again and the multiplexer switch moves on to the subsequent channel. This method is relatively slower than systems where the S/H outputs or even A/D converter outputs are multiplexed, but it has the obvious advantage of having a lower cost due to the sharing of a majority of sub-systems. In cases where the signal variations are extremely slow, sufficient accuracy in measurement can be achieved even without the S/H.

14.4.2 Multiplexing the Outputs of Sample-Holds

When a large number of channels are to be monitored at the same time (i.e. synchronously) but at moderate speeds, the technique of multiplexing the outputs of the sample-hold is particularly attractive. An individual S/H is assigned to each channel, as illustrated in Fig. 14.7, and they are updated synchronously by a timing circuit. The sample-hold outputs are connected to an A/D converter through a multiplexer, resulting in sequential read-out of the outputs. Applications that might require this approach include wind-tunnel measurements, seismographic experimentation, and radar and fire control systems. The event to be measured is often a one-shot phenomenon and the information is required at a critical point during a one-shot event, e.g., when a supersonic air blast hits the scaled model of an aircraft in a wind tunnel.

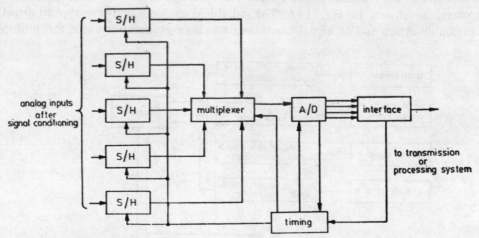

Fig. 14.7 Simultaneously sampled system multiplexer

14.4.3 Multiplexing after A/D Conversion

The cost of A/D converters has been reducing drastically over the past five years, and today it is economically feasible to employ an A/D converter for each analog input and multiplex the digital outputs. Since each ADC is assigned to an individual channel, the conversion rate of the ADC need be only as fast as is needed for that channel, compared to the higher rates that would be needed if it were used as in Sec. 14.4.1. The reduced conversion rate can mean using lower cost ADCs, and due to this the system cost may not be significantly different from that employing a scheme as in Sec. 14.4.1.

The parallel conversion scheme, as shown in Fig. 14.8 provides additional advantage in industrial data acquisition systems where many strain gauges, thermocouples, and LVDTs are distributed over a large plant area. Since the analog signals are digitized at the source, the digital transmission of the data to the data centre (from where it can go on to a communication channel) can provide enhanced immunity against line frequency and other ground-loop interferences.

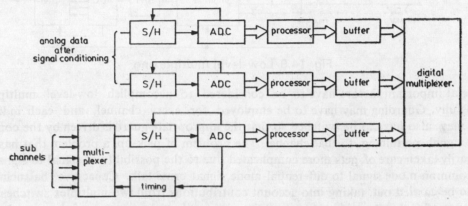

Fig. 14.8 Multi-channel DAS using digital multiplexing

The data which are converted to digital form are used to perform logic operations and decisions so that, based on the relative speed at which changes occur in the data, scanning rate can also be increased or decreased. Alternatively, input channels having slowly varying data can be premultiplexed in any of the forms suggested earlier so that a set of sequentially multiplexed sub-channels can then replace one channel of the main digital multiplex system as indicated in Fig. 14.8.

The ADC outputs are sometimes passed through a processor which acts on the data in a prespecified manner to produce a digital word corresponding to a function of the data input, e.g., the running average or rate of change.

14.4.4. Multiplexing Low-Level Data

A low-level multiplexing system, as shown in Fig. 14.9 enables the use of a single high-quality data amplifier for handling multi-channel low-level inputs. While the present-day availability of high-quality amplifiers at moderate cost does allow the use of individual amplifiers for each low-level signal, low-level multiplexing can be attractive when a large number of channels (twenty-five or more) all having low-level outputs need to be monitored at moderate speeds. A typical application is a 200 channel stress measurement system in a transmission tower test set-up.

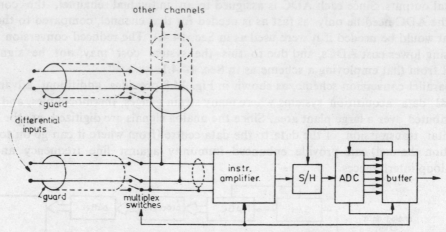

Fig. 14.9 Low-level multiplexing

Several important factors have to be considered to accomplish low-level multiplexing successfully. Guarding may have to be employed for every channel, and each individual guard may also have to be switched so that the appropriate guard is driven by the common-mode signal pertaining to that channel. The problem of pick-up, a problem that has to be necessarily taken care of, gets more complicated due to the possibility of signal to signal, and even common-mode signal to differential-mode signal cross-talk. Capacitive balancing may have to be carried out, taking into account contributions from two multiplex switches.

The use of a programmable gain amplifier enables the enhancement of the signal range. With a 12-bit converter, for example, a resolution of 2.5 mV is typical for a normalized full-scale input of 10 V. When the input level is about 1 V, a gain of 10 in the programmable gain amplifier yields an equivalent resolution of $\dfrac{2.5 \text{ mV}}{10} = 250 \ \mu\text{V}$ at the input. For low-level input signals, the resolution can be improved to $\simeq 32 \ \mu\text{V}$ by switching the gain of the amplifier to 80. (This is comparable to the resolution of a 15-bit converter). Auto-ranging preamplifiers also result in a wide input signal range, e.g., a few μV to about 1 V, a range exceeding 100 dB.

When the number of channels to be multiplexed increases, the problems of stray capacitance and capacitive unbalance are worsened by the parasitic capacitance of the off channels. A practical solution is to use two tiers of multiplexers. In a specific case of a 48 channel system, the input channels are subdivided into groups of eight channels in the first tier. Each of these six subgroups are in turn multiplexed by a six channel multiplexer in the second tier. The main advantage in this case is the reduction of capacitance effects[4].

14.4.5 Present Trends in Data Acquisition Systems

The data system manufacturers are constantly endeavouring to reduce the size and design time of systems and make modular systems with high versatility. A typical example is the Burr Brown SDM 853 which is a complete modular data-acquisition system, as shown in

Fig. 14.10 containing all the components necessary to multiplex and convert ±10 V analog data into equivalent digital outputs yielding resolutions of 2.4 μV to 2.4 mV. For 12-bit conversion a throughput rate of up to 30 kHz is possible. The DAS contains an analog multiplexer (8-channel differential or 16-channel single-ended), an instrumentation amplifier, sample/hold, 12-bit successive approximation ADC, and programming logic. The unit is intended for mounting on a printed-circuit board and requires ±15 V (75 mA) and ±5 V (300 mA) power supplies for operation.

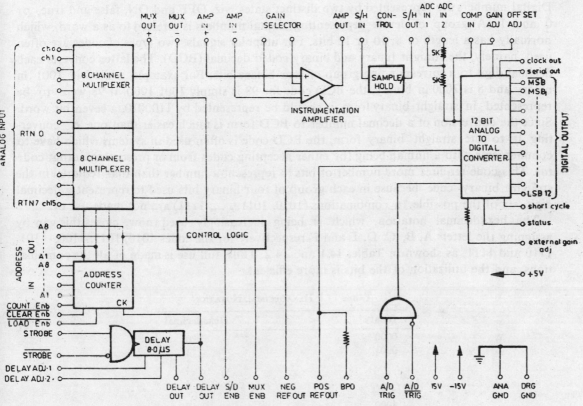

Fig. 14.10 Modular data acquisition system

The ability to accept and multiplex low-level or high-level signals, and the capability of expansion of input channels using additional multiplexers enhance the flexibility of the system. While a cost advantage of 1 : 4 is claimed when compared with other systems using similar individual components, the size of 117 × 76 × 9.5 mm is certainly a distinct advantage. With the advent of microprocessors and associated processing and control, micro-peripheral analog input-output systems (e.g., Burr Brown, Type MP 2216) and micro-computer analog input-output systems (e.g., Burr Brown, Type MP 4102) are steadily gaining importance, both from the point of view of overall system reliability and cost, as well as flexibility and future modification.

14.5 DATA CONVERSION

Analog voltage outputs of electrical transducers are converted to the digital form with analog to digital (A/D) converters in data transmission and digital signal processing. The processed digital outputs can be converted back to analog signals using digital to analog (D/A) converters, for control or further processing and display (e.g., a graph).

14.5.1 Digital Codes

Digital numbers are represented by two distinct states, viz, OFF and ON, false and true, or 0 and 1. A group of levels representing digital numbers is referred to as a word, which normally has a length of 8, 10 or 12 bits. For unipolar signals, two types of codes are often used, namely, the straight binary and binary coded decimal (BCD). The latter converts each decimal digit to a corresponding group of four binary bits. For example, while 9 is 1001 in binary and 8 is 1000 in binary, the BCD code for 98 is simply 1001 1000. If 98 were to be represented in straight binary form, it should be represented by 1100010, a seven bit word. Since the conversion of a decimal number to BCD form is much easier than one of converting it to the straight binary form, the BCD code is often used in systems which have to communicate with a human being (by either accepting codes from or presenting output code to). This code requires more number of bits to represent a number than that required in the straight binary code because in each group of four binary bits used to represent a decimal digit, six of the possible 16 combinations (1010, 1011, . . ., 1111) are not made use of.

The hexadecimal notation, which is being increasingly used now, closes this gap by assigning the letters A, B, C, D, E and F respectively for the codes 1010, 1011, 1100, 1101, 1110 and 1111, as shown in Tables 14.1 and 14.2. Thus, full use is made of all the combinations, and the utilization of the bits is more efficient.

TABLE 14.1 HEXADECIMAL NOTATION

Binary	Hexadecimal
0000	0
0001	1
.	.
.	.
.	.
1000	8
1001	9
1010	A
1011	B
1100	C
1101	D
1110	E
1111	F

Codes for Bipolar Signals

For the representation of bipolar signals, four types of codes are normally used, viz., sign magnitude, two's complement, one's complement, and offset binary. The resulting codes and the manner in which they are related for decimal numbers from +7 to −8 are shown in Table 14.3.

TABLE 14.2 HEXADECIMAL CODES, EXAMPLES

Decimal	Hexadecimal	Straight binary
11	0B	0000 1011
16	10	0001 0000
32	20	0010 0000
65	41	0100 0001
79	4F	0100 1111
252	FC	1111 1100

TABLE 14.3 BIPOLAR CODES

Number	Decimal fraction	Sign + magnitude	One's complement	Two's complement	Offset binary
+7	7/8	0111	0111	0111	1111
+6	6/8	0110	0110	0110	1110
+5	5/8	0101	0101	0101	1101
+4	4/8	0100	0100	0110	1100
+3	3/8	0011	0011	0011	1011
+2	2/8	0010	0010	0010	1010
+1	1/8	0001	0001	0001	1001
0	0+	0000	0000	0000	1000
0	0−	1000	1111	(0000)	(1000)
−1	−1/8	1001	1110	1111	0111
−2	−2/8	1010	1101	1110	0110
−3	−3/8	1011	1100	1101	0101
−4	−4/8	1100	1011	1100	0100
−5	−5/8	1101	1010	1011	0011
−6	−6/8	1110	1001	1010	0010
−7	−7/8	1111	1000	1001	0001
−8	−8/8			(1000)	(0000)

In sign magnitude representation, a '0' in the sign bit signifies positive polarity and a '1' signifies negative polarity. In one's complement representation, the codes for positive polarity are identical to those in sign-magnitude representation, but the codes for negative polarity are obtained as one's complement of the codes representing the same value in positive polarity. In offset binary, as the name implies, the code for zero is offset so that the negative full scale is identified with the all-zero code. In two's complement notation, the codes for negative polarity are obtained as two's complement of the code for the corresponding positive value. This is also equivalent to complementing the code as in one's complement and adding a '1'.

The various codes have come into vogue either due to the ease of generation or ease of computation. In many bipolar digital voltmeters, the sign magnitude BCD is the code that is popularly used. The main drawback is that it is not directly usable for computation—additional software or hardware becomes necessary to digitally interface it with computers. The offset binary is the easiest code to employ with converter circuitry. Except for the fact that the negative full scale is made to correspond to the zero code, the code is really a natural binary code. Besides this ease of implementation, the offset binary has further advantages in that it is compatible with computer input and output, is easily convertible to the more computationally useful two's complement (obtained by merely complementing the MSB), and has a single unambiguous code for zero. The all-zero negative full-scale code is also useful as a converter-checking and adjustment code. The main drawback is that a major-bit transition occurs at 0. This can lead to "glitch" problems dynamically and to linearity problems statically[5]. In addition, the zero errors may be greater than that with sign magnitude because the zero analog level is obtained by taking the difference between the most-significant bit (half-full range) and a bias (half-full range), both of them being two large numbers.

Computationally, the most attractive code is the two's complement. Since the two's complement can be thought of as a set of negative numbers, subtraction is easily performed as this is equivalent to addition of the complement. For example, to subtract 2/8 from 7/8, add 1110 (corresponding to −2/8) to 0111, yielding 0101, i.e. 5/8 (disregarding the extra carry). A comparison of the two's complement code and the offset binary code shows that the MSB of one is its complement in the other. Since both a digit and its complement are available from most flip flops, the conversion of one code to another is easy. The two's complement has the same disadvantages as those of offset binary since the conversion process is on the same lines.

The one's complement is another means of representing negative numbers used by computers. When a number is subtracted by adding its 1's complement, the extra carry (that is disregarded in 2's complement), if present, causes 1 LSB to be added to the total (this is termed as "end-around carry"). Thus, 4/8 is subtracted from 7/8 to give 1011+0111 = 0010 +0001 = 0011 (or 3/8). Besides its ambiguous zero (0000 or 1111), another disadvantage of this code is that in conversion, the implementation of this code is more complex than the two's complement.

The modified sign magnitude and modified one's complement codes are obtained by complementing the MSB in the sign magnitude and one's complement codes respectively.

14.6 DIGITAL TO ANALOG CONVERTER

A basic digital to analog converter consists of a voltage reference, a network of precision-weighted resistors, and a set of switches with their states (ON or OFF) dependent on the input digital code. In a typical circuit, as shown in Fig. 14.11(a) the switches S_1 to S_4 are operated by the input digital binary code. The resulting weighted input currents are summed up by the opamp and converted to an equivalent dc voltage proportional to the magnitude of the voltage the code represents. (Note that an inversion results from the opamp configuration in Fig. 14.11(a).) The input resistors are weighted in 8, 4, 2, 1 sequence corresponding to the weight assigned to the bits in the digital code.

With reference to Fig. 14.11(a), while a next lower significant digit in the straight binary code would be assigned a value of 160 kohm, the weight for the MSB of the next lower significant group of four bits in a BCD code would be 100 kohms. In the case of a 12 bit binary code, if the MSB weighting resistor is 10 kohms, the LSB weighting resistor would be 10 kohms $\times$ 4096 $\simeq$ 41 Megaohms. Hence, the use of this simple D/A conversion arrangement results in the need for a wide range of precision resistors; this range will be

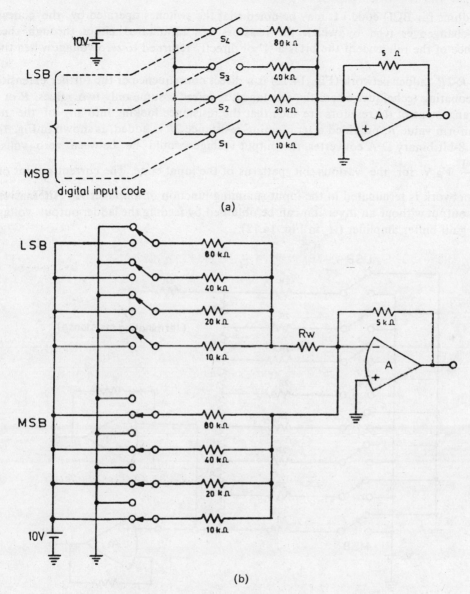

Fig. 14.11 Digital to analog converter: (a) four bit D/A converter; (b) grouping of codes to reduce spread of precision resistors

totally impractical if the resistors are to be manufactured using thin- or thick-film technology.

One of the methods to reduce the resistance range is to attenuate the effective reference voltage being applied to the resistors in the lower significant bit positions. Alternatively, the digital code is grouped as a set of four bits, and the outputs of such four bit groups are summed after appropriate weighting as shown in Fig. 14.11(b). Depending on the code used, the value of the weighting resistor R_W can be chosen. ($R_W = 80$ kohms for binary code and

= 48 kohms for BCD code.) It may be noted that the switches operated by the codes are of the changeover type by which the resistors are terminated either through the low impedance of the reference if the bit is a '1' or directly returned to zero voltage when the bit is a '0'.

The R-$2R$ ladder network (Fig. 14.12) is a direct consequence of the further extension of this attenuating technique, where the resistances required assume only two values, R or $2R$. The arrangement of the resistors are such that the resistance looking into any of the nodes is a uniform value R, provided a terminating resistance $2R$ is added, as shown in Fig. 14.12. For the 8-bit binary D/A converter, the output voltage would lie between zero volts and $-\dfrac{2^8-1}{2^8} V_R$ V for the various bit patterns of the input code. The current output of the ladder network is terminated in the input summing junction of amplifier A_1. Alternatively, a voltage output without an inversion can be obtained by feeding the ladder output voltage to a unity gain buffer amplifier (A_2 in Fig. 14.12).

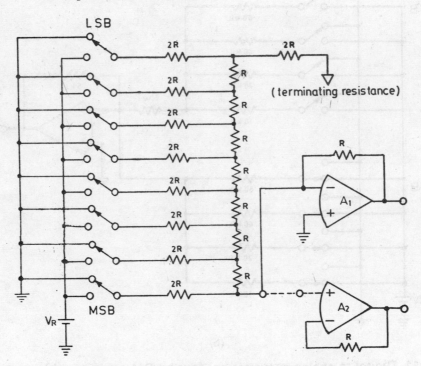

Fig. 14.12 DAC using R-$2R$ network

For the voltage switches shown in the D/A converters of Figs. 14.11 and 14.12, either field effect transistors or bipolar transistors (in inverted mode) can be used to perform the switching action[6]. However, for fast D/A converters where high-speed switching is necessary, current switches are preferred. The advantage is that the reference current is not interrupted as a consequence of code changes, and significant voltage changes appear only at the output and not across the switches. A simplified form of the current switch is shown in Fig. 14.13(a). While a constant current I_R flows through the reference transistor Q_R, weighted currents of

$\dfrac{V_R}{2R}$, $\dfrac{V_R}{4R}$, $\dfrac{V_R}{8R}$, ... flow through transistors Q_1, Q_2, Q_3 ... respectively if the input code

is a "1". (V_R is the reference zener voltage.) When the code becomes a "0", the corresponding diode conducts, "stealing" the current of the respective transistor and thus making it "cut

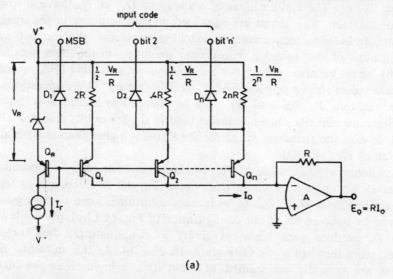

(a)

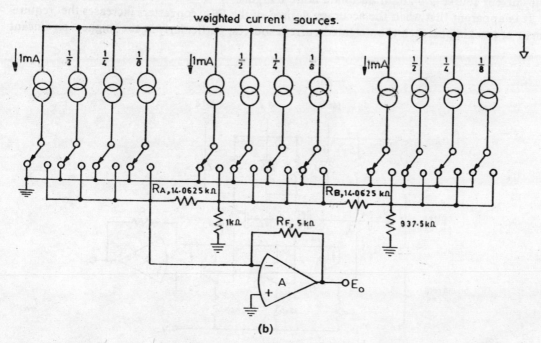

(b)

Fig. 14.13 Digital to analog conversion techniques: (a) DAC using basic current switching technique; (b) 12-bit straight binary DAC using weighted quad current sources

off". With the common base line maintained at about 1.4 V, and assuming 0.6 V diode conduction voltage, the TTL '0' and '1' levels of 0.8 V max. and 2 V min. respectively can directly control the condition of the switched current source. Since the current is not interrupted and the voltage change is small, switching time is quite short (typical settling time to within 1 LSB $\simeq$ 200 ns). The emitter areas of transistors Q_1 to Q_n have a power-of-two relationship so that the V_{BE} drops are equalized, in turn resulting in the tracking of V_{BE} with temperature. In order to reduce current matching problems, the current switches are also used in groups of four (quads), with proper weighting of the lesser significant quads. Figure 14.13(b) shows an arrangement for a 12-bit current switching D/A converter wherein the component values shown provide 12-bit straight binary D/A operation. For BCD operation, the resistors R_A, R_B and R_f may be changed to 8.1325, 8.4375 and 4 kohms respectively[7]. Since the effective current sources used in the lower bits also are always in the range of 1 to 1/16 mA, the switching speed for the LSB's is higher than that obtainable from the configuration of Fig. 14.13(a).

The simple switching configuration of Fig. 14.13(a) is not adequate for obtaining an accuracy better than 12 bits and a wide temperature operation, due to errors arising from the leakage currents in the diodes D_1 to D_n. In such cases, additional logic buffering as shown in Fig. 14.14 has to be resorted to. In the configuration of Fig. 14.13(a), the diode capacitances across D_1 to D_n produce such transient errors by coupling input data transients to the current sources, when they are in the OFF state. In Fig. 14.14, the currents through the buffer switches are typically maintained at about 10% or higher than the currents in the bit-current sources, to attain adequate noise margins.

It is apparent that when the accuracy desired of the D/A converters increases the requirement of tracking between the weighted current sources, particularly in the higher significant

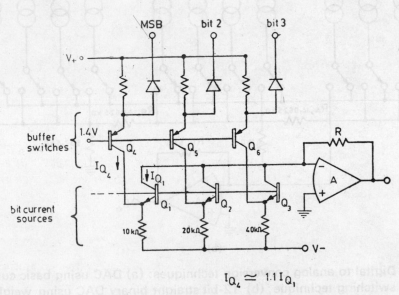

$$I_{Q_4} \simeq 1.1 I_{Q_1}$$

Fig. 14.14 Logic buffering in DAC

quads becomes stringent. The same applies to the weighting resistors used for 8-4-2-1 weighting of current used in any quad, and to those used in interquad weighting networks. Monolithic quad current sources and monolithic thin-film resistor arrays are thus invariably used when the accuracy exceeds about 10 bits. Typical quad current sources which are commercially available are the Analog Devices, AD 550 and AD 551 and Fairchild 9650. Monolithic thin-film resistor arrays having temperature coefficients tracking to within 2 ppm are available as AD 850 and AD 851 (Analog Devices) and RA 15 (National Semiconductors).

14.6.1 DAC with Memory

The basic DAC circuit has the characteristic that the analog output continually reflects the state of the input digital code. When a DAC is desired to respond only at selected time instants to the input digital code and memorize (infinite holding) the output until the next "update" occurs, it is necessary to incorporate an additional memory register at the input so that the input digital code can be "strobed" into the memory and held at desired time instants, as shown in Fig. 14.15. The maximum rate at which a logic input can be meaningfully "strobed" into the buffer memory is limited mainly by the settling time of the DAC. DACs incorporating memory buffers are particularly useful in data acquisition systems handling data from remote locations using serial transmission.

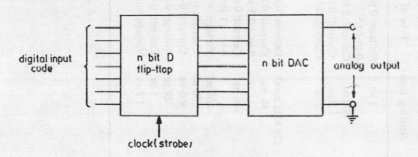

Fig. 14.15 DAC with memory buffer

14.6.2 Multiplying DACs

When the reference current or voltage used within a DAC is made variable according to an external input voltage, the output corresponds to the product of the input code and the reference control voltage. Such multiplying DACs are useful in ratiometric systems, computing systems, and for scale-factor adjustments.

14.6.3 Commercial DACs

Many types of DACs of various speed and resolution are available commercially. Brief details of some of the important commercial DACs are given in Table 14.4.

TABLE 14.4 COMPARISON OF COMMERCIAL DACs

Type No. & Make	Resolution	Settling time	Type of output	Comments
AD 558, Analog Devices	8	1 μs	Voltage: 0 to 2.56 V or 0 to 10 V	IC, digital buffered, single supply
AD 7533 -do-	10	600 ns	Current: 0 to 2 mA	CMOS IC; 4 quadrant multiplying, low cost
AD 563 -do-	12	1.5 μs	Current: 0 to 2 mA	12 bit accuracy; low cost
AD 7542 -do-	12	2 μs	Current: 0 to ±0.7 mA	CMOS IC; 4 quadrant multiplying; 4- or 8-bit μp compatible; double buffered; low power, single supply
AD 7110 -do-	14	(20 kHz max)	External opamp required	Digitally-controlled audio attenuator
DAC 60-10 Burr Brown	10	40 ns	Current: 0 to −5 mA or 0 to ±2.5 mA	Very high speed
DAC 80 CBI-I -do-	12	300 ns	Current: 0 to −2 mA or 0 to ±1 mA	Low cost
4800 -do-	12	100 ns	Voltage: ±10 V to ±60 V	Power DAC; providing ±200 mA current capability
DAC 70.CSBI -do-	16	50 ns	Current: 0 to −2 mA	High resolution
DAC 98BI, Datel Intersil	8	500 ns	Current: 0−2 mA	Low cost
DAC 198B -do-	8	20 μs	Voltage: 0 to 10 V or ±5 V	Voltage-output type
DAC HA 12 BC -do-	12	5 μs	Current: 0 to ±0.5 mA	Precision DAC. CMOS; Low power
DAC 03 ADX-1 Precision Monolithic	10	1.5 μs	Voltage output: 0 to 10 V	Low power

14.7 ANALOG TO DIGITAL CONVERTERS

While a variety of circuit designs are available for executing analog to digital conversion, by far the most popular of these employ the following techniques:

(a) Successive approximation
(b) Single- and dual-slope integration
(c) Voltage-to-frequency conversion
(d) Counter and servo
(e) Parallel conversion.

The decision as to which type of A/D converter is best suited for a particular application will have to be made based on speed, accuracy, cost, size, and the inherent noise reduction capability.

14.7.1 Successive Approximation Method

The successive approximation method of A/D conversion is capable of both high resolution as well as high speed (throughput rates exceeding 1 MHz). Each conversion is independent of the results of previous ones, and the conversion time is constant and independent of the magnitude of the input voltage.

The converter proceeds to convert the analog input by finding a 'Yes' or 'No' answer for the following sequence of questions:

(a) Is the input greater than half the full scale?
(b) (i) Is the input greater than one-fourth of the full scale? or (ii) Is the input greater than three-fourth of the full scale?

[If the answer to (a) is 'No', check for (b) (i); if "Yes", check for (b) (ii)].

This procedure is continued until the desired resolution is obtained. For an N bit converter, N such questions are asked and the resolution obtained is one in 2^N. The time taken for the conversion is N clock periods and is the same irrespective of the magnitude of the input. A simplified schematic diagram of this type of converter is shown in Fig. 14.16. Initially, the shift register is cleared and on "start conversion" command, a "1" is stored in the MSB. The resulting D/A converter output is compared with the analog input. Depending on the decision of the comparator ("1" if analog input is greater than the D/A converter output, and "0" otherwise), a "1" or "0" is assigned to the MSB and a "1" is stored in the next lower bit. Again, the D/A converter output is compared with the analog input and the earlier procedure is continued. After the last bit has been tried, the "status" line changes state to indicate that the contents of the output register now constitute the valid output of the conversion process. A digital binary code corresponding to the input signal is thus available at the output.

While for slowly-varying signals the input can be considered to be constant over the period of conversion, difficulties arise if the rate of change of input is high, thereby resulting in a change of level during conversion. In such a case, the result of the conversion is invalid. To avoid this situation it is necessary to incorporate a sample-hold circuit ahead of the converter so that the input to the comparator is held constant throughout the conversion period. The S/H can be conveniently operated by the "status" output of the converter.

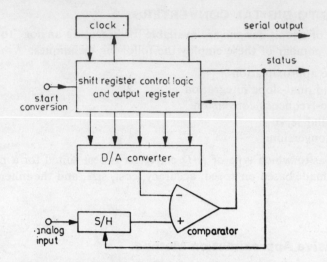

Fig. 14.16 A/D conversion using successive approximation technique

Accuracy, speed, and linearity of this A/D converter are directly dependent on those of the D/A converter and comparator. The throughput rate is generally limited by the settling time of the DAC and the response time of the comparator. Many commercial A/D converters (e.g., Burr Brown ADC 60 series and ADC 80 series, Analog Devices ADC 7570, ADC 1130, etc.) and particularly those recommended for interfacing with computers are designed based on the successive approximation technique.

14.7.2 Single- and Dual-Slope Integration

Single- and dual-slope integration techniques are basically indirect methods of conversion wherein the input voltage is converted to a proportional time period. This period is in turn used to gate a high-frequency clock signal so that a digital representation is obtained. Figure 14.17 shows the schematic diagram of an A/D converter using the single-slope

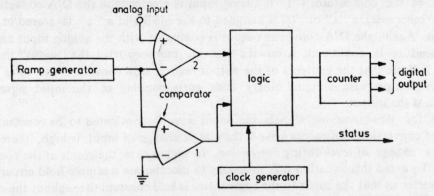

Fig. 14.17 A/D conversion using single slope integration technique

technique. A ramp waveform that swings from below zero volts to a few volts more than the maximum input voltage is applied to two comparators. The comparator 1 output goes high as the ramp voltage becomes positive, and the output of comparator 2 goes low when the ramp voltage exceeds the input voltage. The time period τ, between these transitions is proportional to the input voltage for a fixed ramp rate. By gating a clock during this period τ and counting the gated output, a digital output corresponding to the input voltage is obtained.

The accuracy and stability of this technique is directly dependent on those of the ramp slope and clock frequency. The accuracy achievable is often in the range of 0.1 to 1% (equivalent to 10 bit and lower).

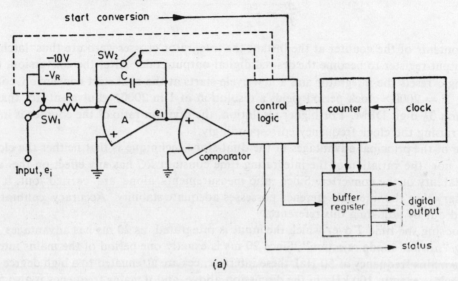

(a)

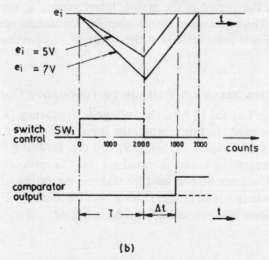

(b)

Fig. 14.18 Dual-slope integration type ADC:
(a) schematic; (b) waveforms

A powerful technique capable of providing accuracy in the range of 0.1 to 0.001% and popularly used in many DPMs (digital panel meters) and DVMs is the dual-slope A/D conversion technique. Using an internal-clock frequency of about 100 kHz, a counter with a division ratio of 2000 provides a time period T of 20 ms during which the input to be measured is gated into an initially reset integrator, as shown in Fig. 14.18(a). At the end of this time period, instead of the external input, an internal stable reference (of opposite polarity) is gated in as the input. At the end of the duration Δt after the reference was gated in, the integrator crosses zero as indicated in Fig. 14.18(b). The time interval Δt can be related to T by the equation

$$\frac{\Delta t}{T} = \frac{e_i}{V_R}$$

The contents of the counter at the instant the integrator crosses zero are thus latched into the output register to become the desired digital output code. After the conversion, the control logic resets the integrator and a new cycle starts at the next start conversion command. Using $T = 2000 \times$ clock period yields a resolution of 1 in 2000, equivalent to that of the common $3\frac{1}{2}$ digit DPM. For higher resolution, the division ratio of the counter is increased, often raising the clock frequency correspondingly.

One of the principal advantages of the dual-slope technique is that neither the clock stability nor the variation of the integrating time constant RC has any effect on the accuracy and stability of the converter. Since ratio measurements alone are carried out, it is only necessary that the internal reference possesses adequate stability. Accuracy calibrations are carried out by adjusting this reference.

Choosing the time T over which the input is integrated as 20 ms has advantages of providing "normal mode rejection". Since 20 ms is exactly one period of the mains interference (with a mains frequency of 50 Hz), these interferences are attenuated to a high degree ($\cong \infty$ if the clock is exactly 100 kHz in the discussion above, and if mains frequency is also 50.0 Hz). If T is within $\pm 1\%$ of the period of the mains interference, a normal mode rejection of about 40 dB results. The rejection is even higher for harmonics present in the interference[8]. The typical conversion rate achievable is in the range of 20 conversions/second.

14.7.3 A/D Converters based on Voltage-to-Frequency Conversion

For accuracies less than about 12 bits, the voltage-to-frequency (V/F) conversion type A/D converter is extensively used. In this scheme, the input is converted to an equivalent frequency by a V/F converter (see Chapter 12, Sec. 5.9) and the resulting frequency is measured in a counter. Since an integrating action is involved in the process, high immunity against periodic interfering signals can be obtained by making the gating time equal to $n \times$ period of the interfering signal, where n is an integer. Using high frequency V/F converters (e.g., 1 MHz), conversion rates exceeding 200 per second can be achieved.

14.7.4 Counter and Servo Types

The typical arrangement used for an A/D converter of this type is shown in Fig. 14.19. The control logic initially resets the counter and on "start conversion command" it opens a gate allowing the counter to start. The output of the D/A converter which is fed by this counter is compared with the analog input continuously, and when the D/A converter output equals the analog input, the comparator inhibits further passage of clock pulses to the counter. The counter output (fed to the output register) forms the digital output of the A/D converter. A primary disadvantage of this type of converter is, again, the speed of conversion. With 10 MHz clock frequency, a conversion time of about 200 μs is required for a 1 in 2000 resolution ($3\frac{1}{2}$ digit) A/D conversion. Depending on the type of counter used, the output can be in direct binary or BCD form.

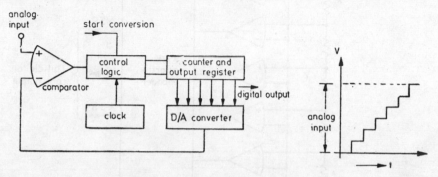

Fig. 14.19 'Counter and servo' type ADC

A variation of this technique is the servo type wherein, using an updown counter controlling a D/A converter, the D/A converter output is forced to track the input signal. When the input signal is less than the D/A converter output, the counter is in the "count up" mode, and when the input signal exceeds the D/A converter output, the counter reverts to the "count down" mode. If the analog input is constant, the D/A converter "hunts" between two adjacent bit values. An advantage is that small changes are rapidly followed by the converter, though full-scale step changes require the full count time before the output becomes valid. A buffer storage register may often be necessary to store the results of a previous conversion, while the counter attempts to "servo" onto the next value. If the "up" or "down" count of the counter is disabled, the counter can also act as a "valley" or "peak" follower.

14.7.5 Parallel Types

In the parallel type of A/D conversion, the input is simultaneously compared with the various reference voltages which are one LSB apart, as shown in Fig. 14.20. The outputs of these comparators are then logically combined to give the output digital code by the priority encoder which puts out the digital code for the highest-order input received by it. An obvious advantage of this type of converter is that very high speed of conversion is possible, since speed is only limited by the switching time of the comparators and gates. The complexity is of course the main disadvantage. For 4-bit resolution, 15 comparators and two 8-bit priority encoders are required, and for 5-bit resolution, 31 comparators and four 8-bit encoders are needed. For higher resolutions, the increased cost makes the technique prohibitive. A compromise yielding better resolution at lesser cost is possible by a proper combination of the parallel conversion technique and successive approximation method.

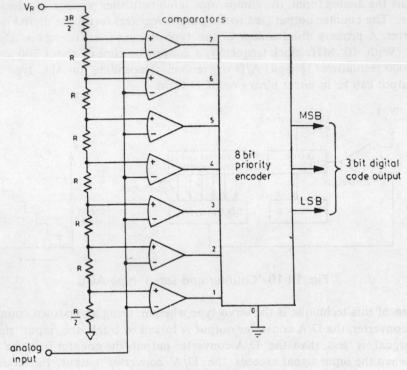

Fig. 14.20 Parallel type, 3-bit, ADC

14.7.6 Comparison of Commercial ADC's

Various commercial models of ADCs are available from reputed manufacturers, such as Analog Devices, Burr Brown and Datel-Intersil. A chart giving brief details of some of these is given in Table 14.5. More details of the various types (some are not included in the table) can be obtained from the manufacturers' catalogues.

14.7.7 A/D Converter Terminology

In order that an A/D converter desired for a specific job can be ordered for from a manufacturer or be developed by a design department, a clear understanding of the various specifications becomes a necessity. The specifications for a standard A/D converter are given in Table 14.6. Some of the terms that aid understanding of the specification are given below.

Absolute Accuracy

The *absolute accuracy* error of the converter is the tolerance of the full-scale set point

TABLE 14.5 COMPARISON OF COMMERCIAL ANALOG TO DIGITAL CONVERTERS

Principle	Type No. & Make	No. of bits	Conversion time	Input	Power	Comments
Successive approxn.	AD 570 Analog Devices	8	25 µs	±5 V 0 to 10 V	+5 V, 5 mA −15 V, 10 mA	Self-contained clock and comparator
-do-	AD 572 Analog Devices	12	25 µs	±5 V 0 to 10 V	±15 V, 25 mA 5 V, 50 mA	±0.012% max, non-linearity
-do-	AD 574 Analog Devices	12	25 µs	±5 V, 0 to 10 V	5 V, 30 mA +15 V, 2 mA −15 V, 20 mA	3-state output for µp interface
-do-	AD 578 Analog Devices	12	4 µs	±5 V, ±10 V	5 V, 80 mA +15 V, 3 mA −15 V, 25 mA	Very fast
Integrating, quadslope	AD 7555 Analog Devices	5½ digits 200,000 counts	200 ms	±5 V	±5 V, 5 mA	CMOS Integrating type, slow
Integrating, quadslope	AD 7583 Analog Devices	8	4 ms	0 to 12 V	5 V, 2 mA 12 V, 2 V mA	Multi-channel (nine channels) single supply, integrating type, medium speed
Successive approxn.	ADC 60-08 Burr Brown	8	0.88 µs	±10 V, ±5 V, ±2.5 V, 0 to 20 V, 0 to 10 V	±15 V, 50 mA +5 V, 270 mA	Very high speed
Successive approxn.	ADC 80 AG-10 Burr Brown	10	21 µs	±2.5, ±5 V, ±10 V 0 to 10 V	±15 V, 20 mA +5 V, 70 mA	Low cost
Integrating Delta sigma modulation	ADC 100 USB Burr Brown	16	50 ms	±10 V	±15 V, 25 mA +5 V, 300 mA	High resolution Medium speed
Integrating	ADC ET 12 BM Datel Intersil	12	24 ms	±5 V 0 to 10 V	±5 V, 3.5 mA	Low power CMOS, Tristate output
Fast dual slope	ADC E 10 B Datel Intersil	10	1.25 ms	±1 V, ±5 V, ±10 V	±15 V, 50 mA +5 V, 150 mA	Differential input, high input impedance (100 MΩ)
Successive approxn.	ADCH×12 BMM Datel Intersil	12	20 µs	0 to 5 V, 0 to 10 V, ±2.5 V	±15 V, 55 mA +5 V, 100 mA	Fast, high accuracy type
Successive approxn.	AD-02 Precision Monolithics	8	8 µs	±5 V, ±10 V ±2.5 V, ±5 V ±10 V, 0 to 5 mA, 0 to 10 V	±15 V, 12 mA +5 V, 30 mA	Low power, high speed

TABLE 14.6 SPECIFICATIONS OF AN A/D CONVERTER

Parameter	Specifications
Model	ADC-QU Analog Devices
ADC 10 QU	10 bits
ADC 12 QU	12 bits
Accuracy: Relative	±1/2 LSB
Quantization	±1/2 LSB
Monotonicity	Monotonic from 0°C to +70°C
Differential Linearity	±1/2 LSB
Differential Linearity TC	±3 ppm/°C max (ADC—12 QU)
Temperature Coefficient: Gain	±5 ppm/°C of Range
Zero	±50 μ V/°C
Long term stability of linearity	±1/2 LSB
Conversion time: ADC—10 QU	8 μs max
12 QU	15 μs max
	(from trailing edge of convert command to "1→0" change of status signal)
Input voltage ranges	±5 V, ±10 V, 0 to +10 V, 0 to +5 V
Input Impedance: Buffer	100 megohms, min.
Direct—0 to +10 V, or ±5 V	5 kohms
±10 V	10 kohms
Input Trigger (convert command)	Positive pulse, 100 ns wide, min.
	Leading edge ("0" to "1") resets previous data
	Trailing edge ("1" to "0") initiates conversion
	TTL/DTL compatible, 1 TTL/DTL load
Output Signals	Parallel TTL/DTL compatible 4 TTL loads per bit
	Serial, RZ, TTL compatible, 1 TTL load
Output levels: 0	+0.4 V TTL Compatible
1	2.4 V
Status	'1' during conversion, 10 TTL loads
Status complement	'0' during conversion, 4 TTL loads
Power (separate analog and digital ground)	+15 V ±3%, +25 mA—(Analog)
	−15 V ±3%, −50 mA
	+5 V ±5%, 300 mA—(Digital)
Power Supply Sensitivity	±0.002%/% ΔV_s, for ±15 V only
Temperature range: Operating	0 to +70°C
Storage	−55°C to +125°C
Adjustment (with external potentiometers): Zero	100 kohm potentiometer across ± 15 V supply, with slider connected to pin 20 through 3 MΩ
Gain	100 kohm potentiometer across ±15 V supply, with slider connected to pin 1 through 30 kΩ
Dimensions	5 cm × 10 cm × 1 cm, nominal

referred to an absolute voltage standard. The full-scale point of a converter is adjusted by the manufacturer with reference to a recognized voltage standard.

Acquisition Time

The acquisition time is the time taken by a sample-hold circuit to acquire the input signal within a stated accuracy. Since the output of a sample-hold is not meaningful until it has settled, the specifications should normally also include the settling time of the output amplifier.

Conversion Time

The conversion time refers to the time required for a complete measurement by an analog to digital converter.

Differential Linearity

The variation in the analog value of transition between adjacent pairs of digital numbers over the full range of digital input or output in a converter is specified by differential linearity. If the maximum differential non-linearity is $\pm 1/2$ LSB, the converter has a monotonic behaviour. Non-monotonic D/A converters can lead to missing codes in A/D converters based on them.

Droop Rate

When a sample-hold circuit using a capacitor for storage is in the "hold" mode, the information cannot be held forever. The rate at which the output voltage changes is termed the droop rate. When using a sample-hold amplifier ahead of an ADC, its droop rate should not be more than 0.1 LSB during the conversion time of the ADC.

Feedthrough

This refers to the undesirable signal leakage around switches or other devices expected to be turned off or to provide isolation. Both digital and analog signals can cause feedthrough errors.

Glitch

Due to unmatched switching delays from ON to OFF and vice versa, in the various bits of a digital to analog converter, the resulting staircase type waveform, as shown in Fig. 14.21, often has additional undesired transient spikes, referred to as "glitch". The most major transition is when input changes from 01111... to 10000.... Improvement is obtained by using a "deglitcher" which is a sample-hold circuit holding the DAC output constant until the switches reach equilibrium. Due to the fast action required, the deglitcher is often incorporated within the DAC module itself.

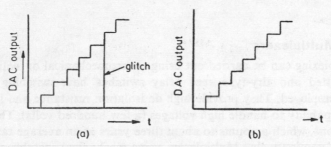

Fig. 14.21 DAC output: (a) with glitches; (b) deglitched output

Linearity

Linearity is conventionally equal to the deviation of the performance of the converter from a "best straight line" fit. In many practical converters, the non-linearity referred to is the deviation from a straight line drawn between the end points after carrying out a normal adjustment and calibration procedure for zero offset and full scale. Linearity of a converter directly determines the relative accuracy of the converter. The relative accuracy refers to the errors resulting from the difference between the nominal and actual ratios to the full scale of the analog value corresponding to a given digital input independently of the full scale calibration. Usually, the error is specified at less than $\pm 1/2$ LSB.

Monotonicity

In response to a continuously-increasing input signal, the output of an A/D converter should not, at any point, decrease or skip one or more codes. Referred to D/A converters for continuously increasing the input code value, the output should not decrease below the value attained for the previous code. Monotonic behaviour requires that the differential non-linearity is less than 1 LSB.

Settling Time

Settling time is the time that a DAC takes to settle for a full-scale code change, usually to within $\pm\frac{1}{2}$ LSB.

Zero Setting

The zero level is set to zero volts at the code corresponding to 0 V in a unipolar DAC. The LSB transition of an ADC is offset by $\frac{1}{2}$ LSB so that all subsequent transitions ideally occur midway between the nominal code values (see also Fig. 14.20).

14.8 MULTIPLEXERS AND SAMPLE-HOLD CIRCUITS

When more than one parameter has to be converted to digital form, either the inputs are scanned by analog multiplexers and then converted to digital form using a single A/D converter or an A/D converter is provided for each parameter and the converter outputs are digitally multiplexed.

14.8.1 Analog Multiplexers

The analog multiplexing can be carried out using electromechanical or solid-state switches. Both mercury-wetted and dry-type reed relay switches have switching times less than a millisecond are employed. They provide high dc isolation resistance and low-contact resistance and have capability to handle high voltages (a few hundred volts). They have a typical life of 10^9 operations, which amounts to about three years at an average rate of 10 operations per second continuously. Multiplexers using mechanical switches are suited for low speed applications and interface well with high resolution integrating type A/D converters.

Solid-state switches are capable of high-speed operation ($\simeq 30$ ns switching time) and have a life likely to exceed most equipment requirements. Field effect transistors (FETs) are universally used in multiplexers because of their lower errors and have superseded bipolar transistors as switches. Due to higher mobility of electrons which are the majority carriers in n-channel FETs, the n-channel FETs have a lower ON resistance. Since the *n*-channel structures also have lower capacitance, they are preferred for use in multiplexers. Typical ON resistance of these types is in the range of 10 to 100 ohms. In the OFF state, the drain to source leakage is of the order of 100 pA in junction FETs.

The complementary MOS switch (CMOS, COSMOS) combines the advantages of *p*-type and *n*-type structures by incorporating them in each switch, as shown in Fig. 14.22. Using this configuration, analog inputs over a ± 10 V range can be handled with $V^+ = +10$ V and $V^- = -10$ V. In addition, the effective ON resistance is lower, being the parallel combination of the resistance of *p*-channel and *n*-channel switches.

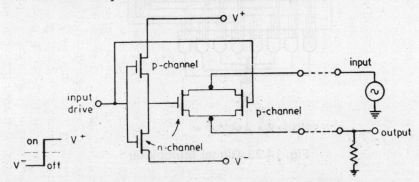

Fig. 14.22 Complementary MOS switches

Due to the non-zero capacitances present between gate and source and between drain and source, the high frequency dynamic performance of multiplexers using solid state switches should be optimized to obtain low settling time and to minimize cross talk. In low level multiplexers, proper selection and matching of the low level signal cable needs careful consideration in order to realise meaningful common mode rejection ratios at higher frequencies[9].

14.8.2 Digital Multiplexers

A typical digital multiplexer capable of selecting one of eight input levels is shown in Fig. 14.23 (SN 74151). For an 8-bit system, eight such ICs will be required to enable multiplexing the outputs of eight different A/D converters. When larger numbers of A/D converters are to be multiplexed, the data bus technique is employed. In this, using tristate drivers at the output of each A/D converter, an 8 bit-data bus enables the connection of a display unit or data link to the 8-bit output of a selected A/D converter.

14.8.3 Sample-Hold Circuits

In data-acquisition systems, sample-holds are often used to "freeze" fast-moving signals so that the level at a chosen instant can be converted to the digital form. When using multiplexers, they can serve to store the output of the multiplexer so that the multiplexer can be allowed to seek the next signal to be converted. They are also used to store data between updates in data distribution systems.

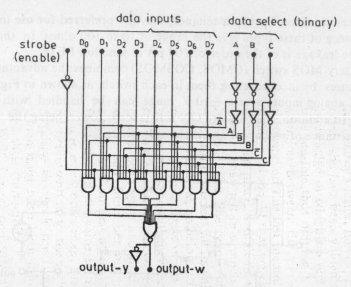

Fig. 14.23 Digital Multiplexer

The various factors of importance in a sample-hold circuit are the aperture time, settling time, droop, and feedthrough.

The aperture time is the time elapsed between the command to "hold" and the actual opening of the "hold" switch. The time required for the output to settle to a final value within a specified fraction of the full scale, after the opening of the switch, is referred to as the settling time. Droop is the result of leakage currents and appears as a slow change, approximately at a constant rate, of the held value. The ratio of the droop rate to the settling time can form a figure of merit for comparison between various sample-holds. The feedthrough caused by capacitance across the switch makes a fraction of the input signal appear at the output in the "hold" mode. It is measured at a fixed frequency and is specified as a percentage of the full scale. The practical circuitry for sample-hold has been discussed in Sec. 12.5.4.

EXERCISES

14.1 Show the complete schematic for a data acquisition system capable of logging data from five stations, sequentially, and dumping the data into a memory. Data is to be collected over 5 seconds, at a rate not less than 10 Hz/sec from each channel. Desired accuracy is 0.5%. The outputs from the various channels are as follows:

Channel 1: 200 mV max across 10 kohm

Channel 2: 10 mV max across 100 ohms

Channel 3: 10 mA max across 100 ohms

Channel 4: 50 mV across 1 kohm, with a common mode voltage of 2 V

Channel 5: 5V max from a piezoelectric transducer (Z_o = 10 Mohms).

14.2 Differentiate between multi-channel DAS using digital multiplexing before transmission, and that employing multiplexing of outputs of sample/holds. Give examples of systems that require these two different schemes of data acquisition.

14.3 In the D/A converter of Fig. 14.11(b), estimate the tolerance required for the resistors, if the overall linearity should be within $\pm 1/2$ LSB for an 8 bit BCD converter.

14.4 In Fig. 14.13(b), verify the validity of the choice of R_A and R_B as 14.0625 kohms.

14.5 What are the modifications required in the dual slope converter of Fig. 14.18(a), if the output digital word should represent logarithm of the input voltage? (*Hint*: the voltage across C will decay exponentially, if a resistor is connected across it.)

14.6 Show how the parallel converter of Fig. 14.20 can be combined with the successive approximation type ADC of Fig. 14.16, to provide a 12 bit conversion. (Assume that the successive approximation ADC provides 8 bit conversion in 10 μs.) What is the conversion time required for this converter?

14.7 What is meant by normal mode rejection? An A/D Converter has 20 ms integration time. What is the normal mode rejection offered by this ADC for signals having frequency of (i) 150 Hz and (ii) 145 Hz?

14.8 Show how the V/F converter of Fig. 12.43 can be combined with a 4 bit precision D/A converter to provide 5 digit display of DC voltages. (*Hint*: Use the D/A converter to decide the maximum significant digit, subtract a corresponding voltage from the input, and use the difference as input to V/F converter.)

REFERENCES

1. Sheingold, D.H. (Ed.), *Analog to Digital Conversion Handbook*, p. I-15, Analog Devices, Norwood, Masschusetts, 1972.

2. Gaffney, J.E. and Doersam, C.H., "Data handling equipment", in: Gruenberg E.L. (Ed. in Chief), *Handbook of Telemetry and Remote Control*, pp. 11-6 to 11-11, McGraw Hill Book Co., N.Y., 1967.

3. Sheingold, D.H. (Ed.), *Non-linear Circuits Handbook*, p. 103, Analog Devices, Norwood, Massachusetts, 1974.

4. Ibid. 1, p. I-33.

5. Ibid. 1, p. II-21.

6. Hoeschele, D.F., *Analog-to-Digital/Digital-to-Analog Conversion Techniques*, Ch. IV, John Wiley and Sons Inc., N.Y., 1968.

7. Ibid. 1, p. II-41.

8. Randall R.B., *Application of B and K Equipment to Frequency Analysis*, p. 64, Bruel and Kjaer, Denmark, 1977.

9. Ibid. 1, pp. III-54-69.

BIBLIOGRAPHY

Balmer, C., "Data logging from the user's viewpoint", *Instruments and Control Systems*, Vol. 51, No. 8, pp. 39-42, Aug. 1978.

Bowers, D., "Analogue multiplexers: their technology and operation", *Electronic Engineering*, Vol. 50, No. 612, pp. 23-31, Mid September, 1978.

Data Acquisition Components and Subsystems, Analog Devices, Massachusetts, 1980.

"Digital panel meter survey", *Instruments and Control Systems*, Vol. 45, No. 2, pp. 93-99, Feb. 1972.

Donn Soderquist, "Exponential digitally controlled oscillator using DAC-76", Application Note, AN-20, Precision Monolithics Inc., California, 1979.

Fullagar, D., et. al., "Interfacing data converters and microprocessors", *Electronics*, Vol. 49. No. 25, p. 81, Dec. 9, 1976.

General Catalog, Burr Brown, Tucson, Arizona, 1976.

Gadway, R., "Sample and hold or high speed A/D converters, how do you decide?" Application Note, AN 56, Burr Brown Res. Crop., Tucson, Arizona, 1973.

Hnatek, E.R., *A Users' Handbook of D/A and A/D Converters*, John Wiley and Sons, N.Y., 1976.

IEE Conference Publication No. 106, *Conference on Digital Instrumentation*, The Institution of Electrical Engineers, London, 1973.

Janson, E., "Beware of data acquisition pitfalls", *Instruments and Control Systems*, Vol. 52, No. 8, pp. 57-59, Aug. 1979.

Kaufman, E.N., "Thinking of changing from analog to digital for data acquisition?", *Instruments and Control Systems*, Vol. 50, No. 7, pp. 29-31. July 1977,

Linear and Conversion IC Products, Precision Monolithics Inc., California, 1976.

Reynolds, B., "Guide to analog I/O boards, Part I", *Instruments and Control Systems*, Vol. 51, No. 8, pp. 53-59, Aug. 1978; and Part II, Vol. 51, No. 9, pp. 157-161, Sept. 1978.

Schmid, H., *Electronic Analog to Digital Conversions*, Van Nostrand Reinhold, N.Y., 1970.

Vesser, B., "A flexible way to handle multichannel data acquisition", *Instruments and Control Systems*, Vol. 51, No. 5, pp. 55-57, May 1978.

Widenka, R., "Recorders with digital storage capture transients for analysis", *Control and Instrumentation*, Vol. 11, No. 4, pp. 51-53, April 1979.

Yuen, M., "D/A Converters, low-glitch design lowers parts count in graphic displays", *Electronics*, Vol. 52, No. 16, pp. 131-135, Aug. 2, 1979.

15
DIGITAL SIGNAL TRANSMISSION AND PROCESSING

15.1 INTRODUCTION

The primary objective of data transmission is the transfer of information from one location to another. In contrast to the analog signal that has an infinite number of voltage levels, the digital signal information is "binary" or two-valued. A binary symbol is called a binary digit or bit, and a group of bits representing an information unit is called a byte. A selective arrangement of seven bits provide 2^7 (or 128) distinct character combinations or 128 bytes. The American Standard Code for Information Interchange (ASCII) is an excellent example of such an arrangement used in the transmission of numbers, alphanumeric characters, and miscellaneous information.

The major points that must be agreed upon by the sender and receiver, to accomplish uniform flow of data are:

(i) The nominal rate of transmission, or how many bits are to be emitted per second by the sender

(ii) The specified information code providing a one-to-one mapping ratio of the information to bit-pattern and vice versa

(iii) A particular scheme by which each bit can be positioned properly, within a byte by the receiver of the data (in the case of bit-serial transmission)

(iv) A protocol (handshaking) sequence necessary to ensure an orderly flow of information

(v) The electrical stress representing the logic values of each bit and the particular pulse code to be used.

The items (ii), (iii), and (iv) are essentially "software" type decisions and do not affect the characteristics of the actual signal sent along the transmission line or any other media used for transmission of information. Items (i) and (v) are directly influenced by the characteristics of the line-drivers, the line-receivers, and the transmission-lines used for data transmission.

15.2 DATA-TRANSMISSION SYSTEMS

A typical data-transmission system contains the information source from which data has to be transmitted through a suitable medium to the destination termed as the "information sink". The information source can be a computer terminal, a digitized transducer output, or any other device generating a stream of bits at the rate of one bit in every t_B seconds. The "information rate" of the system is then $1/t_B$ bits per second. As shown in Fig. 15.1, the information source feeds to a "source encoder" which performs logic operations not only on the data but also on the associated clock, and perhaps, the past data bits as well. Thus the source encoder produces a data stream controlling the line driver. The line driver interfaces the internal logic levels of the source (viz., TTL, MOS, etc.) with the transmission line. The transmission line in turn carries the signal produced by the line driver to the line receiver. The line receiver makes a decision on the signal logic state by comparing the received signal to a decision threshold level, and the "sink-decoder" performs logic operations on the binary bit stream recovered by the line receiver. For example, the sink decoder may contract the clock rate from the data or perhaps detect and correct errors in the data. From the optional sink decoder, the recovered binary data passes to the "information sink", which is the destination for the information-source data

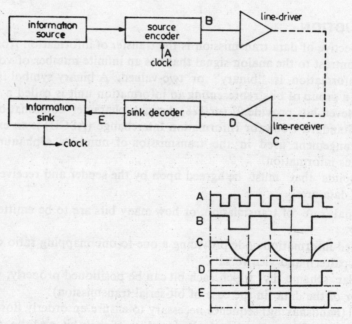

Fig. 15.1 Block schematic of a data transmission system

One of the most common forms of data found in the TTL logic systems is the 'Non-Return-to-Zero (NRZ)' data[1], the details of which are given in Sec. 15.3. The data source in this case emits a fresh bit in every t_B seconds, as shown in Fig. 15.2. The arrows at the top represent the ideal instants at which the signal can change state. The time duration of the shortest signalling element is referred to as the "unit interval", which in this case is the one bit time, t_B. The "modulation rate" is indicative of the signalling speed and is spoken of in terms of "bauds", the baud rate being basically the reciprocal of the time for one unit interval. A modulation rate of 1 baud corresponds to the transmission of one unit interval per second. The clock pulses associated with the NRZ data becomes invariably necessary at the receiver end so that the receiver can use it to sample the data signal at appropriate intervals in order to determine the current logic state. For the example of Fig. 15.2, the falling edge of the clock corresponds to the middle of the data bits so that it can be used to transfer the line-receiver data output into a binary latch. The falling edge of the clock is thus the "sampling instant" for the data. The line receiver has a decision threshold or slicing point so that voltages above that threshold produce one logic state output and voltages below it produce the other logic state at the receiver output. The receiver can have "hysteresis" to reduce the possibility of oscillation in response to slow rise or fall time signals applied to the input of the receiver.

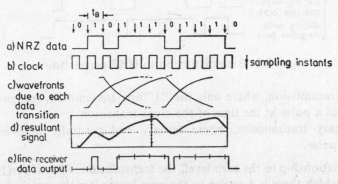

Fig. 15.2 NRZ signalling

The dispersion and attenuation of the transmission line tends to slow down and round off the fast rise-and-fall transitions of the transmitted signal, as illustrated in Fig. 15.2(c). A time displacement of the transition can occur, as shown in Fig. 15.2(e) due to the new wave arriving at the receiver site before the previous wave has reached its final value. This phenomenon, called "inter-symbol interference", can be reduced by making unit interval of the data signal quite long in comparison to the rise/fall time of the signal at the ·receiver. This requires the reduction of the modulation rate for a given line length, or the reduction of the line length for a given modulation rate.

Another type of time distortion that arises in the received signal is due to the misplacement of the decision threshold point from its optimum value. This is shown in Fig. 15.3. If the decision threshold of the receiver is shifted up towards the "1" level, then the time duration of the "1" bits shortens with respect to that of "0" bits, and vice versa. This is termed as "bias distortion" and may be due to the receiver threshold offset (bias) or asymmetrical output levels of the driver.

15.3 PULSE CODE FORMATS

There are many different code formats of pulse waveforms. The classification is based on three criteria, viz., form of information-transmission, relation to zero level, and direction. Based on the form of information-transmission, the format used can be any one of the following:

(i) Full binary transmission, where both the "0" and "1" bits are part of the formats.

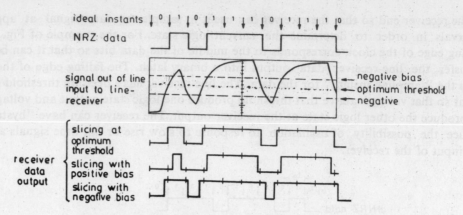

Fig. 15.3 Bias distortion in NRZ pulse train

(ii) **Half binary transmission**, where only the "1" are transmitted, recognizing the "0" by the absence of a pulse at the time of the clock transition.

(iii) **Multiple binary transmission**, where ternary and quadratic codes are used for each transmitted pulse.

Based on the relationship to the zero level, the transmission format can be either "return-to-zero (RZ)" in which there is a return to the zero level after the transmission of each bit of information, or "non-return-to-zero (NRZ)", where there is no voltage level change if

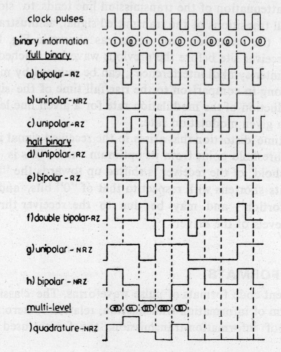

Fig. 15.4 Pulse code formats used in data transmission

consecutive bits are transmitted, although there is a level change when there is an information variation from "0" to "1" or "1" to "0". In the case of the third criterion of classification, namely that of direction, the code format used can be either unipolar, where the pulses are in a single direction, or bipolar, where the pulses are in both directions. Some of these code formats are illustrated in Fig. 15.4.

15.3.1 Full Binary Transmission

The full binary bipolar RZ format shown in Fig. 15.4(a) is one of the most reliable pulse code formats that is employed for slow-speed transmission, typically up to 600 bits/s, using frequency shift keying (FSK). It may be noted that opposite polarity pulses are used to transmit "1" and "0" bits. Between the pulses, no power is transmitted, resulting in a "space" between each pulse.

In the non-return-to-zero (NRZ) unipolar type of transmission shown in Fig. 15.4(b), the pulses are spread out in time so that they occupy the full-time slot, and permit an increased rate of transmission. The term NRZ is directly related to the fact that the pulses do not return to zero between successive pulses of "0" and "1"s. This format is most popularly used in serial computer applications and for data-transmission speeds of 600, 1200, and 2400 bits/s. The transmission bandwidth is efficiently utilized, since the entire bit period contains signal information.

The return-to-zero (RZ) unipolar format, as shown in Fig. 15.4(c) has a symmetrical format characterized by the absence of a dc level. The pulse format has a zero crossing for each bit period, a feature that simplifies synchronization, though at the expense of increasing the total bandwidth required. This code is also referred to as a split phase, biphase, or Manchester code. Due to the reliable synchronization characteristics, this code is also used for airborne to ground slow-speed data transmission.

15.3.2 Half-Binary Transmission

In the half-binary transmission, the binary "1"s are represented by a pulse or a polarity change, but the "0"s are seen as spaces. This is based on the statistical assumption that the number of "1"s in a pulse train is equal to the number of "0"s, resulting in a reduction of the transmission power with a possible increase of transmission speed. The return-to-zero, unipolar format in half-binary transmission is shown in Fig. 15.4(d). The pulse train is similar to that in Fig. 15.4(a) except that the pulses corresponding to the "0" bits are absent. As a result of this, the frequency spectrum of the pulse train has less high frequency components and, in turn, results in less cross-talk. However, a dc component also results, which is difficult to transmit. The coding method is not efficient since 50% of the bandwidth is wasted as information is contained in only half of the bit periods.

The return-to-zero, bipolar format shown in Fig. 15.4(e) is obtained by reversing each consecutive pulse of Fig. 15.4(d). Because of this inversion action, the dc component is removed. Further, error detection is facilitated, since all one is required to remember is the polarity of the last pulse received. However, with the "0"s not transmitted, no indication is available regarding the location of the error. This code is popular for the transmission of the pulse code modulation (PCM) signals at very high speeds. The format is popularly known as "pseudo-ternary".

If the inversion of the pulses be done only after every two consecutive "1" bits, the return-to-zero, double bipolar pulse sequence of Fig. 15.4(f) results. This format further reduces the inter-symbol interference, enabling better utilization of the bandwidth.

The non-return-to-zero, unipolar format is shown in Fig. 15.4(g). A polarity reversal takes place each time a 1 bit is transmitted, while no polarity reversal takes place for "0" bit. This method, known as the "NRZ 1 code format", is widely used for applications in digital tape recording. The non-return-to-zero, bipolar format is a three level code and is also known as "duo-binary code". The "0" bit is represented in this case by a zero level while the binary "1" is reversed only when the number of consecutive "0"s between the "1"s is odd. If the number of consecutive "0"s between the "1"s is even, no reversal occurs. This special code enables doubling of the transmission rate and is used in frequency modulation (FM) systems.

15.3.3 Multi-Level Transmission

In most data-transmission systems, each bit transmitted corresponds to one symbol. By using one symbol to represent a number of bits, the speed of transmission can be increased. The penalty paid is that the data is more vulnerable to noise and other distortion, since the individual states are more difficult to distinguish in a multi-level method than in a two-level method.

The non-return-to-zero, quadrature binary format shown in Fig. 15.4(i) is a typical example of a multi-level transmission format. This is a four-level code in which each level represents two binary bits, i.e., a bit pair of 00, 01, 10, or 11. The two-bit pair, referred to as a "dibit" is transmitted in a one-bit period corresponding to the previous formats resulting in a higher transmission rate. Due to the necessity of guarding against noise and distortion, high-quality lines with low attenuation and delay distortion are required for handling multi-level transmission. Nevertheless, it has been possible to achieve transmission speeds of 9600 bits per second over automatically-equalized telephone lines using an eight-level code[2].

15.4 MODULATION TECHNIQUES FOR DIGITAL-DATA TRANSMISSION

The following modulation techniques are widely employed for transmission of digital data: (i) amplitude modulation, (ii) frequency modulation, and (iii) phase modulation. Another modulation technique that is sometimes used is a combination of amplitude modulation and phase modulation.

In each of these techniques, a sinewave carrier is employed to convey the data by means of a change of its amplitude, frequency, or phase. In principle, the three modulation techniques follow the block diagram of Fig. 15.5. In designing data-transmission networks, the main aspect to be considered is the efficient utilization of the transmission path. This means transferring the maximum amount of data with negligible errors, at a reasonable price, using the full bandwidth available.

For data transmission over voice telephone lines, the available frequency band is from 300 to 3300 Hz. Thus, theoretically, the maximum speed at which signal elements can be

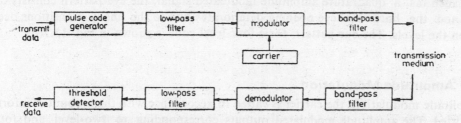

Fig. 15.5 Block diagram of modulation/demodulation system

transmitted is 6000 bits/s. However, about twice this bandwidth is required to achieve a transmission rate of 6000 bits/s. Nevertheless, faster speeds have been possible by suitable coding of the data, using one signal element to signify a number of bits.

Transmission rates approaching the theoretical limit can be achieved by minimizing the influence of noise and controlling the intersymbol interference. Since the output of a low-pass filter for a rectangular pulse is of the $\frac{\sin x}{x}$ form, the reception of a binary bit can be affected by the existence of outputs arising from previous bits. This intersymbol interference can be reduced by modifying the pulse shape of the transmitted data so that the build up and decay of the voltage follows a "cosine" roll-off, as shown in Fig. 15.6.

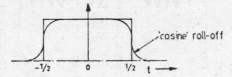

Fig. 15.6 Modified pulse shape using cosine roll-off

A useful concept in evaluating the intersymbol interference and hence the quality of the received demodulated data is the "eye pattern". The eye pattern for a two-level code is illustrated in Fig. 15.7(a). The intersymbol interference is evaluated by the available threshold, which is defined as the interval at the centre of the opening. The slicing level is chosen to be at the centre of the vertical eye opening. When the received signal is affected beyond a specific threshold, the data, as received, will be in error. When transmitting a multi-level

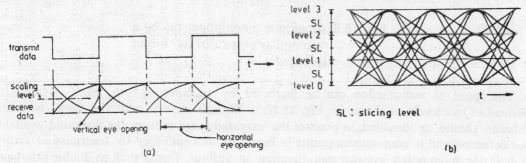

Fig. 15.7 Eye pattern for: (a) two-level code; (b) four-level code

signal such as a quadrature amplitude modulated signal, the eye pattern consists of three levels and the horizontal eye opening deteriorates due to the many transitions occurring between the levels. The eye pattern for a four-level code is shown in Fig. 15.7(b).

15.4.1 Amplitude Modulation

In amplitude modulation, the carrier is varied in accordance with the amount of information transmitted. The amplitude modulated outputs corresponding to two-level and four-level digital signals are shown in Figs. 15.8(a) and (b). The amplitude modulation produces two identical symmetrical side-bands around the carrier. Since the same information is contained in both the side-bands, only one side-band is required to transmit a message. The removal of one of the side-bands can be done by filtering or by quadrature modulation[3]. While the single side-band suppressed-carrier is the most widely used AM technique, its use is limited by its extreme vulnerability to common types of noise, attenuation, and delay distortion in the transmission path, and due to echo and inter-symbol interference.

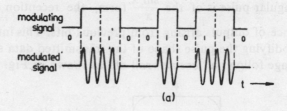

(a)

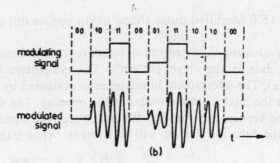

(b)

Fig. 15.8 Amplitude modulation: (a) by a
rectangular pulse; (b) by a four
level pulse

The speed of transmission can be increased by transmitting four levels of amplitude instead of two levels, as shown in Fig. 15.8(b). Though theoretically the speed of transmission should be doubled, in practice the increased speed reduces the threshold available for detection and in consequence results in increased susceptibility to transmission errors. Amplitude modulation systems can function in various forms such as double side-band (DSB), double side-band suppressed-carrier (DSBSC), single side-band (SSB), single side-band suppressed-carrier (SSBSC), vestigial side-band (VSB), and independent single side-band (ISSB). The last technique mentioned is also known as quadrature amplitude modulation (QAM), wherein, two independent signals modulate the same carrier through individual single-side-band modulators. The upper side-band of one and the lower side-band of the other are then combined and transmitted. These two side-bands containing different information operate in quadrature phase which can be separately and coherently detected in the receiver. QAM and VSB systems can enable speeds of up to 9600 bits/s, for transmission of signals over telephone lines.

15.4.2 Frequency Modulation

In frequency modulation, the carrier frequency is changed according to the information transmitted. The ON/OFF data transmission shifts the transmitted frequency in one direction to indicate a "1" and in the other direction to indicate a "0". The amount of frequency shift in both directions is the same. This frequency modulation scheme is known as frequency shift-keying (FSK).

Frequency modulation is less vulnerable to amplitude level variations, caused due to any impulse noise and hence is superior to amplitude modulation. The price paid for this is the bandwidth. For modems (transmission systems based on modulation and demodulation process) operating at speeds up to 1200-1800 bits/s, FM is used. Two basic types of code formats frequently used with FM systems are the RZ and the NRZ codes. In RZ, as shown in Fig. 15.9(a), two discrete frequencies (f_c+f_m) and (f_c-f_m) are used to transmit the binary states, while the carrier f_c is used to transmit the intervals between pulses. In NRZ, the frequency is shifted between the two values (f_1 and f_2), as shown in Fig. 15.9(b) The higher frequency is assumed to have the value of "1" binary state and the lower frequency represents the "0" state. With no information transmitted, the upper frequency is usually transmitted continuously. When varying the frequency between "1" and "0" states, the phase

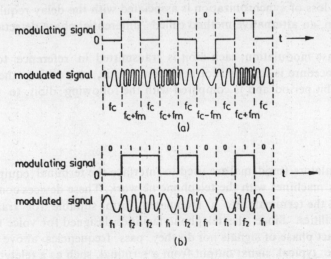

Fig. 15.9 Frequency modulation: (a) by an RZ pulse
train; (b) by an NRZ pulse train

must be preserved. This is usually done by having a single oscillator wherein a capacitor is varied to achieve modulation. The FM technique is particularly employed with the duo-binary format of coding mentioned in Sec. 15.3.2, since it enables full utilization of the bandwidth of the FM technique[4].

15.4.3 Phase Modulation

In phase modulation, the phase of the carrier frequency is changed according to the data transmitted, as shown in Fig. 15.10. This is also referred to as phase-shift-keying (PSK). Phase modulation is often employed for high-speed data transmission, since both the amplitude and frequency of the signal remain constant throughout the transmission period. The main drawback in employing phase modulation is the complexity of the equipment. In spite of this, high-speed data transmission systems invariably employ phase modulation[5].

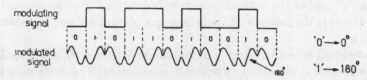

Fig. 15.10 Phase modulation

Multi-level codes can be transmitted by phase modulation by suitable selection of the phase shift required for each level. For the transmission of four levels, the phase shifts can be 0°, 90°, 180°, and 270°. Alternatively, they can be 45°, 135°, 225°, and 315°. In order that the receiver can identify the phase angles appropriately, it is necessary to provide some form of reference signal to the receiver. In "fixed reference phase detection", the transmitted frequency and reference phase is recovered by full-wave detection of the received wave-forms. In this case the "phase jitter" of the transmission medium can create problems. Since a loss of synchronization is associated with the delay required to re-establish synchronization, an alternative method called "differential phase detection" is used in high-speed systems.

In differential-phase modulation, each dibit is transmitted in reference to the previous dibit. A similar procedure is followed for detection: in this, each dibit in the received signal is delayed by one dibit period and is compared with the following dibit to reconstruct the transmitted data.

15.4.4 Modems

Modulators-demodulators (modems) are used to interface the terminal equipment of computers and business machines with the telephone network. These devices convert the electrical waveforms from the terminals into a modulated form suitable for transmission over voice-telephone facilities. Since the telephone facilities designed for voice transmission do not preserve the exact phase of signals nor do they pass frequencies above 3400 Hz and below 300 Hz, the typical signal output from a terminal, such as a teletypewriter can become distorted and unrecognizable if transmitted directly over a telephone channel without the use of modems.

The standard high-speed rates for voice-band modems are 4800, 7200, and 9600 bits/s. The typical methods of modulation used include FSK, PSK, VSB, quadrature amplitude modulation (QAM), or a combination of PSK and AM[6].

15.5 TELEMETRY SYSTEMS

A telemetry system is intended to collect data from various remote locations and transfer the information to a centralized installation. For this, a series of electrical sensors are used which perpetually measure the system operation. The various sensor output readings are scanned at fixed intervals and multiplexed before transmitting through a suitable link to the data-collection centre. In the receiver, the data is reconstructed, demultiplexed, and distributed to individual display and recording systems.

15.5.1 Frequency Division Multiplexing

In frequency division multiplexing, the transmission bandwidth is divided between the various sensors, as illustrated in Fig. 15.11(a). Each channel has associated with it a subcarrier frequency which is modulated by information from that channel. In the figure shown, the output of sensor 1 modulates a fixed carrier so that information from sensor 1 is restricted to the band of frequencies from 32 to 36 kHz. In a similar way, information from sensor 2 is restricted to the band of frequencies from 28 to 32 kHz. The information from all sensors is thus distributed in the band of frequencies from 20 to 36 kHz, which is the bandwidth over which transmission is carried out. In the receiver, the bands corresponding to the individual channels are separated out by band-pass filters. The signals are retrieved from various bands by demodulation and displayed separately.

The particular frequencies assigned to each channel are referred to as the sub-carrier frequencies. In Fig. 15.11(b), channel 1 corresponding to sensor 1 output modulates the sub-carrier oscillator (SCO) 1, and so on. Modulation is usually carried out by FM techniques. The outputs of individual sub-carriers are mixed in an adder and transmitted, often after a further frequency modulation of a high-frequency carrier. In such an FM/FM telemetry system[7], the high-frequency signal received is amplified and frequency demodulated. The subsequent individual sub-carrier filters then separate the signals and feed to the corresponding demodulators. The output of the demodulators corresponds to the information from the individual sensors, and is displayed or recorded as necessary.

15.5.2 Time Division Multiplexing

The signals from various sensors are sampled sequentially and the samples are converted to suitable formats, in the time-division-multiplexing scheme. The process of scanning produces a train of pulses, with the samples corresponding to a particular sensor repeating at regular intervals, as shown in Fig. 15.11(c). Each sensor output thus receives a time slot in the time pulse sequence. The individual amplitudes corresponding to the sample values can be sent as such, or after further conversion. In pulse amplitude modulation (PAM), as shown in Fig. 15.12(b), the sample values of the sensors are directly sent through the transmission medium to the receiver without any further change. Due to the susceptibility of the signal to get affected by the noise in the medium, this method is seldom employed in practice.

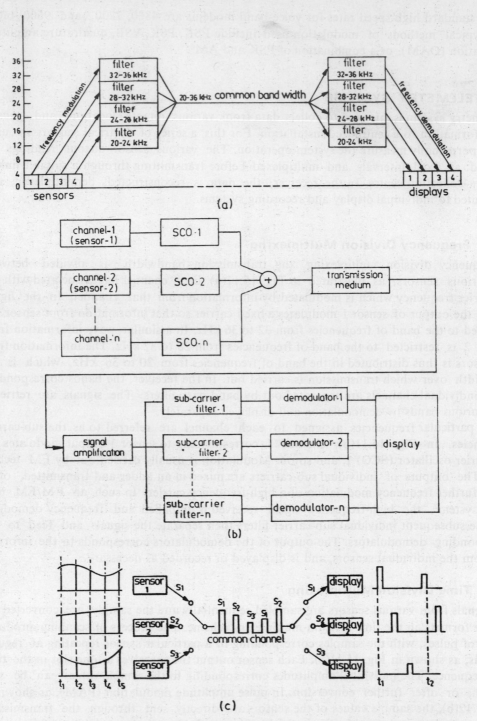

Fig. 15.11 Telemetry: (a) frequency division multiplexing; (b) FM/FM analog telemetry system; (c) time division multiplexing

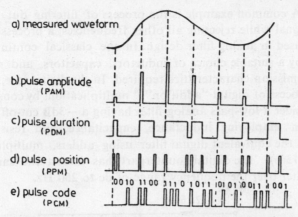

Fig. 15.12 Various pulse modulation techniques

The amplitude information in PAM can be converted to equivalent pulse durations, as shown in Fig. 15.12(c). This is referred to as pulse duration modulation (PDM). Here all the pulses start at the same relative point, but the duration of the pulse is proportional to the sampled value of the signal. PDM is far less susceptible to noise than PAM since most of the disturbances affect the pulse height rather than its duration. Nevertheless, any distortion of the pulse shape will be misrepresented in the reconstructed display. The problem becomes severe at high sampling rates, since the inductance and capacitance of the transmission line can introduce severe distortion of the pulse duration of the signal. In pulse position modulation (PPM), two pulses corresponding to the beginning and end of the "duration" is transmitted, as shown in Fig. 15.12(d). This scheme is superior to PAM and PDM since it is not susceptible to amplitude or shape distortion. However, the "spikes" in noisy lines can seriously affect the reconstruction scheme. In addition, the bandwidth required for transmission of the short duration pulses is also higher. For higher immunity against interferences, the pulse duration can be coded and the codes corresponding to each sample can then be sent over to the receiver. This scheme is called pulse code modulation (PCM). The PCM represents the most efficient and the most practical coding technique today. PCM however requires a wide bandwidth as required for PPM. Nevertheless, the position of the pulses is not so critical, and hence PCM is one of the most popular schemes used for digital transmission of analog data.[8]

15.6 DIGITAL-SIGNAL PROCESSING

The use of digital techniques for various signal-processing applications has increased tremendously in the last few years. Engineering personnel at all levels are now required to deal with many digital analysers, and the impact on the design and development of the hardware is most significant.

The important tools for modern digital-signal processing are: (i) digital filters, and (ii) fast Fourier transforms.

A digital filter is a computational process in which the sequence of input numbers is converted into a sequence of output numbers, representing the alteration of the data in a prescribed manner. A common example is the process of filtering out a certain range of frequencies in a signal while rejecting all other frequencies, a process that is basic for the general approaches used in analog filter design. In the classical continuous-time case, the filtering is achieved by a suitable choice of inductors, capacitors, and resistors arranged as dictated by the transmission characteristics required. In the digital case, this can be achieved completely by the process of digital "addition", "multiplications by constants", and "delay". As an example, consider a low-pass analog filter having a -3dB cut-off frequency of 50 Hz. The analog version employing inductance, capacitance, and resistance is shown in Fig. 15.13(a), while the equivalent digital filter using adders, multipliers, and delays are shown in Fig. 15.13(b). The digital counterpart has almost the same characteristics as that of the analog filter over the frequency range of dc to 250 Hz.

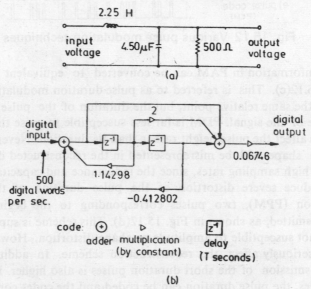

Fig. 15.13 Filters having similar characteristics:
(a) analog; (b) digital

The other important concept in digital signal processing today is that of the fast **Fourier transform** (FFT). The FFT emerged into importance when Cooley and Tukey[9] introduced in 1966, new algorithms that could considerably speed up computation of the Fourier spectrum. Using this approach, the spectrum of signals containing many thousands of sample points can be achieved in a matter of milli-seconds. At present, it is quite feasible to filter a signal by FFT transformation, numerical alteration of the spectrum, and inverse FFT computation. FFT has opened up new potential applications in many varied scientific disciplines that utilize spectral analysis in one form or the other. Spectroscopy, vibration and communication signal analysis, oceanographic wave analysis, and statistical analysis are but a few of the more important application fields of FFT, at present. For many applications, special FFT processors that can be used for real-time processing of signals are already available, and FFT on a chip is now a confirmed reality.

The process by which digital-signal processing is achieved for an analog signal is illustrated in the simplified block diagram of Fig. 15.14. Since the digital operations can be carried out only on identified digital numbers, the analog values are first sampled and converted to digital numbers in an A/D converter. The pre-sampling filter ensures that aliasing errors do not arise due to the process of sampling. The "digital-signal-processor" block operates on the digital numbers, and the output is rendered analog by the following D/A converter and associated smoothing filters.

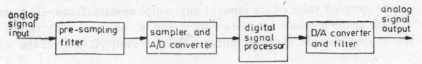

Fig. 15.14 Block diagram of a digital processing system

An important advantage of digital processing is that the same "digital-signal-processing" block can be time-shared using suitable multiplexers and demultiplexers so that multi-channel analog data can be handled without having to duplicate the digital-signal-processing hardware. This is illustrated in Fig. 15.15. It is important to note that though the same digital-signal processor is processing the data of all channels, it is not mandatory that the process carried out be identical for each channel; by appropriate selection of coefficients and even configurations, the digital-signal processor can do varied functions on data pertaining to each of the different input signals. For example, if the processor is used for averaging data, the number of samples over which average is taken need not be the same for signal inputs from different channels.

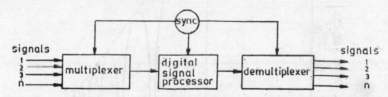

Fig. 15.15 Multiplexed digital processing system

When the data obtained after processing is intended for scientific data reduction and computation, the last block, viz., D/A conversion and filtering of Fig. 15.15 may be altogether avoided; hence, digital-signal processing becomes more attractive and useful in contrast to analog processing.

15.7 DIGITAL FILTERS

The term "digital filter" is used to represent a digital processor which receives a sequence of input data values, carries out some digital operation on them, and outputs a corresponding sequence of digital values which are filtered in a prescribed manner with respect to the input. The input to a digital filter is a number sequence obtained by sampling the signal to be filtered. A digital low-pass filter, for example, can be used to provide the average value of a fluctuating input, as shown in Fig. 15.16. The simplest example of a digital averager is "linear averaging" wherein for every N sample values of the input, the digital processor provides the average of the N samples as the output. The input-output relationship for the linear averager is governed by the algorithm

$$y(n) = \frac{1}{N} \sum_{i=0}^{N-1} x(n-i)$$

where $x(n)$ is the sampled value of the input at any sampling instant, $x(n-1)$ is the sampled value of the input at the previous sampling instant, and so on, and $y(n)$ is the computed value of the output sample at the instant at which the sampled value of the input is $x(n)$.

Fig. 15.16 Input and output of a digital filter

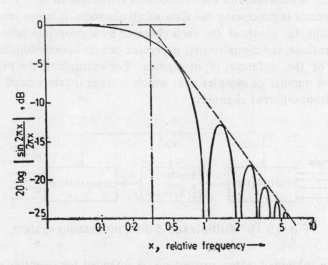

Fig. 15.17 Frequency response of a "linear averager"

The equivalent frequency response resulting from linear averaging, shown in Fig. 15.17, is the familiar $\frac{\sin x}{x}$ function.

The digital equivalent of a first-order low-pass filter is shown symbolically in Fig. 15.18(a) and is widely used for "exponential averaging". The filter comprises standard digital components, such as adders, multipliers, and delay units. The input-output relationship is given by the algorithm,

$$y(n) = Ax(n) - By(n-1) \tag{15.1}$$

The response of this filter for sampled values of a step function is illustrated in Fig. 15.18(b) for $A = 0.1$ and $B = -0.9$. The similarity of the response with that of a first-order low-pass filter can be clearly seen.

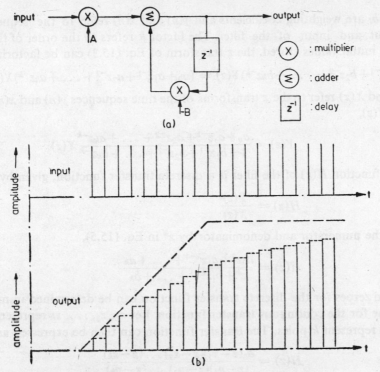

Fig. 15.18 First order low-pass: (a) filter realisation;
(b) step response

15.7.1 The z Transform

The role of the z transform in digital filters is analogous to the role of the Laplace transform in analog-filter theory. The z transform $A(z)$ of the number sequence $(a_0, a_1, a_2, \ldots)$ is given by

$$A(z) = a_0 + a_1 z^{-1} + a_2 z^{-2} + \ldots \tag{15.2}$$

where z is the z transform operator.

The number sequence $(a_0, a_1, a_2, \ldots)$ is assumed to be derived from sampling the input data at consecutive sampling instants. For example, the sequence $(1, 1, 1, -1, 1)$ has the z transform $(1 + z^{-1} + z^{-2} - z^{-3} + z^{-4})$. The inversion of the z transform to yield the time sequence is simplified if the z transform is expressed as a series. For example, the inversion of the z transform, $\dfrac{1}{\left(1 - \dfrac{1}{2} z^{-1}\right)}$, can be done by expressing it in a series form as $1 + \dfrac{1}{2} z^{-1}$

$+ \dfrac{1}{4} z^{-2} + \dfrac{1}{8} z^{-3} + \ldots$. The corresponding time series is then, $1, \dfrac{1}{2}, \dfrac{1}{4}, \dfrac{1}{8}, \ldots$. A more powerful technique for obtaining the inverse z transform is the inversion integral method[10].

The input-output relationship of a digital filter can be expressed in the form of a difference equation as

$$y(n) = \sum_{i=0}^{k} a_i x(n-i) - \sum_{i=1}^{k} b_i y(n-i), \tag{15.3}$$

where a_i and b_i are weighting coefficients and $y(n)$ and $x(n)$ refer to the sequential samples of the output and input of the filter. The factor k refers to the order of the filter. For a filter with no initial values stored, the z transform of Eq. (15.3) can be factorized to yield

$$(1+b_1z^{-1}+b_2z^{-2}+ \ldots +b_kz^{-k})Y(z) = (a_0+a_1z^{-1}+a_2z^{-2}+ \ldots ,+a_kz^{-k})X(z) \qquad (15.4)$$

where $Y(z)$ and $X(z)$ refer to the z transforms of the time sequences $y(n)$ and $x(n)$ respectively. Solving for $Y(z)$,

$$Y(z) = \frac{a_0+a_1z^{-1}+a_2z^{-2}+ \ldots +a_kz^{-k}}{1+b_1z^{-1}+b_2z^{-2}+ \ldots +b_kz^{-k}}X(z) \qquad (15.5)$$

The transfer function $H(z)$ of the filter is a discrete transfer function, given by,

$$H(z) = \frac{Y(z)}{X(z)} \qquad (15.6)$$

Multiplying the numerator and denominator by z^k in Eq. (15.5),

$$H(z) = \frac{a_0z^k+a_1z^{k-1}+ \ldots +a_k}{z^k+b_1z^{k-1}+ \ldots +b_k} \qquad (15.7)$$

The poles and zeroes for the discrete transfer function can be determined in much the same way as is done for the continuous transfer function. Let $z_1, z_2, \ldots, z_k$ represent k zeroes and $p_1, p_2, \ldots, p_k$ represent k poles. The transfer function can then be expressed as

$$H(z) = \frac{a_0(z-z_1)(z-z_2) \ldots (z-z_k)}{(z-p_1)(z-p_2) \ldots (z-p_k)} \qquad (15.8)$$

15.7.2 Direct Realization Forms

Two direct forms exist for the realization of digital filters. In the first form, known as the direct form I method, the difference equation given by Eq. (15.3) is directly implemented, as shown in Fig. 15.19. It may be noted that the delay operations on the left provide

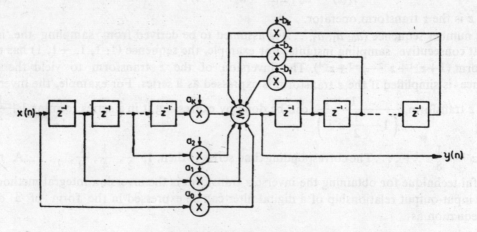

Fig. 15.19 Direct form I realization

successively-shifted values of $x(n)$ while those on the right provide comparable values of $y(n)$. One disadvantage of the direct form I method is that it may require up to $2k$ delay elements for a kth order system.

In the second form, termed the direct form II method, the $H(z)$ is rewritten in the form

$$H(z) = \frac{N(z)}{D(z)} \tag{15.9}$$

Since $Y(z) = H(z)X(z)$, it follows that

$$Y(z) = \frac{N(z)X(z)}{D(z)} = N(z)W(z) \tag{15.10}$$

where $W(z)$ is a new variable given by

$$W(z) = \frac{X(z)}{D(z)} \tag{15.11}$$

The inverse transforms can be expressed as

$$w(n) = x(n) - \sum_{i=1}^{k} b_i w(n-i) \tag{15.12}$$

and

$$y(n) = \sum_{i=0}^{k} a_i w(n-i) \tag{15.13}$$

The direct form II realization is shown in Fig. 15.20. Assuming that $w(n)$ is available, $w(n-1)$, $w(n-2)$, etc. are generated by unit delays. These are then weighted by appropriate $-b_n$'s and summed with $x(n)$ to obtain $w(n)$, according to Eq. (15.12). The output $y(n)$ is then obtained by summation of weighted values of $w(n)$ to $w(n-k)$ according to Eq. (15.13). It may be noted that this method requires only k delay elements. This method is also sometimes referred to as the "canonic form"

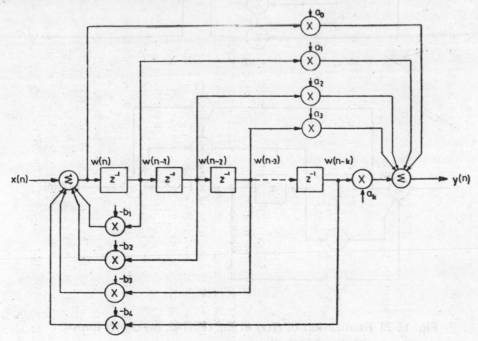

Fig. 15.20 Direct form II realization

EXAMPLE 15.1 For the $H(z)$ of Eq. (15.14), develop the direct forms I and II.

$$H(z) = \frac{2+2.2z^{-1}+0.48z^{-2}}{1+0.1z^{-1}-0.3z^{-2}} \qquad (15.14)$$

Solution: For obtaining the direct form I, express $y(n)$ as a difference equation,

$$y(n) = 2x(n)+2.2x(n-1)+0.48x(n-2)-0.1y(n-1)+0.3y(n-2) \qquad (15.15)$$

The direct form I, shown in Fig. 15.21(a), readily follows.

To obtain the direct form II, we can solve for $W(z)$ and $Y(z)$ as indicated by Eqs. (15.10) and (15.11) and invert them using Eqs. (15.12) and (15.13). This yields

$$w(n) = x(n)-0.1w(n-1)+0.3w(n-2) \qquad (15.16)$$

and

$$y(n) = 2w(n)+2.2w(n-1)+0.48(n-2) \qquad (15.17)$$

The corresponding realization is shown in Fig. 15.21(b).

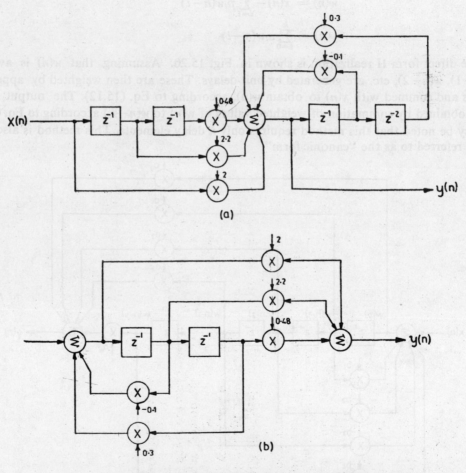

(a)

(b)

Fig. 15.21 Realization of $H(z)$ of Eq. (15.14): (a) direct form I; (b) direct form II

15.7.3 Parameter Quantization Effects

In the practical realization of digital filters three major sources of parameter quantization error arise, viz., (i) quantization of the input signal into a finite number of discrete levels, (ii) accumulation of round-off errors in the arithmetic operations in the systems, and (iii) quantization of the transfer function coefficients a_l and b_i, when represented by a finite number of bits.

The resulting errors due to these sources have different characteristics. The quantization errors can often be considered equivalent to addition of a white noise with an rms value equal to $\dfrac{q}{\sqrt{12}}$ where q is the interval between successive levels in the quantizer. The round-off errors from arithmetic operations can appear as a dead-band effect, in which the output remains the same for a small range of input, or can produce small oscillations about the correct signal output value. The errors due to the finite-length representation of the coefficients produce changes in the frequency response characteristics of the filter. The problem becomes severe when (i) the sampling rate increases in relation to the frequency range of the transfer function being realized, or (ii) the order of the difference equation increases. In view of the last-mentioned effect, it may be noted that the coefficient truncation errors reduce drastically, if higher-order difference equations are realized by a combination of lower-order difference equations rather than as a single higher-order equation[11].

15.7.4 Cascade and Parallel Realizations

By decomposing the transfer function $H(z)$ into the product of several simpler transfer functions, as given by

$$H(z) = a_0 H_1(z) H_2(z) \ldots H_p(z) \tag{15.18}$$

where $H_1(z)$, $H_2(z)$ etc. refer to the transfer function of the individual sections, it is possible

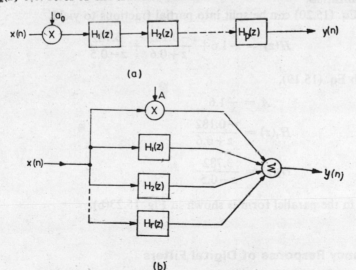

(a)

(b)

Fig. 15.22 Realization of transfer functions: (a) series realization; (b) parallel realization

to realize the transfer function $H(z)$ as a cascaded or series realization form shown in Fig. 15.22(a). On the other hand, if $H(z)$ is decomposed into the sum of several simpler transfer functions as

$$H(z) = A + H_1(z) + H_2(z) + \ldots + H_r(z) \qquad (15.19)$$

then the parallel realization form shown in Fig. 15.22(b) can be used to realize $H(z)$.

EXAMPLE 15.2 For the $H(z)$ of Eq. (15.14), develop the cascaded and parallel realization schemes.

Solution: (i) Cascade Realization:
Expressing $H(z)$ of Eq. (15.14) in positive powers of z,

$$H(z) = \frac{2z^2 + 2.2z + 0.48}{z^2 + 0.1z - 0.3} \qquad (15.20)$$

Factorization yields,

$$H(z) = \frac{2(z + 0.8)(z + 0.3)}{(z + 0.6)(z - 0.5)} \qquad (15.21)$$

The zeroes are at -0.8 and -0.3, and the poles are at -0.6 and 0.5. By grouping one pole with one zero, the transfer function can be expressed as a product, $2 \times H_1(z) \times H_2(z)$, where

$$H_1(z) = \frac{1 + 0.8z^{-1}}{1 + 0.6z^{-1}} \qquad (15.22)$$

and

$$H_2(z) = \frac{1 + 0.3z^{-1}}{1 - 0.5z^{-1}} \qquad (15.23)$$

The resulting realization is shown in Fig. 15.23(a).

(ii) Parallel Realization:
   The $H(z)$ of Eq. (15.20) can be split into partial fractions to yield,

$$H(z) = -1.6 + \frac{-0.182}{z + 0.6} + \frac{3.782}{z - 0.5}$$

Comparing with Eq. (15.19),

$$A = -1.6$$

$$H_1(z) = \frac{-0.182}{z + 0.6}$$

and

$$H_2(z) = \frac{3.782}{z - 0.5}$$

The realization in the parallel form is shown in Fig. 15.23(b).

15.7.5 Frequency Response of Digital Filters

For the steady-state response to be meaningful, it is necessary that the realized system is stable, i.e., all the poles of the transfer function should lie inside the unit circle in the z plane.

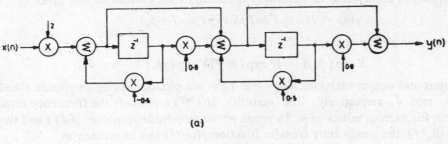

(a)

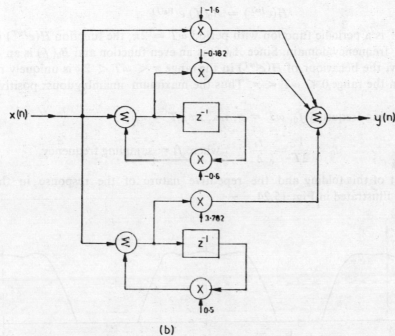

(b)

Fig. 15.23 Realization of $H(z)$ of Eq. (15.14): (a) series
form; (b) parallel form

If the input is a sinusoid, the stready-state output of the filter will be a sampled sinusoid of
the same frequency as the input sinusoid. If $x(n)$ is given by

$$x(n) = X \exp (j(n\omega T + \phi_x)) \qquad (15.24)$$

where X = amplitude, ω = radian frequency = $2\pi f$, ϕ_x = arbitrary phase, and T = period
of sampling frequency, the output $y(n)$ can be expressed in the form

$$y(n) = Y \exp (j(n\omega T + \phi_y)) \qquad (15.25)$$

where Y and ϕ_y are the amplitude and phase respectively.

Taking z transform of $x(n)$ and multiplying by the transfer function $H(z)$, it follows that[12]

$$Y(z) = \frac{zX \exp (j\phi_x)}{z - \exp (j\omega T)} H(z) \qquad (15.26)$$

The inversion of Eq. (15.26) to yield only the steady-state portion of $y(n)$ gives

$$y(n) = H \exp(j\omega T) X \exp(jn\omega T + \phi_x) \qquad (15.27)$$

Substituting for $y(n)$ from Eq. (15.25) in Eq. (15.27),

$$Y \exp(j\phi_y) = H \exp(j\omega T) X \exp(j\phi_x) \qquad (15.28)$$

The input and output variables $Xe^{j\phi_x}$ and $Ye^{j\phi_y}$ are phasors having amplitude X and Y and phase ϕ_x and ϕ_y respectively. The quantity $H(e^{j\omega T})$ represents the frequency response of the system for various values of ω. In terms of the amplitude response $A_0(f)$ and the phase response $B_0(f)$, the steady state transfer function $H(e^{j\omega T})$ can be written as

$$H(e^{j\omega T}) = A_0(f) \, e^{jB_0(f)} \qquad (15.29)$$

Since $e^{j\omega T}$ is a periodic function with period $\omega T = 2\pi$, the function $H(e^{j\omega T})$ is also periodic in the frequency domain. Since $A_0(f)$ is an even function and $B_0(f)$ is an odd function of frequency, the behaviour of $H(e^{j\omega T})$ in the range $\pi < \omega T < 2\mu$ is uniquely related to its behaviour in the range $0 < \omega T < \pi$. Thus the maximum unambiguous positive value for ωT is π.

At the folding frequency f_0, $\omega T = \pi$, i.e., $2\pi f_0 T = \pi$,

$$f_0 = \frac{1}{2T} = \frac{f_s}{2} \qquad \text{where } f_s = \text{sampling frequency.}$$

The effect of this folding and the repetitive nature of the response in the frequency domain are illustrated in Fig. 15.24.

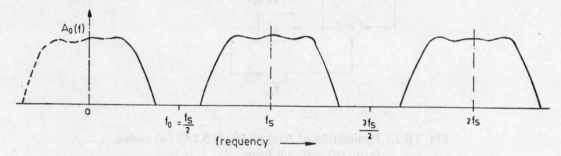

Fig. 15.24 Frequency response of digital filters showing "folding"

15.7.6 Digital Filter Design—Approaches

The primary goal in achieving a prescribed signal-filtering requirement by digital filters is that of determining the difference equation or discrete transfer function of the digital filter. The concept of frequency response plays an important role in digital filter design though other concepts, such as time variable, adaptive, and non-linear filters are possibilities with digital systems. Digital filters of the discrete time linear time invariant type can be classified, based on the duration of the impulse response, as "infinite impulse response (IIR)" and "finite impulse response (FIR)" types. An IIR filter is one in which the impulse response has an infinite number of samples. Thus the impulse response $h(n)$ is non-zero at an infinite number of points in the range $n_1 \leqslant n \leqslant \infty$. In contrast, the FIR filter is one in which the impulse response $h(n)$ is limited to a finite number of samples defined over the range $n_1 \leqslant n \leqslant n_2$, where n_1 and n_2 are both finite.

The possible realization procedures can be divided into three broad classes, viz., (a) recursive realization, (b) non-recursive realization, and (c) FFT realization.

(a) Recursive Realization

In recursive realization, the present output value depends both on the input (present and past values) as well as on previous values of the output. It can be usually recognized by the presence of both a_i and b_i terms in the input-output relationship of Eq. (15.3). The recursive realization is illustrated in Fig. 15.25(a). Since the impulse response of recursive filters extends to infinity, this realization is particularly suited for implementation of IIR filters.

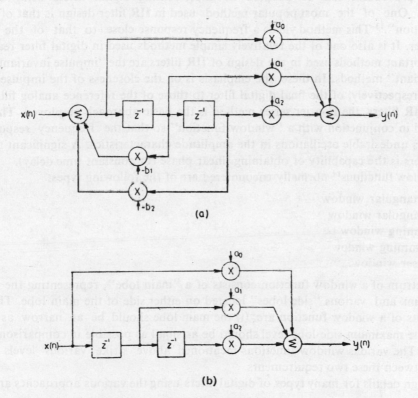

(a)

(b)

Fig. 15.25 Realization of digital filters: (a) recursive realization;
(b) non-recursive realization

(b) Non-Recursive Realization

In this realization the present value of the output depends only on the present and past values of the input. Equivalently, the coefficients b_i in Eq. (15.3) are zero for this case. A typical realization is shown in Fig. 15.25(b). Since the impulse response yielded by this type of realization is finite, the resulting filters are always stable in contrast to possible instability of the filters resulting from the recursive realization.

(c) *FFT Realization*

In FFT realization, the input signal is transformed by FFT, filtering done in the frequency domain by modification of the frequency spectrum, and then the inverse transform performed. A schematic block diagram of this technique is shown in Fig. 15.26.

Fig. 15.26 Digital filtering using FFT

Various procedures can be adopted in implementing digital filters using the above techniques. One of the most popular methods used in IIR filter design is that of "bilinear transformation".[13] This method yields a frequency response close to that of the reference analog filter. It is also one of the relatively simple methods used in digital filter realizations. Other important methods used in the design of IIR filters are the "impulse invariant" and the "step invariant" methods. In these, the emphasis is on the closeness of the impulse and step responses respectively, of the final digital filter to those of the reference analog filter. In the design of FIR filters, the Fourier series method is the basic approach employed. The method is best used in conjunction with a "window function" so that the frequency response does not possess undesirable oscillations in the amplitude characteristics. A significant advantage of FIR filters is the capability of obtaining linear phase (or constant time delay).

The window functions[14] normally encountered are of the following types:

   (a) Rectangular window
   (b) Triangular window
   (c) Hanning window
   (d) Hamming window
   (e) Kaiser window.

The spectrum of a window function consists of a "main lobe", representing the middle of the spectrum and various "side lobes" located on either side of the main lobe. The general requirements of a window function are: (i) the main lobe should be as narrow as possible, and (ii) the maximum side·lobe level should be as small as possible in comparison with the main lobe. The various window functions mentioned above strike various levels of compromise between these two requirements.

The design details for many types of digital filters using the various approaches are detailed in Ref. 15.

15.8 FAST FOURIER TRANSFORM

The fast fourier transform is a computational tool which facilitates signal analysis, such as power spectrum analysis and filter simulation using digital computers.

In the digital analysis of signals, the continuous waveform to be analysed is first sampled and then converted to digits that represent the amplitude of the samples. The digital analyser operates on this number sequence, and produces another number sequence as a result of the digital processing. If the resulting sequence represents the samples of a time sequence, it can be converted to the analog form by D/A converters to form a continuous waveform in the time domain. In the case of Fourier transformation of the number sequence, the result of the digital process is a number sequence representing in the frequency domain the characteristics of the continuous waveform that formed the basis for the input number sequence.

The Fourier transform of a number sequence is referred to as the "discrete Fourier transform (DFT)" and is analogous to the Fourier series transform and the Fourier integral transform of continuous and transient time signals. The DFT defines the spectrum of a time series. The convolution of two-time series is equivalent to the multiplication of the DFTs of the two-time series.

The fast Fourier transform is a highly-efficient procedure for computing the DFT of a time series. For the calculation of the DFT of a time series having $N = 2^n$ samples, while the straight-forward calculation of DFT involves N^2 arithmetic operations, the same can be done by FFT with only $2N_n = 2N \log_2 N$ arithmetic operations[16]. In a computer that takes about half an hour to do the DFT calculations in the conventional way for $N = 8192$ samples, the calculation time required using FFT is only about five seconds.

15.8.1 The Discrete Fourier Transform

The DFT is defined by

$$A_r = \sum_{k=0}^{N-1} X_k e^{-(2\pi jrk/N)}, \ r = 0, 1, \ldots, N-1 \tag{15.30}$$

where A_r is the rth coefficient of the DFT, X_k denotes the kth sample of the time series which consists of N samples, and $j = \sqrt{-1}$. The X_ks can be complex numbers and the A_rs are almost always complex. For notational convenience, Eq. (15.30) can be written as

$$A_r = \sum_{k=0}^{N-1} X_k W^{rk}, \ r = 0, 1, \ldots, N-1 \tag{15.31}$$

where

$$W = e^{-(2\pi j/N)} \tag{15.32}$$

The inverse transform of the DFT, (IDFT), is given by

$$X_l = \frac{1}{N} \sum_{r=0}^{N-1} A_r W^{rl}, \ l = 0, 1, \ldots, N-1 \tag{15.33}$$

The insertion of this into Eq. (15.31) can be done easily to confirm tnat Eq. (15.33) indeed represents IDFT.

15.8.2 Fast Fourier Transform from DFT

FFT is an algorithm that makes possible the computation of the DFT of a time series more rapidly than by other algorithms available. As an example of the computation of the DFT of a trivial time series containing only two sample values, consider X_k for $k = 0$ and 1.

The number of samples N is equal to 2, and the DFT will have only two terms, obtained by evaluating Eq. (15.30) for $r = 0$ and 1.

$$A_r = \sum_{k=0}^{1} X_k \, e^{-2\pi jrk/2}, \, r = 0, 1 \tag{15.34}$$

Using Eq. (15.32), this yields,

$$A_0 = X_0 + W^0 X_1 \tag{15.35}$$

and

$$A_1 = X_0 + W^1 X_1 \tag{15.36}$$

The simple DFT of a two-point sequence is represented schematically in Fig. 15.27 (the weighting factors W^0 and W^1 are indicated near the arrow head).

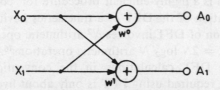

Fig. 15.27 Two-point DFT

Consider now a four-point series having sample values as X_k, $k = 0, 1, 2$ and 3. Using Eqs. (15.30) and (15.31)

$$A_r = \sum_{k=0}^{3} X_k \, e^{-2\pi jrk/4}, \, r = 0, 1, 2, 3 \tag{15.37}$$

$$= X_0 + X_1 W^r + X_2 W^{2r} + X_3 W^{3r}, \, r = 0, 1, 2, 3 \tag{15.38}$$

The individual DFT values are:

$$A_0 = X_0 + X_1 W^0 + X_2 W^0 + X_3 W^0 \tag{15.39}$$

$$A_1 = X_0 + X_1 W^1 + X_2 W^2 + X_3 W^3 \tag{15.40}$$

$$A_2 = X_0 + X_1 W^2 + X_2 W^4 + X_3 W^6 \tag{15.41}$$

$$A_3 = X_0 + X_1 W^3 + X_2 W^6 + X_3 W^9 \tag{15.42}$$

Since $W^0 = 1$, $W^2 = -1$, $W^3 = -W^1$, $W^4 = 1$, and so on, we can rewrite Eqs. (15.39) to (15.42) as:

$$A_0 = X_0 + X_1 + X_2 + X_3 \tag{15.43}$$

$$A_1 = X_0 + X_1 W^1 - X_2 - X_3 W^1 \tag{15.44}$$

$$A_2 = X_0 + X_1 W^2 + X_2 + X_3 W^2 \tag{15.45}$$

$$A_3 = X_0 + X_1 W^3 - X_2 - X_3 W^3 \tag{15.46}$$

This set of equations can be again regrouped as

$$A_0 = X_0 + W^0 X_2 + W^0 (X_1 + W^0 X_3) \tag{15.47}$$

$$A_1 = X_0 + W^2 X_2 + W^1 (X_1 + W^2 X_3) \tag{15.48}$$

$$A_2 = X_0 + W^0 X_2 + W^2 (X_1 + W^0 X_3) \tag{15.49}$$

$$A_3 = X_0 + W^2 X_2 + W^3 (X_1 + W^2 X_3) \tag{15.50}$$

The advantage gained by this regrouping is that the DFT of the four-point sequence can be obtained from the DFT of two sets of two-point sequences, as illustrated in Fig. 15.28. It may be noted that by grouping X_0 and X_2 and performing a two-point DFT, and adding this to weighted DFTs obtained from a two-point DFT operation on X_1 and X_3, the final DFT values A_0, A_1, A_2, and A_3 can be obtained.

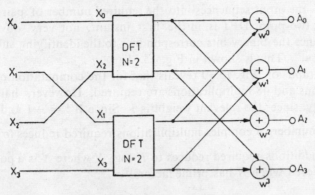

Fig. 15.28 Four-point FFT

The procedure for obtaining the DFT values of an eight-point time series follows in the same lines. As illustrated in Fig. 15.29, the signal-flow graph shows that A_0, A_1, ..., A_7 are the weighted sums of B_0, B_1, B_2, B_3 and C_0, C_1, C_2, C_3 where B_0 to B_3 and C_0 to C_3 are respectively, the DFT coefficients of the even numbered sequences X_0, X_4, X_2, X_6 and that of the odd-numbered sequences X_1, X_5, X_3, X_7. Further, B_0 to B_3 are shown to be weighted sums of DFT's obtained from two-point DFT operations on the pairs X_0, X_4 and X_2, X_6. The DFT values C_0 to C_3 are similarly obtained. The complete operation for the calculation of DFT of the eight-point time sequence reduces to multiplications and additions as shown

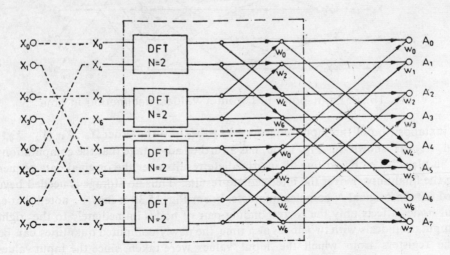

Fig. 15.29 Eight-point FFT from four-point FFT

in Fig. 15.30. Each node represents a variable obtained by summing the weighted values of the variables connected to that node through indicating arrows. The weights, if other than unity, are indicated at the arrow heads. The DFT value A_3, for example, is related to the X values as follows:

$$A_3 = X_0 + W^4 X_4 + W^6(X_2 + W^4 X_6) + W^3 [(X_1 + W^4 X_5) + W^6(X_3 + W^4 X_7)] \qquad (15.51)$$

The grouping of the input sequences into the required number of pairs that can then be operated upon by a two-point DFT is, in the first instant, not very obvious. Fortunately, this becomes clear once the binary bits corresponding to the identifying subscript are examined after "bit-reversal". This is shown in Fig. 15.31.

The signal-flow graph of Fig. 15.30 reveals that for the computation of DFT's A_0 to A_7, a total of 24 additions and 48 multiplications are required. However, half of the multiplications are by unity since the relevant weight is 1. Since $W^4 = -1$ and $W^6 = -W^2$ etc., generally, the total number of complex multiplications required reduces to about $\frac{N}{2} \log_2 N$ and the number of additions required reduces to $N \log_2 N$ where N is a power of 2. Further simplification is achieved when N has prime factors[17].

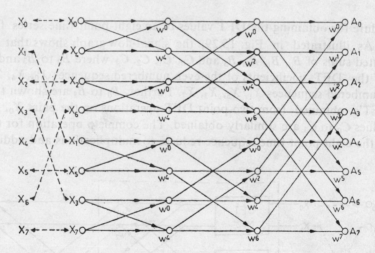

Fig. 15.30 Eight-point FFT from X values; decimation in time

The juxtaposition of the input sequences X_0 to X_7 into the order X_0, X_4, X_2, X_6, X_1, X_5, X_3 and X_4, as shown in Fig. 15.30 has a further advantage that the computations can be done "in place", i.e., by writing all intermediate results over the original data sequence, and writing the final answer over the intermediate results. Thus no storage is needed beyond that required for the original N complex numbers. From Fig. 15.30 it may be noted that each pair of input nodes affects only the corresponding pair of nodes immediately to the right and if the computation deals with two nodes at a time, the newly-computed quantities can be written into the registers from which the input values were taken, since the input values are no longer needed for further computation.

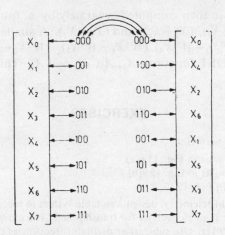

Fig. 15.31 Bit reversal to obtain the appropriate
input pairs

15.8.3 Decimation in Time and Decimation in Frequency

For the eight-point DFT considered as an example in Sec. 15.8.2, the samples X_0 to X_7 are divided into two groups, viz., X_0, X_4, X_2 and X_6, and X_1, X_5. X_3 and X_7. The DFT operations on the two groups are separately carried out, and the final DFT coefficients are obtained by the weighted sum of the results of DFT operations on the individual groups. It may be noted that the grouping is done by arranging the odd-numbered points into one group and the even-numbered points into another. This procedure is referred to as decimation in time.

An altogether different method of obtaining the DFT is by decimation in frequency. This is carried out by splitting the number sequence into two groups so that X_0 to X_3 form one group and X_4 to X_7 another group, in the eight-point case. The even-numbered transform

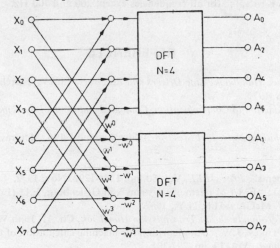

Fig. 15.32 Decimation in frequency

points A_0, A_2, A_4 and A_6 are then computed separately by a four-point DFT operation on the sums (X_0+X_4), (X_1+X_5), (X_2+X_6), and (X_3+X_7). A similar four-point DFT computation on weighted sums $(W^0X_0 - W^0X_4)$, $(W^1X_1 - W^1X_5)$, $(W^2X_2 - W^2X_6)$, and $(W^3X_3 - W^3X_7)$ yields the odd-numbered DFT functions A_1, A_3, A_5, and A_7. This is illustrated in Fig. 15.32.

EXERCISES

15.1 Design simple circuits to perform:

(a) Amplitude modulation, as in Fig. 15.8(a)
(b) Frequency modulation, as in Fig. 15.9(b)
(c) Phase modulation as in Fig. 15.10.

15.2 Using the principles of FM telemetry, design a suitable system to record the instantaneous values of three parameters, using a single carrier for transmission. The individual parameters have frequency components limited to 100 Hz. Use sub-carrier oscillator frequencies compatible with this requirement.

15.3 Design an 8 channel PCM system for transmission of low frequency data in the range DC to 10 Hz. If the overall accuracy desired is $\pm 1\%$ estimate the minimum bit rate required for transmission. (Hint: One additional channel can be used to transmit a bit-stream for frame synchronization.)

15.4 The following averaging is performed on a calculator. For every five input entries, the average is obtained and printed out. If the input is entered at a rate of one entry per second, estimate the frequency response resulting from this process.

15.5 A "running average" system utilizes the following algorithm:

$$y_n = \frac{x_n}{1.1} + \frac{y_{n-1}}{11}$$

If the input rate is 100 samples per second, estimate the RC value of the equivalent low-pass filter.

15.6 Design a digital filter complete with ADC and DAC for executing the algorithm of Problem 15.5, using TTL circuits. Use 8 bit 2's complement sign magnitude binary representation of numbers. Assume input to be -5 V to $+5$ V.

15.7 Proceeding in the same lines as described to obtain the FFT as shown in Fig. 15.30 for the case of eight input samples, construct the flow graph for the calculation of FFT from 16 input samples.

15.8 Two sinusoids having frequencies of 200 Hz (amplitude 1 V) and 700 Hz (amplitude of 3 V) are sampled at a rate of 1600 samples/s. From a set of 16 known samples, calculate the FFT and show that the FFT function has a zero value for all frequencies except 200 and 700 Hz.

REFERENCES

1. True, K.M., *Interface Handbook: Line Drivers and Receivers*, Ch IV, Fairchild Semiconductor, Mountainview, California, 1975.
2. Morris, D.J., *Introduction to Communication, Command and Control Systems*, p. 74, Pergamon Press, Oxford, 1977.
3. Panter, P.F., *Modulation, Noise and Spectral Analysis*, pp. 192-196, McGraw-Hill, N.Y., 1965.
4. Ibid. 2, p. 68.
5. Ibid. 2, pp. 71-74.
6. Davey, J.R., "Modems", *Proc. IEEE*, Vol. 60, pp. 1284-1292, Nov. 1972.
7. Albright, C.D. et. al., "FM-FM telemetry systems", in Gruenberg, E.L. (Ed.), *Handbook of Telemetry and Remote Control*, McGraw-Hill, N.Y., 1967.
8. Freeman, R.L., *Telecommunication Transmission Handbook*, Ch. 11, John Wiley & Sons, N.Y., 1975.
9. Cooley, J.W. and Tukey, J.W., "An algorithm for machine calculation of complex fourier series", pp. 297-301, *Math. Comput.*, Vol. 19, pp. 297-301.

10. Stanley, W.D., *Digital Signal Processing*, p. 72, Reston Publishing Co. Inc., Virginia, 1975.
11. Ibid. 10, p. 92.
12. Ibid. 10, pp. 101-102.
13. Ibid. 9, pp. 168-184.
14. Rabiner, L.R. and Gold, B., *Theory and Application of Digital Signal Processing*, pp. 88-105, Prentice Hall of India, New Delhi, 1978.
15. Ibid. 10, Chapters VII and VIII.
16. Cochran, W.T. et. al., "What is fast Fourier transform?" *Proc. IEEE*, Vol. 55, pp. 1664-1677, Oct. 1967.
17. Rader, C.M., "Discrete convolutions via Mersenne transforms", *IEEE Trans. Comput.*, Vol. C. 21, pp. 1269-1273, Dec. 1972.

BIBLIOGRAPHY

Bennett, W.R. and Davey, J.R., *Data Transmission*, McGraw-Hill, N.Y., 1965.

Bergland, G.O., "A Guided tour of the fast Fourier transform", *IEEE Spectrum*, Vol. 6, No. 7, pp. 41-52, July 1969.

Butler, D. and Harvey, G., "The fast Fourier transform and its implementation", in Griffiths, J.W.R (Ed.) *Signal Processing*, Academic Press, London, p. 165, 1973.

Bylanski, P. and Ingram, D.G.W., *Digital Transmission Systems*, IEE Telecomm. Series 4, Inst. of Engineers, London, 1976.

Cappellini, V. et. al., *Digital Filters and their Applications*, Academic Press, London, 1978.

Chu, W.N., *Advances in Computer Communications*, Artech House Inc., Massachusetts, 1976.

Davenport, W.P., *Modern Data Communications*, Hayden Book Co., Inc., N.Y., 1971.

"Digital instrumentation", *Conference Publication No. 106*, Inst. of Electrical Engineers, London, 1973.

Digital signal processing committee, IEEE Acoustic Speech and Signal Processing Society, *Selected Papers in Digital Signal Processing*, II, IEEE Press, N.Y., 1975.

Doll, D.R., *Data Communications*, John Wiley & Sons, N.Y., 1978.

Foster, L.E., *Telemetry Systems*, John Wiley & Sons, N.Y., 1965.

Hersch, P., "Data communication", *IEEE Spectrum*, Vol. 8, No. 2, pp. 47-60, Feb. 1971.

Hewlett-Packard Inc., "Fourier analyzer training manual", Application Note, 140-0, Hewlett Packard, Palo Alto, California, 1975.

Hirsch, D. and Wolf, W.F., "A simple adaptive equalizer for efficient data transmission", *IEEE Trans. Comm. Tech.*, Vol. COM-18, No. 1, pp. 5-11, Feb., 1978.

Jury, E.I., *Theory and Application of the Transform Method*, John Wiley & Sons, N.Y., 1964.

Merritt, R., "Sizing up long distance data transmission needs", *Instruments and Control Systems*, Vol. 51, No. 9, pp. 23-29, Sept. 1978.

Nelson, G.E. and Ricci, D.W., "A practical interface system for electronic instruments", *Hewlett-Packard Journal*, Vol. 23, No. 10, pp. 2-7, Oct. 1972.

Oppenheim, A.V. (Ed.), *Applications of Digital Signal Processing*, Prentice-Hall, Inc., New Jersey, 1978.

Oppenheim, A.V. and Schafer, R.W., *Digital Signal Processing*, Prentice-Hall, Inc., New Jersey, 1975.

Parker S.R. and Hess, S.F., "Limit cycle oscillations in digital filters", *IEEE Trans. on Circuit Theory*, Vol. CT-18, No. 6, pp. 687-697, Nov. 1971.

Parks, T.W. and McClellan, J H., "Chebyshev approximation for non-recursive digital filters with linear phase", *IEEE Trans. on Circuit Theory*, Vol. CT-19, No. 2, pp. 189-194, March 1972.

Peled, A. and Lin, B., *Digital Signal Processing*, John Wiley & Sons, New Jersey, 1976.

Rabiner, L.R. and Rader, C.M. (Ed.), *Digital Signal Processing*, IEEE Press, New York, 1972.

Robinson, E.A. and Silvia, M.J., *Digital Signal Processing and Time Series Analysis*, Holden Day Inc., San Francisco, 1978.

Special Issue on FFT, *IEEE Trans. on Audio and Electroacoustics*, Vol. AU-15, No. 2, June 1967.

Special Issue on Digital Filtering, *IEEE Trans. on Audio and Electroacoustics*, Vol. AU-18, No. 2, June 1970.

Special Issue on Digital Signal Processing, *IEEE Trans. on Audio and Electroacoustics*, Vol. AU-20, No. 4, Oct. 1972.

Washburn, J., "Communications interface primer—Part I", *Instruments and Control Systems*, Vol. 51, No. 3, pp. 43-48, March 1978.

Weissberger, A.J., "Modems: The key to interfacing digital data to analog telecommunication lines", *Electronic Design*, Vol. 27, No. 10, pp. 82-89, May 10, 1979.

Wier, J.M., "Digital data communication techniques", *Proc. IRE*, Vol. 49, No. 5, pp. 196-209, Jan. 1961.

16

MICROPROCESSORS

16.1 INTRODUCTION

A microprocessor is an LSI (large scale integration) chip that is capable of performing arithmetic and logic functions as defined by a given program. The system by itself does not form an operational computer, and additional circuits for memory and input/output must be supplied and interfaced with the system. The "software", viz., the program for controlling the operation of the microprocessor itself is also to be necessarily provided. Since the microprocessor forms only a part—though, an important part—of a microcomputer, it is also necessary to study the various elements of a microcomputer to properly understand the usefulness of the microprocessor.

16.1.1 Microcomputer

A microcomputer comprises the following elements: (i) microprocessor/central processing unit (CPU), (ii) random access memory (RAM), (iii) read only memory (ROM), (iv) input/output devices (I/O), and (v) interface components.

The simplified block diagram of a microcomputer, as shown in Fig. 16.1, comprises an arithmetic logic unit (ALU), memories for temporary and semi-permanent storage, input/output devices, and a control unit. The memory contains in coded form the operations to be performed and the information to be processed. The arithmetic and logic operations are carried out by the ALU. Information is transferred from outside the computer into it and vice versa by the I/O devices. The control unit coordinates the activities of the various elements. The microprocessor used in a mircrocomputer consists of the control unit and ALU, which in combination forms the central processing unit (CPU). It has the ability to control the I/O devices and to transfer information to and from the memory.

The organizational structure of a computing system is normally termed as the "Architecture". Different types of architecture arise due to variations in the simplified block diagram structure shown in Fig. 16.1. The design of many microcomputers (and microprocessors) is based on the Von Neumann type architecture. The control section operates on the basis of a sequence of instructions called a "program", which is stored in a memory. Each instruction consists of two parts, viz., an "operator" and an "operand". The "operator"

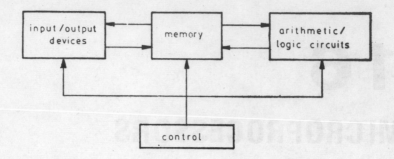

Fig. 16.1 Block diagram of a microcomputer

specifies the specific operation to be performed by the processor (arithmetic operations, such as ADD, logic operations such as OR, and control operations such as JUMP) and the operand specifies the data or address of memory location to be operated upon.

The sequence of instructions or the program corresponds to the operations to be performed by the system. To expedite data and instruction transfers between the control section and memory, special hardware structures shown in Fig. 16.2 are provided in microprocessors. They are: (i) instruction register, (ii) program counter, (iii) accumulator, and (iv) arithmetic logic unit (ALU).

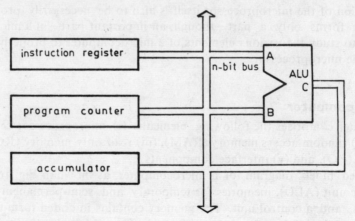

Fig. 16.2 Bidirectional bus structure in a microprocessor

The instruction register, program counter, and accumulator are the most fundamental elements of the "memory" block of Fig. 16.1. These elements are registers or storage cells typically having a capacity of bits equal to the word length of the machine. The program counter stores the "location" in the memory of the next instruction to be executed by the computer. The instruction register stores the next instruction to be executed by the computer. The accumulator stores data that are to be used in the arithmetic or logic operations or accepts data that result therefrom. The ALU performs the specified arithmetic/logic operation indicated by the instruction. It may be noted that the ALU has two inputs A and B, and the result of the logic operations performed on A and B is placed at output C.

The data entry and transfer between these hardware structures are carried through "busses" that interconnect these elements. The busses are n bit wide, where n is the word length of the machine. In an eight-bit system, the data bus thus has eight individual lines that are shared by the individual elements. The necessary time-multiplexing of the bus is handled by the bus control hardware, and is synchronized by the control unit of the microcomputer.

The control unit performs the basic supervision and synchronization of all other units of the microcomputer. Microcomputer and microprocessor systems are typically synchronous sequential digital circuits. The basis of synchronization is a standard clock signal that is provided throughout the system. Each element is designed to make a sequential transition after a predetermined number of clock pulses.

16.2 MICROPROCESSORS

The important aspects of a microprocessor are its internal organization or architecture, the concepts of stacks, resource sharing, memory access, and the software necessary to handle the various operations that the processor can perform. For a total system design, a basic understanding of the functioning of the internal hardware becomes essential.

16.2.1 Microprocessor Architecture

The basic functional building blocks of a microprocessor are: (i) the arithmetic logic unit, (ii) internal registers, (iii) instruction decoder, and (iv) control and synchronization. With reference to these basic building blocks shown in Fig. 16.3, the microprocessor may be considered to be an IC component that is capable of performing arithmetic and logic operations under program control, in a bit parallel fashion.

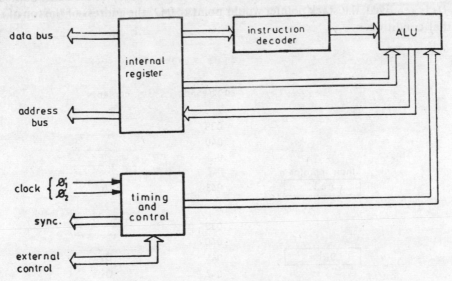

Fig. 16.3 Microprocessor architecture

The ALU performs basic arithmetic and logic operations on binary data stored in two registers of the microprocessor. Such operations are performed by an 'adder' as well as by 'logic gates'. The instruction decoder is typically an internal read only memory which translates the machine instruction code into micro-instructions which are executed by the processor. Versatility is added to modern microprocessors by permitting the user to define these micro-instructions on an external control read only memory chip. The control and synchronization block interprets the micro-instructions, to put out appropriate control and synchronization pulses to other parts of the system. Transfer of data, addresses, and control signals between the system elements are carried out by time shared busses.

Additional architectural features normally incorporated in microprocessors are: (i) stacks, (ii) resource sharing, (iii) memory access and transfer, and (iv) interrupts.

16.2.2 Stacks

A stack is a temporary storage facility that operates to store information in a sequence. This may be done in a specific portion of the main memory or in a separate buffer memory. As new information is entered into the stack, other information already stored is "moved down" in the stack. As information is removed from the stack, data is moved up in the reverse order. Thus the last information placed on the top of the stack is the first information out. This last-in first-out (LIFO) feature is realized by having a stack pointer, which is a register that contains the address of the memory location considered to be the "top" of the stack. The process of entering information into the stack is termed "push", while "pop" refers to removing information from the stack. The arrangement of data in a stack is shown in Fig. 16.4. When only one datum D_1 is stored in the stack, the stack pointer points to the address 043 relating to the top of the stack. When additional data D_2 and D_3 are pushed into the stack, the stack pointer points to 041 which is the present top of the stack address. If the datum D_3 is removed, the stack pointer would point to 042, the address of the top of the stack under that condition.

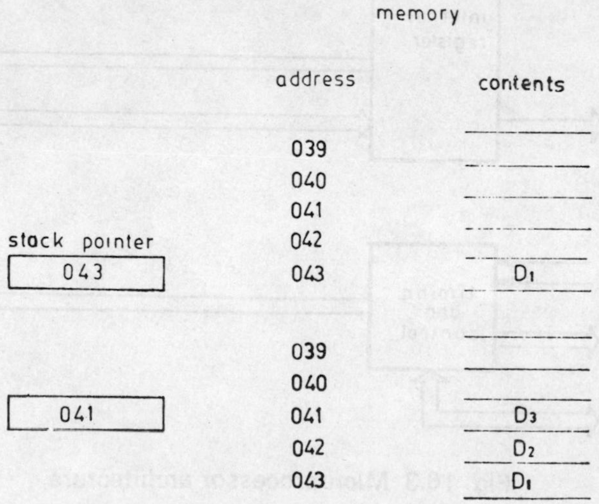

Fig. 16.4 Stack implementation

16.2.3 Resource Sharing

With the aim of reducing the pin counts in a microprocessor chip, and in order to optimize the utilization of the various internal elements, a number of scarce resources such as registers, I/O pins, busses, memory, and control programs are shared by the different individual elements by time-division multiplexing. The control and synchronization section of the microprocessor defines specific time periods or sub-cycles during which certain operations are allowed to take place. These operations may be both internal to the processor or refer to external operations, such as data or instruction fetch from memory. As a consequence of this resource sharing, the microprocessor supplies information only, during brief periods of time, which may not coincide with those periods when other system elements are prepared to accept and utilize that information. Additional hardware in the form of decoders and latches must be used to capture this information and supply it to other system elements.

16.2.4 Memory Access and Transfer

High-speed operations, particularly those requiring considerable data transfer between memory and peripheral device, utilize the memory access arrangement known as direct memory access (DMA). DMA refers to the direct transfer of data from or to predetermined memory locations to or from a peripheral device without direct control by the processor. DMA is implemented by means of an external bus that connects the external random access memory, peripherals, and microprocessor. When the microprocessor is not using the external bus, external hardware can be activated to effect a data transfer along the bus between the peripheral device and the memory.

The starting and ending addresses of the data to be transferred by DMA as well as the amount of data are indicated by external hardware. The peripheral device then transfers the data from or to the memory by a process called "cycle stealing". Since the microprocessor operates on the basis of synchronous digital circuits, certain operations are performed by it at predetermined clock cycles during which the external busses (I/O) are utilized. During other clock cycles when internal operations are performed, the busses are free for use by the peripherals and memory. By decoding the synchronization and state information, an indication that the bus is free for use can be transferred to the peripherals and memory. This is referred to as cycle stealing. This concept is a very important one for efficient microprocessor system design using high-speed peripherals.

16.2.5 Interrupts

While a microprocessor is executing a program sequence, a situation can arise in certain applications requiring immediate response of the processor to an external condition. In such a case, the processor must interrupt the program presently being executed and begin a new program to handle the external condition or "interrupt". A "simple interrupt" merely indicates that a single external device requires servicing by the processor. When several external devices exist, the particular device that requires servicing is specified by the "vectored interrupt", this being done by a data field or "vector" which specifies the identity of the external device. In "priority interrupt", the priority which a particular device has over other devices is also specified and recognized by the microprocessor. The "interrupt" condition is made known to the micropocessor by an external condition, such as an "interrupt request" applied to a specified pin of the microprocessor. The timing and control section responds to such external control signals and gears itself up to the task by performing the appropriate saving and resetting operations, prior to handling the interrupt routine. The "saving" operation is one of storing the contents of the program counter in a stack when an interrupt request is received, so that after the interrupt has been "serviced", the program counter is restored to the initial value.

16.2.6 Microprocessor Software

The sequence of instructions given to the microprocessor constitutes the software of the system. The use of the microprocessor software as a replacement for hardware components is one of the key advantages of the microprocessor systems. While for repeated addition, the hardware requirement in terms of adders are determined by the number of additions required in a conventional system, in a microprocessor, this is done by using only one adder and a sequence of instructions which uses the same adder repeatedly, by time sharing. Except for some very high-speed systems, the longer execution time resulting by such time sharing is quite tolerable and thus results in a lower overall cost of the system. Another advantage of software over hardware is that it is a non-recurring cost item, while hardware, which must be duplicated in every system is a recurring cost item. Once the software for a system has been designed and tested, it can be duplicated and stored in the memory of any number of systems. Thus the total development cost for the software is spread over the total system production. In random logic hardware systems (i.e., conventional hardware systems), though the cost of ICs themselves may not be high, the cost for the assembly and testing of the system is also a recurring item, increasing the overall cost per system.

Each microprocessor system has a software, viz., the sequence of instructions that controls the operation; but a notable difference exists between these and large-scale computers. While in the latter the software is loaded into the computer at the beginning of each computation, the software for the microcomputer is stored within the computer itself in a read-only-memory (ROM) chip. The modification of the program is achieved by merely replacing the ROM IC with another ROM IC containing a different control program. This is one of the most significant advantages of software implementation in a microcomputer system.

The different levels of software in a microprocessor can be classified as: (i) system executive, (ii) programs, (iii) sub-routines, and (iv) microprograms.

The system executive is concerned with the overall job, task, and data management for the system. A program is a set of instructions for performing a specific operation or function. A program often consists of a discrete number of individual "routines" or "sub-routines" which perform a specific calculation or algorithm. Frequently-used routines are often encoded and stored in the form of microinstructions which directly control the hardware operations. For example, instead of specifying a sequence of microprocessor instructions for performing an integer "multiply" operation, the user may specify that "multiply" is to be a new "microprogram" instruction. The microinstructions that constitute the microprogram perform the operations of multiplication in the microprocessor much more efficiently than a series of microprocessor instructions. Since the microinstructions are executed on the basis of internal microinstruction cycle times, a significant time advantage over regular microprocessor programming is achieved. In addition, for long programs or those utilizing complex operations and functions, microprogramming considerably simplifies the programming task.

16.3 MICROPROCESSOR ACCESSORIES

The various auxiliary hardware required for the microprocessor in order to make it fully operative include read only memories, random access memories, latches, tristate buffers, input-output interface circuits, and I/O devices. For application in the instrumentation field, A/D and D/A converters may also have to be used in addition to clock drivers and power supplies required for any microprocessor system in general.

16.3.1 Random Access Memory

In a micro-computer, the memory is used to store programs and data used by the microprocessor. The complexity of the program and the amount of data handled by the processor determine the memory capacity required for an application.

RAM refers to a memory in which arbitrary binary data may be written into or read from the memory. The RAM is volatile, i.e., the memory loses the stored data once the power is cut-off. Any information that is to be subsequently read out has to be "written in" again after power is turned on.

The semiconductor RAM usually uses either bipolar or metal oxide semiconductor technology. A typical cellular array consists of flip-flop memory cells as shown in Fig. 16.5(a). In memories fabricated with on-chip decoding, a decoder internal to the chip decodes the "address" (a binary word) and connects the output lines to the appropriate (addressed) memory cell, thus reducing the number of pins necessary on the chip. Memories are available in various sizes (such as 256 bit, 1024 bit, 4096 bit and 8192 bit) and are "organized" as 1024×1 bit, 32×8 bit, 512×8 bit, and so on.

In MOS memories, two types of designs are available, viz., static and dynamic. The static memory cell is similar to that in Fig. 16.5(a) but uses MOS devices. In the dynamic MOS memory shown in Fig. 16.5(b), information is stored in a capacitor, and a periodic "refresh" cycle (from a clock) is used to ensure retention of the information.

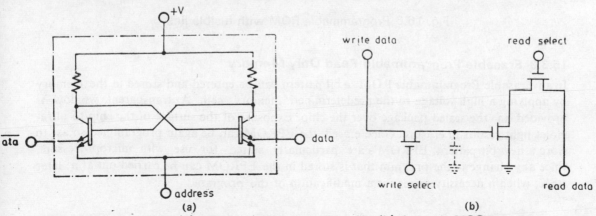

Fig. 16.5 Memories: (a) bipolar memory storage cell; (b) dynamic MOS memory

16.3.2 Read Only Memory

In an ROM, a binary pattern (such as a look-up table) is initially stored at the time of manufacture and it is only possible to read this information from time to time. The data stored in ROM is non-volatile; that is, the memory retains the stored data irrespective of whether the memory is energized or not.

While information can be either "read from" or "written into" an RAM, the ROM permits only the "read out" of the memory contents. The bit pattern that is "written in" at the time of manufacture is permanently stored in the ROM. ROMs are typically used to supply dot-matrix patterns for use in character generation on a CRT alphanumeric display. They are used in a microprocessor system for storing programs for execution. In microprogrammed computers, they are used to store the microinstructions. In the "masked" ROM, which is particularly suited for high-volume applications, the memory bit pattern is produced during the actual fabrication of the chip by the manufacturer by means of masking operations.

The field programmable ROM is based on a memory matrix in which each storage cell contains a transistor or diode including a fuse (or "fusible link") in series with one of the electrodes, as illustrated in Fig. 16.6. By addressing a particular location, the cell content at that location can be changed from a "0" to a "1" by blowing-up the fuse link. This is done by sending a high current pulse and can be carried out in the "field". However, the programming is permanent in that once it is programmed, the bit pattern cannot be altered.

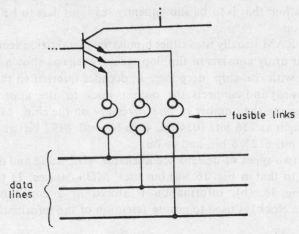

fusible links

data lines

Fig. 16.6 Programmable ROM with fusible link

16.3.3 Erasable Programmable Read Only Memory

In an Erasable Programmable ROM, a bit pattern can be entered and stored in the memory by applying a high voltage to the predetermined memory cell. A transparent window is provided in the sealed package over the chip. Exposure of the surface of the chip to ultra-violet light results in erasure. Once erased, the EPROM can be again programmed so as to store a new bit pattern. EPROM's are particularly suited for use with microprocessors, since any change in the program that is stored in the EPROM can be carried out at a later stage, when a necessity arises for a modification of the program.

16.3.4 Non-Volatile RAMs

One of the latest developments in semiconductor memories is the non-volatile RAM that uses a non-volatile storage to back-up or "shadow" a random access memory[1]. A typical device available with an organization of 1 k by 1 bit has a 1024 by 1 bit static RAM with an access time of less than 250 ns. A 1 k non-volatile electrically erasable programmable read only memory (EEPROM) "shadows" the RAM on a bit-by-bit basis. Data is written from the RAM into its non-volatile counterpart by applying a TTL level signal to a single pin. If power fails, the RAM's data can be saved by transferring it to the back-up. When the power is turned on, the reverse happens automatically and the same data will reappear in the RAM.

16.3.5 Latches

Many microprocessors have to be interfaced with the rest of the microcomputer system through appropriate latches and decoding logic. The purpose of such interfacing logic is to synchronize the operation of the microprocessor with that of the rest of the system. Latches are provided so that, in the particular time inverval when the microprocessor requests data, they are available for "reading into" the microprocessor, and when the microprocessor is ready to output data, they can be outputted and stored for use later.

Another important aspect of interfacing is to improve the "fan-out" (driving capability) of the output stage of the microprocessor. The typical drive capability of the microprocessor is one TTL load. Since a higher drive capability is often required in most systems, it is necessary to interface the microprocessor output through latches or buffers.

16.3.6 Tristate Logic

As has been mentioned in Sec. 16.2.3, the busses inside the microprocessor are time shared by the various elements. This is carried out using tristate logic busses. In contrast to the normal busses which at any time carry a "1" or "0", the tristate logic busses have an additional state wherein they can be disabled or driven to a high impedance state. Thus when the ALU has to transfer information into a memory, the logic connecting the I/O, for example, to the same bus is driven into a high impedance state. Similarly, all other logics that connect the common bus to any other element than the ALU and memory, are also driven into the high impedance state. (A similar situation exists in the "hold" mode in a microprocessor, wherein all the logic connecting the microprocessor to the data and address busses are driven into a high impedance state and they are thus suspended in a floating state. External peripheral devices can now access the busses for direct data transfer without intervention or interference by processor operations.)

16.3.7 Status Decoders

As was noted earlier, the microprocessor is in a position to deliver data to and take data from I/O ports only at specific times within its machine cycle. The exact moment for transfer of data into the microprocessor has to be identified by decoding the state of the microprocessor. The status information is provided by the microprocessor on the data bus, but the system designer has to decode the status data given by the data bus and transfer data from the I/O port into the microprocessor or vice versa at a particular instant decided by the decoded status information. A combination of decoder and latches with a tristate logic output is used for this purpose (e.g., Intel 8212).

16.3.8 Input-Output Devices

Some of the standard input-output devices used with microcomputers are:

Input: Keyboard (solid state or teletype)
Tape readers (paper or magnetic)
Card readers (paper or magnetic)
Disk drives (standard or floppy)
Optical readers (mark or character)

Output: Punches (card and paper tape)
Printers (impact or non-impact)
Displays
Plotters.

The system designer has to decide which of these devices is most suitable for a given application and interface the device to the computer. This interfacing is done through proper interfacing ICs, and by utilizing special hardware or software to make the external device compatible with the logic levels, timing, and synchronization of the processor.

16.3.9 Interface Logic

Interface logic is one of the most important elements of the microcomputer system. While the microprocessor operates on its own internal characteristics that cannot be modified by the user, the external I/O devices also likewise have their own characteristics. To enable the processor to control and process the data associated with such external devices, it is necessary to properly code and synchronize the various elements of the system. The basic physical and electrical compatibility among the diverse elements is achieved by using appropriate latches, encoders, decoders, and converters. The appropriate "codes" can then be achieved in software, e.g., conversion of binary code to ASC II Code, etc.

When the microcomputer has to communicate with remote devices, some type of communication interface device must be provided. This device performs the functions of parallel to serial or serial to parallel conversion, synchronization, and transmission control. The necessary interface functions are implemented on a LSI chip, referred to as the universal asynchronous receiver transmitter (UART), shown in Fig. 16.7, or asynchronous communication interface adaptor (ACIA). Both these LSI devices utilize clocked shift registers to transfer parallel information to serial format and vice versa. Transmission-control bits, such as start and stop bits, as well as a parity bit are also automatically added to the serial data stream.

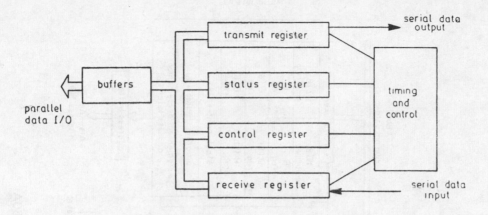

Fig. 16.7 Block schematic of UART or ACIA

16.4 INTERNAL STRUCTURE OF A MICROPROCESSOR

Having considered the general features available in microprocessors, the sequence of operations involved in a specific practical microprocessor is considered in this section. The necessity for the various internal registers and other electronic hardware built within the microprocessor chip can thus be better understood.

16.4.1 Functional Description of Intel 8080 A

A typical microprocessor that is popular and possesses many features of other microprocessors available commercially, is the Intel 8080. The basic machine architecture of Intel 8080 A is organized around an 8 bit data bus, and it consists of the following basic elements that are directly attached to the internal data bus: (i) a bidirectional I/O data bus, (ii) accumulator, (iii) five flag flip-flops, (iv) instruction register, (v) arithmetic logic unit, (iv) six general purpose registers, and (vii) temporary registers.

In addition, it also has a timing and control unit and an address buffer associated with the 16-bit address bus, as shown in the schematic diagram of Fig. 16.8.

The communication of data between the microprocessor and external logic takes place over an 8-bit bidirectional data bus. The data bus is connected to an 8-bit buffer or latch which captures the data on the data bus at appropriate points during the machine cycle. The 8-bit buffer is controlled by the timing and control unit to fully synchronize the I/O data bus with the internal data transfer operations.

A separate 8-bit internal data bus enables the communication of data between the various internal registers. The timing and control unit specifies which register will capture the data appearing on the internal data bus at appropriate points during the machine cycle.

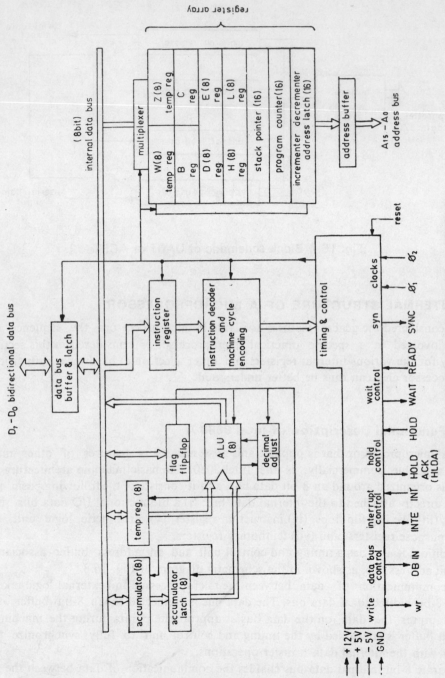

Fig. 16.8 Schematic block diagram of Intel 8080A

The accumulator serves as a latch for storing data that are to be processed by the ALU or for receiving such data that have already been processed. The temporary register is an internal register not under user control which temporarily stores data which have been transferred from another register.

The flag flip-flops are utilized to indicate certain arithmetical conditions during microprocessor operation. These conditions viz., "carry", "parity", "sign", and "zero" are used to set the flag flip-flops when the ALU performs a calculation which produces an output resulting in an overflow or underflow, an even number, a negative number, or zero. The individual flag flip-flops can be tested by later instructions for the presence or absence of a given condition, and subsequent program routines can follow depending on that given condition.

The instruction register is a register which is connected to the internal data bus. At an appropriate point of the machine cycle, an instruction code appears on the internal data bus, and the control unit indicates to the instruction register that the instruction should be "fetched". Once the instruction code is in the instruction register, the control unit generates the basic signals necessary to decode the instruction in the instruction decoder and issue the necessary internal data transfer operations.

The Intel 8080A is an internally-microprogrammed microprocessor. The internal microprogram stored in an ROM translates the instruction code into a sequence of microinstructions necessary to perform the arithmetic or logical operation required by the user. The nature of these microinstructions and the contents of the ROM storing the microinstructions is not accessible to the user. (This is really not necessary either, since in a small number of critical applications where there is a necessity to change the microinstructions or the microcode, microprocessors with this feature of microprogrammability can be used.)

Six 8-bit general purpose registers (B, C, D, E, H, and L in Fig. 16.8) are arranged in pairs so that they may be addressed either singly for single-precision operation (i.e., 8-bit precision), or in pairs for double precision operation (16-bit precision). Registers H and L are used for referencing the memory. Register H refers to the eight higher-order bits of the memory address location, and register L refers to the eight lower-order bits.

As was discussed in Sec. 16.2.2, stacks are often used in microprocessors for temporary storage of information. The 8080 does not have the "stack" in itself but has a 16-bit stack pointer register. The stack is located in a RAM external to 8080, but the stack pointer in 8080A "points to" the address of the top of the stack. The size of the stack is thus limited only by the "width" of the stack pointer which in this case is 16-bit wide.

Three 8-bit temporary registers shown in the Fig. 16.8 are for the internal use by the processor for arithmetic operations and transfer of data. When the transfer of data is requested from one of the general purpose registers to another, the data is first transferred from a specified general purpose register to the temporary register and then transferred back to another specified general purpose register. The registers W and Z are temporary registers associated with operations of the six general purpose registers B, C, D, E, H, and L. The multiplexer transfers the data from various registers to the internal data bus in a time multiplexed sequence during double-precision operations.

The program counter contains the address of the next instruction to be executed by the processor. This counter is automatically updated and advanced by the processor during memory cycles. A 16-bit incrementer/decrementer address latch is provided to store addresses associated with increment and decrement instructions.

The processor addresses the external memory by means of the address bus. The address buffer stores the address bits to be put on the address bus. Since the address bus is 16-bit wide, up to 64 k of 8-bit words in the external memory can be accessed directly by the processor. When the address lines are organized by external logic to indicate a particular I/O device, up to 256 such devices can be referenced by the processor.

16.4.2 Operational Sequence

A microprocessor is a synchronous sequential machine. The program, which is a sequence of steps or instructions to be carried out by the processor, is numbered sequentially and this number is stored in the program counter. On the application of power to the system, the program counter is forced to a particular starting address (or number) that corresponds to the first line of the program.

Each instruction is executed in a microprocessor in two phases: (i) the fetch phase and (ii) the execution phase. In Intel 8080A, each instruction is executed in typically one to five machine cycles. Thus, depending on the particular instruction, the time taken to complete the fetch phase and the execution phase varies between one and five machine cycles. Each machine cycle, in turn, consists of three to five states, where each state occupies typically one clock period. Hence, it is important to note that the time taken by the processor to fetch and execute one instruction may be several clock periods depending on the instruction.

The "instruction set" in a microprocessor is the set of instructions that the microprocessor has been microprogrammed for by the manufacturer. Each instruction has a "machine code" or "object code" assigned to it. This object code is a binary word assigned to the particular instruction. In order that users can avoid the drudgery of knowing and interpreting the various binary sequences corresponding to each instruction, a mnemonic code is also assigned for each instruction. The mnemonic code is translated into the binary bit pattern by an appropriate "assembler". Certain operations are also indicated symbolically, and the manufacturer gives the list of the instruction set as well as the meaning of the symbols that may have been used. The latter is only necessary to describe the operation corresponding to each mnemonic code which in turn represents an instruction set. For Intel 8080A, the symbol "$< B2 >$" means "second byte of the instruction", the symbol "r" means one of the scratch pad register references, A, B, C, D, E, H, or L, the symbol "$\leftarrow$" means "is transferred to" etc. The mnemonic instruction "ADD r" represents the symbolic operation: "$(A) \leftarrow (A)+(r)$" interpreted as "add the contents of the register r to the contents of register A and place the result in register A". Similarly, the mnemonic "INR r" describes the operation "$(r) \leftarrow (r)+1$", meaning "the contents of register r is incremented by one". Each instruction occupies a time duration of a certain number of cycles for execution, and this is specified by the manufacturer. The word length in number of bytes (1, 2, or 3) that each instruction occupies in memory is also similarly specified.

Consider the instruction "ADD B". This mnemonic instruction indicates the operation "add the contents of register B to the accumulator". The time taken to execute (to be exact, to fetch and execute) this instruction is "one machine cycle" consisting of four states. These states are T_1, T_2, T_3 and T_4, each state occupying a time duration of one clock period. Since the maximum number of states in a cycle is five, the sequence of operations for these possible five states is, in general, as indicated in Fig. 16.9. Each of the states T_1 to T_5 start with a pulse repeating at the rate of the clock frequency. The biphase clock signals ϕ_1 and ϕ_2 are non-overlapping and the typical timings for these for proper operation of the microprocessor are specified by the manufacturer. The period of the clock needed for Intel 8080A is between 0.48 μs (min) and 2 μs (max).

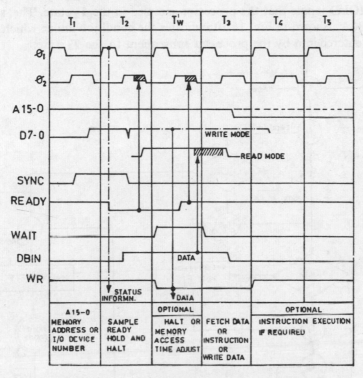

Fig. 16.9 Timing diagram of Intel 8080A

During the T_1 cycle, the contents of the program counter register are placed on the address bus ($A_0 - A_{15}$). Since the program counter contains only the "address" of the instruction and not the instruction itself, it is now the task of the external logic to locate the instruction (in a memory external to the processor) and make it available to the processor at a later state (T_3).

Following the leading edge of the ϕ_2 pulse in the T_1 state, a synchronization pulse is outputted by the microprocessor on the sync line. The designer can use this signal to activate external circuits to perform the required memory input and output functions. At the time the sync signal is outputted, the status information is also outputted on the data bus $D_0 - D_7$. The designer can transfer this information to the external latches and decode the same to determine the present status of the machine. A sync pulse thus identifies the start of each machine cycle.

The T_1 state is always followed by a T_2 state. In this state the processor determines the next state that it should enter depending on the logic levels of three signals, namely, the **READY** and **HOLD** inputs and **HALT ACKNOWLEDGE** output. Since the logic levels of the READY and HOLD inputs are governed by external logic, the user can utilize these signals to synchronize the operation of the processor with the external devices, such as memories with various access times, or with manual switches or other processors.

T_w is an optional state that the processor can enter after T_2; otherwise the processor enters the T_3 state. The entry to the T_w state or otherwise is determined by the logic levels on the READY and HOLD inputs that the processor sampled in the T_2 state. The state transition diagram for 8080A, shown in Fig. 16.10 indicates the condition under which the T_w state or T_3 state can be entered into by the processor subsequent to the T_2 state.

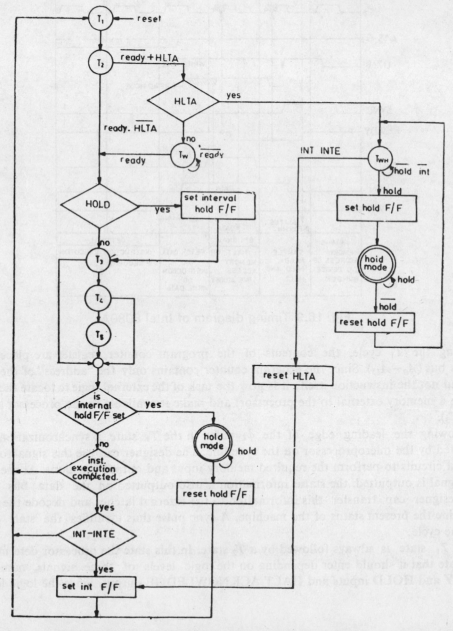

Fig. 16.10 State transition diagram of Intel 8080A

If the processor should enter the T_w state, it first determines whether a HALT instruction is being executed by it. If so, the processor enters a WAIT state designated as T_{WH} in Fig. 16.10. The processor will remain in this "wait" state until either a HOLD or an INTERRUPT signal is received by it. If the hold signal is received, the processor sets a hold flip-flop and remains in the hold state until this flip-flop is reset by an external signal. Since in the HOLD mode, the address and data busses are driven into a high impedance state, the external devices can utilize these busses without interference from the processor in this state. On resetting the hold flip-flop, the processor returns to the wait state. If the INTERRUPT signal is received as indicated by a signal on the interrupt request input line, the processor goes out of the "wait" state and begins the execution of the interrupt routine.

If in the T_w state a HALT instruction is not being executed, the processor remains in this state until the READY line goes high, indicating that valid data are available for the processor on the data bus. If no HOLD signal is received, the processor goes on to the T_3 state.

It is in the T_3 state that the data available in the data bus (these data represent the code for the particular instruction) are transferred into the instruction register. This completes the "fetch" phase. In the execution phase starting with state T_4, the instruction in the instruction register is decoded and after identifying the number of machine cycles or states required to execute that instruction, the processor generates the appropriate timing and synchronization signals.

For the "ADD B" instruction considered earlier, the instruction is completely executed by the processor in the T_4 state itself, and the processor returns to the T_1 state of the following machine cycle, the beginning of a new fetch and execute cycle. For this instruction, the T_5 state is thus absent.

The mnemonic instruction "IN, $\lhd B_2 \rhd$", requires three machine cycles to do the following symbolic operation: $(A) \leftarrow$ (input data), interpreted as "at T_1 time of the third cycle, byte two of the instruction which denotes the I/O device number, is sent to the I/O device through the address lines, and the INP status information is sent out at sync time. New data for the accumulator are loaded from the data bus when DBIN control signal (see Sec. 16.4.3) is "active".

In the first machine cycle of the three machine cycles required to execute this instruction, the processor fetches the instruction in the T_3 state and identifies in the T_4 state that the second byte is to be read from the memory. In the second machine cycle, the second byte is read, and the actual execution is done in the third cycle when, in the T_3 state, the data available from the I/O device that was addressed through the address lines by the binary "byte two" pattern is inputted into the A register. Since each cycle of this instruction relates to different status in the processor, the status decoder would identify the first cycle as instruction fetch, the second as "memory read", and the third as "input read". The type of machine cycle and the corresponding status word for other operations are shown in Fig. 16.11. The timing diagram for the fetch and execution of this instruction is illustrated in Fig. 16.12.

type of machine cycle

data bus bit	status information	instruction fetch ①	memory read ②	memory write ③	stack read ④	stack write ⑤	input read ⑥	output write ⑦	interrupt acknowledge ⑧	halt acknowledge ⑨	interrupt acknowledge while halt ⑩
D_0	INTA	0	0	0	0	0	0	0	1	0	1
D_1	$\overline{WO}$	1	1	0	1	0	1	0	1	1	0
D_2	STACK	0	0	0	1	1	0	0	0	0	0
D_3	HLTA	0	0	0	0	0	0	0	0	1	1
D_4	OUT	0	0	0	0	0	0	1	0	0	0
D_5	M_1	1	0	0	0	0	0	0	1	0	1
D_6	INP	0	0	0	0	0	1	0	0	0	0
D_7	MEMR	1	1	0	1	0	0	0	0	1	0

Ⓝ status word

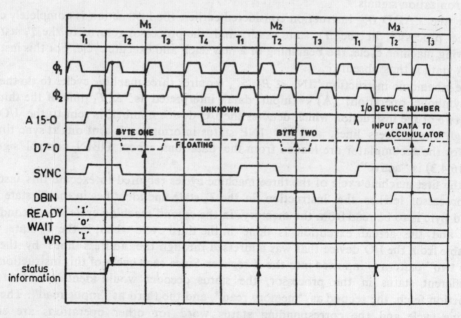

Fig. 16.11 Status decoding chart

Fig. 16.12 8080A 'IN' instruction cycle

16.4.3 Description of Input-Output Pins for 8080A

The various pin functions of the INTEL 8080A microprocessor chip shown in Fig. 16.13 are described in this section[2].

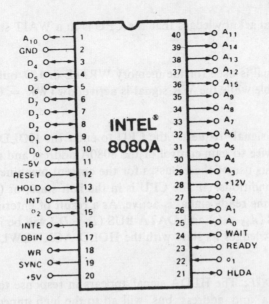

Fig. 16.13 Pin-diagram of 8080A

$A_{15} - A_0$ (output, three state)

Address Bus: The address bus provides the address to the memory (up to 64 k 8-bit words) or denotes the I/O device number for up to 256 input and 256 output devices. A_0 is the least significant bit.

$D_7 - D_0$ (input/output, three state)

Data Bus: The data bus provides bidirectional communication between the CPU, memory and I/O devices for instructions and data transfers. Also, during the first clock of each machine cycle, the 8080A outputs a status word on the data bus that describes the current machine cycle. D_0 is the least significant bit.

SYNC (output)

Synchronizing Signal: The SYNC pin provides a signal to indicate the beginning of each machine cycle.

DBIN (output)

Data Bus IN: The DBIN signal indicates to the external circuits that the data bus is in the input mode. This signal should be used to enable the gating of data onto the 8080A data bus from the memory or I/O.

READY (input)

READY: The READY signal indicates to the 8080A that the valid memory or input data is available on the 8080A data bus. This signal is used to synchronize the CPU with a slower memory or I/O device. If after sending an address out, the 8080A does not receive a READY input, the 8080A will enter a WAIT state for as long as the READY line is low. READY can also be used to single step the CPU.

WAIT (output)
WAIT: The wait signal acknowledges that the CPU is in a WAIT state.

$\overline{WR}$ (output)
WRITE: The $\overline{WR}$ signal is used for the memory WRITE or I/O output control. The data on the data bus is stable while the $\overline{WR}$ signal is active low ($\overline{WR}$ = 0).

HOLD (input)
HOLD: The HOLD signal requests the CPU to enter the HOLD state. The HOLD state allows an external device to gain control of the 8080A address and data bus as soon as the 8080A has completed its use of these busses for the current machine cycle. It is recognized under the following conditions: (i) The CPU is in the halt state, or (ii) the CPU is in the T_2 or Tw state and the ready signal is active. As a result of entering the HOLD state, the CPU ADDRESS BUS ($A_{15} - A_0$) and DATA BUS ($D_7 - D_0$) will be in their high impedance state. The CPU acknowledges its state with the HOLD ACKNOWLEDGE (HLDA) pin.

HLDA (output)
HOLD ACKNOWLEDGE: The HLDA signal appears in response to the HOLD signal and indicates that the data and address bus will go to the high impedance state. The HLDA signal begins at T_3 for READ memory or input operation, or at the clock period following T_3 for WRITE memory or OUTPUT operation.

In either case, the HLDA signal appears after the rising edge of ϕ_1 and high impedance occurs after the rising edge of ϕ_2.

INTE (output)
INTERRUPT ENABLE: It indicates the content of the internal interrupt enable flip-flop. This flip-flop may be set or reset by the enable and disable interrupt instructions, and inhibits interrupts from being accepted by the CPU, when it is reset. This flip-flop is automatically reset (disabling further interrupts) at time T_1 of the instruction fetch cycle (M_1) when an interrupt is accepted and is also reset by the RESET signal.

INT (input)
INTERRUPT REQUEST: The CPU recognizes an interrupt request on this line at the end of the current instruction or while it is halted. If the CPU is in the HOLD state or if the interrupt enable flip-flop is reset, it will not honour the request.

RESET (output)
RESET: While the RESET signal is activated, the content of the program counter is cleared. After RESET, the program will start at location 0 in the memory. The INTE and HOLD flip-flops are also reset. It may be noted that the flags, accumulator, stack pointer, and registers are not cleared. (Note: the RESET signal must be active for a minimum of 3 clock cycles.)

16.4.4 Timing and Synchronization of Interfaces

The microprocessor has to be interfaced with the rest of the microcomputer system using appropriate latches and decoding logic. As was discussed in Sec. 16.3.5, latches are used in order to store data that the microprocessor can output when it is ready so that these data can be provided to the interface devices when they are ready to accept them. The latches are used for a similar function in the reverse order when data is to be entered into the processor. The Intel 8228 system controller interface can be used with the Intel 8080A microprocessor for the purposes of interfacing. The bidirectional buffer in the Intel 8228 enables the data lines D_7-D_0 of the microprocessor to be interfaced with an external data bus (8 bit) while ensuring that the output drive capability—typically one TTL load—of the microprocessor data lines is not exceeded[3].

16.4.5 Functional Description of 8085A

The 8085A is a complete eight-bit parallel central processor operating with basic clock speeds up to 3 MHz. As against the requirements of additional support chips, such as 8224 (clock generator) and 8228 (system controller) for the 8080A, the 8085A incorporates all of these features on the chip itself. To assemble a minimum system with 8085A, only two additional chips are required, viz., a RAM/IO chip and a PROM/IO chip.

The 8085A uses a multiplexed data bus. The address is split between the higher eight-bit address bus and the lower eight-bit address/data bus. The lower eight bits are latched into the peripherals by the Address Latch Enable (ALE) signal. The 8085A provides RD, WR and IO/MEMORY signals for bus control. It has in addition, three maskable restart interrupts and a non-markable restart interrupt, for efficient interrupt handling. The 8085A also provides serial input data (SID) and serial output data (SOD) lines for simple serial interfaces, such as CRT and line printers.

16.4.6. Microcomputer Kits

A microcomputer kit essentially is an operational microcomputer available in kit form. After assembly, the microcomputer can be used for educational purposes, developing actual programs, and as part of dedicated microprocessor based systems.

Typically, a kit consists of the hardware required to make up a system, as shown, in Fig. 16.14. The system in general consists of a microprocessor, 1 kilobyte of RAM (expandable to 4 kilobytes), 2 kilobytes of PROM (expandable to 8 kilobytes), a hexadecimal keyboard with about 12 additional keys for other functions described below, an eight-digit hexadecimal display, and serial input/output data lines for communication with an external teletypewriter (TTY) or CRT. Some kits also provide circuitry for cassette interface by which data from a section of the memory can be stored in the cassette and reloaded into the microcomputer when necessary.

A monitor program stored in the PROM coordinates the activities of the microcomputer and enables keyboard entry of data, hex display and communication with the peripherals. In addition to the hexadecimal keys, keys are provided to perform operations, such as memory load, memory read, memory address increment and decrement, examine register contents, single step, program run, cassette load, and so on. The programs required for controlling the various operations associated with these keys also reside in the monitor. The single step mode is often useful in executing a program step by step, and is necessary in the "debugging" of programs.

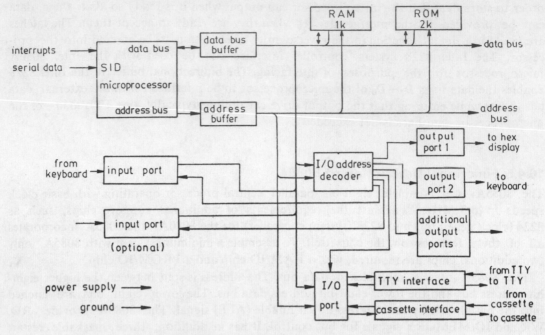

Fig. 16.14 Block schematic of a microcomputer kit

Some additional input/output ports, interrupt inputs, input-output lines for cassettes and TTY interface, and also buffered data and address lines are brought out in an edge connector for appropriate usage and expansion. The power supply for the operation of the kit has to be generally provided externally, and the edge connectors will contain necessary pins for these connections as well.

16.5 APPLICATION FIELDS

Microprocessors are being used today in a wide variety of applications in the fields of instrumentation, communication, data processing, industrial process instrumentation, commerce, and consumer products. A few exemplifying applications in each field are:

Instrumentation: Automatic test equipment; electronic instruments; and analytical, chemical, and medical equipment.

Communication: Remote terminals; programmable controllers; switching systems; multiplexers; message handling; and error detection.

Data Processing: Programmable calculators; peripheral processors; I/O controllers; and communication interface.

Industrial: Data acquisition systems; numerical control; environmental monitoring; and process control and instrumentation.

Commercial: Inventory control systems; pay roll, banking, and financial systems; and auto transaction systems.

Consumer: Educational systems; intelligent toys; games; automative systems; and programmable appliances.

The three most important industries that have changed complexion due to the impact of microprocessor are the mini or small business computer industry, the electronics industry, and the large-scale data-processing industry. The electronics industry has benefitted by the introduction of microprocessors in the three broad areas of flexibility, reliability, and cost.

16.5.1 A Microprocessor-based Data Logger

As an example of the application of microprocessors in instrumentation, the use of a microprocessor in data logging can be examined. A typical data-logging system can use varied types of signal conditioners, amplifiers, and output devices. A printer is most commonly employed in the logging of slowly-varying data. A certain amount of processing of data may be involved in certain cases, such as linearization of the thermocouple output, computation of the average value of a certain set of data inputs, or conversion to engineering units. In addition, the comparison of the measured data with preset minimum and maximum limits, and actuation of out-of-limit indicators or initiation of alarms can also be carried out. Eventually, the system can also be made to sequentially shut down energization systems, when maximum tolerable limits of working systems are reached.

An exemplifying requirement of a data-logging system which is to collect data periodically from 100 locations can be the following:

(a) The provision to collect load information from 60 locations. Transducer used: load cell. The load information from each individual station is to be measured at least once in every five seconds. The measured data with the time at which measurement is made should be printed out as well as stored in digital cassettes for analysis later.

(b) The provision to monitor temperature at twenty points. Temperature range: 0 to 1000°C. Transducer used: K-type thermocouple. Output data are to be linearized to provide direct display of temperature to within ±0.1% ±1°C. Visual indicators are to be actuated when the set temperature limits (settable for each station) are exceeded. Reading rate: once in every 5 minutes.

(c) The provision to monitor twenty control point voltages. Aural alarms are to be set when any of them falls out of the range of ±5 V. Simultaneous visual indication of the particular station where the voltage is out of range is to be displayed.

A data logger of this nature can be efficiently handled by a microprocessor-based system. The system can be designed in such a way that a built-in clock is used to function as a "real time" clock so that each measurement is logged along with the time at which it is done. Invariably, the channel number identifying the channel on which measurement is made can also be logged. In the case of the load-cell measurement, balancing of the individual strain gauges can also be done by the processor. The processor can do this by calling sub-routines at the start of logging by noting the outputs of the load cells when no load is applied and storing these for later subtraction from individual measurements (auto zero). The rate of reading (e.g., the necessity to take readings of the load in every five seconds) can be tailored to the requirement. The processor can command low-level or high-level multiplexers at appropriate times to access data from a desired channel, convert the data into digital values, store these in RAMs within the system, and proceed to log data from other locations. It can efficiently utilize the time available to it for doing the various functions by commanding the

RAM data to be stored in cassettes in a serial form after adding parity and synchronization bits.

For the monitoring and display of temperature, the thermocouple output will be amplified and linearized by look-up tables stored within the system in read only memories. The linearized output can be transferred to output ports that control the displayed digits. Constant comparison can be made of the temperature with the limit values set in the operating console or fed to the microprocessor system at the start of a process. Visual annunciators can be actuated based on this comparison, when the limits are exceeded. The monitoring of the other twenty voltage levels corresponding to the control functions can also be carried out in much the same way.

This data-logging system can obviously have incorporated within it programmable data amplifiers and multiplexers to handle the inputs. It can also have a fast ADC for conversion of the analog inputs. Its output device can be a teleprinter (TTY) or a line printer that will provide the print-out of the data. It can have an operating console with keyboards for the entry of necessary data and commands, a panel display that displays the temperature of the various stations monitored by it, and visual and other alarms. It can also have a cassette interface for recording the "load cell" data from the 60 stations. The block schematic of the system is shown in Fig. 16.15.

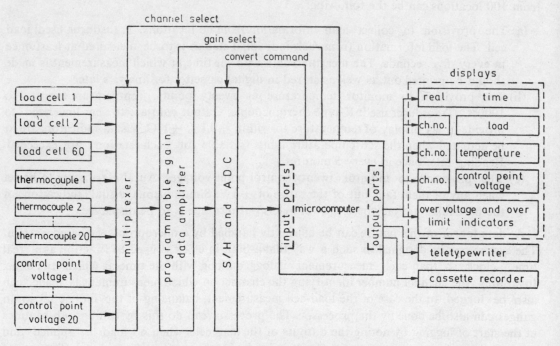

Fig. 16.15 A microprocessor-based data logger

While the microprocessor has to necessarily operate on instructions sequentially, the fast speed at which it operates enables it to access, convert, compute, display and record information from various stations. It is thus ideally suited for logging of many parameters and to take intelligent decisions based on computations carried out on these measured data.

16.5.2 Microprocessor Control of a Petrol Engine

Another example of the use of microprocessors in instrumentation is the application of a microcomputer in the control of a petrol engine to achieve better fuel efficiency.

A promising new method of measuring the engine power and hence the specific fuel consumption (SFC) is based on the computation of the thermodynamic work done per cycle per cylinder[4]. The measurements have to be made on a cyclic basis so that the direct effect of SFC for particular values of fuel and timing at the start of the four-stroke cycle can be seen at the end of the cycle. The scheme shown in Fig. 16.16(a) envisages to control the fuel delivery and ignition timing of each cylinder for every firing cycle. To execute this control, the microcomputer has to first obtain data from the engine, act on this data by using it in an algorithm, and finally output the fuel data and timing values. This sequence of events has to be phased with the engine crank angle in such a manner that data is obtained from the engine at the beginning of each exhaust stroke and the new value of the fuel is outputted before the end of each exhaust stroke. Control algorithms can be formed relating the fuel required to be injected in the next stroke in terms of the measured timing angle, work done, set value of the fuel, and crank angle information. Similarly, the spark timing angle is also computed from these same parameters. Using an iterative procedure in which the fuel and timing angle information calculated for a previous cycle forms the input information for the following cycle, the additional information required for the calculations are those relating to (i) crank angle and (ii) work done.

The work done is computed as the integral of the product of the pressure and the incremental volume. The pressure is sensed by quartz crystal pressure transducers flush mounted in the combustion chamber of each cylinder. The volume information is one of the four values selected based on the crank angle. The crank angle information is required to synchronize the microcomputer to the engine operation and to give information regarding the cylinder for which the measured inputs are valid. This information is obtained from a slotted disc mounted on the crank-shaft and an inductive probe sensing the cam-shaft position.

 · The output peripheral hardware translates the calculated timing and fuel values into signals which directly adjust the fuelling and timing of the engine. The fuel is delivered by a fuel injector which is kept open for a period proportional to the computed value of the fuel needed. For this, the fuel data is loaded into the fuel unit counter, and the fuel injector is kept open until this counter is decremented to zero. The timing control is also achieved in a similar fashion by loading a timing unit counter with the timing data and decrementing the counter to zero. A spark is produced when the count reaches zero.

Figure 16.16(b) indicates the control cycle operation. The sequence of operations are: (i) Measure engine variables (P in Fig. 16.16(b)), (ii) Compute new timing and fuel values (Q in Fig. 16.16(b)), (iii) Load fuel unit counter (R in Fig. 16.16(b)), and (iv) Load timing unit counter (S in Fig. 16.16(b)).

Due to the limited time available for the computation of the work done using the software, this computation is carried out by the hardware. The processor reads the A/D converter to get this data, and based on the measured crank angle data and previously computed values of timing and fuel (for the previous cycle), new values of timing and fuel are calculated. The estimated fuel savings by such a microcomputer control over conventional control system are estimated to be about 10%.

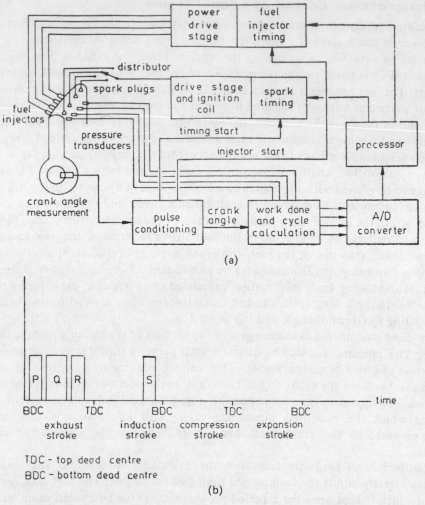

(a)

(b)

Fig. 16.16 Controller for petrol engine: (a) schematic layout; (b) control cycle

16.6 GLOSSARY OF TERMS

Some of the often used terminology in the microprocessor field, parts of a microprocessor, and programming are briefly described below.[5,6,7]

16.6.1 Basics

Bit: A minimum logic element—A binary number of 0 or 1.
Word: Any group of bits indicating a single number or expression.
Byte: A word consisting of typically eight bits.
Address: A specific memory location that is called out by the program counter.

Hex: Abbreviated form for hexadecimal; a scheme of calculating numbers to the base 16 (0 to 9 for the normal BCD sequence from 0000 to 1001 and A, B, C, D, E, and F designated by the sequences from 1010 to 1111 respectively).

Register: A device that stores one word of data and often consists of several flip-flops.

RAM (random access memory): A data storage device that can retain and produce on demand any data placed on it.

ROM (read only memory): A device that has data permanently entered into it to be outputted on demand.

PROM: A programmable ROM in which a program is entered by the user before installation into the equipment, in contrast to a factory-programmed ROM.

EPROM: A PROM that can be erased and reused indefinitely. Most EPROMS are erased under ultraviolet light and can be recognized by the transparent cover over the silicon "chip".

Decoder: Usually a device that detects a certain specific address on the address bus.

Bus: A group of wires that carry related binary signals, usually a word, as in a 16-wire address bus. A bus can be bidirectional, as in the case of a data bus.

16.6.2 Parts of a Microprocessor

Accumulator: A register in the microprocessor that operates on data.

ALU: (Arithmetic and logic unit): The circuitry that performs the manipulations on data held in the accumulator.

I/O (Input/Output): The hardware that interfaces a microprocessor system with the outside world.

Port: A place through which the input and output — either data or instructions — are channelled. A microprocessor can have more than one port or can address many. The port size, often specified in bits, ranges from 4 to 16.

Program Counter (PC): Two 8-bit registers used to generate the 16-bit address. The registers are called PCH and PCL and are used for higher-order and lower-order bytes respectively.

R/W (Read/Write): A control output of the microprocessor that indicates if data are being transferred from the microprocessor to memory or vice versa.

Scratchpad: An area of the main memory set aside for calculations that are short and performed often.

Stack: Storage for data during sub-routines or interrupts.

Stack pointer: Two 8-bit registers containing the address of the top (most recent end) of the stack.

16.6.3 Programming

Assembly language: A compromise between the user's thoughts and the numerical notation of the microprocessor. The assembly language is the closest technique to the actual numerical codes that still retains some speaking-language characteristics.

Branch: Depending on the status of a particular bit in the status register, the program will jump by the indicated amount if the condition is met, or merely increment if not met.

Cross-assembler: A program on a large computer that allows a microprocessor programmer to use assembly language. The assembler reduces the program to the machine language.

DMA (*Direct memory access*): A process in which a microprocessor is removed temporarily from a system to allow data to be transferred rapidly in or out of the memory without the microprocessor control.

Interrupt: An external signal that causes a microprocessor to jump to a specific sub-routine. Interrupts are maskable or non-maskable. A maskable interrupt can be delayed, until a mask bit is lowered.

Iterative loop: A programming technique whereby a process is repeated a specified number of times.

Jump: A programming instruction that breaks the consecutive instruction program sequence and resumes elsewhere in the program.

Machine language: Numerical coding, representing instructions, usually in the form of groups of bytes used by the microprocessor.

Peripheral: A unit operated with the microprocessor system, such as a keyboard or printer.

Program: A set of sequential instructions that a computer follows.

Sub-routine: A program within a program that performs a specific, often used function.

Vector: A specified address loaded into a microprocessor's program counter to force the microprocessor to start processing at a specific address.

REFERENCES

1. Klein, R. et al., "5 Volt only non-volatile memory owes it all to polysilicon", *Electronics*, Vol. 52, No. 21, pp. 111-116, October 11, 1979.
2. *Intel Component Data Catalog*, p. 9.12, Intel Corporation, Santa Clara, California, 1979.
3 McGlynn, D.R., *Microprocessors: Technology, Architecture and Applications*, pp. 123-124, John Wiley and Sons, N.Y., 1976.
4. Werson and Trotter, "Real time computer control of a petrol engine", *Trends in On-line Computer Control Systems*, IEE publication No. 172, IEE, London, 1979.
5. Gellender, E., "Microprocessor Basics, Part 20: Microprocessor Data Manual", *Electronic Design*, Vol. 25, No. 21, pp, 74-79, Oct. 11, 1977.
6. Sippl and Kidd, *Microprocessor Dictionary and Guide*, Matrix Publishers, Champaign, IL, 1975.
7. Electrical Research Association, *The Engineering of Microprocessor Systems*, Electrical Research Association, Leatherhead, Surrey, England—Pergamon Press, New York, 1979.

BIBLIOGRAPHY

Altman, L. and Scrupski, S.E. (Ed.), *Applying Microprocessors*, Electronics Magazine Book Series, McGraw-Hill, N.Y., 1976.
Aspinall, D. (Ed.), *The Microprocessor and its Application*, Cambridge University Press, Cambridge, London, 1978.
Athani, V.V., "Microprocessor based data acquisition systems", *Microprocessors aad Microsystems*, Vol. 3, No. 8, pp. 359-364, Oct. 1979.
Barden, W.J., *How to Program Microcomputers*, Howard W. Sams and Co., Indiana, 1977.
Boyce, J.C., *Microprocessor and Microcomputer Basics*, Prentice-Hall, Inc., New Jersey, 1979.

Edelman, S., "Glossary of microprocessor based control system terms", *Instruments and Control Systems*, Vol. 52, No. 5, pp. 43-48, May 1979.

Elphick, M.S. (Ed.), *Microprocessor Basics*, Hayden Book Co., Inc., New Jersey, 1977.

Findley, R., *Scelbi 8080 Software Gourmet Guide and Cookbook*, Scelbi Computer Consulting Inc., Connecticut, 1976.

Hordeski, M., "Interfacing Microcomputers in Control Systems", *Instruments and Control Systems*, Vol. 51, No. 11, pp. 59-62, Nov. 1978.

Intel 8080 Microcomputer System User's Manual, Intel Corp., Santa Clara, California, 1975.

Lesea, A. and Zaks, R., *Microprocessor Interfacing Techniques*, SYBEX, Berkeley, California, 1977.

Leventhal, L.A., *8080A/8085 Assembly Language Programming*, Osborne and Associates Inc., Berkeley, California, 1978.

Linear and Interface Data Book, Advanced Microdevices Inc., Sunnyvale, California, 1976.

Motorola 6800, Microprocessor Applications Manual, Motorola Inc., Phoenix, Arizona, 1975.

Motorola 6800, Microprocessor Course, Motorola Inc., Phoenix, Arizona, 1977.

Noble, P., "A multiprocessor systems provides new approach to motor rpm control", *Control and Instrumentation*, Vol. 11, No. 7, pp. 29-31, July/Aug., 1979.

Osborne, A., *8080 Programming for Logic Design*, Osborne and Associates Inc., Berkeley, California, 1976.

Osborne, A. et. al., *Z 80 Programming for Logic Design*, Osborne and Associates Inc., Berkeley, California, 1978.

Poe, E., *Using the 6800 Microprocessor*, Howard W. Sams and Co., Indiana, 1978.

SC/MP Microprocessor Applications Handbook, National Semiconductor Corp., Sunnyvale, California, 1976.

Special Issue on Microprocessors, *Proc. IEEE*, Vol. 66. No. 2, 1978.

Streitmatter, G.A. and Fiore, V., *Microprocessors, Theory and Applications*, Reston Publishing Co.. Virginia 1979.

Tocci, R.J. and Laskowski, I.P., *Microprocessors and Microcomputers: Hardware and Software*, Prentice-Hall Inc., New Jersey, 1979.

The Pace Microprocessor: Logic Designer's Guide to Programmed Equivalents to TTL Functions, National Semiconductors Corp., Santa Clara, California, 1976.

Weller, W.J., *Assembly Level Programming for Small Computers*, D.C. Heath and Co., Lexington, Massachusetts, 1975.

Wester, *Software Design for Microprocessors*, Texas Instruments Inc., Dallas, Texas, 1976.

Zaks, R., *Microprocessor: From Chips to Systems*, SYBEX, Berkeley, California, 1977.

17

INPUT-OUTPUT DEVICES AND DISPLAYS

17.1 INTRODUCTION

All instrumentation systems have to possess either a display that a human operator can read out from and interpret, or an output device that enables the transfer of information from the instrumentation system to a general purpose or dedicated computer. Input-output devices are of various forms depending on (i) the type of data viz., analog or digital, and (ii) such factors as speed, type of record required, and type of system to which data is fed. The typical input-output devices and displays that are normally used for data handling in a modern instrumentation system are discussed in this chapter.

17.2 ANALOG DISPLAYS AND RECORDERS

Various methods are used in instrumentation systems for the display and recording of analog voltages and currents. Indicating devices usually operate on the principle of the d'Arsonval galvanometer. The recording methods vary, depending on (i) the speed of recording and frequency response desired, and (ii) whether the parameter is recorded against time or against another variable parameter.

17.2.1 D'Arsonval Meter

Analog indicators are basically current-operated devices, working on the d'Arsonval type galvanometer principle. The device consists essentially of a circular or rectangular coil of a large number of turns of fine wire, suspended between the poles of a permanent magnet. The coil is mounted in position with a jewel bearing and is coupled to a pointer-indicator moving over a graduated scale. The restoring force for equilibrium is provided through a control spring. The sensitivity and the torque produced depend upon the coil dimensions, number of turns, flux density, and the control spring constant.

The resulting deflection is given as

$$\delta = KIB \cos \theta$$

where δ = deflection, K = a constant of proportionality, I = current through coil, B = flux density, and θ = angle between the plane of the coil and magnetic field when no current is flowing.

The basic movement can be adapted to measure dc voltages with a series resistor and to measure ac voltages with a rectifying diode and resistor.

17.2.2 Graphic Recorder

In order that the value of the parameter being measured can be recorded continuously, it is necessary to provide a means of transferring the galvanometer motion onto a paper while moving the paper at a known speed. The recording effect is usually achieved by mounting an ink pen at the end of an arm and letting it move over the chart paper. The arm is driven by the galvanometer coil, and hence the motion of the arm is directly proportional to the current in the coil. Special linkages enable the conversion of the angular rotation of the coil into a straight-line motion of the writing arm. In some cases, the writing action is obtained by a heated stylus mounted at the end of the arm and moved against a heat-sensitive chart paper. Due to the high torque required to drive the writing arm, the sensitivity of this type of recorders is low, requiring a few tens of milliamperes of current for full scale. The frequency response is limited to 200 Hz or less.

17.2.3 Optical Oscillograph

The optical oscillograph is an instrument wherein a sensitive galvanometer is employed to obtain a visible permanent record of the signal trace on a photosensitive paper. A beam of high-intensity ultraviolet light is focussed through a suitable collimating lens system on a mirror mounted on the coil of the galvanometer. The reflected beam, sharply focussed, is made to fall on a light-sensitive paper moved precisely over a drum with a clock mechanism as shown in Fig. 17.1. The recording spot sensitivity is controlled by adjusting the light intensity of the source, and the paper movement speed is suitably altered depending on the frequency of the signal to be recorded.

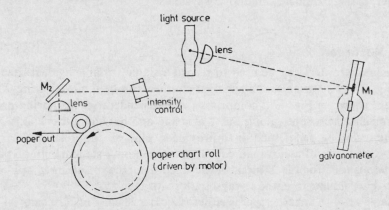

Fig. 17.1 Principle of operation of an optical oscillograph

Two main considerations of importance for an optical oscillograph are the frequency response and sensitivity. In a typical instrument, the frequency response is flat from dc up to 10 kHz, the sensitivity is about 1 to 10 mV per cm, and the linearity and accuracy are approximately 1 and 2% respectively. The coil system is either fluid-damped or magnetically damped. The recording paper width is typically 10 to 25 cm wide. By a suitable mechanical mounting arrangement, it is possible to have as many as 16 or more galvanometers recording on the same paper. The records can overlap, enabling full coverage over the width of the paper by the signal in any of the galvanometers. Suitable trace identification markers help identify the individual records. In certain applications, one of the galvanometers can be used as a time marker by feeding pulses from a crystal oscillator/divider unit.

17.2.4 Self-balancing Potentiometer

A self-balancing potentiometer is an electrical equipment which measures the unknown emf by balancing it against a known potential which in turn is obtained from a slide-wire potentiometer operated from a reference source. The position of the contactor of the slide wire potentiometer actuated by a servo motor is directly interpreted as a measure of the input signal.

The input voltage to be measured is compared with the output dc potential of the slide-wire potentiometer and the difference voltage is converted to an ac signal with a mechanical or electronic chopper and amplified. The ac amplifier output is fed to a two-phase low inertia servomotor whose shaft is suitably coupled to the wiper of the slide-wire potentiometer. Because of the feedback action, the wiper attains a stable position such that the error voltage is infinitesimally small. The wiper is coupled to an ink-operated recording stylus writing on a mechanically-driven chart paper for permanent record.

The main advantages of this type of recorders are the high sensitivity (1 mV F.S.), good linearity (0.1%), wide chart width (25 cm), and extreme ruggedness. The dynamic response is limited to the range of 2 to 10 Hz. As such, this type of recorder is ideally suited for many low-speed measurements, such as continuous recording of output of thermocouples. They are very popular in process control, chemical, metallurgical, and textile industries and in many other analog parameter-monitoring systems.

17.2.5 X-Y Recorder

While strip-chart recorders can be used to record a single variable against time in one axis, the recording of two variables, one against another, can be achieved using X-Y recorders. The equipment shown in Fig. 17.2 comprises two independent self-balancing potentiometric-type drive mechanisms, one along the X axis and another along the Y axis. The resulting motion of the recording pen is such as to provide a plot of the relationship between the variables in the form of a cartesian coordinate graph on a standard graph paper. When a linear time base is used for the X input of the recorder, the resulting graph of Y is a plot of Y against time, similar to cathode-ray-oscilloscope display.

The normal size of the chart paper is either (22 cm × 28 cm) or (28 cm × 44 cm). Typical sensitivities for X and Y channels range from 100 μV/cm to 20 volts/cm, with a linearity of 0.1%.

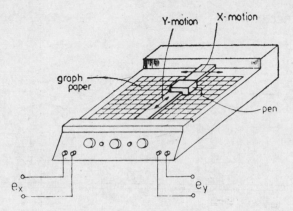

Fig. 17.2 *X-Y* recorder

17.2.6 Magnetic Recorder

The magnetic tape recorder/reproducer has a distinct advantage over other forms of recording in that they can be used to record and store an electrical voltage on a magnetic tape over a considerable length of time and can be used later to reproduce the stored voltage in a format identical to its original form.

Magnetic recording is the process of magnetizing an extremely small volume of a thin material which has essentially the properties of a permanent magnet. Recording may be done in the direct form, in the FM form, or in the digital form. In the direct method, which is limited to the recording of ac waveforms typically having frequencies higher than 50 Hz, the input voltage is converted to a proportional current and passed through the winding on the "record head", as shown in Fig. 17.3. A dc or high frequency ac is added to the signal, to improve linearity[1]. The resulting magnetic field produced in the recording gap enables magnetic recording of the input information on a tape (a flexible material such as Mylar with a nominal thickness of 0.04 mm, coated with a magnetic material such as iron oxide) that passes under the gap. For reproduction, the tape is passed over a "reproduce head", thereby resulting in an output voltage proportional to the magnetic flux in the tape, across the coil of the reproduce head. Since the reproducing head has a differentiating characteristic, the reproduce amplifier should have a compensating integrator characteristic so that the recording and reproduction processes together have a flat frequency response. The high-frequency response is dependent on the tape speed. With a gap width of 0.002 mm, and a tape speed of 300 cm/s, the frequency response can extend from 50 Hz up to about 1 MHz. The main drawback of the direct method is its poor signal-to-noise ratio, which is typically 25 dB.

The FM (frequency modulation) type tape recording enables the extension of low-frequency response down to dc and the improvement of signal-to-noise ratio to 50 dB. In this case, the input voltage frequency modulates a sinusoidal "carrier", and the frequency-modulated carrier is recorded linearly using an ac bias, or non-linearly without a bias, in a magnetic tape. On reproduction, the recorded information is reconstructed after frequency demodulation and filtering. A carrier deviation of $\pm 15\%$ is normally used, and the resulting

RECORD HEAD

REPRODUCE HEAD

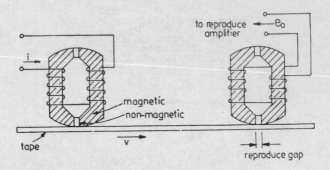

Fig. 17.3 Record and reproduce heads in a magnetic recorder

input signal bandwidth over which the response is flat is typically from dc to 40% of the carrier frequency used. The carrier frequency is typically 11.25 kHz for a tape speed of 3.75 cm/s, increasing to 900 kHz at a tape speed of 300 cm/s.

The digital methods of magnetic tape recording are discussed in Sec. 17.3.5.

17.3 DIGITAL INPUT-OUTPUT DEVICES

The input-output devices serve as communication links through which data is fed into the digital computer for processing. The input devices accept data from machines or operators and transmit to a storage unit. The output unit accepts data from the storage unit and transmits to the recorder or to other peripherals. Both the units, in effect, perform the translation function, transferring data from human language symbols to machine language symbols.

Input-output (I/O) devices may operate on-line or off-line. The on-line peripheral equipment operates under the direction of the control unit of a computer as an integral part, transmitting data to the storage unit or obtaining data from it. On the other hand, the off-line equipment operates independently of the control unit of the computer, neither supplying data directly to the storage unit nor obtaining data directly from it. The "hard-copy" devices principally operate in the off-line mode, and the user does not have to be present at the computer at run-time. The other devices present the output directly to the user in a non-permanent form, or they read the input directly as a result of some operation by the user, such as typing.

All I/O equipment have a basic operating cycle and pattern, with appropriate techniques and suitable media for the transfer of information. The media typically used are ink on paper (numbers, letters, symbols, and characters), magnetization on a magnetizable material (magnetic tape), changes in electrical voltages in devices, holes punched into paper base or plastic base materials (punched card and punched tape), and presence/absence of light on the face of a cathode-ray-tube (CRT) display. An important characteristic of the I/O units is the speed of operation, measured in cycles or number of character per unit time.

17.3.1 Punched Card

Punched cards are common for the input and output for small- and medium-sized computers. The normal size of the card that is universally used is 8.3 cm wide, 18.9 cm long, and 0.178 mm thick. The card, as shown in Fig. 17.4, can be punched with a hole in any one of 960 positions on a 12 by 80 rectangular array of positions. The normal punch codes are Hollerith, ASCII (American Standard Code for Information Interchange), row binary and column binary, and EBCDIC (Extended Binary Coded Decimal Interactive Code).

The card reader is based on the physical movement of the card past a sensing mechanism which is usually either an electrical contact or a photoelectric device. The card readers can serve in either an on-line or off-line basis and have speeds of 1000 to 2000 cards per minute. The cards, in the order in which they are to be read, are placed in a feed hopper, fed one at a time for the leading edge of the stack, and passed over the reading station. In certain equipment, a checking station is also incorporated for comparison or error detection. Electrical pulses obtained from the reader unit is later translated into the code needed by the computer.

The card punch unit operates much like the reader unit and has a speed of 200 to 400 cards per minute. Sharp rods, one for each row or column, are thrust through the card once or as many times as needed to make the holes in each row or column in the required pattern, as commanded by the code. The pattern of holes punched depends upon the position of the card and the timing of the punching action. Punch checks such as hole count, read and compare, and echo-checking[2] are made with a reader similar to the punched card reader, and after passing the reading station, the cards are stocked in decks and files.

17.3.2 Paper Tape

A punched paper tape is very similar to punched cards in that it consists of a heavy paper stock in which information is presented by the presence or absence of punched holes. It differs from cards in that the paper tape is in continuous strips of arbitrary lengths, whereas cards are of fixed size. The tape is commonly used in three different widths containing five, seven, or eight possible information hole positions across the tape. Each of these positions is called a channel. A 2.5 cm eight-channel tape is shown in Fig. 17.5. It may be seen that in addition to the eight information positions or channels, there is a ninth position that is always punched with a sprocket hole. This is to locate the position where the information should appear along the tape. Without these sprocket holes, a series of characters consisting of no punched holes can lead to a strip of a completely blank tape. It cannot then be possible to tell how many characters there are in such a string of tape except by measuring the length of the tape, a procedure that can lead to errors. The sprocket hole is also used to mesh with a sprocket gear on the slower mechanical readers. Since the paper tape is prone to error, it is very common to use one of the information channels as a parity bit for other information channels.

Punched paper tape readers are either photoelectrically or electromechanically operated units. The reader mechanism is similar to that used in punched card readers, with the tapes in continuous strips and eight channels instead of eighty columns and twelve rows. The speed is as much as 2000 characters per second. The paper tape punches are relatively

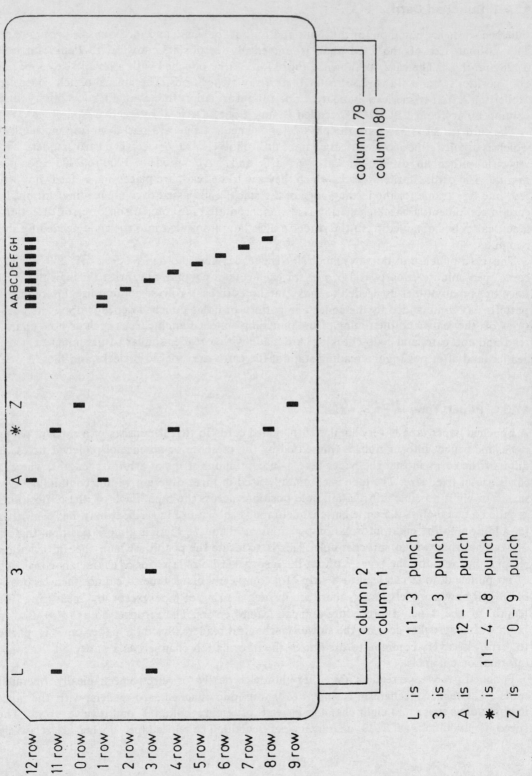

Fig. 17.4 Hollerith punched card

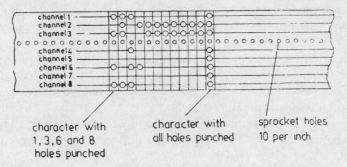

character with
1, 3, 6 and 8
holes punched

character with
all holes punched

sprocket holes
10 per inch

Fig. 17.5 Paper tape

slower and have a speed of 100 to 500 characters per second. The punching action is very similar to that of card punches. In general, paper tape is cheaper (both in terms of the cost of reading and punching equipment and in terms of the cost of the paper itself) than cards and hence tends to be used in small low-speed computers.

17.3.3 Output Equipment

Some of the equipment that are exclusively used for the output of the computer are printers, plotters, displays, and actuators. Printers are synchronous equipment, used normally for the registration of graphic characters, mostly numerals on paper. Alphabetic letters and marks of punctuation can also be provided. A serial printer prints out one character at a time, similar to the way in which an ordinary typewriter operates. Parallel printers print all the characters on a given line simultaneously, and hence the speed is much higher than that for serial printers.

A specific example of a serial printer is the teleprinter. It is operated from its keyboard which is similar to the typewriter keyboard though only capital letters are generally available in the teleprinter. Alternatively, it can also receive its input data through a series of pulses. The rate at which printing is done is typically 5 to 40 characters per second. The electrical input for each character consists of $7\frac{1}{2}$ unit pulses as shown in Fig. 17.6, made up of a start signal (one unit pulse), five code signals (corresponding to the character desired), and a $1\frac{1}{2}$ unit stop signal. For a teleprinter speed of 50 bauds, the time taken per character is typically 150 ms.

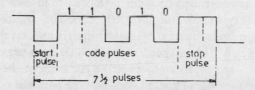

Fig. 17.6 Teleprinter code pulses

The teleprinter is a form of type bar character printer using a basket of type bars, a fixed print position, and a movable paper-holding carriage. The keys are operated with an electromagnet. The required data is fed from a buffer that translates computer output language into the required format. The desired characters are selected by the choice of type bars. Other forms of character printers use selectable hammer, matrix, thermal and electrostatic techniques.

Selectable hammer character printers use one of four different forms of the hammer and a stationary paper-holding carriage. After printing each character, the hammer moves to the next selected print position along the line of the paper. On receiving a command, the hammer, mounted on a spherical ball rotates about its vertical axis, to align the desired character shape opposite the printer position, and strikes the ribbon against the paper. Thereafter, the hammer moves to the next print position to the right, in preparation to print the next character.

Another form uses a matrix of character shapes, each character shape fixed on the end of its own push rod and held in a block by a guide mechanism. The mechanism moves up or down and left or right to position the desired character shape at the print position. Then a single hammer strikes the end of the push rod that is in the printing position to force the ribbon against the paper. Matrix character printers operate in a manner similar to matrix line printers but produce only one character at a time[3].

Thermal character printers operate in much the same manner as the selectable hammer or matrix character printers, but instead of a ribbon, they use a hot hammer to print on the surface of a heat-sensitive paper. They produce only one copy at a time, since they are not impact printers.

In electrostatic character printers, the electrostatic force directs a stream of fluid ink against the paper. The print mechanism consists of a supply of electrically-charged ink and a closely-spaced series of small electrostatic guides to direct the ink on its way to the paper.

17.3.4 Line Printer

Line printers are used to print high-speed data since they can print an entire line of characters simultaneously. The common speed range for line printers is from 600 to 1200 lines per minute. Most of the line printers are impact printers, and can print a full alpha-numeric character set ranging from 43 to 63 different characters (26 letters, 10 digits, and a variety of symbols). The print-out normally has 120, 132, or 144 character positions in a line, and the printer normally prints about five to six lines in a vertical span of 2.5 cm with 0.5 cm line spacing. To avoid printing a part of any line, the printer prints "spaces" or "blanks" which are the absence of a graphic. To leave unprinted lines, the printers can be asked to skip one or more lines, as controlled by a carriage control tape in which holes are punched appropriately[4]. Six major types of line printers, classified by the means for producing characters, employ bars, wheels, chains, cylinders, matrix and cathode ray tubes.

Type bar printers typically have a speed of 100 to 200 lines per minute and operate by making a set of solenoid-operated hammers strike the back of the paper against the ribbon and the character on the type bars (Fig. 17.7). The type bars are positioned by input data so that the desired characters are aligned against the hammer head. There is one type bar associated with each print position, and the number of print columns is usually 10 to 100. The input data for each print column is also presented to the printer in a parallel form. In Fig. 17.7, the numbers to be printed (730456) are shown positioned correctly along the type line.

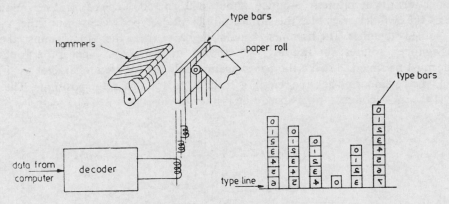

Fig. 17.7 Basic bar printer

Type wheel line printers operate in much the same fashion as type bar printers with one type wheel for each possible print position along the line. The type wheel shown in Fig. 17.8 contains the characters to be printed, and the appropriate character is positioned against the impact head by the input buffer/decoder. Speed is usually about 200 lines per minute with 70 to 120 characters per line.

In chain printers, the character shapes are mounted on the links in a chain in the form of a loop. The chain is rotated continuously, against a sheet of paper with a ribbon in between. A hammer, mounted behind the paper forces the paper against the moving chain to form the printed characters. The selection of the correct timing for the firing of hammers as the desired characters on the chain pass the print positions, requires some fairly complex buffering. The speed depends on the number of various characters that can be printed and is about 600 lines per minute for 60 characters along the chain.

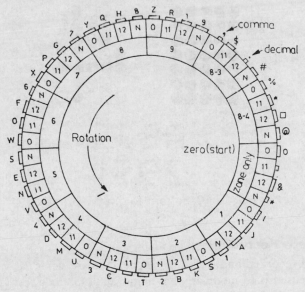

Fig. 17.8 Type wheel print pattern

Cylinder or drum printers produce about 600 to 1500 lines of print per minute. The surface of the cylinder resembles the surface of a bank of type wheels with the individual wheels joined together. The hammers behind the paper force the paper against the ribbon as the cylinder rotates continuously, as shown in Fig. 17.9. Hence, the firing of each hammer must be timed to strike the paper against only the desired character as it rotates past on the cylinder. The line length is from 10 to 150 character positions. The cylinder printer is the most common high-speed line printer.

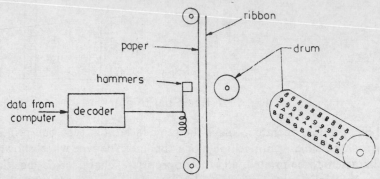

Fig. 17.9 Basic drum printer

Matrix line printers operate at speeds ranging from 500 to 1000 lines per minute. They operate like character printers, but instead of using only one matrix for printing the entire line, the printer uses one matrix for every second or fourth character position of the 120 possible character positions per line. Partly because of their speed, the buffering needed with these printers is complex. Figure 17.10 shows the patterns for some characters for line printers with a 35-part matrix.

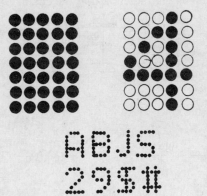

Fig. 17.10 Pattern for matrix printers

17.3.5 Digital Tape Recording

Digital data can be recorded and stored in magnetic tapes using a variety of techniques. The basic principle used is to modulate the digital data in some form or the other and then record this modulated data in the tape, as shown in Fig. 17.11. On playback, the output after amplification is demodulated and used to reconstruct the original data.

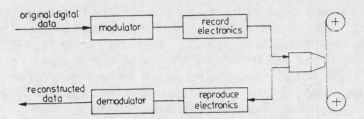

Fig. 17.11 Basic system for digital tape recording

In the return to bias (RB) type of recording, the "1"s in the data are presumed to be in the form of positive pulses, shown as e_i in Fig. 17.12(a). A "0" is represented by the absence of a pulse at clock time. A biasing current $-I_R$ holds the tape at a saturation flux level of $-\phi_{sat}$ except when the recording current switches to the level $+I_R$. The monostable multivibrator shown in Fig. 17.12(b) extends the input voltage pulse duration to allow sufficient time for the flux to build up in the head and stay within the head tape resolution. The playback voltage shown as e_{PB} has a differentiated form since e_{PB} is proportional to rate of change of flux $\dfrac{d\phi}{dt}$. The playback amplifier raises the voltage level and shortens the rise time. The rectified output fed to a monostable multivibrator enables the reconstruction of the recorded digital data.

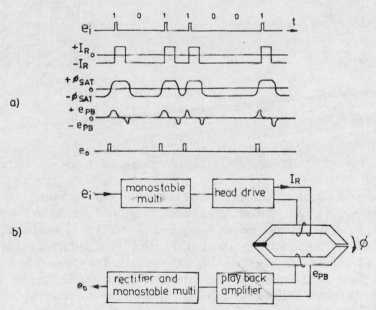

Fig. 17.12 Return to bias (RB) recording system:
(a) waveforms; (b) block schematic

While the electronic circuits required are relatively simple and economical, the main drawbacks of this method are the absence of a "self-clocking" characteristic on account of the zeroes being represented by the absence of any change in state, and a reduced storage density capability due to the requirement of two flux transitions per bit of stored data[5].

The return to zero (RZ) mode of recording, illustrated in Fig. 17.13(a), provides self clocking both for "1"s as well as "0"s. While a positive current pulse is fed to the recording head for a '1' in the data, a negative current pulse is fed for a 'zero'. The playback waveform e_{PB} consists of pulse doublets differing in phase by 180°. The demodulator differentiates between these waveforms and reconstructs the input pulse train.

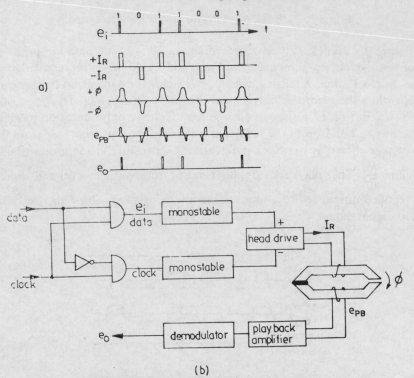

Fig. 17.13 RZ recording: (a) waveforms; (b) block schematic

One of the most popular methods employed in digital tape recording is the non-return to zero-Mark (NRZ-M) type of modulating the input data. Referring to Fig. 17.14 it may be noted that only one flux change per bit is required in this type of recording. As a result, the packing density is higher, being about 320 bits/cm. The system is not self-clocking, and hence a clock track must be recorded along with the data. The system is however independent of the tape velocity, and requires no readjustment of recording electronics for lower tape speeds. In the "non-return to zero change" method, which is a variation of the NRZ method, the flux is reversed only when a "1" is followed by a "0" or vice versa. A consecutive series of "1"s or "0"s result in no change. The relevant waveforms and schematic diagrams are shown in Fig. 17.15(a) and (b).

Modern recording and playback systems use double-pulse techniques of recording, employing phase modulation or frequency modulation. While the NRZ technique offers packing densities of 320 bits/cm and rates of 120,000 bits/s, the phase modulation systems

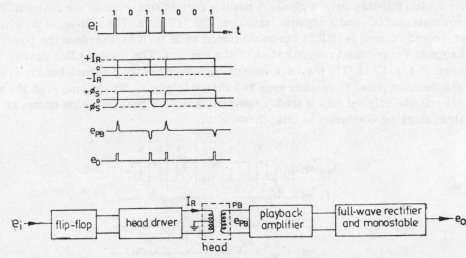

Fig. 17.14 NRZ-M method of recording: (a) waveforms; (b) block schematic

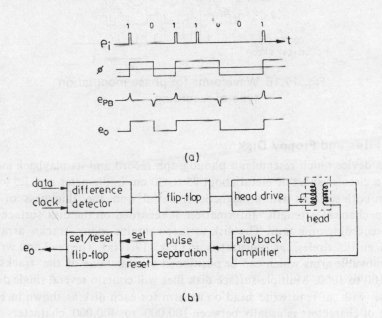

Fig. 17.15 NRZ-C method of recording: (a) waveforms;
(b) block schematic

yield densities of 600 bits/cm and rates of 300,000 bits/s. Figure 17.16 illustrates one type of phase-modulation technique. The main advantage of this technique is that while random sequences of "1"s and "0"s in the data can produce a very wide frequency band when recorded in the NRZ form, the phase-modulation technique used generally reduces the bandwidth to a single octave. It may be noted that the recording head current is a series of complete cycles, differing only in phase. A positive current transition at the centre of the bit cell represents a "0" and a negative transition, the "1" state. The individual positive and negative record current I_R (NRZ) can be shortened as in I_R (RZ), to reduce the power with little change in the resultant magnetization of the medium. The resultant flux density ϕ_H is also shown in Fig. 17.16. The playback voltage e_{PB} induced in the playback head is equalized in the playback amplifier to produce e_{PBE} and shaped to give e_o. By strobing e_o at the centre of the bit cell, the original data is readily retrieved. Since a signal transition occurs at every bit of time, clocking is inherent in this scheme also.

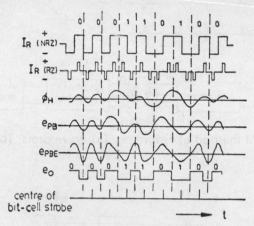

Fig. 17.16 Waveforms for phase modulation
type of recording

17.3.6 Disk Files and Floppy Disk

A disk file is a device which resembles a phonograph record and its playback mechanism. A single disk is a circular sheet of metal about 25 to 50 cm in diameter and 1.5 to 6 mm thick. It is coated on both surfaces with a magnetic material and the thickness of the disk is mainly for mechanical strength. Information is recorded on the disk surface in much the same way as recording on a tape. The disk surface contains many tracks arranged in the form of concentric circles, as illustrated in Fig. 17.17(a). The read and write heads are mounted on movable arms which can be positioned over any one of the tracks which can range from 100 to 1000. Multiple-surface disk files will contain several single disks mounted concentrically, with a read/write head on an arm for each disk as shown in Fig. 17.17(b). The data rate of characters is usually between 100,000 to 400,000 characters per second, as compared to 30,000 to 180,000 per second for the tape. While tapes contain about 20×10^6 characters per spool (about 720 m with a density of 400 characters per cm), a disk file typically contains 10×10^6 to 400×10^6 characters. In order to use a disk file, the heads must be moved to the right track before the read or write operation can be done. This is known as the "seek" operation. The information is usually written on the magnetic disk in "blocks" of serial data. A typical block can contain 10,000 characters. A timing track is prerecorded on one surface of the file so that bits are always stored in the same physical position in repeated "write" operations[6].

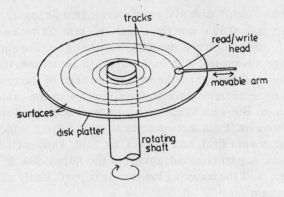

(a)

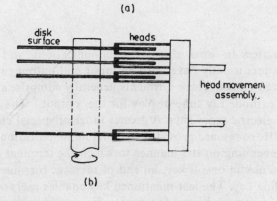

(b)

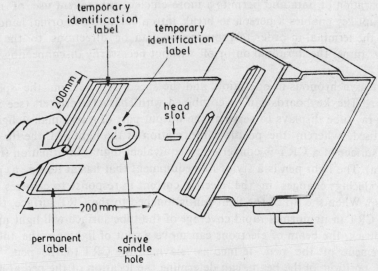

(c)

Fig. 17.17 Magnetic disk: (a) single disk; (b) multiple-surface disk file;
            (c) floppy disk

A variation of the older "rigid" disk system is the modern floppy disk. The floppy disk or "diskette" is a Mylar disk 0.125 mm thick and 195 mm dia with a 27.5 mm hole in the centre. It is coated with oxide to form a magnetic recording surface and is packaged in a flexible plastic envelope to protect the oxide layer. In actual use, the diskette and plastic envelope are inserted into the drive, and the read/write head of the drive is fitted into a slot on one edge of the envelope, thereby maintaining contact with the oxide layer.

The IBM (International Business Machines) format divides the disk into 77 tracks, each track consisting of 26 sections. Each section consists of 123 bytes which includes a blank field, an address field, a data field, and a check bit field. Thus each diskette has a storage capacity of 246,000 bytes. A particular advantage of the floppy disk is that it is relatively simple to manufacture, and the resulting lower cost is particularly suitable in the low-cost microcomputer environment[7].

17.3.7 Terminals

Terminals such as those used in time sharing, communications and as part of control consoles of larger computers usually have both an input and output capability built into the same physical piece of equipment. These terminals generally comprise a keyboard and a light pen for the input and a cathode ray tube display for the output. The keyboard resembles that used in an ordinary electric typewriter. A greater range of special characters, as required in EBCDIC and ASCII codes are provided by suitable modifications. Additional control functions needed vary depending on the manner in which the terminal is to be used but the functions, often included are an on-off key, an end of message (or line) key, an interrupt key, and an on-line off-line key. The last-mentioned key enables users to use the terminal for the off-line preparation of data and permits a more efficient subsequent use of the on-line time. The interrupt key enables a person to break into a computer's normal handling of the data from or to the terminal in order to provide new data or directions to the computer. The on-off key turns the terminal on or off without necessarily disconnecting it from the computer.

Keyboards are asynchronous in operation, and the speed depends on the speed of the human operator. The keyboards can be combined with character printers (see Sec. 17.3.3) or with cathode-ray-tube displays to serve as the output part of a terminal. A light pen can sometimes be used, wherein the position information of the light pen, the tip of which is touched to the surface of a CRT is converted to equivalent digital information (in X and Y co-ordinate form). The light pen is a stylus-like equipment that has at its tip, a photosensitive element producing changes in the electric current in response to changes in the light applied to its tip. When the tip of the light pen is touched to the CRT surface, the beam of electrons in the CRT in its normal rapid coverage of the tube surface will light up the tip of the pen. By feedback, the beam of electrons can move a spot of light on the tube face to match the movement of the pen, termed as "slaving" the CRT to the pen. The CRT, by sensing the position of the beam, can determine the location of the pen at any time its tip is close to the tube surface.

17.3.8 CRT Display

The CRT used with automatic computers is similar to the TV picture tube. A stream of electrons produced by the cathode in the narrow neck of the CRT is used to direct electron beams so that the beam can hit any part of the flat or slightly curved face (screen) of the tube. The intensity is controlled by a voltage applied to the grid. To form characters or lines, the input buffer produces the required pulse signals corresponding to the shape of the character and intensity so that the beam is moved to the desired place on the tube face and is focussed to form the desired shape. In one of the techniques the beam covers the entire face with scans producing rasters that move left to right and top to bottom. When the beam is intense the tube face is lit. The resulting characters look as though they are made of spots, as shown in Fig. 17.10. In a second version, the beam passes through a matrix of characters that has an opening for each character shape, and the shaped beam falls on the screen in a raster pattern. Any character shape can be placed anywhere on the tube surface. In an alternative scheme, electrostatic and magnetic forces are used to drive the beam in any direction at any time, enabling the tracing of any pattern. This vector technique gives the greatest flexibility in producing patterns. CRTs using this technique commonly serve as data plotters.

The buffering requirements for CRT are complex and have to fulfil many functions, viz., (i) the buffer must translate data from digital to analog form, which determine the beam position and intensity, (ii) the buffer must refresh the image on the tube face in excess of thirty times a second to avoid flicker, (iii) the buffer must maintain sufficient accuracy to hit any one place out of about five million possible places on the tube face, and (iv) to reduce the amount of data needed from the computer to drive the raster and vector CRTs, the buffer must be able to fill in details of the intensity and movement needed for the continual control of the beam and to combine this with data needed to refresh the image.

17.3.9 Data Plotter

A data plotter is a versatile output equipment for a computer wherein the information provided as data for the computer is plotted in a graphical form. For each point for which the computer provides data, the data plotter will either print a symbol or dot, or draw a line connecting that and the proceeding point. The plotting itself is done by the pen or symbol plotter located on the writing arm which can be positioned over any place on the paper on which the graph is to be plotted. Mechanical data plotters can be used both off-line and on-line. Punched cards, paper tape, and magnetic tape form the common data sources for off-line plotters.

In some data plotters, the received information on a series of points can be used to calculate the intervening points by interpolation so that the plot appears smoother. In others which have only the facility to translate input information directly into positions of the writing arm, the computer should provide as many points as are required so that the plot can appear continuous. Some of the high-speed plotters use the vector-plotting ability of CRTs and produce hard copies by photography. The production of graphic images, especially on a CRT, as a computer output, is known as "computer graphics".

17.4 DISPLAYS

Various types of displays are available today for the presentation of outputs of digital systems in visual form. The light emitting diode (LED) and liquid crystal displays (LCD) are very popular due to their common use in hand-held and other calculators. Some of the other forms used in displays include incandescent displays, cold cathode displays, and fluorescent displays.[8] The CRT display which is an important terminal equipment in computer systems has been described in Sec. 17.3.8.

17.4.1 Incandescent Displays

Incandescent displays can be made in a wide range of sizes and colours, and are among the brightest displays available for use. Though their main disadvantage is the low reliability due to segment failure, newer methods and materials have improved the reliability of this type of display. Many newer incandescent displays have seven segment filaments contained within a single vacuum envelope and are compatible with standard TTL voltages. Multiplexing is not very advantageous for this type of display, since each display segment often requires a diode to prevent leakage paths.

17.4.2 Cold Cathode Displays

These are also known as neon or gas-discharge displays. In the older versions, each display tube has 10 numerical cathodes placed at different depths. The inherent disadvantage is that the numbers displayed are not on the same plane. Seven segment displays of the cold cathode type are now available in sizes up to 1.7 cm high. The requirement of a high anode potential is a basic disadvantage of this type of display. This display typically has a red-orange colour.

17.4.3 Fluorescent Displays

Mainly used in calculators, the typical colour of this type is blue-green with the character height up to 1.5 cm. Their low current ($\cong 1$ mA) and voltage ($\cong 30$ V) requirements render them ideal for multiplexing.

17.4.4 Light Emitting Diodes

Light emitting diodes (LED) are p-n junction diodes usually using gallium arsenide and gallium arsenide phosphide, which emit visible electromagnetic radiation usually red in colour under forward bias condition. Combinations of other semiconductor materials enable other colours, such as amber, green, and yellow to be achieved. The low power requirements, high operating speed, and high reliability have made the LEDs one of the most favoured types of displays for a host of applications. In the seven segment numeric displays (display of numbers 0 to 9), it is usual to employ one LED per segment (the segments are shown in Fig 17.18(a)). The typical size range is from 0.25 to 2 cm.

The wiring pattern of LED seven segment displays is simplified by having one terminal as common for all the seven segments. Figure 17.18(b) and (c) show the "common-anode" and

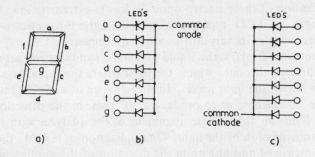

Fig. 17.18 LED seven-segment display: (a) display
format; (b) common-anode configuration;
(c) common-cathode configuration

"common-cathode" internal connections for LED displays. The common-cathode LEDs have to be driven by "active-high" decoder ICs, and the common-anode LEDs have to be driven by "active-low" decoders. Figure 17.19 shows this type of decoder connected to a seven-segment display digit. It may be noted that series resistors are included for each of the LEDs corresponding to the seven segments. Further, an additional LED corresponding to the decimal point is also provided in the display, which again has a current limiting series resistance. The typical value of the series resistance is 150 ohms for a segment current of about 20 mA.

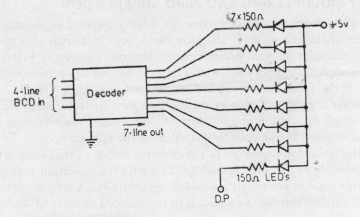

Fig. 17.19 LED seven-segment display driver

17.4.5 Liquid Crystal Displays[8]

In contrast to LEDs which are active devices that generate light, liquid crystal displays (LCDs) are passive devices that modify the light by scattering. The light from a separate light source is controlled by placing the liquid crystal cell in the light path and altering the optical transmission characteristics of the cell by the application of electric fields. The operation of the LCD may be based on one of the three processes viz., (i) dynamic scattering mode (DSM), (ii) field induced birefringence, and (iii) alignment of a twisted nematic (TN).

The power consumption of these electro-optic devices is extremely low, which is one of the foremost advantages of LCD types of displays. Of the three electro-optic devices, TN is more popular on account of its very low power requirements.

In the twisted nematic displays, the liquid crystal is sandwiched between two pieces of glass, one a 'polarizer' through which the light enters the liquid crystal and the other an 'analyzer' through which the light leaves. In the absence of a field, the molecules in the liquid crystal are so oriented as to produce a 90° twist in the direction of polarization of the incident light. Thus an appropriate alignment of the analyzer with respect to the polarizer results in full transmission of the light. On application of a field, the molecules of the liquid crystal are untwisted and line up in the direction of the applied field. As a result, the light is not rotated on passing through the crystal and is blocked by the analyzer, which is aligned for the twisted condition. The opposite effects may be achieved by turning the polarizer so that it is aligned parallel to the analyzer. In this case no transmission occurs in the absence of the field and the background appears dark. An important advantage of the twisted nematic structure is that very small voltages, typically less than 10 V, are sufficient to align the molecules. The power consumed is of the order of a few microwatts. An ac is generally used for the excitation, since the material failure is rapid with dc excitation.

The response time of LCDs typically range between 10 and 100 ms. The main disadvantages of LCDs are a limited temperature range of operation (0 to 60°C), low reliability, and short operating life.

17.5 DISPLAY MULTIPLEXING AND ZERO SUPPRESSION

By time sharing the decoder used for driving the display digits, it is possible to considerably reduce the count of the components and interconnections in display systems. A typical circuit scheme for multiplexing eight seven-segment displays is shown in Fig. 17.20 The input in BCD form is applied to the latches whose outputs are fed to open-collector control gates. The outputs of the gates are "wired-OR"ed and fed to a single "BCD to seven-segment" decoder. The seven segments of each of the eight display digits are paralleled and fed from the decoder through current-limiting resistors. At any instant however, only one of the digits is displayed as selected by the decoder output from the scan controller. For any particular digit selected, the transistor connected to the common anode of that digit is turned ON, and the gate corresponding to that digit is enabled. This strobing operation then progresses to the next digit. In this manner each digit is enabled sequentially. A refresh rate of 50 to 100 Hz is typical for flicker-free display. In addition to the reduced number of decoders necessary, the multiplex scheme requires less average dc power for getting nearly the same intensity, due to the fact that the luminous efficiency of LEDs increases with the peak current level. Further, the display intensity is also controllable by varying the strobe time. Other displays, such as incandescent and fluorescent as well as gas-discharge displays can also be multiplexed in a similar manner.

17.5.1 Zero Suppression

In multi-digit displays with the decimal point, it is advantageous to be able to suppress zeroes preceding the significant digits and following the decimal point. Conforming to normal

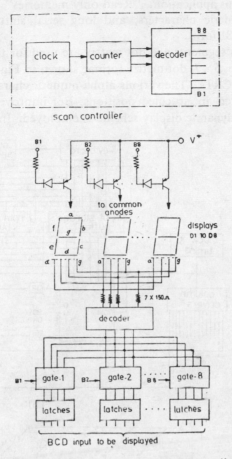

Fig. 17.20 Multiplexed seven-segment display

practice, the display 0007.200 can then be displayed as 7.2. In order to facilitate leading-edge zero suppression, the decoder-drivers of many seven-segment displays are provided with additional, input/output controls termed ripple blanking input (RBI) and ripple blanking output (RBO). The RBO assumes a "1" level when the character being displayed is a "'0'. The application of this '1' level as RBI for the decoder in the next lower significant digit position will ensure that its display will be blanked if the displayed character is zero. The RBO of the second decoder will in turn form the RBI for the next lower significant digit decoder and so on. Since the suppression of the least significant integer zero in a number is not usually desired, the RBI input of this decoder stage should be left open. A similar procedure in the reverse order is used for the blanking of trailing-edge zeroes.

17.5.2 Alpha-numeric Display

The display of alphabets as well as numerals in response to electrical inputs is the primary goal of alpha-numeric displays. Arrays of LEDs as well as CRTs (cathode-ray-tube displays) are extremely useful in this application. "Read only memories" that are used to facilitate generation of alpha-numeric characters, and long serial shift registers for memories are now available in MOS/LSI form.

Many formats, such as segments and dot matrix are used for the representation of alpha-numeric characters. The 5×7 dot-matrix format shown in Fig. 17.21(a) is most popularly used in LED arrays and CRTs. The various alpha-numeric characters are displayed by lighting up the LEDs located in specified positions. For improved brightness of display and economy in hardware, a dynamic display scheme is employed. In this the LEDs are not lit

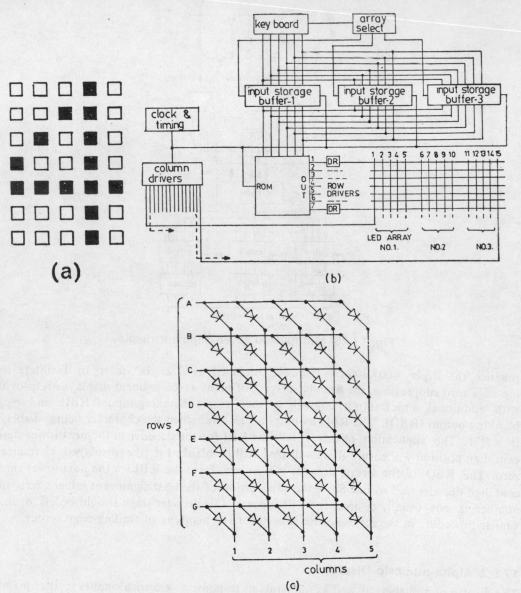

Fig. 17.21 Dot matrix display: (a) 5×7 dot matrix; (b) 3-digit alpha-numeric display using horizontal strobing; (c) internal arrangement of LED's in 5×7 dot matrix

continuously but are sequentially lit by scanning in a "vertical strobe" or "horizontal strobe" mode. In the vertical strobe mode, information is addressed to the display by selecting a single row at a time, energizing the appropriate LEDs in that row, and then proceeding to the next row. In the horizontal strobe mode, a single column is selected at a time. The vertical strobing scheme is similar to the horizontal raster scan technique used in CRT displays.

The functional diagram for a three-digit alpha-numeric display system using horizontal strobing is shown in Fig. 17.21(b). The alpha-numeric characters are represented by a code of a specified word length, generated by the keyboard. The ASCII code is one of the most popular formats used with keyboards, providing 64 alpha-numeric characters, including the 26 English alphabets, 10 numerals, and several other symbols. The different characters are represented by a six-bit code, and each code provides a unique row address and column address so that appropriate LEDs arranged in a 5×7 dot-matrix can be energized. Hence, the ROM has a storage capacity of $64 \times 5 \times 7 = 2240$ bits.

Referring to Fig. 17.21(b), the six-bit, ASCII code from the keyboard is sequentially entered and stored in three input storage buffers. The codes in the input buffers refer to the three individual characters to be displayed. The array selector selects the buffer, and the six-bit output of the decoder is entered in parallel into the selected buffer. The first input storage buffer output is enabled by a timing pulse so that the six-bit code from it controls the character output from the ROM. If all the five columns of the LED array, shown in Fig. 17.21(c) are driven now, the appropriate character can be displayed. In the dynamic display however only one column is energized or driven at a time, and the five columns are driven sequentially. When the first five columns have been driven, a timing pulse changes the code input to the ROM to correspond to that stored in buffer-2. Similarly when columns 11 to 15 are being driven, the data to the ROM is from input buffer-3. After all the columns have been driven, the sequence repeats; if the repetition rate is more than about 20 per second, a flicker-free array display of alpha-numeric characters results. Hewlett Packard 5082-7100 series LED alpha-numeric indicator arrays is a typical example of a display usable in this manner[9].

17.5.3 Bar-graph Display[10]

The bar-graph display is basically an array of LEDs, LCDs, or gas-discharge panels, arranged in an $n \times m$ matrix form, by which the signal magnitude is indicated in a linear or angular format. The light-emitting diode bar-graph consists of a number of LED arrays (row-wise) arranged in a single or multiple column. The packed density may be as much as 50 to 200 devices per cm^2, and the display signs can be as large as $5\ cm \times 10$ cm. The main advantages of this type of display are the solid-state nature (without any moving parts) and good speed of response. Such displays find wide applications in process instrumentation systems.

REFERENCES

1. Pear, C.B. (Ed.), *Magnetic Recording in Science and Industry*, pp. 39-42, Reinhold Publishing Corp., New York, 1967.

2. Gear, C.W., *Computer Organization and Programming*, pp. 219-220, McGraw-Hill, New York, 1969.
3. Chapin, N., *Computers: A Systems Approach*, p. 178, Van Nostrand Reinhold Co., New York, 1971.
4. Ibid. 3, p. 180.
5. Ibid. 1, pp. 150-151.
6. Ibid. 2, pp. 215-220.
7. McGlynn, D.R., *Microprocessors, Technology, Architecture and Applications*, pp. 128-129, John Wiley and Sons, New York, 1976.
8. Sol Sherr, *Electronic Displays*, pp. 221-232, John Wiley and Sons, New York, 1979.
9. "Solid state alphanumeric display", *Application Note 931*, Hewlett Packard, Palo Alto, California, 1973.
10. Ibid. 8, pp. 506-519.

BIBLIOGRAPHY

Anderson, P.L., "Optical character recognition—a survey", *Datamation*, Vol. 15, No. 7, pp. 43-48, July 1969.

Applications Engg. Staff, (H-P), *Opto Electronics Applications Manual*, McGraw-Hill, New York, 1977.

Barden, W., Jr., *How to Buy and Use Minicomputers and Microcomputers?* Howard W. Sams and Co., Indiana, 1977.

Berkeley, E.C. (Ed.), *The Computer Directory and Buyer's Guide*, Berkeley Enterprises Inc., Newtonville, Massachusetts, 1979.

Borut, R.W. et al., "Display systems", Ch. 15 in: Considine, D.M. (Ed.), *Process Instruments and Controls Handbook*, McGraw-Hill, New York, 1974.

Chapin, N., *Computers: A Systems Approach*, Van Nostrand Reinhold Co., New York, 1971.

Chappell, A., *Optoelectronics: Theory and Practice*, McGraw-Hill, New York, 1978.

Crooke, R.S., "Dynamic accuracy of analogue *X-Y* recorders", *Electronic Engg.*, Vol. 51, No. 623, pp. 41-48, Mid May 1979.

Davis, S., "OEM printers", *EDN*, Vol. 24. No. 4, pp. 68-69. Feb. 20, 1979.

Ewing, G.W. and Ashworth, H.A., *The Laboratory Recorder*, Plenum Press, New York, 1974.

Figueroa, J.A., "PHI, the HP-IB interface chip", *Hewlett Packard Journal*, Vol. 29, No. 7, pp. 16-17, July 1978.

Fuori, W.M. et al., *Introduction to Computer Operations*, McGraw-Hill, New York, 1973.

Hackmeister, D., "Focus on plotters: under μP control, they bring complex images to reality", *Electronic Design*, Vol. 27, No. 21. pp. 173-180, Oct. 11, 1979.

London, A., "Reviewing the recent developments in recorder technology", *Control and Instrumentation*, Vol. 10, No. 12, pp. 34-48, Dec. 1978.

Matheson, W.G., "A computer input/output system based on the H.P. interface bus", *Hewlett Packard Journal*, Vol. 30, No. 7, pp. 9-13, July 1979.

Matick, R.E., *Computer Storage System and Technology*, John Wiley and Sons, New York, 1977.

Optoelectronics Designer's Catalog, Hewlett Packard Components, California, 1979.

Oringen, R.S., *Audio Control Handbook*, Hastings House, New York, 1972.

Rich, M., "CRT terminals—an update", *Instruments and Control Systems*, Vol. 52, No. 5. pp. 20-26, May 1979.

Richards, C.J., *Electronic Display and Data Systems*, McGraw-Hill, London, 1973.

Salmon, G. and Lawries, L., "Hard copy from oscilloscopes", *Electronic Engg.*, Vol. 51, No. 623, pp. 86-88, Mid May 1979.

Sherr, S., *Electronic Displays*, John Wiley and Sons, New York, 1979.

"Strip chart recorder survey", *Instruments and Control Systems*, Vol. 44, No. 7, pp. 69-81, July 1971.

Standeven, J. et al., "Multiconsole—computer display systems utilizing television techniques", *Proc. IEEE*, Vol. 115, No. 10, pp. 1375-1379, Oct. 1978.

"The instrumentation recorder and its niche in industry", *Control and Instrumentation*, Vol. 11, No. 10, pp. 41-45, Oct. 1979.

Theis, D.F. and Hobbs, L.C., "Low cost remote CRT terminals", *Datamation*, Vol. 14, No. 6, pp. 22-29, June 1968.

Waye, C., "The computer and its peripherals", *Instruments and Control Systems*, Vol. 52, No. 1, pp. 63-69, Jan. 1979.

Weiner, R.J., "Rely on a floppy-disc controller IC to handle 'any density' floppy drives", *Electron Des.*, Vol. 27, No. 4, pp. 72-76, Feb. 15, 1979.

Wilson, R.A., *Optical Page Reading Devices*, Van Nostrand Reinhold Co., New York, 1966.

18

GENERAL PURPOSE ELECTRONIC TEST EQUIPMENT

18.1 INTRODUCTION

Some of the basic electronic-test and measuring instruments used in instrumentation systems are described in this chapter. These include: (i) cathode ray oscilloscope, (ii) digital voltmeter/DPM/DMM, (iii) electronic counter, (iv) ac milli-voltmeter, (v) wave analyzer and spectrum analyzer, (vi) signal and noise generators, (vii) regulated power supplies, (viii) frequency synthesizer, (ix) lock-in amplifier, and (x) frequency response analyzer and phase meter.

18.2 CATHODE-RAY OSCILLOSCOPES

The cathode-ray oscilloscope (CRO) is one of the most versatile instruments used in the development of electronic circuits and systems, and for trouble-shooting and monitoring the performance of instrumentation systems. The basic functional block diagram of a CRO is shown in Fig. 18.1. The instrument is widely used for visual display of complex signals and pulse waveforms and comprises a vertical amplifier and horizontal amplifier that deflects a beam of electrons originating from the cathode of the cathode ray tube (CRT). The signal to be displayed is normally fed through a calibrated input attenuator and a wideband high-gain vertical amplifier to the Y deflection plates of the CRT. The horizontal amplifier, connected to the X plates of the CRT, is normally fed from an internally-generated time base which is usually a saw-tooth waveform generator. Alternatively, the X amplifier can be fed from an externally-connected X input voltage. The high voltage supply required for acceleration and focussing of the electron beam also forms a part of the equipment. An internal vertical calibration signal is often included in almost all oscilloscopes. The various sub-sections are energized from a regulated power supply system.

The bandwidth of an oscilloscope normally refers to the 3 dB bandwidth of the vertical amplifier in the normal sensitivity ranges (to enhance the sensitivity in the Y amplifier, a $\times$ 5 or $\times$ 10 switch can also be present, but this often results in reduced bandwidth). The bandwidth is approximately related to the rise time, τ, by the relationship (bandwidth)$\times \tau \simeq 0.35$.

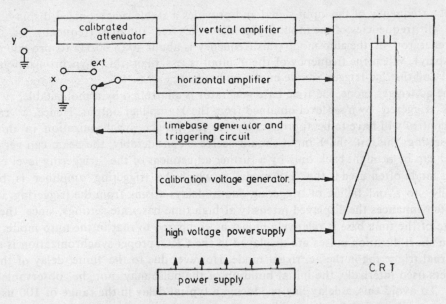

Fig. 18.1 Schematic block diagram of a cathode-ray oscilloscope

The rise time is of specific importance when the oscilloscope is to be used for observing short duration high-frequency pulses. In order to maintain the frequency response constant at various sensitivity settings, the attenuator in the vertical channel is invariably a compensated attenuator. The input impedance of most of the oscilloscopes is typically 1 megaohm in parallel with a 30 pF input capacitance (C_{in}). The effect of the input capacitance can be quite significant when the source impedance is high. For example, a 5 MHz vertical amplifier may offer effectively only a bandwidth of about 500 kHz when the resistance of the source connected to the scope is about 10 kΩ and $C_{in} \simeq 30$ pF. The accuracy of the vertical amplifier section for various sensitivity settings is normally of the order of $\pm 3\%$.

The time base generator in a scope is provided with step and continuous controls to obtain variable time base rates in the range 500 ms/cm to as high as 0.5 or 0.1 μs/cm. For oscilloscopes possessing a vertical amplifier bandwidth much higher than 10 MHz, the time base rates can extend to 50 ns/cm and higher. When external X inputs need to be applied to the scope, the internal time base circuit is disconnected, and the X amplifier gets connected to the X input by a switch which can often be an additional throw position in the time base control switch. The bandwidth in this case is determined by that of the X amplifier. It is particularly important to consider the effect of the X amplifier bandwidth on phase when the oscilloscope is being used to measure the phase shift between two sinusoidal signals at a high frequency.

The time base is triggered by a triggering circuit which can function in one of three or more modes. A commonly encountered and used mode is the "auto" mode. The time base is used in this case in a self-oscillating condition, i.e., it gives an output even in the absence of any Y input. The advantage of this mode is that the beam is visible on the CRT under all conditions, including the zero input. When the input exceeds a certain magnitude (often about half a division in the vertical display) the internal free-running oscillator locks on to the frequency of the input signal and provides a stable synchronized display. This is so for all frequencies of the input higher than the free running frequency of the time base generator in the auto mode (this frequency is about 40 to 60 Hz to provide a flicker-free display). When the frequency of the Y input is less than this, synchronization is not assured and the "ac trigger" mode has to be used.

In the ac trigger mode, the time base generator is controlled by a monostable, which in turn is triggered by a set level obtained from the Y amplifier output. Hence, a "triggering level" control will have to be appropriately set for proper synchronization in this mode. After setting this, if the Y input should decrease considerably, the beam can get blanked out and can be brought back only by a further adjustment of the "triggering level control". A third mode often used is the "HF mode" in which the triggering amplifier is bypassed internally, to avoid failure of triggering due to delays arising from the triggering amplifier. This often enhances the displayed intensity at high time-base-rate settings, since the repetition rate of the time base is relatively higher as compared to that in the auto mode.

When short duration pulses are displayed in the CRO, proper synchronization is achieved by internal triggering in the ac trigger mode. However due to the finite delay of the trigger amplifiers used internally, the initial build-up of the pulse may not be observable in the display. To avoid this, a delay line producing a typical delay in the range of 100 ns to 1 μs is often incorporated in the Y amplifier.

The "delayed sweep" is an additional facility available in some oscilloscopes, enabling enhanced resolution in time measurements. The "delaying sweep" allows the operator to select any specific delay time by means of a 10-turn calibrated dial. This delay is generated by applying a sweep ramp to a voltage comparator that produces a trigger pulse at a later point in time. The delayed sweep starts at the selected time, and is usually a decade or two faster than the delaying sweep. Using a very high speed for the delayed sweep, considerable magnification is achieved so that short duration phenomena occurring after a delay period following a trigger can be conveniently observed.

The measurement of the phase difference between two sinusoidal signals of the same frequency can be carried out in a CRO by means of "Lissajous figures". By applying one of the inputs to the Y amplifier and the other to the X amplifier (external X-input mode), the Lissajous pattern is obtained. While for phase shifts of 0°, 180°, and 360°, the Lissajous pattern is a straight line, the same for phase differences of 90° and 270° is a circle, provided input sensitivities are adjusted properly. For other phase shift values, the Lissajous pattern is an ellipse. Lissajous patterns can also be used to compare the frequency of two signals if they are harmonically related.

Z modulation is another additional facility available in many general purpose scopes. The voltage applied to the grid of the CRT in this case can be controlled by an external signal connected to the Z mode input. The input required at this point can often be 5 to 10 V to effect discernible changes in the intensity of the displayed beam. "Time markers" can be conveniently connected to this input in order to elicit precise time information from the CRT display.

An useful accessory for the oscilloscope is the "oscilloscope probe". A 1:1 passive probe is a thin metal prod connected to the oscilloscope input terminal through an insulated, shielded, flexible, lead. A "low-capacitance probe" is generally an attenuating type (10:1) with an adjustable compensating capacitor. The input capacitance of the probe is approximately one-tenth of the input capacitance of the connecting-cable and the amplifier. Because of the 10 : 1 attenuation, the sensitivity of the CRO is reduced by a factor of ten. To achieve very low input capacitance, active probes are used. In an active probe, the input feeds to a high impedance circuit, such as the ones using FET's situated at the input end of the probe. The supply voltage for the operation of the FET stage is also fed through the probe leads.

18.3 DIGITAL VOLTMETERS AND MULTIMETERS

Several A/D conversion techniques were outlined in Chapter 14. Of these, the dual slope integration technique is widely employed in digital voltmeters of medium accuracy and low speed. The digital outputs of A/D converter shown in Fig. 14.18 are connected through suitable decoders to digital display devices, such as LED or LCD seven-segment arrays or Nixie tubes. The sensitivity of a DVM is controlled by incorporating calibrated attenuators in the input section. For a $4\frac{1}{2}$ digit DVM, the calibration accuracy of the input attenuator will be typically about 0.01 to 0.05%. To facilitate periodic recalibration, a dc standard voltage of a higher level of accuracy can also be incorporated in the DVM.

The input resistance in the normally encountered 0.2 and 2 V ranges is often about 1000 megaohms or higher, while for higher input ranges, the input resistance may be limited to 10 megaohms in order to ensure adequate accuracy. (High accuracy, high value resistances are not easy to come by and are in addition affected by stray leakage across them; a 10 megohms resistance gets altered by 0.01% if a 100 gigaohms leakage resistance develops across it.) The accuracy specifications of DVM's normally include two quantities: (i) a percentage of the range, and (ii) a percentage of the reading. As a result, the ambiguity of a measurement is highest in any range at the lowest input that cannot be measured in a lower range. For example, a $4\frac{1}{2}$ digit DVM possessing an accuracy specification of $\pm 0.05\%$ of reading $\pm 0.01\%$ of range may indicate anywhere from 2.018 to 2.022 V in the 10 V range, for a standard input of 2.020 V. (The total error, here, is equivalent to about $\pm 0.1\%$ of the applied input.)

Depending on the resolution possible, a DPM may be referred to as 3 digit, $3\frac{1}{2}$ digit, 4 digit, etc. A three-digit DPM has a resolution of 1/1000th of the range and has a maximum display of 999. In contrast, the $3\frac{1}{2}$ digit DPM has a resolution of 1/2000th of the range, and the maximum displayed value is 1999. Similarly, the resolution of a four digit DPM is 1/10000th of its range, and that of the $4\frac{1}{2}$ digit is 1/20000th of the range, with the display range extending to 19999 for the latter.

With the additional capability to measure ac voltage and current, dc current, and resistance, the digital multimeter (DMM) offers increased versatility. The schematic block diagram of a DMM is shown in Fig. 18.2. In the ac voltage mode, the applied input is fed through a calibrated, compensated attenuator, to a precision full-wave rectifier circuit followed by a ripple-reduction filter. The resulting dc is fed to the ADC and the subsequent display system. For current measurements, the drop across an internal calibrated shunt is measured, directly by the ADC in the dc current mode, and after ac to dc conversion in the ac current mode. This drop is often in the range of 200 mV (corresponding to full scale.) Due to the lack of precision in the ac-dc conversion, the accuracy in the ac ranges is in general of the order of 0.2 to 0.5%. In addition, the measurement range is often limited

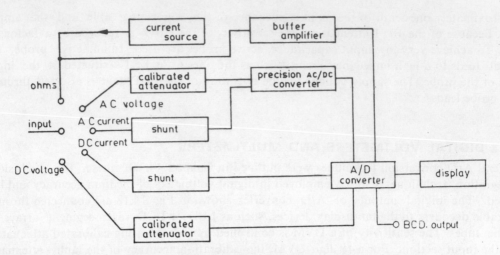

Fig. 18.2 Schematic block diagram of a digital multimeter

to about 50 Hz at the lower frequency end owing to the ripple in the rectified signal becoming a non-negligible percentage of the display and hence resulting in fluctuation of the displayed number. At the higher frequency end, deterioration of the performance of the ac-dc converter limits the accuracy. The ac measurement range is often average reading, rms calibrated.

In the resistance range the DMM operates by measuring the voltage across the externally-connected resistance, resulting from a current forced through it from a calibrated internal current source. The accuracy of the resistance measurement is of the order of 0.1 to 0.5% depending on the accuracy and stability of the internal current sources. The accuracy may by poorer in the highest range which is often about 10 or 20 megaohms. In the lowest range, the full scale may be $\simeq$ 200 ohms with a resolution of about 0.01 ohms for a $4\frac{1}{2}$ digit DMM. The effect of lead resistances will have to be carefully considered in this range of resistance measurement.

18.4 ELECTRONIC COUNTERS

Due to the high accuracy of measurement achievable from electronic digital counters, they have become the standard test equipment for frequency monitoring in laboratory measurements. A schematic block diagram is shown in Fig. 18.3. In the frequency measurement mode, the input (after getting converted into digital pulses) is gated into a counter for a selectable, accurate period in the range 10 μs to 10 s, derived from an ...ernal clock. The single pulse selector driven from the internal repetition-rate generator, selects out one pulse from the pulse train output of the divider chain-2. After presentation of the counted output in the display for a convenient time, the counter is reset, and the process is repeated when another single pulse is selected out by the repetition-rate generator. In the manual mode, a manual control replaces the internal repetition-rate generator, and in the hold mode the internal rate generator is disabled after a display has been obtained so that the displayed value can be held indefinitely.

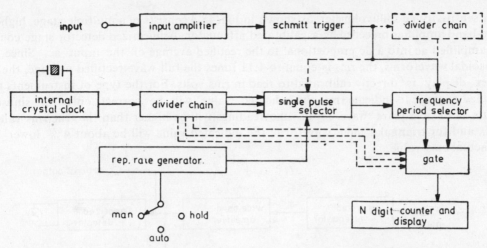

Fig. 18.3 Schematic block diagram of an electronic counter

The period measurement mode is often used at frequencies less than about 100 Hz, the frequency being computed as the inverse of the period. In this mode the single pulse selector is connected to the schmitt trigger that follows the input amplifier, and a standard clock frequency from the divider chain is gated into the counter and display unit over a single period of the input pulse train. Depending on the clock frequency used, the resolution may vary in the range 1 μs to 1 s. In the multiple period mode, a further divider chain-1 coupled to the schmitt trigger provides period averaging over 10, 100, 1000, etc. of the input pulse periods. Many counters also have the facility to measure the time interval between two external command inputs provided as pulse or as contact closures. In this case the gating is done by a flip-flop that operates from the external inputs, by "gating in" a standard output from the internal clock divider chain-2 over the period between the two external contact closures.

The accuracy of a counter is directly dependent on the accuracy of the basic crystal clock used within the counter. Employing oven-controlled crystals for the basic internal clock, a stability of the order of 1 in 10^8 is normally achievable over laboratory temperature conditions. The accuracy is also of this order, provided the calibration is done with respect to an absolute standard of frequency.

For the measurement of frequencies above a few. hundred megahertz, the principle of heterodyning is sometimes employed. In this case, the high frequency to be measured is converted to a lower frequency at which the counter can operate, by heterodyning the input with a fixed high-frequency signal. In another method employed in the measurement of high frequencies, a 'prescaler' is used to scale down the input frequency by a fixed ratio. The prescaler is normally designed to cover specifically a high frequency range, e.g., from 100 to 500 MHz.

18.5 AC MILLIVOLTMETERS

AC millivoltmeters can be classified into three broad categories: (a) average-responding voltmeters, (b) peak-responding voltmeters and (c) true rms-responding voltmeters. A typical high sensitivity ac millivoltmeter, as shown in Fig. 18.4 consists of a multiple-stage, high-gain wide-band amplifier preceded by a calibrated attenuator. A linearized detector stage converts the amplified ac into a dc proportional to the rectified average of the input ac. Since, for sinusoidal waveforms, the rms is equal to 1.11 times the full wave rectified average, the final meter display is directly calibrated to read in rms volts. For the type of instruments using rectified average to indicate rms, the indicated value will be correct only for sinusoidal inputs. For a square wave input, the readings will be higher than the true rms value by 11%, and for triangular input waveform, the indicated value will be about 4% lower than the actual rms value.

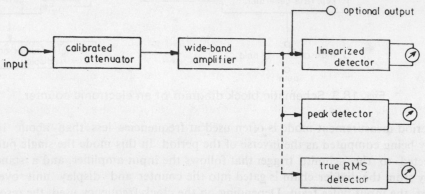

Fig. 18.4 Schematic block diagram of an ac millivoltmeter

The bandwidth capability of the ac voltmeter needs to be considered carefully when high frequency signals are to be measured. While in a majority of instruments the bandwidth is constant for all the ranges, in certain cases the bandwidth decreases at some of the high sensitivity settings (usually for full-scale values in fractions of a mV). The bandwidth referred to is generally the frequency range over which the instrument operates within a certain specified error expressed as a percentage or in dB.

In peak-reading voltmeters, the amplifier output is fed to a peak detector (see Chapter 12), and its output is displayed. The peak detector normally has a fast response for increasing amplitude signals, but if the signal should decrease in amplitude, the detector output will not immediately follow the input change. Ideally, of course, the peak would be "held" indefinitely, but in practice a suitable decay time constant is incorporated to facilitate practical usage.

A true rms voltmeter provides an output directly proportional to the rms value of the input, irrespective of the waveform of the input. Since the amplifier and associated circuitry should be kept in the linear region for proper operation, normal operation of a true rms indicator is specified for a certain maximum value of the crest factor. This refers to the ratio of the peak value of the signal to its rms value. In general, it is less than 5 for a variety of signals. Only in a very few special cases, such as a pulse train with very low duty ratio, the crest factor goes beyond 5. Hence a true rms meter is often specified for this value of crest factor and for an input having an rms value equal to the full-scale value. Typical applications of such meters are in noise analysis, turbulence studies, rms power measurement of phase controlled thyristor powered systems, etc. The methods used for obtaining the true RMS value have been discussed in Sec. 12.5.5.

18.6 WAVE ANALYZERS AND SPECTRUM ANALYZERS

The analysis of the spectrum of a complex wave is often desired to identify the origin of certain interferences, and helps establish malfunctions and predict possible failures. The methods of analysis employed in general have been described in Chapter 13. One of the methods used is based on the heterodyne principle, as shown in Fig. 18.5, where the amplitude information at an arbitrarily-selectable frequency in the input is converted into a proportional amplitude at a standard frequency within the analyzer, and the amplitude of this signal is measured after filtering. Consider for example, that the component at a frequency of 1.5 kHz in the input is to be measured. The first mixer (shown in Fig. 18.5) converts this component to a standard frequency of 100 kHz by mixing the input with an internally-generated frequency of 101.5 kHz. For measuring an input at 22.5 kHz, the internal frequency used to mix with the input is 122.5 kHz. In this fashion, the filtering can always be carried out at a fixed frequency (100 kHz in the example), and at the bandwidth of this intermediate frequency filter. This type of arrangement results in constant bandwidth analysis, and the bandwidth of analysis may be one of a few selectable values. An auxiliary BFO output can also be incorporated, obtained as the beat output of the internal variable frequency oscillator and another fixed standard frequency generator at the intermediate frequency. It may be noted that the frequency of this output is precisely the frequency to which the analyzer is tuned. This arrangement is thus very convenient when the signal being analyzed is the output of a system that can possibly be excited by the BFO output itself as in filter response measurements.

18.6.1 Swept Filter Analyzers

In swept filter analysis, the signal to be analyzed is fed to a tuned filter whose centre frequency can be continuously varied either mechanically or electrically. The output of the tuned filter is fed to an X-Y recorder after rectification and averaging. The X input of the recorder is fed from a voltage proportional to the instantaneous centre frequency of the filter being swept. The record obtained is thus directly the frequency spectrum of the signal being analyzed. Generally, the spectrum obtained is a plot of the signal level in dB against the frequency in a log scale. A typical application of a swept filter analyzer is in plotting the frequency response of the telephone transmitter (mouth piece) and receiver (ear piece).

18.6.2 Spectrum Analyzers

While sophisticated spectrum analyzers based on the time compression techniques and FFT processsing are available, many modern oscilloscopes have the capability to display the frequency spectrum of the input applied to it. The basic arrangement is shown in Fig. 18.6, which resembles the block diagram of Fig. 18.5. The frequency range over which the spectrum is displayed is controlled by the "span" adjustment in the sweep generator. The displayed spectrum is centred around the centre frequency as set in the swept local oscillator. The relative input level over which the amplitude spectrum is displayed is set by the input level control of the input attenuator. The new generation of spectrum analyzers incorporate many facilities which include (i) direct frequency readout, (ii) digital storage—in order to

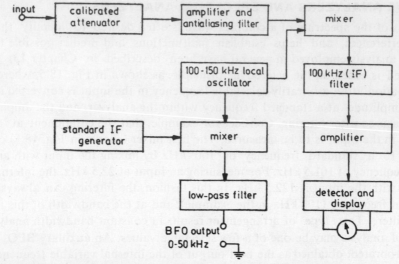

Fig. 18.5 Schematic block diagram of a heterodyne wave analyzer

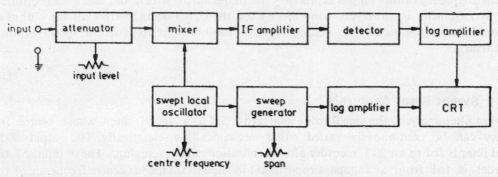

Fig. 18.6 Schematic block diagram of a swept-frequency spectrum analyzer

avoid flicker effect at low rates of sweep, (iii) high stability—obtained by incorporating the frequency synthesizer principle in the local oscillator, and (iv) wide dynamic range—as high as 80 dB with ability to detect nanovolt level signals[1].

18.7 SIGNAL GENERATORS

Signal generators are of various types based on the techniques used. In the frequency range up to 200 kHz generally employed in Instrumentation Systems the *RC* generator using the Wien network is one of the most popular methods used to obtain low distortion outputs. The desired frequency range is subdivided into suitable decade ranges, and in each range, the frequency is continuously variable. Capacitors are switched to provide various decade ranges, while resistors are either continuously changed or changed in steps to provide any frequency within a decade range. The important characteristics to look for in a generator are: (i) frequency stability, (ii) frequency accuracy, (iii) frequency range, (iv) resolution, settability and repeatability, (v) amplitude stability, (vi) distortion and (vii) output impedance.

The frequency stability of *RC* oscillators is in the range of 0.1% of setting for ordinary oscillators, bettering to 0.001% after warm-up in sophisticated types. The frequency accuracy may be only ±3%, though better figures (e.g. ±0.2%) are achievable by proper trimming of components (Hewlett Packard Type 4204A digital oscillator is a typical example of a high-accuracy oscillator). In sophisticated signal generators, a digital readout of the frequency is provided. While the settability˙ is often about 1%, this can be improved to ±0.01% of the range by using vernier control or by multiple switch control of frequency. The majority of oscillators employ some form of feedback stabilization for amplitude, yielding amplitude stability of the order of ±1 dB or better for any set value. The typical output impedance is 600Ω, and the actual output is often directly indicated by a built-in meter. Some oscillators may not be provided with a dc return path in the equipment (i.e., the output may have been connected to the internal generator through a large value capacitor which is also internal to the oscillator), and in such a case connecting a suitable resistance across the output will help avoiding certain undesirable effects resulting therefrom. The distortion figure of *RC* oscillators is often dependent on the set frequency, the figure being as good as 0.1% over a medium range of frequencies, deteriorating to 1% or higher at the lower and higher ends of operation. The lowest frequency is often about 1 Hz.

18.7.1 Function Generators

Another popular method of generation of particularly low frequencies is by using a basic triangular waveform generator and converting this waveform into a sine wave by a triangular to sine converter. This type of function generator operates at frequencies down to 0.0005 Hz or lower, achieved by the precise control of low value charge and discharge currents of an internal capacitor. The output waveform may be sine, square, or triangular, and the upper frequency may extend to 10 MHz. The distortion figure for the sinusoidal output is limited to 1%. One of the significant advantages of the method employed is that the output amplitude is inherently stable over a wide range of frequencies, without the necessity to incorporate additional feedback techniques to stabilize the amplitude. This also enables fast sweep of the oscillating frequency. Oscillators of this type can often be made voltage controlled with greater ease than is possible with Wien bridge type oscillators. In addition, frequency control requires the variation of only a single resistor, while two resistors have to be varied simultaneously to achieve frequency change in almost all Wien bridge oscillators. A frequency stability of ±0.01% can be maintained by exercising proper care in the selection of components. The triangular output can be made as a ramp output by changing the charging and discharging currents of the generator; the sweep generators often work on this principle. (Note the difference in meaning between sweep generator and swept generator; the former refers to the generator doing the sweep action on the latter.)

18.7.2 Pulse Generators

A pulse generator consists of a basic repetition rate generator coupled to a variable pulse width monostable which provides the final output. To this arrangement, many other facilities can be added for enhanced utility. These are: (i) selection of the repetition rate generator as internal or external, (ii) operation of the monostable in the manual mode, (iii) independent control of the rise/fall times of the output pulse, (iv) amplitude control of the output pulse with ability to drive up to 20 V pp into 50 ohms load, (v) availability of an additional pulse of arbitrary pulse width, delayed by a settable delay time with respect to the start of the basic pulse output (double pulse generation), (vi) inverted and non-inverted outputs, (vii) individual selection of the single basic pulse or the secondary pulse, or the logic OR output or their sum as the final output.

Some of the important factors to be noted in usage are the output impedance, transition times, output amplitude range, overshoot of the output pulse if any, droop, output pulse width jitter, and duty cycle range. A standard unit, such as Hewlett Packard Type 214A, is capable of providing a repetition range from 10 Hz to 1 MHz, source impedance of 50 ohms, output up to 50 V into 50 ohms, transition times less than 15 ns, output amplitude variable in 1, 2, 5 steps over a range of 80 mV to 100 V, and positive or negative polarity. The overshoot and droop is about 5% or less, and the width jitter is less than 0.05% of pulse width. Pulse width ranges from 50 ns to 10 ms in five decade ranges with a maximum duty cycle of 10% between 10 V and 100 V and 50% up to 10 V. In some of the later versions, the repetition rate capability extends to 125 MHz with rise and fall times in the order of 350 picoseconds.

18.7.3 Noise Generators

A noise generator basically consists of a noise source followed by a suitable amplifier and frequency-shaping networks. The basic noise generated should preferably have uniform spectral density over a wide frequency range. In many noise sources where low frequency noise is of importance, the method adopted for noise generation is shown in Fig. 18.7(a). Here the noise generated over a high frequency range (100 to 200 kHz) is heterodyned to a low frequency (0 to 50 kHz) by mixing with a fixed frequency signal centred around the high frequency range (150 kHz), in a balanced modulator. The output is low-pass filtered and amplified to become the final output. This scheme is adopted since, while the noise in a typical noise source, such as a zener diode has uniform spectral density over a wide high-frequency range, the noise spectral density shows a frequency dependence at low frequencies.

If the low-pass filter that is used to filter the mixer output is provided with variable cut-off, the frequency range of the output noise can also be band-limited to selectable values. When a lower cut-off frequency is used, the rms value of the noise decreases since, when the noise spectral density (unit: $mV/\sqrt{Hz}$) is uniform, the total noise over a bandwidth reduces as the square root of the frequency range. To maintain the same noise, the gain in the final amplifier can be increased by an appropriate factor for any reduced cut-off frequency desired. Note that the spectral density increases with increase in gain.[2]

A simple method to generate a noise pattern using digital circuits[3] is by using shift registers in a sequential feedback circuit. A 31-stage shift register provided with linear feedback to produce a maximum-length pseudo-random bit sequence is shown in Fig. 18.7(b). One of the significant features of a pseudo-random sequence is that the noise produced therefrom is repeatable, though the repetition rate for the output of circuit of Fig. 18.7(b) is about once in 2.4 hours, with the clock rate of 250 kHz. The spectral density of the noise output of this circuit is uniform to within ± 1 dB over the frequency range 20 Hz to 20 kHz.

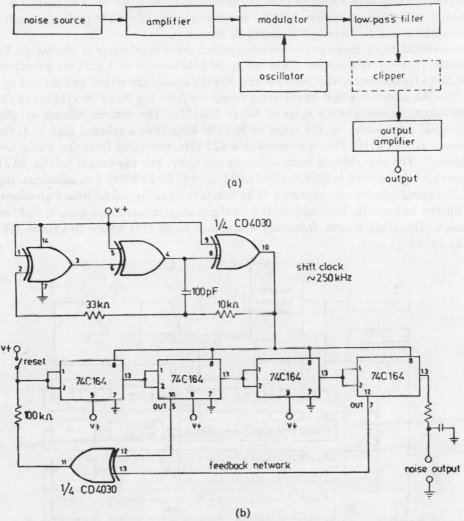

(a)

(b)

Fig. 18.7 Noise generator: (a) schematic block diagram; (b) noise generator based on pseudo-random sequence

18.7.4 Frequency Synthesizers

Frequency synthesizers provide an ac sine wave output with an arbitrarily selectable and yet highly accurate frequency. The frequency synthesizer effectively synthesizes either directly or indirectly the desired frequency output from a single frequency obtained from a stable crystal oscillator.

The direct method of synthesis uses harmonic generators and mixers to produce a particular frequency output. Consider, for example, the generation of 1.32 kHz from a 1 MHz time-base oscillator. Frequencies of 1 kHz, 100 Hz, and 10 Hz are derived from the time base using dividers, and the third harmonic of 100 Hz and the second harmonic of 10 Hz are mixed suitably with 1 kHz to provide the required frequency of 1.32 kHz. A different approach as discussed below enables standardization of certain parts of the circuitry so that resolution can be increased or decreased at will.

A schematic block diagram of a direct-type frequency synthesizer is shown in Fig. 18.8. Consider that 10 frequencies from 30 to 39 kHz in steps of 1 kHz are generated from a basic 500 kHz oscillator. The 500 kHz and 30 kHz signals are mixed and filtered to provide a 470 kHz signal to which one selected frequency from the 30 to 39 kHz set can be mixed to provide a frequency in the range of 500 to 510 kHz. The filtered output is divided by 10 to yield a frequency in the range of 50 to 51 kHz. (For a selected digit of 1, the output frequency is 50.1 kHz). This is mixed with a 420 kHz, generated from the basic time base, in mixer 2. The next chain is identical to the one above and the output will be 50.21 kHz, if the second digit selected is $2[\{(420+50.1)+32\}\div10 = 50.21$ kHz]. For additional digit selection, identical chains are repeated. The resultant signal is mixed with a standard 50 kHz and filtered to form the final output. If four digits were selected and were 1, 2, 3, and 4 in sequence, the final output frequency would then be 50.4321 kHz $-$ 50 kHz $=$ 0.4321 kHz or 432.100 Hz.

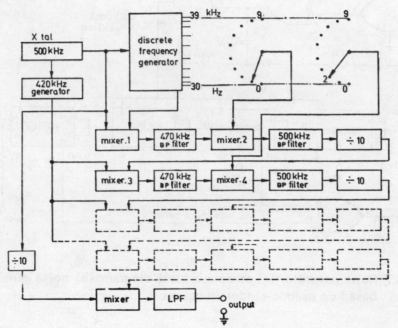

Fig. 18.8 Schematic block diagram of a frequency synthesizer

The zeroes in the 432.100 Hz output are significant since the accuracy of the final output is the same as the accuracy of the crystal used. If the basic time base of 500 kHz was accurate to within 1 ppm, the final output frequency would also be likewise accurate to 1 ppm of the set value. Thus the frequency error for the above cited setting would be only 0.432 mHz.

A frequency synthesizer for low-frequency applications offers one attractive feature. Consider that an accurate frequency of 3.215 Hz is required to excite a mechanical resonance system. If one were to use an ordinary oscillator, hoping that it permits setting with a resolution of 1 mHz it would still not be easy to set the frequency accurately to 3.125 Hz since direct measurement of this frequency in a counter is difficult (it would require a clocking period of 1000 s to obtain 1 mHz resolution of reading). One would have to then measure the period and then take the inverse to obtain the frequency. For any desired change in frequency, this procedure has to be repeated. With the synthesizer, one has to merely dial the required digit, and a highly accurate 3.125 Hz is the resulting output.

To enhance the resolution in the synthesizer and to enable continuous setting or sweep of the frequency, a continuously-adjustable decade can be used as follows. Consider that the input to the second mixer of the chain in Fig. 18.8 is derived from a linear 30 to 40 kHz voltage-controlled oscillator. Depending on the stability of this VCO, the output resolution would be higher. If the VCO output can be set to 30.123 kHz, and if the VCO is feeding to mixer-2, the final output would be 123 MHz (for the case of 3 subsequent chains used in Fig. 18.8), resulting in 1 mHz resolution. In addition, if the VCO output is swept from 30 to 39.99 kHz, the output frequency will vary from xxx.000 to xxx.999 Hz. The VCO can also be used to replace the input to mixer-4 or a corresponding mixer in the following chain. This enables increased swept frequency range, for the output of the synthesizer.

In the indirect method of synthesis, a phase locked loop is normally used, in which the output of a VCO is divided by a settable division ratio N and phase compared with a standard 10 Hz or 100 Hz signal. The phase comparator output, after filtering, controls the VCO so that when lock has been achieved, the frequency of the VCO is exactly N times the frequency of the standard signal. To enhance the resolution, summing loops are employed, and a resolution of 1 Hz in 10 MHz is quite feasible in a synthesiser based on five summing loops[4].

The spectral purity of the signals from a synthesizer is specified in terms of the harmonic and spurious signals present. Typical figures for these are: harmonic signals less than 40 dB below the set level and spurious signals less than 80 dB down. Computer compatible programming of frequency, voltage level, and modulation are unique features available in modern frequency synthesizers.

18.8 REGULATED POWER SUPPLIES

Regulated power supplies are basically highly regulated dc voltage supplies required for energising transducers, operational amplifiers, and other electronic sub-systems. Three basic configurations which are generally used, are shown in Fig. 18.9. In many of the fixed voltage supplies, the circuit arrangement of Fig. 18.9(a) or Fig. 18.9(b) is used. Variable supplies required to be varied from zero to a certain maximum voltage often use the configuration of Fig. 18.9(c). This configuration is not easily realised with single unregulated supplies and needs additional auxiliary supplies for operation. Some of the key factors of importance in a power supply are: (i) output voltage range and current rating, (ii) output regulation—against load variation and against line variation, (iii) output voltage stability over an eight-hour operation, (iv) output noise and ripple, (v) input voltage range over which the operation is specified, (vi) protection circuits incorporated—short circuit protection, over voltage crowbar protection, reverse current protection, etc., (vii) dynamic performance

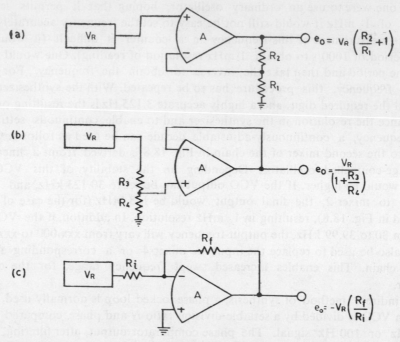

Fig. 18.9 Typical circuit arrangements for power supplies: (a) $e_o > V_R$;
(b) $e_o < V_R$; (c) $e_o = -V_R \times (R_f/R_i)$

of the supply—transient recovery time, and (viii) other features, such as remote sensing, remote shut down etc.

A variety of three terminal voltage regulators are commercially available to meet specific needs. Typical examples are 7800 series of Fairchild and 340 series of Texas and National Semiconductors. These can handle up to 15 W power dissipation with external heat sinks (e.g., μA 7805 KC, LM 340 KC-5). The three terminal regulators provide nominal fixed output voltages between 5 and 24 V. The regulation for input voltage variation from 12.5 to 25 V for LM 340-10 (a 10-V regulator) is typically 200 mV max at a load current of 500 mA. The load regulation for output current variation from 5 mA to 1.5 A is $\simeq$ 200 mV max.

Positive voltage regulators are devices in which the negative line is common for the unregulated input and regulated output. The regulator operates from a positive unregulated input and results in a positive regulated output. In contrast to this, the negative regulator has the positive line as common and gives out a negative regulated output for a negative unregulated input.

The switching type regulator, which is a high-efficiency regulator uses ON and OFF conditions of the pass-transistors in a pulse width modulation circuit to obtain regulation. Pulse-width modulators are available in IC form for use in switching regulators (e.g., Texas SG 1524, SC 2524). The block diagram of a monolithic switching regulator (fixed on-time, variable-frequency type) and its application for obtaining a regulated output more than the applied input, is shown in Figs. 18.10(a) and (b). (For details see Ref. 5.) These monolithic

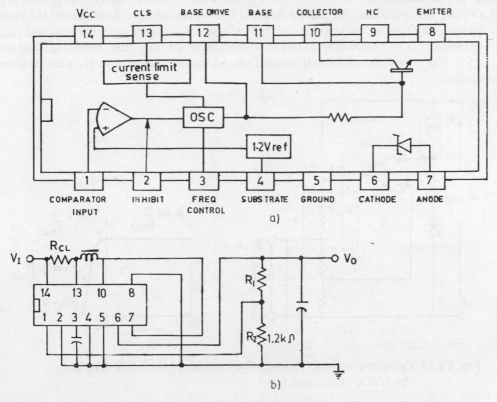

Fig. 18.10 Pulse width modulator for switching mode supplies: (a) schematic block diagram; (b) circuit arrangement for $V_o < V_i$

circuits also feature an internal current limit for protection and have typical maximum power dissipation specifications of 1 W.

Switching regulators are replacing conventional linear regulators because of their higher efficiency which directly results in lower power dissipation, smaller size, and lesser heat-sinking requirements. Though in comparison with linear regulators they often have a higher ripple and hum, in many cases this can be held to be less than 10 mV, and hence does not seriously affect the performance of the system.

18.8.1 Constant-Voltage, Current-Limit (CVCL) Supplies

The general over-current protection schemes used in power supplies fall under three categories. In the constant-voltage, current-limited supplies, a current sense resistor in series with the load but within the regulation loop of the supply monitors the load current, as shown in Fig. 18.11(a). When the load current exceeds a certain value I_{max} so that the voltage across R_{sc} is about 0.6 V required to start conduction of Q_2, the drive-current to the base of the main pass-transistor Q_1 is shunted to its emitter side by Q_2. However the base current necessary for Q_1 to provide an emitter current equal to the current limit value desired is maintained. As a result of this limiting action, the voltage output of the supply falls and the characteristic, as shown in Fig. 18.11(b) results. On short circuit, the current that passes through Q_1 is thus limited, typically to 20% higher than the required I_{max}. It may be noted that to ensure continuous short-circuit protection, the power dissipation in Q_1 under the worst case (shorted output) should be considered, and Q_1 must be selected accordingly.

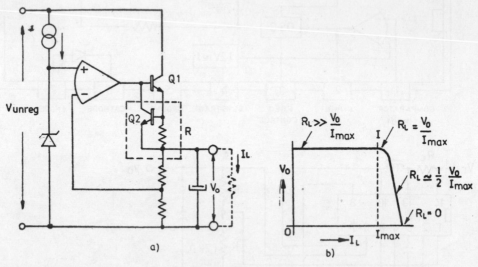

Fig. 18.11 Constant-voltage, current-limit supply: (a) circuit diagram;
(b) CVCL characteristics

18.8.2 Constant-Voltage, Constant-Current (CVCC) Supplies

In constant-voltage, constant-current supplies, the current-limit action is carried out in a current-regulated mode. The voltage across R_{sc} is compared with a standard dc voltage in a high gain differential amplifier, and the control of the output potential is shifted to this amplifier once the load current I_L exceeds a certain critical value, as shown in the circuit of Fig. 18.12(a). In the constant voltage mode (defined as the situation when the load resistance $R_L > R_c$, where the critical load resistance R_c is equal to the set voltage divided by the set value of the current-limit), the op-amp A_1 controls the base current to transistor Q_1 so that the output voltage V_o is equal to $\left(\dfrac{R_3}{R_3+R_4}\right) V_{ref}$, where R_3, R_4, and V_{ref} are as shown in Fig. 18.12(a). When the R_L (external load) is decreased to a value equal to R_c, the voltage across R_{sc} is just equal to the voltage V_x set by the current-limit control (R_v). For any R_L less than this value, the amplifier A_2 takes over control and the power supply operates as a constant current supply. The regulation of the supply in this mode is also high. Further the impedance of the supply is very high, as is expected of a current source. The variation of the load current for any value of the load resistance from $R_L = 0$ to $R_L = R_c$ can be made as little as 0.1% of the set limit value, I_{limit}. The variable reference voltage provided by R_v enables various current limits to be set, as shown in Fig. 18.12(b).

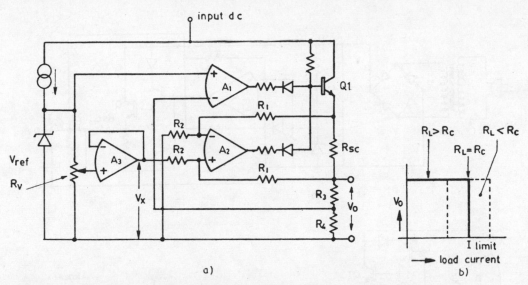

Fig. 18.12 Constant-voltage; constant-current supply: (a) circuit diagram;
(b) CVCC characteristics

18.8.3 Constant Voltage, Fold Back Current-Limit Supplies

The fold back current-limit arrangement is often used in supplies where the power dissipation under output shorted conditions should be optimised so that it is no more than the power required to be dissipated under normal full-load working conditions. In the example shown in Fig. 18.13(a), the circuit schematic is that of a 5 V, 3 A supply using a μA741 and additional drivers. The circuit works as a CVCC supply with the current limit set to approximately 3.3 A (selecting a suitable value of R_{sc1}). This circuit demands that the pass-transistor be capable of dissipating about 31 W power, if continuous short-circuit protection is desired. However, the power that the pass-transistor need handle is only about 16 W under full load conditions.

Using the fold back current-limit technique, as shown in Fig. 18.13(b), the power dissipation required under output short-circuit conditions can be reduced considerably. It may be noted that the current-limiting transistor, in this case, is not driven directly by the voltage developed across the current sense resistor, but from a potential divider connected as shown. As a result, when the load is such that the load current is 3.3 A, the voltage at the emitter of power transistor Q_1 is $\simeq 5+(0.5 \times 3.3) = 6.65$ V for $R_{sc2} = 0.5 \Omega$. The potential divider made up of the 100 Ω and 560 Ω is so chosen that the limiting transistor just starts conduction for this condition for which the base potential of this transistor Q_2 will be about .56/.66 of 6.05, or $\simeq 5.6$ V. If the output is shorted, the short-circuit current that follows is considerably less than 3.3 A, being only about 1.5 A, resulting in a power dissipation demand in the pass-transistor of only 15 W approximately. The characteristics that result are shown in Fig. 18.13(c). Due to the higher drop that exists across the current-limit resistor R_{sc2} under full load, the secondary voltage of the transformer will have to be about 8.5 V (under full load) for the fold back current-limited arrangement.

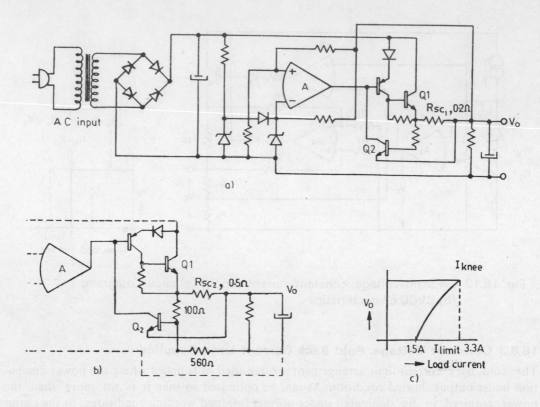

Fig. 18.13 Current limiting in power supplies: (a) constant voltage, current-limit supply; (b) modification yielding constant voltage fold back current-limit supply; (c) characteristics of (b)

18.8.4 Input-Output Differential Dependent Current-Limit Supplies

Another method which is used to reduce the limit current when the voltage across the device—particularly, three-terminal voltage regulators—exceeds a certain minimum value, is shown in Fig. 18.14(a). When the input voltage is such that the voltage between the input and output is less than the breakdown voltage ($\simeq$ 15 V) of the zener ZD, the output current will be limited to a value $\dfrac{V_{BE}}{R_{sc}}$, where V_{BE} is the voltage required by the current-limiting transistor to start limiting action. When the input voltage is much higher, e.g., say about 30 V for an output voltage of 5 V, the input-output differential is about 25 V and the zener diode conducts, resulting in a reduced limit current. This is because a part of the V_{BE} required for the limiting transistor is supplied by the current (approximately $(25-15)$ V/10 kΩ = 1 mA flowing through the base resistance of 180 ohms). The limit current reduces to $\simeq$ 1.6 A from $\simeq$ 2.2 A for the previous condition considered. If the output is short-circuited, the limit current further reduces to about 1.3 A.

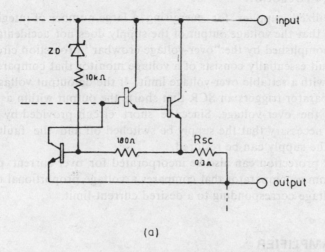

(a)

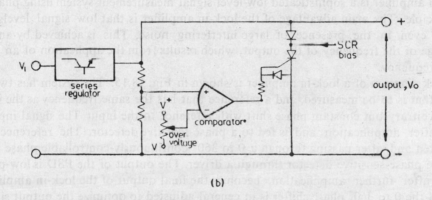

(b)

Fig. 18.14 Power supply protection: (a) current-limit dependent on input
voltage; (b) over-voltage crowbar.

18.8.5 Thermal Shut-Down

Modern monolithic three-terminal regulator chips have a self-protecting feature, termed as
thermal shut-down. This is achieved by having a transistor pre-biased to a fixed voltage of
about 0.45 to 0.5 V and connected so as to divert to ground the current drive from the output stage, when the chip temperature increases beyond a safe value. Due to the decrease of
V_{BE} with increase in temperature, the base-emitter drive voltage required to start conduction
in the thermal shut-down transistor progressively decreases as the chip temperature increases. When the required V_{BE} drops to the pre-bias value, the thermal shut-down action starts.
A low-frequency oscillation of the load current often results at the start of this action. This
is because as soon as current-limit action starts, the power dissipated decreases and the chip
temperature falls, resulting in temporary suspension of the current-limit action until the
temperature increases to a critical value, once again starting the current-limit action.

18.8.6 Crowbar Protection

When using stabilized supplies for energising a large number of integrated circuits, it is essential to ensure that the voltage output of the supply does not accidentally exceed a set value. This is accomplished by the "over-voltage crowbar" protection circuit shown in Fig. 18.14(b). The circuit essentially consists of a voltage monitor that compares the output voltage of the supply with a settable over-voltage limit. If the dc output voltage rises above the set limit, the comparator triggers an SCR that shorts the output within a few microseconds of occurrence of the over-voltage. Since the short circuit provided by the SCR is of the latching type, it is necessary that the supply be switched off and the fault removed before proper action of the supply can be restored.

Similar crowbar protection can also be incorporated for over-current protection by triggering the SCR from a comparator that compares a voltage proportional to the load current with a settable voltage corresponding to a desired current-limit.

18.9 LOCK-IN AMPLIFIER

A lock-in amplifier is a sophisticated low-level signal measurement system using phase detection principle. The main advantage of the lock-in amplifier is that low signal levels can be detected even in the presence of large interfering noise. This is achieved by an *a priori* knowledge of the frequency of the output, which results from the application of an input at known frequency.

A block diagram of a lock-in amplifier is shown in Fig. 18.15. The system has two inputs: a signal that is to be measured, and a reference that has the same frequency as the input and has an arbitrary but constant phase shift with reference to the input. The signal input is prefiltered after amplification and is fed to a phase-sensitive detector. The reference signal is also filtered and, after passing through a 0 to 360° continuously-controllable phase shifter, is fed to the phase-sensitive detector through a driver. The output of the PSD is low-pass filtered and after further amplification, becomes the final output of the lock-in amplifier. The setting of the 0 to 360° phase shifter is in general adjusted to optimize the output signal.

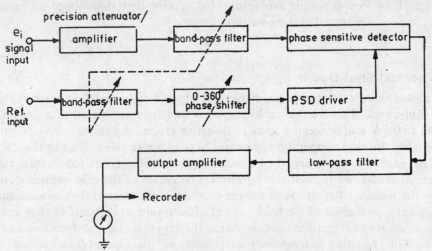

Fig. 18.15 Schematic block diagram of a lock-in amplifier

In effect, the phase-sensitive detector produces a base-band signal proportional to the signal input by a multiplication process using the reference signal as a multiplicand. The output which would contain the base-band signal as well as high-frequency harmonics of the signal frequency is filtered in a variable time constant low-pass filter. Any noise that was present in the input would produce a PSD output that is however filtered out by the low-pass filter. Noise that has frequency components very close to or at the same frequency as the signal are not easily filtered out, but can produce a low frequency beat at the output. By having a time constant as large as 100 s in the low-pass filter, the system will attenuate noise components farther than 0.0016 Hz away from the signal frequency. Thus the noise contribution is all but eliminated, and the system provides high signal to noise ratio improvement, particularly when the noise in the input is wide-band in nature.

Since interferences that have the same frequency as the signal are not attenuated by the system, care should be exercised in choosing the signal frequency so that it is reasonably away from the frequency of known interferences (such as 50 Hz mains hum and its harmonics)[6]. The typical specifications of a standard lock-in amplifier are described in Table 18.1.

TABLE 18.1 SPECIFICATIONS OF A LOCK-IN AMPLIFIER

Signal Channel	
Frequency Range	1.5 Hz to 150 kHz in 5 ranges. Continuous tuning, plus vernier.
Input Impedance	Differential: 10 MΩ minimum plus 20 pF.
	Direct: 100 kΩ plus 25 pF.
Input Sensitivity	Differential 1 μV to 10 mV in decade steps plus linear vernier. Usable to 100 nano-volts.
	Direct: 100 μV to 1.0 V in decade steps, plus linear vernier. Usable to 10 μV.
Internal Noise	Differential: Noise figure at 1 kHz is less than 3 dB for source resistances from 20,000 Ω to 5 MΩ. Equivalent input noise voltage with input shorted is less than 50 nV as seen at the detector.
	Direct: Equivalent input noise voltage with input shorted is less than 100 nV as seen at the detector.
Filter Characteristic	Single tuned, Q = 25.
Reference Channel	
Frequency Range	1.5 Hz to 150 kHz in 5 ranges. Continuous tuning, plus vernier.
Input Impedance	100 kΩ minimum.
Input Sensitivity	20 mV minimum. Continuous gain control.
Operating Modes	Flat : Filter bypassed. Response flat.
	Filtered: Ganged filter, Q = 15.
	"Automatic" : Operates on any waveform signal which has two zero crossings per cycle with equal time between crossings.
	Internal filter ganged with signal filter to preserve tracking.
General	
Phase Adjustment	Range switch and fine phase vernier, plus 180° inversion switch.
Time Constants	3 ms to 100 s in 1-3-10 sequence. External capacitor across binding posts on the rear panel, as option.
Monitor Switch	Meter monitors signal and reference inputs to detector, 100 mV, 10 mV and 1 mA outputs. 10 X switch multiplies meter scale readings when desired.

(Contd.)

TABLE 18.1 (Contd.)

Outputs	Direct signal, reference and phase outputs, Scope-servo output, 10 mV recorder output, 1 mA recorder output, base line control, and external battery connections for use with mV recorders.
Zero Suppression	Ten-turn potentiometer provides up to +300% of full scale suppression.
Marker Switch	Positive and negative marker feeding recorder output.
Size	$17\frac{1}{4}'' \times 5\frac{1}{4}'' \times 14''$ deep.
Weight	Approximately 15 lbs.
Power Requirements	105/125 V 50/60 Hz, Eight watts.

18.10 FREQUENCY-RESPONSE ANALYZER

The frequency response method is one of the well-established methods of testing the performance of feedback control systems. Another associated parameter often required to be measured is the mechanical impedance of a structure, defined as the ratio of the force F to the velocity U.

$$Z\,(j\omega) = \frac{F}{U}\,(j\omega)$$

An impedance-measuring instrument must determine $\frac{E_2}{E_1}\,(j\omega)$ in terms of $\left|\frac{A_2}{A_1}\right|$ in dB and $(\phi_2 - \phi_1)$ in degrees, where E_2 and E_1 are signals proportional to force and velocity, with respective amplitudes A_2 and A_1 and phases ϕ_1 and ϕ_2. Since the signal from the sensors is often rich in harmonic content (either due to the response of the structure under test to the harmonics, or due to nonlinearities), the analyser must strongly discriminate against harmonics and noise present in the signal. At low frequencies, the analyzer should enable conservation of test time.

The schematic block diagram of a frequency response analyzer based on the fourier analysis filter[7] is shown in Fig. 18.16. The test signal generator provides sine and cosine wave forms obtained by diode shaping from triangular wave generators. The frequency is generally voltage controlled, and can be swept over a desired range. The system under test is excited with the "sine" output of the test signal generator, after suitable power amplification. The parameters, "force" and "velocity" are converted into electrical signals using suitable sensors followed by signal-conditioning amplifiers. The output of each amplifier is multiplied by "sine" and "cos" reference signals available from the test signal generator. The multiplier outputs are integrated (for frequencies less than about 10 Hz) over integer number of repetition periods of the signal in the gated integrator. This ensures optimum use of time in obtaining error-free measurement of the signal amplitudes while at the same time offering high rejection for harmonic components. The integrator outputs are held and the ratio A_2/A_1 in dB is computed by the function module block. The integrator outputs corresponding to the in-phase and quadrature components of the signal input also permit calculation of the individual phases ϕ_2 and ϕ_1 and hence their difference as well.

The frequency range of operation is typically 0.01 Hz to about 10 kHz. A built-in sweep generator is also often incorporated that enables sweep speeds as low as 1000 s per decade frequency range.

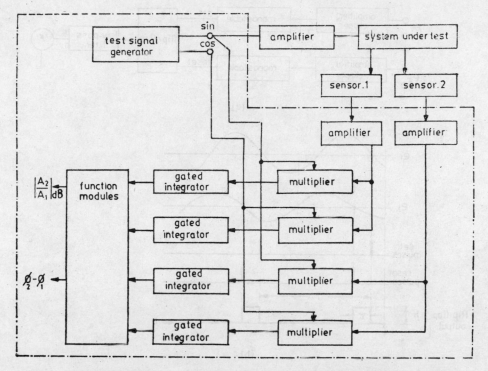

Fig. 18.16 Schematic block diagram of a frequency response analyzer

18.10.1 Phase Meter

The measurement of phase angle between two signals can be carried out using various principles. When two sinusoidal signals have a phase difference ϕ, the Lissajous pattern obtained by feeding them to the X and Y amplifiers of a CRO can yield the phase information. Alternatively, the phase shift between the signals can be read-off from a calibrated phase shifter which, when introduced in series with one of the inputs, produces a straight line corresponding to $0°$ phase, as the Lissajous pattern.

A widely-employed technique[8] for the measurement of phase at low frequencies is based on the relationship of the phase angle to the delay between the zero crossings of the input signals. For a phase shift ϕ between the signals, the delay τ between the zero crossings is related as

$$\frac{\tau}{T} = \frac{\phi}{360}$$

where T is the period of the signal and ϕ is phase shift in degrees. The schematic block diagram of a phase meter based on this principle is shown in Fig. 18.17(a). The input signals e_1 and e_2 are separately amplified and clipped so that the positive zero crossing of signal e_1 sets a flip-flop (FF) while the positive zero crossing of signal e_2 resets it. The output of FF is a rectangular pulse train having constant amplitude pulses of height h and width τ as in Fig.

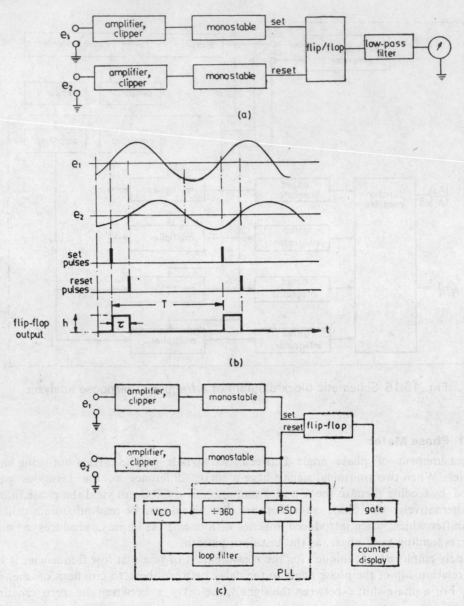

Fig. 18.17 Phase meter: (a) block schematic; (b) waveforms; (c) digital display of the phase angle

18.17(b). The average of this pulse train is $\frac{\tau}{T} h$, a voltage that is proportional to the phase angle ϕ.

A direct indication of the phase angle ϕ in degrees can be obtained if a clock having a frequency $360 \frac{1}{T}$ is gated into a counter for the delay period τ. The required clock whose frequency should be exactly 360 times the frequency of the input, can be realised by a phase locked loop (PLL), as shown in Fig. 18.17(c). By proper design of the PLL, phase measurements in the frequency range 1 Hz to 100 kHz can be carried out using this scheme. A higher resolution of 0.1° can be obtained by choosing a frequency multiplication factor of 3600. However, the accuracy of the phase measurement will be influenced by the slew rate of the clipping amplifier at the high frequency end.

18.11 GENERAL COMPONENTS

Various types of active and passive components need to be used in general in any measurement system. While the active components play a major role in conditioning, processing, and conversion of the signals to suitable forms, the role of the passive components such as resistors and capacitors is equally important. Careful choice of the passive components is demanded if deterioration of the high performance of active devices due to improper choice of associated components is to be avoided.

18.11.1 Resistors

While for commercial use in non-critical applications the ordinary carbon composition type resistors are satisfactory, when resistance stability and tolerance are critical, the metal film resistors or other stable type of resistors should be used. Depending on the performance expected of the system, components of suitable temperature coefficients should be chosen so that over the working temperature range, performance deterioration is within tolerable limits. The metal-film resistors are available in various tolerances between 5 and 0.1%, and their temperature coefficients are typically ± 100, $+50$ and ± 25 ppm. Wire-wound resistances available have temperature coefficients down to ± 10 ppm and tolerances as good as 0.01%. Using wire-wound resistance of the same type and manufactured from the same pool of wire, tracking of the temperature coefficient can be as good as 1 ppm. Such tracking coefficients can be an advantage when the parameter of interest (such as gain in a system) is dependent on the ratio of two resistances. For critical applications, due considerations have to be given to the proper choice of the wattage of the resistance also, since the internal temperature of the resistance may often be higher than the ambient owing to the power dissipation. It is usual practice in critical applications to choose a resistor rated for ten times the nominal power that it is expected to dissipate so that additional error due to self heating is considerably reduced.

18.11.2 Potentiometers

A variety of potentiometers are commercially available for use in different applications. Typically, these include: (i) single-turn type, (ii) multi-turn type, (iii) multi-turn precision potentiometer, and (iv) non-linear potentiometer (such as sine/cosine).

A single-turn potentiometer might be a carbon preset, wire-wound preset, a cermet, or any of these types but intended for continuous operation. While the life in terms of number of cycles may be typically in the range of 10^5 to 10^6 operations for the latter types, the same for the preset types may be only a few hundred cycles. Single-turn potentiometers can often yield a settling resolution between 1/50 to 1/500 of the value of the potentiometer. It is however difficult to realise a resolution better than about 1/100 without the aid of a gear mechanism. In multi-turn potentiometers, this arrangement is internally provided so that the setting resolution is often as good as 1/1000.

Multi-turn Potentiometers

When applications demand precise setting of a potentiometer with repeatability better than 0.2%, precision multi-turn potentiometers are employed. The standard 10-turn potentiometers (often used in analog computers and servo applications) have a linearity of about ±0.15% and setting resolution of 0.05%. With a 10-turn dial that enables the set value to be read out, these potentiometers can be set to the same resistance value (or the same ratio when used as a potential divider) repeatedly with a repeatability of about 0.1%. The rotational life exceeds 10^6 operations, and the temperature coefficient of the resistance is typically ±130 or ±20 ppm depending on the material of the wire used. Digital 10-turn dials enable direct in-line read out of the potentiometer resistance or the ratio of the potential divider. Multi-gang potentiometers are available with individual resistance values close to 1% of each other. A typical application of a double gang ten-turn potentiometer of this type is in the Wien bridge oscillators and filters discussed in Chapters 12 and 13.

18.11.3 Capacitors

The capacitors used in oscillators, filters, and other circuits as part of frequency-determining networks should have the primary features of high stability and low leakage. A low-temperature coefficient enables operation over a wide temperature range, and close tolerance (better than +1%) obviates individual choice or adjustment of circuit components. Typical commercial capacitors are of the following types: paper, metallized paper, polycarbonate, styroflex, mica and ceramic. Very many other materials which are variations of the types mentioned are also used as dielectrics in capacitors.

Metallized polycarbonate capacitors are particularly suited for applications requiring large value and low leakage capacitors. Values up to 10 μF are available commercially. The variation of the capacitance is typically less than 1% from 0° to 70°C. The temperature coefficient is however non-linear. Polystyrene capacitors have temperature coefficients of about −50 to −100 ppm/°C over the temperature range −60 to +60°C. Ceramic capacitors having large dielectric constants (1200 to 6000) such as the physically small ceramic disk capacitors can be used only where capacitance variation and loss are relatively unimportant (e.g., for power supply decoupling). Their variation in capacitance with temperature, frequency, voltage, and time render them practically unusable as part of the frequency determining networks in oscillators and filters. The low-loss ceramic capacitors having low-dielectric constant perform well at high frequencies and are available with a variety of temperature coefficients between +100 and −750 ppm/°C. They can be used as compensating capacitors to correct the thermal drifts in other elements.

Mica capacitors have very low dissipation factors and possess high stability. Very high working voltage operation is also possible. By proper control of the manufacturing process, capacitors with predictable temperature coefficient can be obtained. These capacitors also, find wide application as compensating capacitors. Silvered mica capacitors have lower temperature coefficient and higher stability. Paper capacitors are relatively inexpensive and are widely used where tolerance and dissipation factor are not a primary consideration. Metallized paper capacitors occupy less volume and have relatively low leakage current compared to the paper capacitors.

The power factor is the sine of the angle by which the current flowing into the capacitor fails to be 90° out of phase with the applied voltage. The tangent of this angle is called the dissipation factor. The reciprocal of the dissipation factor is termed as Q and is the ratio of the capacitor reactance to the equivalent series resistance.

Electrolytic capacitors often have a series resistance which limit their effective impedance to a finite value at high frequencies. It thus becomes mandatory to place lower value capacitors across these in decoupling applications to ensure proper bypass action at high frequencies. In order to maintain a low impedance over a wide range of frequencies in power supplies, paralleling of several values (typically 0.01 μF, 0.1 μF and 1 μF, all ceramic) of capacitors across an electrolytic capacitor is often restorted to. This is because the inductive reactance due to the structure of the capacitor and the leads results in a low impedance for a particular value of capacitors over only a limited frequency range.

REFERENCES

1. *Tektronix Product Catalog, Section 12*, Teketronix Inc., Beaverton, Oregon, 1978.
2. "Random noise generator type 1381", *Instruction Manual*, General Radio Company, West Concord, Massachusetts, 1968.
3. Damashek, M., "Shift register with feedback generates white noise", p. 28, in Weber, S. (Ed.), *Circuits for Electronic Engineers*, McGraw-Hill, N.Y., 1977.
4. Shanahan, J.C., "Uniting signal generation and signal synthesis", *Hewlett Packard Journal*, Vol. 23, No. 4, pp. 2-13, Dec. 1971.
5. Spencer, J.D. and Pippengar, D.E. (Compilers), *The Voltage Regulator Handbook*, pp. 137-138, Texas Instruments Inc., Texas, 1977.
6. *Instruction Manual*, "HR-8 lock-in amplifier", Princeton Applied Research, Princeton, New Jersey, 1970.
7. "Two channel frequency response analysis", Technical Publication No. 7172-1, BAFCO Inc., War.minister, Pennsylvania, 1968.
8. Thomas, H.E. and Clarke, C.A., *Handbook of Electronic Instruments and Measuring Techniques*. pp. 140-143, Prentice-Hall Inc., N.J., 1967.

BIBLIOGRAPHY

Amin, D.A. and Kriegel. T., "A multiple output switching power supply for computer applications", *Hewlett-Packard Journal*, Vol. 30, No. 7, pp. 25-28, July 1979.
Bapton, D., *Modern Oscilloscope Handbook*, Reston Publishing Co., Virginia, 1979.
Bardos, P., "Spectrum analysis of rfi can improve power supply deisgn", *Control and Instrumentation*, Vol. 11, No. 6, pp. 37-39, June 1979.
Bartholomew, D., *Electrical Measurements and Instrumentation*, Allyn and Bacon Inc., Boston, 1963.
Botos, B., "Designer's guide to RCL measurements, Part I to IV", *EDN*, Vol. 24, No. 11, pp. 137-174, June 5, 1979.
Braccio, M., *Basic Electrical and Electronic Tests and Measurements*, Reston Publishing Co., Virginia, 1978.

Carr., J.J., *Elements of Electronic Instrumentation and Measurement*, Reston Publishing Co., Virginia, 1979.

Chambers, R.P., "Random noise generators", *IEEE Spectrum*, Vol. 4, No. 2, pp. 48-56, Feb. 1967.

Engelson, M., *Spectrum Analyzer Circuits*, Tektronix Inc., Oregon, 1969.

Faran, J.J. (Jr.), "Random noise generators", *The General Radio Experimenter*, Vol. 42, No. 1, pp. 3-13, Jan. 1968.

Golding, J.F. (Ed.), *Measuring Oscilloscopes*, Illiffe Books, London, 1971.

Hazeu, H.A.G., *Fifty Years of Electronic Components*, Publications Dept. of Product Division Elcoma of N.V. Philips' Gloeilampenfabrieken, 1971.

Herrick, C.N., *Electronic Service Instruments*, Prentice-Hall Inc., New Jersey, 1974.

Herrick, C.N., *Oscilloscope Handbook*, Reston Publishing Co., Virginia, 1974.

Imbens, G. and Rauch, S., "The Right oscilloscope trigger delivers the picture you need", *EDN*, Vol. 24, No. 1, pp. 93-96, Jan. 5, 1979.

Malmstadt, H.V. et al., *Electronic Measurements for Scientists*, W.A. Benjamin Inc., California, 1974.

Manassewitsch, V., *Frequency Synthesizers, Theory and Design*, John Wiley and Sons., N.Y., 1976.

Nelson, G.E. and Thomas, P.L., "Faster gain-phase measurements with new automatic 50 Hz to 13 MHz network analyzers", *Hewlett Packard Journal*, Vol. 24, No. 2, pp. 12-18, Oct. 1972.

Ohr, S., "Passive pack more punch in packaging, power, precision", *Electron. Des.*, Vol. 27, No. 15, pp. 56-62, July 19, 1979.

Patel, R., "Reduce size and cost of buck regulators by running at over 100 kHz frequencies", *Electron. Des.*, Vol. 27, No. 23, pp. 82-86, Nov. 8, 1979.

Podolske, J., "Stable inexpensive low frequency sine wave generator using digital techniques", *Review of Scientific Instruments*, Vol. 50, No. 8, pp. 1010-1012, Aug. 1979.

Prensky, S.D., *Electronic Instrumentation*, Prentice-Hall Inc., New Jersey, 1971.

Ramirez, R.W., "Digitizing oscilloscope systems simplify transmission measurements", *EDN*, Vol. 24, No. 11, pp. 117-123, June 5, 1979.

Schweber, W., "Low frequency spectrum analyzers simplify audio measurements", *EDN*, Vol. 24, No. 11, pp. 107-114, June 5, 1979.

Springer, H., "Breakthroughs throughout push scope to 1 GHZ", *Electron. Des.*, Vol. 27, No. 2, pp. 60-65, Jan. 18, 1979.

Todd, C.D., *Potentiometer Handbook*, McGraw-Hill, N.Y., 1975.

Tuttle, R.K., "The synthesized test oscillator: a new signal source for the 0.1 Hz to 13 MHz range", *Hewlett Packard Journal*, Vol. 23, No. 11, pp. 2-8, July 1972.

Voltage Regulator Handbook, National Semiconductor Corp., Sunnyvale, California, 1980.

INTERNATIONAL STANDARD UNITS SI

The international system of metric units (SI) has been universally accepted by engineers and scientists throughout the world. It provides a coherent and elegant framework of standardization in mechanics, electrics, and other allied disciplines.

The system is based on seven base units and two supplementary units, from which a host of derived units is obtained. The definitions are given below, with symbol shown in paranthesis.

BASE UNITS

Metre (m) The metre is the length equal to 1650763.73 wavelengths in vacuum of the radiation corresponding to the transition between the levels $2p_{10}$ and $5d_5$ of the krypton-86 atom.

Kilogram (kg) The kilogram is the unit of mass; it is equal to the mass of the international prototype of the kilogram. (The international prototype of the kilogram is a particular cylinder of platinum-iridium alloy which is preserved in a vault at Sevres, France, by the International Bureau of Weights and Measures.)

Second (s) The second is the duration of 9 192 631 770 periods of the radiation corresponding to the transition between the two hyperfine levels of the ground state of the cesium-133 atom.

Ampere (A) The ampere is that constant current which, if maintained in two straight parallel conductors of infinite length, of negligible circular cross section and placed 1 meter apart in vacuum, would produce between these conductors a force equal to 2×10^{-7} newton per meter of length.

Kelvin (K) The kelvin, the unit of the thermodynamic temperature is the fraction 1/273.16 of the thermodynamic temperature of the triple point of water.

Note: In addition to the thermodynamic temperature (symbol T) expressed in kelvins, use is also made of celsius temperature (symbol t) defined by the equation $t = T - T_0$, where $T_0 = 273.15$ K by definition. The celsius temperature is in general expressed in degrees celsius (symbol $_a°C$). The unit degree celsius is thus equal to the unit kelvin, and an interval or a difference of celsius temperature may also be expressed in degrees celsius.

Candela (cd) The candela is the luminous intensity, in the perpendicular direction, of a surface 1/600 000 square meter of a blackbody at the temperature of freezing platinum under pressure of 101 325 newtons per square metre.

Mole (Mol) The mole is the amount of substance of a system which contains as many elementary entities as there are atoms in 0.012 kilogram of carbon 12.

SUPPLEMENTARY UNITS

Radian (rad) The radian is the plane angle between two radii of a circle which cuts off on the circumference an arc equal in length to the radius.

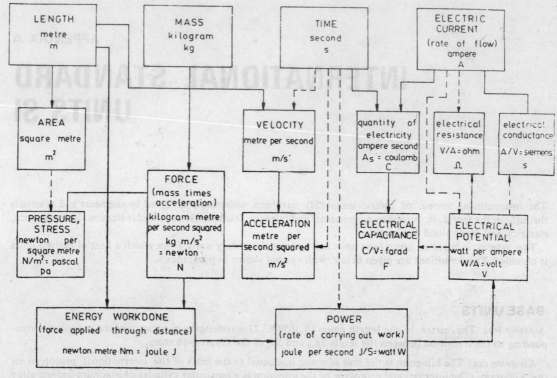

Steradian (sr) The steradian is the solid angle which having its vertex in the centre of a sphere, cuts off an area of the surface of the sphere equal to that of a square having sides of length equal to the radius of the sphere.

DERIVED UNITS

Joule (J) The joule is the work done when the point of application of 1 newton is displaced a distance of 1 metre in the direction of the force.

Watt (W) The watt is the power which gives rise to the production of energy at the rate of 1 joule per second.

Volt (V) The volt is the difference of electric potential between two points of a conducting wire carrying a constant current of 1 ampere, when the power dissipated between these points is equal to 1 watt.

Ohm (Ω) The ohm is the electric resistance between two points of a conductor when a constant difference of potential of 1 volt, applied between these two points, produces in this conductor a current of 1 ampere, this conductor not being the source of any electromotive force.

Coulomb (C) The coulomb is the quantity of electricity transported in 1 second by a current of 1 ampere.

Farad (F) The farad is the capacitance of a capacitor between the plates of which there appears a difference of potential of 1 volt when it is charged by a quantity of electricity equal to 1 coulomb.

Henry (H) The henry is the inductance of a closed circuit in which an electromotive force of 1 volt is produced when the electric current in the circuit varies uniformly at a rate of 1 ampere per second.

Lumen (lm) The lumen is the luminous flux emitted in a solid angle of 1 steradian by a uniform point source having an intensity of 1 candela.

Newton (N) The newton is that force which gives to a mass of 1 kilogram an acceleration of 1 meter per second.

Weber (Wb) The weber is the magnetic flux which, linking a circuit of one turn, produces in it an electromotive force of 1 volt as the flux is reduced to zero at a uniform rate in 1 second.

TABLE A.1 UNITS AND THEIR CONVERSION FACTORS

Quantity	Unit Base unit	Unit Preferred multiple and sub-multiple	Conversion factors
1	2	3	4
Length	m (metre)	km mm	1 statute mile = 1609.344 m 1 International nautical mile = 1852 m 1 ft = 0.304 m 1 in = 25.4 mm
Area	m²	cm², mm²	1 in² = 645.16 mm²
Volume	m³	mm³	1 UK gallon = 4.536 litres
Time	s (second)	minutes, hours	Hours and minutes are not SI, but still used widely
Velocity	m/s	—	1 ft/sec = 0.3048 m/s 1 mph = 1.609344 km/h 1 international knot = 1.852 km/h
Angle	rad (radian)	degree minute second	1° = (2π/360) rad
Angular velocity	rad/s	—	1 rpm = (π/30) rad/s 1 rad/s = 9.5493 rpm
Acceleration	m/s²	—	1 ft/sec² = 0.3048 m/s² 1 m/s² = 0.102 g, where g is the acceleration due to gravity
Angular acceleration	rad/s²		
Frequency	Hz (hertz)	kHz	1 cycle/sec = 1 Hz
Mass	kg (kilogram)	g	1 metric tonne = 1000 kg 1 ton = 1.01605 metric tonne 1 lb = 0.45359237 kg
Mass flow (fuel flow)	kg/s	g/s	1 lb/sec = 0.45359237 kg/s
Volumetric flow rate	m³/s	—	1 gal/min = 6.309 × 10⁻⁵ m³/s 1 gal/min = 1.26280 ml/s
Force (thrust)	N (newtons)	MN kN	1 N = 1 kg m/s² 1 ton f = 9.96402 kN 1 lbf = 4.44822 N 1 kgf = 9.80665 N 1 dyne = 10⁻⁵ N
Torque or Moment of force	Nm		1 Nm = 1 kg m²/s²
Torque/length	N.m/m		1 lbf in/in = 0.2248 N m/m
Specific fuel consumption	mg/Ns µg/J		1 lb/hr/lbf = 28.3255 mg/Ns 1 lb/hr/hp = 168.966 g/J

1	2	3	4
Pressure (stress)	Pa (pascal)	MPa kPa	$1 \text{ Pa} = 1 \text{ N/m}^2 = 1 \text{ kg m/s}^2$ $1 \text{ lbf/in}^2 = 6894.76 \text{ Pa}$ $1 \text{ lbf/in}^2 = 0.070307 \text{ kg/cm}^2$ $1 \text{ tonf/in}^2 = 15.4443 \text{ MPa}$ $1 \text{ mm Hg} = 133.322 \text{ Pa}$ $1 \text{ Torr} = 1 \text{ mm Hg}$ $1 \text{ mm H}_2\text{O} = 9.81302 \text{ Pa}$ $1 \text{ bar} = 100 \text{ kPa} = 0.1 \text{ MPa}$ $1 \text{ pieze} = 1 \text{ kPa}$ $1 \text{ Atm} = 1.01325 \text{ bars}$
Work	J (joule)	kJ	$1 \text{ J} = 1 \text{ N m} = 1 \text{ kg m}^2/\text{s}^2$ $1 \text{ ft lbf} = 1.35582 \text{ J}$
Energy	J		
Quantity of heat	J		$1 \text{ Btu} = 1.05506 \text{ kJ}$ $1 \text{ thermochemical calorie} = 4.184 \text{ J}$
Power	W (watt)	MW kW	$1 \text{ W} = 1 \text{ J/s} = 1 \text{ N m/s} = 1 \text{ kg m}^2/\text{s}^2$ $1 \text{ hp} = 0.7457 \text{ kW}$
Energy	kWh		$1 \text{ kWh} = 3.86 \times 10^6 \text{ J}$
Energy (thermo-chemical)	Cal		$1 \text{ Btu} = 3.96832 \text{ calories}$
Density	kg/m³		$1 \text{ lb/ft}^3 = 16.0185 \text{ kg/m}^3$ $1 \text{ lb/gal} = 99.7764 \text{ kg/m}^3$
Torque	Nm	kNm	$1 \text{ lbf ft} = 1.35582 \text{ N m}$
Viscosity	Pa s		$1 \text{ Pa s} = 1 \text{ kg/m s}$
Dynamic kinematic	Ns/m² m²/s		$1 \text{ centipoise} = 1 \text{ m N s/ms}$ $1 \text{ centistoke} = 1 \text{ mm}^2/\text{s}$
Thermal conductivity	W/m K		$1 \text{ Btu in/ft}^2 \text{ hr } °\text{F} = 0.144131 \text{ W/m K}$
Specific heat (gas constant)	J/kg K	kJ/kg K	$1 \text{ ft/lbf/lb K} = 2.98907 \text{ J/kg K}$
Electric current	A (ampere)	kA, mA	$1 \text{ A} = 1 \text{ V/}\Omega$
Electric potential (electromotive force)	V (volt)	kV	$1 \text{ V} = 1 \text{ W/A}$
Electric charge	C (coulomb)		$1 \text{ C} = 1 \text{ A s}$
Electric resistance	Ω (ohm)	kΩ MΩ	$1 \Omega = 1 \text{ V/A}$
Conductance	S (siemens)		$1 \text{ S} = 1 \text{ A/V}$
Electric capacitance	F (farad)	μF, pF	$1 \text{ F} = 1 \text{ A s/V}$
Inductance	H (henry)	mH μH	$1 \text{ H} = 1 \text{ Vs/A}$
Magnetic flux	Wb (Weber)		$1 \text{ Wb} = 1 \text{ V s}$
Magnetic flux density	T (tesla)		$1 \text{ T} = 1 \text{ Wb/m}^2$ $1 \text{ Gauss} = 10^{-4} \text{ Wb/m}^2$

1	2	3	4
Luminance	Cd/m²		
Luminous flux	lm (lumen)		1 lm = 1 candela steradian
Illuminance	lx (lux)		1 lx = 1 cd sr/m²
Phase angle	rad (radian)		1 rad = 57.29578 degrees
Solid angle	Sr (Steradian)		1 sr = 0.07958 sphere

GLOSSARY OF TRANSDUCER TERMS

Absolute pressure:	The pressure measured relative to vacuum.
Acceleration:	A vector quantity equal to the time rate of change of velocity, with respect to a reference system.
Acceleration error:	The maximum difference, at any measured value within the specified range, between output readings taken with and without the application of a specified constant acceleration along specified axes.
Acceleration sensitivity:	Acceleration error expressed in per cent of full scale output per *g*. The term is indicative of the response of a system due to the acceleration input.
Accelerometer:	A device that measures the acceleration of a moving body and translates it into a corresponding electrical quantity.
Accuracy:	The extent to which the measured value deviates from the true value of the measurand.
Active element:	A device capable of controlling voltages/currents, to produce a gain or switching action in a circuit.
Ambient conditions:	The conditions of the medium surrounding the transducer. This includes temperature, humidity, pressure, radiation and vibration.
Amplifying transducer:	A transducer with an integrally packaged amplifier.
Analog output:	Transducer output which is a continuous function of the measurand (except as modified by the resolution of the transducer).
Attitude:	The relative orientation of a vehicle or object represented by its angles of inclination to three orthogonal reference axes.
Attitude error:	The error due to the orientation of the transducer relative to the direction in which gravity acts upon the transducer.
Bellows:	A mechanical element of generally cylindrical shape with cylindrical walls having deep convolutions.
Best fit straight line:	A line midway between two parallel straight lines close together and enclosing all output vs measurand values, on a calibration curve.
Bondable transducer:	A transducer which is designed to be permanently mounted to a surface by means of adhesives.
Bonded strain gauge:	A resistance strain transducer, permanently attached over the length and width of its active element.
Bourdon tube:	A pressure sensing element consisting of a twisted or curved tube of non-circular cross section which tends to get straightened on the application of internal pressure.
Burst pressure rating:	Maximum pressure which may be applied to the sensing element or the case of a transducer, without rupture of either the sensing element or the case.

Calibration:	A test during which standard values of measurand are applied to the transducer and the corresponding output readings are compared with the standard values.
Calibration curve:	A graphical representation of the calibration record (Plot of calibration data).
Calibration cycle:	The application of known values of the measurand and calibration of the readings of the corresponding output values, over the full (or specified) portion of the range of a transducer, in an ascending or descending order.
Calibration traceability:	The relation of a transducer calibration, through a specified step by step process, to an instrument or group of instruments calibrated by a national standards agency.
Calibration uncertainty:	The maximum calculated error in the output values shown in a calibration record, due to causes not attributable to the transducer.
Capsule:	A pressure sensing element consisting of two corrugated metallic diaphragms joined along their circumference.
Centre of seismic mass:	The point within an acceleration transducer where acceleration forces are considered to be summed.
Compensated temperature range:	The operating temperature range of a transducer incorporating temperature compensation.
Compensation:	The utilization of supplemental device, materials, or processes to minimize known sources of error.
Conduction error:	The error in a temperature transducer due to heat conduction between the sensing element and the mounting of the transducer.
Conformance, conformity:	The closeness of a calibration curve to a specified curve.
Continuous rating:	The rating applicable to a specified operation for a specified uninterrupted length of time.
Creep:	A change in output occurring over a specified period of time, with the measurand applied and all the environmental conditions and other variables remaining constant.
Critical damping:	The degree of damping required to give the most rapid transient response without overshoot or oscillation. It lies between underdamped and overdamped conditions.
Cross sensitivity:	The maximum sensitivity of a transducer to a specified value of transverse measurand applied in a direction orthogonal to the primary axis, expressed in per cent of the sensitivity in the designed major axis.
Damping:	The energy dissipating characteristics which together with a natural frequency determines the limit of frequency response and the response characteristics of a transducer. Any action or influence that extracts energy from a vibratory system in order to suppress the vibration or oscillation.
Damping factor:	The ratio of amplitude of any one series of damped oscillations to that of the following one—also called decrement.
Damping-magnetic:	Damping effect (by use of current in electrical conductors) by changes in magnetic fields.
Damping ratio:	The ratio of the degree of actual damping to the degree of damping required for critical damping.
Damping-viscous:	Damping effected by use of the viscosity of liquids and gases.
Dead band:	The range of values over which a measured variable can change without affecting the output.
Dead time:	The time during which a device or system is insensitive, after receiving a stimulus, to any other inpulse or stimulus.
Dead volume:	The total volume of internal cavity between the sensing element and the external portion of the pressure port of a pressure transducer.
Diaphragm:	A sensing element consisting of a thin flexible circular plate which can be actuated by a pressure differential applied across the plate.

Directivity: The solid angle or the angle in a specified plane over which sound energy or radiant energy, impinging on a transducer, is measured.

Displacement: The extent of spatial distance through which an object or a point is moved.

Displacement transducer: A transducer that converts a linear or angular movement into a corresponding electrical signal.

Differential transformer transducer: A transducer in which movement of the ferromagnetic core of a transformer varies the output voltage across two series opposing secondary windings.

Drift: The random changes in output under constant measurand and normal operating conditions.

Dynamic calibration: A calibration during which the measurement varies with time in a specified manner and the output is recorded as a function of time.

Dynamic characteristics: Characteristics of a transducer which relate to its response to variations of the measurand with time.

Elastic member: The element or elements within the transducer to which a number of sensing elements are attached.

Electro-magnetic transduction: The conversion of the measurand into an induced voltage in a conductor by a change in magnetic flux without any excitation.

End point: The output at the specified upper or lower limit of the range.

End point line: The straight line between the end points.

Environmental conditions: Specified external conditions (shock, vibration, temperature, and humidity) to which a transducer may be exposed during operation, storage, or shipping.

Error: The algebraic difference between the indicated or observed value and the true value of the measurand.

Error-band: The band of maximum deviation of output values from a specified reference line or curve, due to those causes attributable to the transducer, as measured over two consecutive calibration cycles.

Error-curve: A graphical representation of errors obtained from a specified number of calibration cycles.

Excitation (electrical): The external electrical voltage and/or current applied to a transducer.

Fatigue life: The number of load cycles at a specified measurand value, before deterioration of electrical characteristics occurs.

Field of view: The solid angle or angle in a specified plane over which radiant energy incident on a transducer is measured within stated tolerances.

Flow rate: The time rate of motion of a fluid quantity per unit time.

Flow meter: A device that measures/indicates the rate of flow of a liquid or gas.

Fluid: A gas or liquid.

Fluid damping: See viscous damping.

Force: The vector quantity necessary to cause a change in momentum.

Frequency, natural: The frequency of free oscillations of the sensing element of a fully assembled transducer.

Frequency, resonant: The measurand frequency at which the transducer responds with maximum output amplitude.

Frequency response: The range of frequencies over which the faithful reproduction of the measurand is obtained.

Friction error: The maximum change in output before and after minimizing friction within the transducer by dithering.

Friction-free calibration: Calibration under conditions minimizing the effect of static friction, obtained by dithering.

Full-scale output: The algebraic difference between the end points of the range of the device.

Gauge factor: A measure of the ratio of the relative change of resistance to the relative change in length of a resistive strain transducer (strain gauge).

Gauge pressure: Pressure measured relative to ambient pressure.

Gyro (gyroscope):	An inertial device having a spinning mass, the tendency of which is to remain fixed in its angular relationship to inertial space.
Hall effect:	The development of a transverse electric potential gradient between the two edges of a current carrying conductor or semiconductor whose faces are perpendicular to an applied magnetic field.
Harmonic distortion:	The distortion in a transducer's output, in the form of harmonics other than the fundamental component.
Harmonic motion:	A motion whose instantaneous amplitude varies sinusoidally with time.
Heat conduction:	The transfer of heat energy by diffusion through solid material or through stagnant fluids.
Heat convection:	The transfer of heat energy by the movement of a fluid between two points.
Heat flux:	The time rate of flow of heat energy per unit area.
Heat radiation:	The transfer of heat energy by electromagnetic waves.
Hysteresis:	The maximum difference in output for the same measurand value within the transducer's range, one obtained by increasing from zero and the other by decreasing from a higher value of the measurand.
Hysteresis, thermal:	The maximum difference in output, at a given measurand value within the specified range and at a given temperature when this temperature is approached in the increasing and in the decreasing portion of a temperature cycle whose maximum temperature is substantially beyond the given temperature.
Impact pressure:	The pressure in a moving fluid exerted parallel to the direction of flow due to the velocity of the flow.
Inductive transduction:	Conversion of the measurand into a change of the self inductance of a single coil.
Input impedance:	The impedance presented to the excitation source, measured across the excitation terminals of a transducer.
Insulation resistance:	The DC resistance measured between specified insulated portions of a transducer (when a specified DC voltage is applied).
Integrating transducer:	A transducer whose output is a time integral function of the measurand.
Intermittent rating:	The rating applicable to a specified operation over a stated number of time intervals of specified duration.
Ionizing transduction:	Conversion of the measurand into a change in ionization current, such as that through a gas between two electrodes.
Jerk:	A vector unit that specifies the time rate of change of an acceleration.
Leakage rate:	The maximum rate at which a fluid at a specified pressure is leaking through specified sealed portion of a transducer.
Least square line:	The straight line for which the sum of the squares of the residual deviation is minimized.
Life cycling:	The specified minimum number of full range excursions or specified partial range excursions over which a transducer will operate as specified without changing its performance beyond specified tolerances.
Life, operating:	The specified minimum length of time over which the specified continuous or intermittent rating of a transducer applies without changing its performance beyond specified tolerances.
Life, storage:	The specified minimum length of time over which a transducer can be exposed to a specified storage condition, without changing its performance beyond specified tolerances.
Linearity:	The maximum deviation of any calibration point, obtained for either increasing or decreasing input, from the best fit straight line having overall minimum deviation.
Linearity, end point:	Linearity, referred to a straight line between the end points.
Linearity, independent:	Linearity referred to the best straight line passing through zero.

Linearity, least square:	Linearity referred to a straight line for which the sum of the squares of the residuals is minimized.
Linearity, terminal:	Linearity, referred to the terminal line.
Load cell:	The device which generates an output signal proportional to the applied force or weight.
Lead impedance:	The complex impedance presented to the output terminals of a transducer by the associated external circuitry or load.
Loading error:	An error introduced due to the effect of the load impedance on the transducer output.
Magnetostriction:	The change in dimensions of a ferromagnetic object when the object is placed in a magnetic field.
Magnetoresistive effect:	The change in the resistance of a conductor or semiconductor due to the application of a magnetic field.
Mass:	The quantity of matter in a body. Mass is a measure of inertia and determines resistance to acceleration, independently of gravitational force.
Mean output curve:	The curve through the mean values of output during any one calibration cycle of a different specified number of calibration cycles.
Measurand:	The physical quantity, property, or condition that is to be measured.
Measurand medium:	The medium which comes in contact with the sensing element.
Mechanical impedance:	The complex ratio of force to velocity during simple harmonic motion.
Motion:	The change in position of a body or point with respect to a reference system.
Mounting error:	The error resulting from mechanical deformation of the transducer caused by mounting the transducer.
Null:	A condition of balance which results in a minimum absolute value of output.
Non-linearity:	(See linearity).
Output:	The electrical quantity (useful energy) produced by a transducer. The magnitude is a function of the applied measurand.
Output impedance:	The impedance across the output terminals of a transducer presented by the transducer to the associated external circuitry.
Output noise:	The unwanted component (typically of broad frequency spectrum) of the output of a transducer.
Output rated:	The algebraic difference in value between the outputs at no input and rated input of measurand.
Overload:	The maximum magnitude of measurand that can be applied to a transducer without causing a change in performance beyond specified tolerance.
Over range:	(See Overload).
Overshoot:	The amount of output measured beyond the final steady output value in response to a step change in the measurand.
Photoconductive transduction:	Conversion of a measurand into a change in resistance or conductivity by a change in the magnitude of illumination incident upon the material.
Photoemissive transduction:	Conversion of the measurand into a change of emission of electrons due to a change in the incidence of photons on a photocathode.
Photovoltaic transduction:	Conversion of the measurand into a change in voltage generated when a junction between dissimilar materials is illuminated.
Piezoelectric transduction:	Conversion of the measurand into a change in electrostatic charge or voltage generated by certain materials when mechanically stressed.
Piezoresistive transduction:	Conversion of the measurand into a change in the resistance of a conductor or semiconductor by a change in the mechanical stress applied to it.
Potentiometric transduction:	Conversion of the measurand into a voltage ratio by a change in the position of a movable wiper on a resistance element across which excitation is applied.
Precision:	The degree of reproducibility among several independent measurements of the same true value under reference conditions.

Pressure: Force acting on a surface measured as force per unit area (this may be absolute pressure, differential pressure, gauge pressure, or reference pressure).

Pyroelectric effect: The generation of charges in certain crystals when unequally heated or cooled.

Random vibration: Non-periodic vibration described only in statistical terms (mean vibrations characterized by a normal amplitude distribution) within prescribed limits.

Range: The measurand values over which a transducer is intented to measure, specified by upper or lower limits.

Recovery time: The time interval after a specified event after which a transducer again performs within its specified tolerances.

Reference pressure: The pressure relative to which a differential pressure transducer is used.

Reference standard: A transducer or a device whose characteristics are precisely known relative to a primary standard.

Relative humidity: The ratio of the water vapour pressure actually present to the water vapour required for saturation at a given temperature expressed in percentage.

Reliability: A measure of the probability that a transducer/device will continue to perform within specified limits of error over a specified length of time under specified conditions.

Repeatability: The ability of a transducer to reproduce output readings when the same measurand value is applied to it repeatedly under the same environmental conditions and in the same direction.

Resolution: The magnitude of discernable (detectable) output changes as the measurand is continuously varied over the range.

Response time: The time required for the output of a transducer to reach a specified percentage of its final value as a result of a step change of measurand.

Rise time: The time required for the output of a transducer to rise from 10% to 90% of its final value.

Sensing element: That part of the transducer which responds directly to the measurand.

Sensitivity: The ratio of the change in transducer output to a corresponding change in the value of the measurand.

Sensitive axis: The axis along which the input measurand is applied or mounted.

Shock: A short non-periodic or transient excitation of a mechanical system.

Source impedance: The impedance presented to the transducer's excitation terminals by the excitation source.

Span: The algebraic difference between the limits of the range.

Stability: The ability of a transducer to retain its repeatability and other characteristics throughout its specified operating life and storage life.

Stagnation pressure: Sum of the static pressure and the impact pressure in a fluid flow.

Static calibration: A calibration performed by application of the measurand to the transducer at discrete amplitude intervals.

Static error band: The error band applicable at room conditions and in the absence of any vibration, shock, or acceleration. It is the cumulative effect of non-linearity, hysteresis, and non-repeatability.

Strain: The deformation in a body or object resulting from a stress, measured as the ratio of the dimensional change to the total value of the dimension in which the change occurs.

System accuracy: Difference between the value as measured on the system and the true value.

Temperature error: The maximum change in output at any measured value within the specified range, when the temperature of the transducer is changed from one value to another.

Terminal line: A theoretical slope for which the theoretical end points are 0% and 100% of both measurand and output.

Thermal co-efficient of resistance:	The relative change in resistance of a conductor or semiconductor per unit change in temperature, over a stated range of temperature.
Thermoelectric transduction:	Conversion of the measurand into a change in emf generated by a temperature difference between the junctions of two selected dissimilar metals.
Threshold:	The smallest change in the measurand that produces a detectable change in the transducer output.
Time constant:	The time required for the output of a transducer to rise to 63.2% of its final value as a result of a step change in the measurand.
Torque:	The moment of force.
Transfer function:	A mathematical relationship between the input and the output, expressed as a ratio of two polynomials.
Traceability:	The step transfer process by which the transducer calibration can be related to the reference standards.
Transducer:	A device which provides a usable output in response to a specified measurand.
Transduction element:	The part of the transducer in which the output information originates.
Transient response:	The response of a transducer to a step/fast change in measurand.
Transverse acceleration:	An acceleration perpendicular to the sensitive axis of transducer.
Transverse sensitivity:	The sensitivity of a transducer to a specified value of inputs applied in an axis orthogonal to the designed sensitive axis.
Triboelectric effect:	The generation of electric charge by friction between surfaces.
Velocity:	A vector quantity equal to the time rate of change of displacement with respect to a reference system.
Warm-up period:	The period of time, starting with the application of power to the transducer, required to assure that the transducer will perform within specified tolerance.
Zero shift:	A change in output over a specified period of time at specified ambient conditions with input held constant.

INDEX